AUTOMOT
MANUAL
DRIVETRAIN AND
AUTOMATIC
TRANSMISSIONS

James D. Halderman

Edited by Jeffrey Rehkopf

Taken from

Manual Drivetrains and Axles, 7th Edition

By James D. Halderman and Tom Birch

Automatic Transmissions and Transaxles, 6th Edition

By James D. Halderman and Tom Birch

PEARSON

Boston Columbus Hoboken Indianapolis New York San Francisco
Amsterdam Cape Town Dubai London Madrid Milan Munich Paris Montréal
Toronto Delhi Mexico City São Paulo Sydney Hong Kong Seoul Singapore Taipei Tokyo

Editorial Director: Andrew Gilfillan
Editorial Assistant: Nancy Kesterson
Director of Marketing: David Gesell
Program Manager: Holly Shufeldt
Project Manager: Janet Portisch
Procurement Specialist:
  Deidra Skahill
Senior Art Director: Diane Ernsberger

Cover Designer: Cenveo Publisher
  Services
Media Project Manager: April Cleland
**Full-Service Project Management and
  Composition:** Integra Software
  Services, Ltd.
Printer/Binder: RR Donnelley/Owensville
Cover Printer: Phoenix Color/Hagerstown

Taken from
Manual Drivetrains and Axles, 7th Edition
By James D. Halderman and Tom Birch
Copyright © 2015 by Pearson Education

Automatic Transmissions and Transaxles, 6th Edition
By James D. Halderman and Tom Birch
Copyright © 2015 by Pearson Education

PEARSON

ISBN 10:   0-13-416176-9
ISBN 13: 978-0-13-416176-1

BRIEF CONTENTS

Technical and Content Reviewers

TECHNICAL AND CONTENT REVIEWERS The following people helped in checking this text for technical accuracy and clarity of presentation. Their suggestions and recommendations were included in the final version of the page proofs. Their valuable input helped make this textbook clear and technically accurate while maintaining the easy-to-read style that has made other books in this series so popular.

Alan Crouch
J. Sargeant Reynolds Community College

Josh Gilbert
Guilford Technical College

Joe Jackson
Ranken Technical College

Marty Kamimoto
Fresno City College

Darrin Marshall
University of Alaska, Anchorage

Kelly Smith
University of Alaska, Anchorage

Martin Smith
British Columbia Institute of Technology, Canada

Charles Taylor
Sinclair Community College, Dayton OH

Timothy A. Wawerczyk
Broward College

Chris Gallo
Camden County College

Raytheon Technical Services, LLC

chapter 1

INTRODUCTION TO DRIVETRAINS

LEARNING OBJECTIVES

After studying this chapter, the reader should be able to:

1. Define torque, and explain the relationship between torque and horsepower.
2. Describe the various gear types and their effect on speed, torque, and direction of rotation.
3. Explain gear ratios and their effect on vehicle operation.
4. Discuss the types of manual transmissions and transaxles that are currently in use.
5. Discuss automatic transmissions and the planetary gear sets used for automatic transmissions.
6. Compare rear-wheel drive, front-wheel drive, four-wheel drive, and all-wheel drive.
7. Explain the characteristics of driveshafts and drive axle assemblies.

This chapter will help you prepare for ASE Manual Drive Train and Axles (A3) certification test content area "B" (Transmission Diagnosis and Repair) and area "C" (Transaxle Diagnosis and Repair).

KEY TERMS

All-wheel drive (AWD) 16
Automatic transmission 9
Bevel gear 6
Clutch 8
Constant-velocity (CV) joint 14
Differential 14
Dynamometer 4
Drive axle 14
Driveshaft 14
Final drive 13
Four-wheel drive (4WD) 16
Front-wheel drive (FWD) 13
Gear ratio 7
Half shaft 13
Helical gear 5
Horsepower 4
Hypoid gear 6
Manual transmission 8
Overdrive 7
Pinion gear 8
Pitch diameter 4
Planet carrier 11
Planetary gear set 11
Power transfer unit 16
Rear-wheel drive (RWD) 13
Ring gear 11
Spiral bevel gear 6
Spur gear 5
Sun gear 11
Torque 2
Torque converter 11
Transaxle 13
Transfer case 16
Transmission 8
Universal joint (U-joint) 14
Worm gear 6

GM STC OBJECTIVES

GM Service Technical College topics covered in this chapter are as follows:

1. General features of drivetrain components as used in General Motors vehicles.

DRIVETRAINS

PURPOSE AND FUNCTION

The purpose of a vehicle drivetrain is to transfer power from the engine to the drive wheels. The drivetrain, also called a powertrain, serves the following functions:

- It allows the driver to control the power flow.
- It multiplies the engine torque.
- It controls the engine speed.

TORQUE

DEFINITION

Torque is a rotating or twisting force that may or may not result in motion. A vehicle moves because of the torque the drive axle exerts on the wheels and tires to make them rotate. Being a form of mechanical energy, torque cannot be created or destroyed—it is converted from one form of energy to another form of energy.

In a gasoline or diesel engine, torque is developed when combustion pressure pushes a piston downward to rotate the crankshaft. ● **SEE FIGURE 1–1.**

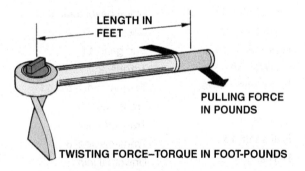

LENGTH IN FEET

PULLING FORCE IN POUNDS

TWISTING FORCE–TORQUE IN FOOT-POUNDS

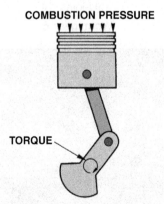

COMBUSTION PRESSURE

TORQUE

FIGURE 1–1 Torque, a twisting force, is produced when you pull on a wrench. An engine produces torque at the crankshaft as combustion pressure pushes the piston downward.

? FREQUENTLY ASKED QUESTION

Is It Lb-Ft or Ft-Lb of Torque?

The unit for torque is expressed as a force times the distance (leverage) from the object. Therefore, the official unit for torque is lb-ft (pound-feet) or Newton-meters (a force times a distance). However, it is commonly expressed in ft-lb and most torque wrenches are labeled with this unit.

The amount of torque produced will vary depending on the size and design of the engine and the throttle opening. A factor that greatly affects drivetrain design is that very little or no torque is developed at engine speeds below 1000 RPM (revolutions per minute). An engine begins producing usable torque at about 1200 RPM and peak torque at about 2500 to 4000 RPM, with an upper usable speed limit of 5000 to 7000 RPM. The gear ratios in the transmission and drive axle are used to match the engine speed and torque output to the vehicle speed and torque requirements. ● **SEE FIGURE 1–2.**

UNITS OF TORQUE

Torque is measured in pounds-feet (lb-ft) or Newton-meters (N-m). One Newton-meter of torque is equal to 0.737 lb-ft.

DRIVE VS. DRIVEN GEARS

The *drive* gear is the gear that is the source of the engine torque and rotation. The *driven* gear is the gear that is driven or rotated by the drive gear. Two gears meshed together are used to transmit torque and rotational motion. The driven gear can then rotate yet another gear. In this case, the second gear becomes the drive gear and the third gear is the driven gear.

TORQUE MULTIPLICATION

The gear teeth are cut proportional to the diameter of the gear. If one of two mating gears were twice as large as the other, it would have twice as many teeth. For example, if the smaller gear has 10 teeth, a gear twice as large will have 20 teeth. If the teeth of these gears are intermeshed, 10 teeth of each gear will come into contact when the smaller gear rotates one revolution. This will require one revolution of the small gear and one-half revolution of the larger gear. It will take two revolutions of the small gear to produce one revolution of the larger gear. This is a gear ratio of 2:1, assuming that the small gear is the drive gear. To determine a gear ratio, divide the driven gear by the driving gear. ● **SEE FIGURE 1–3.**

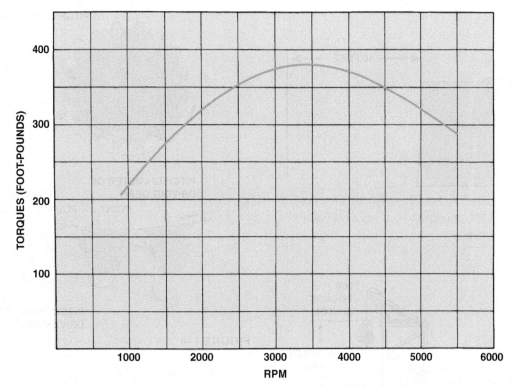

FIGURE 1–2 The torque produced by a 5.7 L engine as plotted on a graph. Note that the engine begins producing usable torque at 1000 to 1200 RPM and a maximum torque (381 ft-lb) at 3500 RPM. The torque produced by the engine decreases at higher RPM due to a decrease in volumetric efficiency.

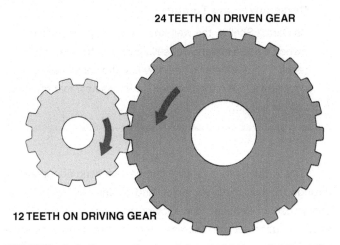

24 TEETH ON DRIVEN GEAR

12 TEETH ON DRIVING GEAR

FIGURE 1–3 Gear ratio is determined by dividing the number of teeth of the driven (output) gear (24 teeth) by the number of teeth on the driving (input) gear (12 teeth). The ratio illustrated is 2:1.

GEARS ARE LEVERS Torque is increased because of the length of the gear lever, as measured from the center of the gear. Think of each tooth as a lever, with the fulcrum being the center of the gear. The lever lengths of the two gears can provide leverage much like that of a simple lever. Physics

does not allow energy to become lost in a gear set, other than what is lost as heat in overcoming friction. Therefore, whatever power that comes in one shaft goes out through another.

- If the speed is reduced, torque will increase by the same amount.
- If speed is increased, torque will decrease by the same amount.

For example, if the driving gear has 20 lb-ft (27 N-m) of torque at 500 RPM and the ratio is 2:1, the driven gear will have 40 lb-ft (54 N-m) of torque (twice as much) at 250 RPM (half the speed).

HORSEPOWER

DEFINITION The term "power" means the rate of doing work. Power equals work divided by time.

- Work is done when a certain amount of mass (weight) is moved a certain distance by a force. Whether the object is moved in 10 seconds or 10 minutes does not make a difference in the amount of work accomplished, but it does affect the amount of power needed. ● **SEE FIGURE 1–4.**

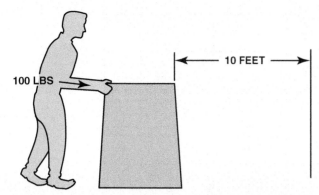

FIGURE 1–4 Work is calculated by multiplying force times distance. If you push 100 pounds 10 feet, you have done 1000 foot-pounds of work.

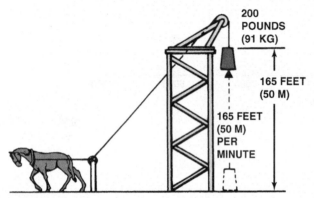

FIGURE 1–5 One horsepower is equal to 33,000 foot-pounds (200 lbs × 165 ft) of work per minute.

- Power is expressed in units of foot-pounds per minute. One **horsepower** is the power required to move 550 pounds one foot in one second, or 33,000 pounds one foot in one minute (550 lb × 60 sec = 33,000 lb). This is expressed as 550 foot-pounds (ft-lb) per second or 33,000 foot-pounds per minute. ● **SEE FIGURE 1–5.**

HORSEPOWER AND TORQUE RELATIONSHIP To determine horsepower, a **dynamometer** is used to measure the amount of torque an engine can produce at various points through its operating range. The formula used to convert torque at a certain revolution per minute (RPM) into a horsepower reading is

$$\textbf{Horsepower} = \textbf{Torque} \times \textbf{RPM/5252}$$

The various readings are then plotted into a curve. A typical horsepower and torque curve shows us that an engine does not produce very much torque at low RPM. The most usable torque is produced in the mid-RPM range. Torque decreases with an increase in horsepower at a higher RPM.

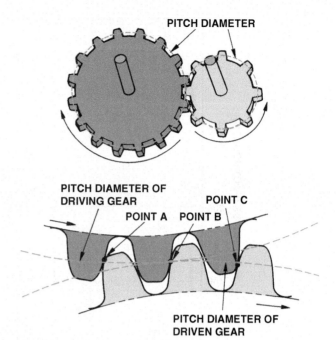

FIGURE 1–6 The pitch diameter is the effective diameter of the gear. Note how the contact points slide on the gear teeth as they move in and out of contact.

  TECH TIP

How to Explain the Difference between Horsepower and Torque

As Carroll Shelby, the well-known racer and business owner, said, "Horsepower sells cars, but torque wins races." Torque determines how fast the vehicle will accelerate, and horsepower determines how fast the vehicle will go.

The torque from an engine can be increased or decreased through the use of gears, belts, and chains. Gears, belts, or chains cannot increase horsepower; they can only modify its effect. A gear set can increase torque, but it will decrease speed by the same amount.

GEARS

TERMINOLOGY The effective diameter of a gear is the **pitch diameter** (or *pitch line*). ● **SEE FIGURE 1–6.**

The pitch diameter is the diameter of the gear at the point where the teeth of the two gears meet and transfer power. The gear teeth are shaped to be able to slide in and out of mesh

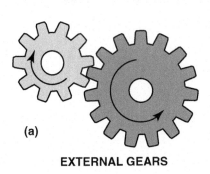

(a)

EXTERNAL GEARS

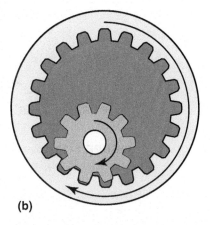

(b)

INTERNAL AND
EXTERNAL GEARS

FIGURE 1–7 (a) When one external gear drives another, the direction of rotation is always reversed. (b) When an external gear drives an internal gear, the two gears will rotate in the same direction.

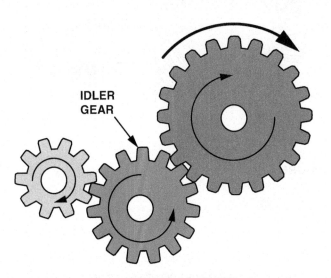

IDLER
GEAR

EXTERNAL GEARS

FIGURE 1–8 An idler gear reverses the direction of rotation so that the driving and driven gears rotate in the same direction.

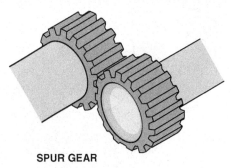

SPUR GEAR

FIGURE 1–9 The teeth of a spur gear are cut parallel to the shaft, and this produces a straight pressure between the driving and the driven gear teeth.

REVERSING DIRECTION OF ROTATION   External gears reverse the direction of rotation when the drive gear transfers power to the driven gear. When it is necessary to change the ratio without changing the direction of power flow, an idler gear is added. An idler gear changes the rotational direction but does not affect the ratio. ● **SEE FIGURE 1–8.**

GEAR TYPES   Gears come in different types depending on the cut and relationship of the teeth to the shafts.

- **Spur gears**—Spur gears, the simplest gears, are on parallel shafts with teeth cut straight or parallel to the shaft. ● **SEE FIGURE 1–9.**
- **Helical gear**—Helical gears are the most used of all gears used in transmissions. These gears have teeth cut in a spiral or helix shape. ● **SEE FIGURE 1–10.**

Helical gears are quieter than spur gears, but generate axial or end thrust under a load. A helical gear is stronger than a comparable-sized spur gear and has an almost continuous power flow because of the angled teeth. ● **SEE FIGURE 1–10.**

with a minimum amount of friction and wear. Major points include the following:

- Driven and driving gears will rotate in opposite directions.
- External gears will always reverse shaft motion.
- If same-direction motion is required, the power will be routed through two gear sets.
- When power goes through a series of gears, an even number of gears (2, 4, 6, and 8) will cause a reversal in direction and an odd number of gears (3, 5, 7, and 9) will produce same direction of rotation.

● **SEE FIGURE 1–7.**

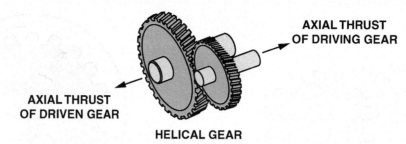

FIGURE 1–10 The teeth of a helical gear are cut on a slant, and this produces an axial or side thrust.

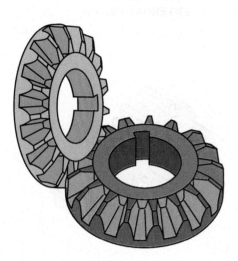

FIGURE 1–11 Bevel gears are commonly used in differentials.

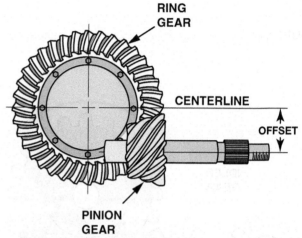

FIGURE 1–12 A hypoid gear set uses a pinion gear that is located below the centerline of the ring gear and is commonly used in drive axles.

NOTE: When discussing gears, a pinion gear is the smaller gear of a pair.

- **Bevel gears**—Bevel gears are used on nonparallel shafts. The outer edge of the gear must be cut on the angle that bisects the angle of the two shafts. In other words, if the two shafts meet at an angle of 90° and the two gears are the same size, the outer edge of the gears will be cut at 45°. The simplest bevel gears have teeth cut straight and are called spur bevel gears. They are inexpensive but noisy. ● SEE FIGURE 1–11.

- **Spiral bevel gears**—Spiral bevel gears, like helical gears, have curved teeth for quieter operation.

- **Hypoid gear**—A variation of the spiral bevel gear is the hypoid gear, also called an *offset-bevel gear*. Hypoid gears are used in most drive axles and transaxles that have longitudinal mounted engines. The hypoid gear

design places the drive pinion gear lower in the housing (below the centerline) of the ring gear and axle shafts. ● SEE FIGURE 1–12.

- **Worm gear**—A gear set used with shafts that cross each other but do not intersect is the worm gear. The worm gear or drive pinion is cut in a rather severe helix, much like a bolt thread, and the ring gear or wheel is cut almost like a spur gear. Worm gears are used in vehicle speed sensor drives. To determine the ratio of a worm gear, divide the number of teeth on the wheel by the pitch of the worm gear. For example, a single-pitch worm gear tooth driving a 20-tooth ring gear will have a ratio of 20:1, a very low ratio, and the wheel does not have to be 20 times larger than the worm gear. A 20:1 ratio in most gear sets requires the driven gear to be 20 times larger than the driving gear. ● SEE FIGURE 1–13.

FIGURE 1–13 A worm gear set is also used to transmit power between angled shafts.

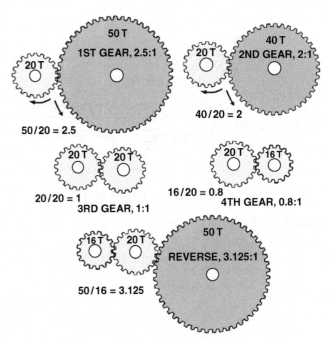

FIGURE 1–14 The gear ratio is determined by dividing the number of teeth on the driven (output) gear by the number of teeth on the driving (input) gear.

GEAR RATIOS

TERMINOLOGY **Gear ratios** are determined by the following methods:

- Divide the number of teeth on the driven gear (output) by the number of teeth on the driving gear (input). Most of the time, this means dividing a larger number, such as 20, by a smaller number, such as 5. In this case, $20 \div 5 = 4$, so the ratio will be 4:1.

- Gear ratio is equal to driven gear/drive gear.

- The driving gear will turn four times for each revolution of the driven gear. This results in a speed reduction and a torque increase. The speed of the output will be four times slower than the input speed, but the output torque will be four times more than the input torque. The higher the ratio number, the lower the gear ratio. A 5:1 ratio is higher numerically, but, in terms of speed of the driven gear, it is a lower ratio than 4:1. ● **SEE FIGURE 1–14.**

Most of the time, the ratio will not end up as whole numbers. It will be something like an 11-tooth driving gear and a 19-tooth driven gear, which results in a ratio of 19 divided by 11, which equals 1.7272727 and can be rounded off to 1.73.

COMMONLY USED RATIOS The automotive industry commonly rounds off gear ratios to two decimal points. Drivetrain engineers usually do not use even ratios like 3:1 or 4:1 but instead use ratios that are at least 10% greater or less than even numbers. An even ratio, like 3:1, repeats the same gear tooth contacts every third revolution. If there is a damaged tooth, a noise will be repeated continuously, and most drivers will not like the noise. A gear set with a ratio such as 3.23:1 is called a hunting gear set, and a tooth of one gear contacts all of the other gear teeth, which produces quieter operation.

? FREQUENTLY ASKED QUESTION

What is the Relationship between Speed and Gear Ratio?

The following formulas can be used to determine the vehicle speed based on the gear ratio and engine speed, or the engine speed based on the gear ratio and MPH (miles per hour):

- MPH = (RPM × tire diameter) ÷ (gear ratio × 336)
- Engine RPM = (MPH × gear ratio × 336) ÷ tire diameter

NOTE: Use the loaded tire radius times two for the tire diameter.

OVERDRIVE If the driving gear has more teeth (20) than the driven gear (5), there will be an increase in speed and a reduction in torque. This is called an **overdrive**. The ratio is computed by dividing 5 by 20, $5 \div 20 = 0.25$, so the ratio would be expressed as 0.25:1. The driving gear will turn 0.25 or one-fourth of a revolution for each turn of the driven gear. Note that a gear ratio is always written with the number 1 to the right of the colon. This represents one turn of the output gear, while the number to the left represents the revolutions of the input gear.

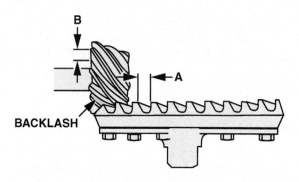

A - B = BACKLASH

FIGURE 1–15 Backlash is the clearance between the teeth of two meshing gears. There has to be some clearance (backlash) to prevent the gears from getting into a bind condition when they are transmitting torque; the gears also expand slightly when heated to operating temperature.

CALCULATING OVERALL RATIOS When power goes through more than one gear set, two or more ratios are involved. In most cases, the simplest way to handle this is to figure the ratio of each set and then multiply the ratios. An example of this is a vehicle with a first-gear ratio of 2.68:1 and a rear axle ratio of 3.45:1. The overall ratio in first gear is 2.68×3.45 or 9.246:1.

- At the same time there will be 9.246 times as much torque at the rear wheels than the engine produced.

- The engine will rotate at a speed that is 9.246 times faster than the rear axle shafts. The overall ratios for the other transmission gears would be figured in the same manner.

GEAR SET SUMMARY Typical rules about gear sets include the following:

- Two mated external gears will always rotate in opposite directions.

- Gear sets will multiply torque but at a reduced speed.

- An idler gear allows the drive and driven gears to rotate in the same direction.

- To find the ratio, divide the driven gear by the drive gear.

- When power transfers through an even number (two or four) of gears, the input and output gears will rotate in opposite directions.

- When power transfers through an uneven number (one, three, or five) of gears, the input and output gears will rotate in the same direction.

- To find the overall ratio of multiple gear sets, multiply the ratios of the gear sets.

- Two gears transferring power push away from each other in an action called *gear separation*. The gear separation force (thrust) is proportional to the torque being transferred.

- The smaller gear(s) in a gear set may also be called a **pinion gear**.

- All gear sets *must* have backlash to prevent binding. ● **SEE FIGURE 1–15.**

TRANSMISSIONS

PURPOSE AND FUNCTION The purpose and function of gears in a **transmission** include the following:

- Low/first gear must provide enough torque to get the vehicle moving.

- High gear should provide an engine speed for fuel-efficient operation at highway speeds.

- The intermediate ratios should be spaced to provide adequate acceleration while minimizing the potential of overrevving the engine before the shift or lugging the engine after the shift.

TRENDS The majority of vehicles up to the 1970s used three-speed transmissions while some added an overdrive unit for a fourth gear ratio to lower engine RPM at cruise speeds. As the need to improve fuel economy and reduce exhaust emissions has improved, five-, six-, seven-, eight-, and even nine- speed transmissions have been introduced to provide lower first gears, overdrive, and/or smaller steps between gear ratios.

MANUAL TRANSMISSIONS

PURPOSE AND FUNCTION A **manual transmission**, also called a *standard transmission*, is constructed with a group of paths through which power can flow with each path used being a different gear ratio. ● **SEE FIGURE 1–16.**

Synchronizer assemblies or sliding gears and the shift linkage are used to control or engage the power paths.

CLUTCH Engine power must be stopped when making a shift in a manual transmission. The **clutch** is used to stop the power flow to allow the transmission to be shifted. It is also

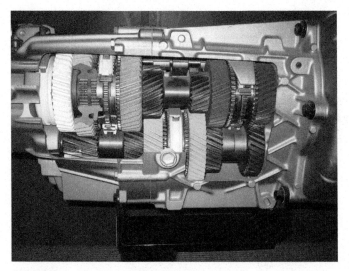

FIGURE 1–16 A manual transmission provides several gear ratios and a method to shift them.

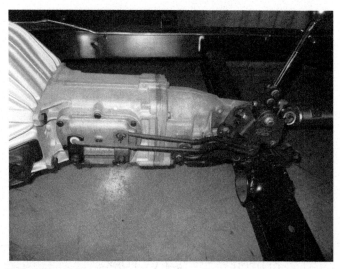

FIGURE 1–17 An older Muncie four-speed manual transmission, showing the external linkage and "side shifter" cover plate.

used to ease the engagement of the power flow when the vehicle starts from a standstill. The slight slippage as the clutch engages allows the engine speed to stay up where it produces usable torque as the vehicle begins moving.

Most vehicles use a foot-pedal-operated single-plate clutch assembly that is mounted on the engine flywheel. When the pedal is pushed down, the power flow is disengaged and when the pedal is released, power can flow from the engine to the transmission through the engaged clutch. ● **SEE FIGURE 1–18.**

AUTOMATIC TRANSMISSIONS

PURPOSE AND FUNCTION The purpose and function of an **automatic transmission** are to provide the forward and reverse gear ratios needed without requiring the driver to make the change in gearing as with a manual transmission. An automatic transmission has various gear ratios, but the paths of power flow are different from those of a manual transmission.

GEAR RANGES The transmission provides the various gear ratios for forward and reverse operations as well as two methods for the engine to run without moving the vehicle. Most automatic transmissions and transaxles include the following gear ranges (shift modes). ● **SEE FIGURE 1–19.**

- **Park**—In the park position, the output shaft is locked to the case of the transmission/transaxle which keeps the

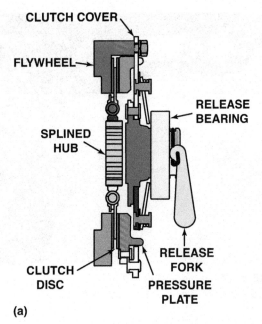

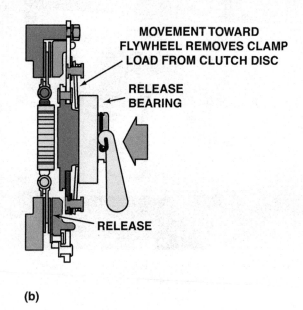

(a)

(b)

FIGURE 1–18 (a) A clutch cover (pressure plate assembly) is bolted onto the flywheel with the clutch disc between them. The release bearing and fork provide a method to release (disengage) the clutch. (b) When the clutch is engaged, the disc is squeezed against the flywheel by the pressure plate. Releasing the clutch separates the disc from the flywheel and pressure plate.

FIGURE 1–19 This gear selector includes a "M" position that allows the driver to manually select the gear ranges. (Courtesy of General Motors.)

vehicle from moving. No power is transmitted through the unit so the engine can remain running while the vehicle is held stationary.

In the park position

1. The engine can be started by the driver.
2. To move the shifter out of the park position on a late model vehicle, the brake pedal must be depressed to release the transmission shift interlock.

- **Reverse**—The reverse gear selector position is used to move the vehicle in reverse. Reverse usually uses a gear ratio similar to first gear.

- **Neutral**—In the neutral position, no torque is being transmitted through the automatic transmission/transaxle. In this position, the engine can be started by the driver.

CAUTION: The vehicle is free to roll when the gear selector is placed in the neutral position unless the brake pedal is depressed to prevent the vehicle from moving.

- **Drive (D)**—The D position includes the overdrive ratios in most vehicles. Use this position when driving on the highway. The "overdrive (OD)" button found on some older automatic transmissions is used to turn off overdrive and while towing or when driving in city traffic to prevent the transmission from shifting in and out of overdrive.

- **Manual (M)**—The shift selector may have a "Manual" position that allows the driver to manually select gears using push buttons, paddle shifters on the steering wheel, or some other selection method. This position also allows the driver to upshift or downshift manually using movements of the shift lever, paddle shifters, or "up (+)" and "down (−)" buttons on the shifter.

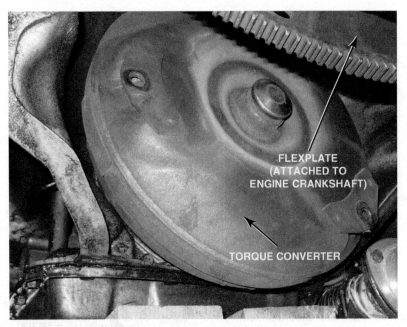

FLEXPLATE
(ATTACHED TO
ENGINE CRANKSHAFT)

TORQUE CONVERTER

FIGURE 1–20 A torque converter is attached to the engine crankshaft and the other end is splined to the input shaft of the automatic transmission. The torque converter is used to transmit engine torque to the transmission yet slip when the engine is at idle speed.

- **Third (3)—**In the third position (found on older vehicles), the transmission/transaxle will upshift normally to third gear but will not upshift to a higher gear. When the third position is selected while driving in a higher gear, the transmission will downshift into third if the vehicle speed is low enough. This gear selection is used for descending gentle grades at a moderate vehicle speed when compression braking is needed.

- **Second (2)—**Also found in older vehicles, the second position is used for slowing the vehicle while descending long grades. In this gear selection, the vehicle speed is controlled and the engine is used to provide engine compression braking. This gear selection is used for the gentle grades at a moderate vehicle speed.

- **First (1 or Low)—**The first (or low) position is used for slowing the vehicle while descending steep grades. In this gear selection, the vehicle speed is controlled and engine compression braking is used to slow the vehicle. This gear selection is used for the steepest grades at the lowest possible speed.

TORQUE CONVERTERS A **torque converter** replaces the manual transmission clutch. It is a type of fluid coupling that can release the power flow at slow engine speeds and also multiply the engine torque during acceleration. The torque converter assembly also includes a friction clutch that locks up to eliminate slippage at cruising speeds, improving fuel economy and reducing exhaust emissions. ● **SEE FIGURE 1–20.**

PLANETARY GEAR SETS Most automatic transmissions use **planetary gear sets**, which are a combination of gears. When the gear set is assembled, the sun gear is in the center and meshed with the planet gears, which are located around it, somewhat like the planets in our solar system. The ring gear is meshed around the outside of the planet gears. The three main members of the planetary gear set include the following:

1. **Sun gear**—It is the gear in the center.

2. **Ring gear**—It is also called an *annulus gear* or *internal gear*.

3. **Planet carrier**—It holds the planet gears (also called *pinions*) in position. ● **SEE FIGURE 1–21.**

Each of these gears can have two possible actions: They can rotate or stand still.

The planet gears/pinions have the following three possible actions.

1. They can rotate on their shafts in a stationary carrier and act like idler gears.

2. They can rotate on their shafts in a rotating carrier; the planet gears are walking.

3. They can stand still on their shafts and rotate with the carrier.

Planetary gear sets are used and combined in a complex manner so that transmissions with seven or eight speeds forward plus reverse are possible. Shifts are made by engaging or releasing one or more internal clutches that drive a gear set member, or by engaging or releasing other clutches or bands that hold a gear set member stationary. An automatic transmission might have as many as seven of these power control units

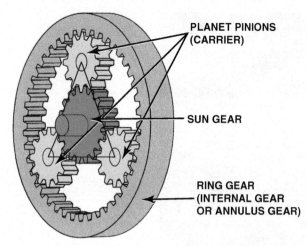

PLANET PINIONS (CARRIER)

SUN GEAR

RING GEAR (INTERNAL GEAR OR ANNULUS GEAR)

FIGURE 1–21 A typical planetary gear set showing the terms that are used to describe each member.

(clutches or bands). One-way clutches are also used that self-release and overrun when the next gear is engaged. The control units can operate without the interruption of the power flow.

PLANETARY GEAR SET OPERATION
Planetary gear sets are so arranged that power enters through one of the members and leaves through one of the other members, while the third member is held stationary in reaction. Power flow through a planetary gear set is controlled by clutches, bands, and one-way clutches. One or more clutches will control the power coming to a planetary member and one or more reaction members can hold a gear set member stationary. The third planetary member will be the output. ● **SEE FIGURE 1–22.**

PLANETARY GEAR SET RATIOS
A simple planetary gear set can produce one of the following:

- A neutral if either the input clutch or reaction member is not applied
- Two reduction ratios
- Two overdrive ratios
- Two reverse ratios, one a reduction and one an overdrive
- The reduction, overdrive, and reverse ratios will require one driving member, one output member, and one reaction member in the gear set.

NOTE: A 1:1, direct-drive ratio is achieved if two gear set members are driven.

ADVANTAGES OF PLANETARY GEAR SETS
Planetary gear sets offer several advantages over conventional gear sets.

1. Because there is more than one gear transferring power, the torque load is spread over several gear teeth.

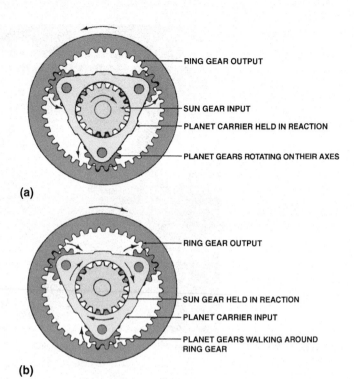

RING GEAR OUTPUT

SUN GEAR INPUT

PLANET CARRIER HELD IN REACTION

PLANET GEARS ROTATING ON THEIR AXES

(a)

RING GEAR OUTPUT

SUN GEAR HELD IN REACTION

PLANET CARRIER INPUT

PLANET GEARS WALKING AROUND RING GEAR

(b)

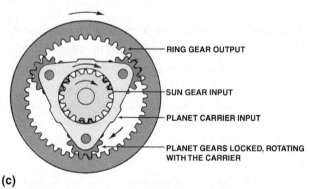

RING GEAR OUTPUT

SUN GEAR INPUT

PLANET CARRIER INPUT

PLANET GEARS LOCKED, ROTATING WITH THE CARRIER

(c)

FIGURE 1–22 (a) If the planet carrier is held with the sun gear rotating, the planet gears simply rotate in the carrier and act as idler gears between the sun and ring gears. (b) If the sun or ring is held, the planet gears will walk around that stationary gear; they rotate on their shafts as the carrier rotates. (c) If two parts are driven and no parts are held, the planet gears are stationary on their shafts, and the whole assembly rotates as a unit.

2. Also, any gear separation forces (as gears transfer power, they tend to push away from each other) are contained within the planetary gear set, preventing this load from being transmitted to the transmission case.

3. Another advantage is the small relative size of the planetary gear set. Conventional gears are normally side by side, and for a 2:1 gear ratio, one gear has to be twice the size of the other. A planetary gear set can easily produce this same ratio in a smaller package.

4. Also, planetary gear sets are in constant mesh and no coupling or uncoupling of the gears is required.

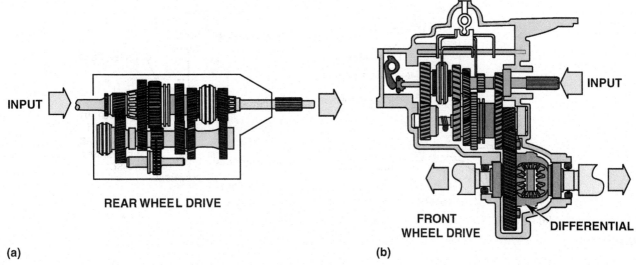

(a)
REAR WHEEL DRIVE

INPUT

(b)
INPUT

FRONT
WHEEL DRIVE   DIFFERENTIAL

FIGURE 1–23 A RWD drivetrain uses a transmission to provide the necessary gear ratio and a single driveshaft to transfer power to the rear axle (a). A FWD drivetrain uses a transaxle that combines the transmission's final drive, and differential (b). A driveshaft is used for each front drive wheel.

? FREQUENTLY ASKED QUESTION

What Do All the Letters and Numbers Mean In Transmission Designations?

The numbers and letters usually mean the following:

- **Number of forward speeds.** The number of forward speeds may include four, five, or six such as the GM 4T60-E four-speed unit and the ZF 5HP24 five-speed unit.
- **Front-wheel drive or rear-wheel drive.** The letter **T** usually means *transverse* (front-wheel-drive transaxle) such as the General Motors 6T65-E; and the **L** means *longitudinal* (rear-wheel-drive transmission) such as the General Motors 6L80.
- **Electronically controlled.** The letter **E** is often used to indicate that the unit is electronically controlled, and **M** or **H** is used to designate older mechanically (hydraulically) controlled units. Most automatic transmissions built since the early 1990s are electronically controlled and therefore the **E** is often included in the designation of newer designs of transmission or transaxles.
- **Torque rating.** The torque rating is usually designated by a number, where the higher the number, the higher the amount of torque load the unit is designed to handle. In a GM 6L80-E, the torque rating is 80. Always check service information for the exact transmission designation for the vehicle being studied.

REAR-WHEEL DRIVE VS. FRONT-WHEEL DRIVE

At one time, most vehicles had the transmission mounted behind the engine and used a driveshaft to transfer power to the rear axle and driving wheels. This drivetrain is called **rear-wheel drive (RWD)**.

Many vehicles use a transaxle to drive the front wheels, called **front-wheel drive (FWD)**. Most FWD vehicles have the engine mounted in a transverse position, crosswise in the vehicle. Some are longitudinally mounted, in a lengthwise position as in RWD vehicles.

Two short driveshafts, called **half shafts**, are used to connect the transaxle to the front wheels. Driving only two wheels is adequate for most driving conditions. When the roads are slippery or when driving off road, driving all four wheels provides better vehicle control. ● **SEE FIGURE 1–23.**

TRANSAXLES

TERMINOLOGY A **transaxle** is a compact combination of a transmission, the **final drive** gear reduction, and the differential. It can be either a manual, automatic, or continuously variable transaxle. Transaxles are used in nearly all front-wheel-drive vehicles, some mid-engine vehicles, rear engine, and even a few rear-wheel-drive vehicles. ● **SEE FIGURE 1–24.**

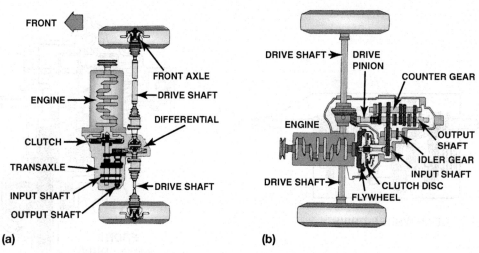

FIGURE 1–24 Transverse (a) and longitudinal (b) mounted front-wheel-drive (FWD) drivetrains.

OPERATION A transmission normally has one output shaft that couples to the rear axle through the driveshaft. A transaxle has two output shafts that couple to the two front wheels through a pair of driveshafts. The **differential** used in transaxles or drive axles is a torque-splitting device that allows the two axle shafts to operate at different speeds so that a vehicle can turn corners. When a vehicle turns a corner, the wheel on the outer side of the turning radius must travel farther than the inner wheel, but it must do this in the same period of time. Therefore, it must rotate faster while turning. Most differentials are composed of a group of four or more gears. One gear is coupled to each axle and two are mounted on the differential pinion shaft.

DRIVESHAFTS

Driveshafts, also called a *propeller shaft* or *prop shaft*, transfer power from one component to another. Rear-wheel-drive vehicle driveshafts are usually made from steel tubing, and normally have either a **universal joint (U-joint)** or a **constant-velocity (CV) joint** at each end. Most front-wheel-drive vehicles use driveshafts that are a solid shaft or hollow steel tubing. A U-joint allows the shaft to change angle as the drive axle moves up and down when the wheels travel over bumps. Speed fluctuations occur in the driveshaft as the U-joints transfer power at an angle, but these fluctuations are canceled out or eliminated by the position of the U-joint at the other end of the driveshaft.

A front-wheel-drive vehicle driveshaft must use a CV joint at its ends because the front wheels must be steered at sharp angles. The short driveshafts used with transaxles and independent rear suspension drive axles are often called half shafts. ● **SEE FIGURE 1–25.**

DRIVE AXLE ASSEMBLIES

Rear-wheel-drive vehicles use a drive axle assembly at the rear. A **drive axle** performs four functions:

1. It supports the weight of the rear of the vehicle.
2. It contains the final drive reduction gears.
3. It contains the differential, which transfers torque to both drive wheels and allows the wheels to rotate at different speeds when cornering.
4. It allows the power to turn 90°.

Most axle assemblies use strong axle shafts to transfer the torque from the differential gears to the wheels and tires. A bearing at the outer end of the axle housing serves to transfer vehicle weight to the axle and then to the wheels and tires while allowing the shaft to rotate.

The term "final drive" refers to the last set of reduction gears in a gear train. The torque that is applied to the drive wheels, and cruising speed engine RPM, is determined by the reduction gears and the drive wheel diameter. ● **SEE FIGURE 1–26.**

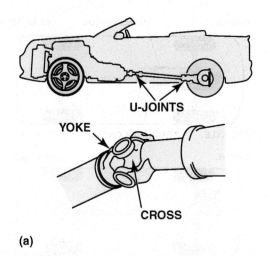

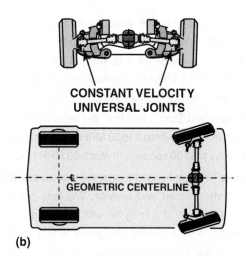

FIGURE 1–25 (a) A rear-wheel-drive driveshaft uses a pair of universal joints to allow the rear axle to move up and down. (b) A front-wheel-drive driveshaft uses constant-velocity joints to allow the front wheels to move up and down and steer.

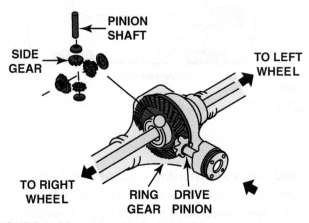

FIGURE 1–26 A drive axle includes a ring and pinion gear to produce a lower gear ratio as it turns the power flow 90° and a differential (differential pinion and side gears) to allow the drive wheels to rotate at different speeds.

? FREQUENTLY ASKED QUESTION

What Must the Powertrain Overcome to Move the Vehicle?

To propel the vehicle, the engine and drivetrain must overcome the following:

- Rolling friction, which is the drag of the tires on the road, and bearing friction. These frictions increase at a constant rate, doubling as the speed is doubled.
- Aerodynamic drag, which is the wind resistance of air moving over the size and shape of the vehicle. It increases at a rapid rate, roughly four times as the speed is doubled (actually, velocity squared).
- Grade resistance, which is equal to 0.01 times the vehicle weight times the angle of the grade in percent.

TOWING CAPABILITY

DRIVETRAIN REQUIREMENTS Trucks are often used to tow trailers or heavy loads. In order for a vehicle to tow a heavy load, the vehicle must have the following features:

- An engine that can produce the needed torque and horsepower.
- A strong frame to withstand the forces involved.
- A strong trailer hitch properly installed and attached to the frame of the vehicle.

- A strong drivetrain (transmission, driveshaft, and drive axle(s)) that can transmit the engine torque to the drive wheels.
- Heavy-duty brakes so that the heavy load can be slowed and stopped safely.

SAE J2807 STANDARD Starting in 2013, the Society of Automotive Engineers (SAE) established a standardized test procedure to determine the tow rating for vehicles. The standard includes three vehicle performance standards including the following:

1. **Climbing test** During the climbing test, the vehicle with the loaded trailer (at the specified rating that the vehicle

manufacture states is the capacity of the vehicle) has 12 seconds to climb a hill that rises 3000 feet (900 m) over a length of 11.4 miles (18 km) without dropping below 40 MPH (64 km/h). This test is based on a stretch of interstate I-15 between Los Angeles and Las Vegas.

2. **Acceleration test** During this test, the vehicle with loaded trailer must accelerate from 0 to 30 MPH (48 km/h) in 12 seconds and less than 30 seconds to reach 60 MPH (100 km/h).

3. **Launching** This test is used to test the vehicle and loaded trailer in both forward and reverse. The test places the vehicle at the base of a long hill with a 12% grade. The vehicle must be able to climb the grade 16 feet (5 m) from a stop five times within five minutes.

These tests test not only the power of the vehicle but also that the engine and transmission can be kept at the proper temperature, meaning that the engine and transmission (if automatic) be equipped with a cooler.

NOTE: Not all vehicle manufactures adhere to the SAE standard when reporting their recommended tow rating because, while standardized, the use of the SAE J2807 is voluntary.

FOUR-WHEEL DRIVE

TERMINOLOGY Four-wheel drive (4WD) is often designated as "4 × 4" and refers to a vehicle that has four driven wheels.

- The first 4 indicates that the vehicle has four wheels.
- The second 4 indicates that all four wheels are driven.

A vehicle will have more pulling power and traction if all of its wheels are driven. This requires a drive axle at each end of the vehicle, another driveshaft, and a **transfer case** or **power transfer unit** to drive the additional driveshaft and drive axle. The transfer case is normally attached to the rear of the transmission. It has a single input shaft from the transmission and two output shafts, one to the front drive axle and one to the rear drive axle. Some transfer cases are two-speed and include a set of reduction gears for lower-speed, higher-torque operation. Four-wheel drive can be built into

- A front-engine rear-wheel drive
- A front-engine front-wheel drive
- A rear-engine rear-wheel drive

● **SEE FIGURE 1-27.**

ALL-WHEEL DRIVE All-wheel-drive (AWD) vehicles are designed with a number of different operating characteristics for improved on-road handling.

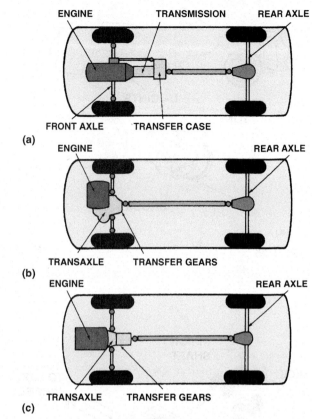

FIGURE 1-27 Three major 4WD configurations. The traditional form (a) uses a transfer case to split the torque for the front and rear drive axles. Both (b) and (c) are typical AWD configurations.

- **Full-time four-wheel drive**—Full-time 4WD allows the driver to select two-wheel drive (2WD) or 4WD with similar selector positions as part-time 4WD. Unlike part-time configurations, full-time 4WD includes a center (interaxle) differential or viscous coupling that allows the front and rear axles to rotate at different speeds. This allows full-time 4WD configurations to operate in 4WD on any road surface. Normally, the driver selects 2WD to decrease fuel consumption when 4WD is not needed.

- **All-the-time 4WD**—The all-the-time 4WD configuration can only be driven in 4WD. This type is also called all-wheel drive. Transfer case controls may allow the driver to select 4WD high, neutral, and 4WD low. Like full-time 4WD, all-the-time 4WD uses a center differential in the transfer case to prevent driveline windup.

- **All-wheel drive (power transfer system)**—This system is used on front-wheel-drive vehicles with a transversely mounted engine. Both axles can drive the vehicle. A single speed transfer case with a differential, a viscous coupling, a center differential, or transfer clutch assembly (located at the transmission or at the rear axle) directs power to the rear axles and assures that both axles are able to rotate at different speeds. A special clutch in the transfer case varies power to the rear axle, depending on the amount of available traction.

- **Automatic AWD**—An automatic four-wheel drive system operates much like an automatic transmission, selecting automatically between 2WD and 4WD, depending upon the driving conditions. It uses an automatic transfer case control module, which monitors input speeds from the front and rear drive shaft speed sensors to monitor wheel slip. These speed sensors are located on the transfer case near the output shafts.

SUMMARY

1. Vehicles are built as rear-wheel drive, front-wheel drive, and four- or all-wheel drive.
2. Engines develop torque and the drivetrains modify that torque to move the vehicle.
3. A variety of gears are used to modify torque.
4. The gear ratio is determined by dividing the number of driven gear teeth by the number of teeth on the driving gear.
5. Transmissions have different gear ratios that are selectable by the driver.
6. Manual transmissions use a clutch and automatic transmissions use a torque converter.
7. Transaxles combine the final drive gears and differential with the transmissions.
8. Driveshafts and the drive axle complete the drivetrain.
9. Four-wheel-drive and all-wheel-drive vehicles have a transfer case or transfer gears and a second drive axle.

REVIEW QUESTIONS

1. What is the difference between torque and horsepower?
2. How is a gear ratio calculated?
3. What are the common shift modes used in an automatic transmission?
4. What is an inter-axle differential?

CHAPTER QUIZ

1. Torque is _____.
   - **a.** A twisting force
   - **b.** The rate of doing work
   - **c.** Results in motion
   - **d.** The gear ratio

2. Gears can be used to _____.
   - **a.** Increase speed
   - **b.** Increase torque
   - **c.** Reverse direction
   - **d.** All of the above

3. If a gear with 20 teeth is driving a gear with 60 teeth, the gear ratio is _____.
   - **a.** 2:6
   - **b.** 3:1
   - **c.** 1:3
   - **d.** 0.33:1

4. Technician A says a helical gear is stronger than a spur gear. Technician B says a helical gear is noisier than a spur gear. Which technician is correct?
   - **a.** Technician A only
   - **b.** Technician B only
   - **c.** Both Technicians A and B
   - **d.** Neither Technician A nor B

5. Which type of gear may be found in a rear-wheel-drive axle?
   - **a.** Hypoid
   - **b.** Spiral Bevel
   - **c.** Planetary
   - **d.** Helical

6. The transmission is in first gear, which has a 2.5:1 ratio, and the rear axle has a ratio of 2:1. What is the overall ratio?
   - **a.** 2:1
   - **b.** 2.5:1
   - **c.** 4.5:1
   - **d.** 5:1

7. The type of gear set used in most automatic transmissions is _____.
   - **a.** Spur gears
   - **b.** Planetary gears
   - **c.** Helical gears
   - **d.** Any of the above

8. What shift mode should be used when descending a steep hill?
   - **a.** Drive (D)
   - **b.** Second (2)
   - **c.** Neutral (N)
   - **d.** Low (L)

9. Full-time four-wheel-drive vehicles may use _____.
   - **a.** Transfer case
   - **b.** Spiral bevel drive axles
   - **c.** Three differentials
   - **d.** Both a and c

10. What is used to transfer engine torque to all four wheels?
    - **a.** Four driveshafts
    - **b.** A transfer case or power transfer unit
    - **c.** Four differentials
    - **d.** All of the above

chapter 2

CLUTCH PARTS AND OPERATION

LEARNING OBJECTIVES

After studying this chapter, the reader will be able to:

1. List the major parts that are included in the clutch system and describe how the clutch works.
2. Discuss the purpose and function of clutch discs.
3. Discuss the purpose and function of pressure plates.
4. State the characteristics of a flywheel and explain how a dual-mass flywheel works.
5. Describe how a clutch pedal linkage and a clutch pedal switch work.
6. Describe the operation of the release bearing and state the types of release bearings.

This chapter will help you prepare for ASE Manual Drive Train and Axles (A3) certification test content area "A" (Clutch Diagnosis and Repair).

KEY TERMS

Belleville spring 23
Clutch disc 19
Coefficient of friction (COF) 21
Coil spring style 23
Cushion spring 22
Diaphragm spring style 23
Dual-mass flywheel 26
Front bearing retainer 21

Inertia 25
Marcel spring 22
Pilot bearing 27
Pressure plate 19
Release bearing 19
Slave cylinder 28
Torsional dampers 22
Throwout bearing 19

GM STC OBJECTIVES

GM Service Technical College topics covered in this chapter are as follows:

1. Various clutch designs that may be used on General Motors vehicles.
2. Operation of cable and hydraulic clutch control systems used on General Motors vehicles.
3. Proper inspection and replacement of a single and dual mass flywheel.

CLUTCHES

PURPOSE AND FUNCTION The clutch assembly is located between the engine and the transmission/transaxle. The purpose and function of a clutch include the following:

- To disconnect engine power from the transmission/transaxle to permit the engine to remain running when the vehicle is stopped and to permit the transmission/transaxle to be shifted into different gears including reverse.
- To connect and transmit engine torque to the transmission/transaxle.
- To dampen and absorb engine power impulses and drivetrain vibration.
- To provide a smooth engagement and disengagement of torque between the engine and the transmission/transaxle.

PARTS INVOLVED A clutch assembly consists of a **clutch disc** that is splined to the input shaft of the transmission/transaxle. When the driver depresses the clutch pedal, a **release** bearing, also called a **throwout bearing**, is forced against the release levers (fingers) of the **pressure plate**. The pressure plate is bolted to and rotates with the flywheel. ● **SEE FIGURE 2–1.**

CLUTCH OPERATION When force is exerted on the center of the pressure plate by the release bearing, the applied force is released from the clutch disc that had been squeezed between the engine flywheel and the pressure plate. With the pressure removed from the clutch disc, the engine can be operated without transferring torque to the transmission/transaxle. Using a clutch also permits the transmission/transaxle to be shifted easily because a shift cannot be made easily if the transmission/transaxle is transferring engine torque. When the driver releases force on the clutch pedal, the pedal return spring and the pressure plate spring combine to return the clutch pedal to its at-rest position (clutch-engaged position). When the clutch pedal moves up, the pressure on the release bearing is released and the force against the pressure plate spring(s) is released, allowing the spring force of the pressure plate to clamp the clutch disc tightly between the flywheel and the pressure plate. ● **SEE FIGURE 2–2.**

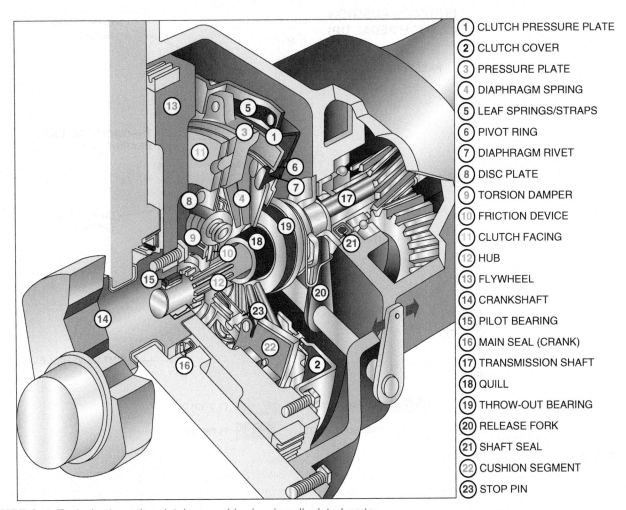

1. CLUTCH PRESSURE PLATE
2. CLUTCH COVER
3. PRESSURE PLATE
4. DIAPHRAGM SPRING
5. LEAF SPRINGS/STRAPS
6. PIVOT RING
7. DIAPHRAGM RIVET
8. DISC PLATE
9. TORSION DAMPER
10. FRICTION DEVICE
11. CLUTCH FACING
12. HUB
13. FLYWHEEL
14. CRANKSHAFT
15. PILOT BEARING
16. MAIN SEAL (CRANK)
17. TRANSMISSION SHAFT
18. QUILL
19. THROW-OUT BEARING
20. RELEASE FORK
21. SHAFT SEAL
22. CUSHION SEGMENT
23. STOP PIN

FIGURE 2–1 Typical automotive clutch assembly showing all related parts.

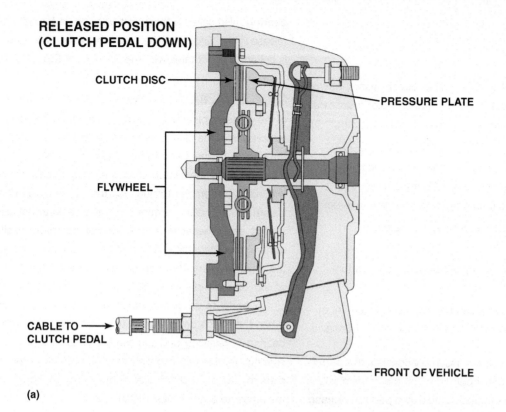

RELEASED POSITION
(CLUTCH PEDAL DOWN)

CLUTCH DISC

PRESSURE PLATE

FLYWHEEL

CABLE TO
CLUTCH PEDAL

FRONT OF VEHICLE

(a)

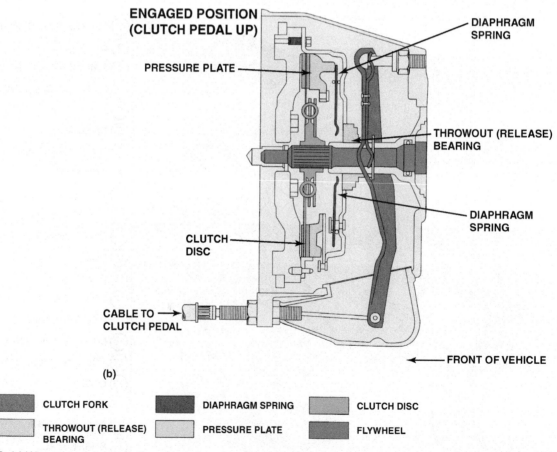

ENGAGED POSITION
(CLUTCH PEDAL UP)

DIAPHRAGM
SPRING

PRESSURE PLATE

THROWOUT (RELEASE)
BEARING

DIAPHRAGM
SPRING

CLUTCH
DISC

CABLE TO
CLUTCH PEDAL

FRONT OF VEHICLE

(b)

CLUTCH FORK   DIAPHRAGM SPRING   CLUTCH DISC

THROWOUT (RELEASE)   PRESSURE PLATE   FLYWHEEL
BEARING

FIGURE 2–2 (a) When the clutch is in the released position (clutch pedal depressed), the clutch fork is applying a force to the throwout (release) bearing, which pushes on the diaphragm spring, releasing the pressure on the friction disc. (b) When the clutch is in the engaged position (clutch pedal up), the diaphragm spring exerts force on the clutch disc, holding it between the flywheel and the pressure plate.

The release bearing is often supported and rides on the transmission/transaxle **front bearing retainer** (also called the *quill*).

To summarize:

- When the clutch pedal is up, the clutch is *engaged*. (The pressure plate presses the clutch disc against the flywheel and rotating together.)
- When the clutch pedal is down, the clutch is *disengaged*. (The clutch disc is free and not rotating with the pressure plate.)

CLUTCH DISCS

PURPOSE AND FUNCTION   The purpose of the clutch disc is to transfer engine torque from the flywheel to the input shaft of the transmission/transaxle. The clutch disc is located between the flywheel and the pressure plate where it connects the two parts when the clutch is engaged and the pressure plate spring exerts spring pressure against the disc and forces it against the flywheel.

COEFFICIENT OF FRICTION   The **coefficient of friction (COF)**, abbreviated with the Greek letter μ (mu), is the relative amount of friction between two surfaces. There has to be friction between the members of the clutch friction surfaces for the clutch to function correctly.

- If the coefficient of friction of the clutch is less than correct (COF too low), it might slip and not transmit the required torque.
- If the coefficient of friction is greater than what it should be (COF too high), the clutch would become more aggressive and grabby, and engagement would be harsh and severe.

The coefficient of friction, also referred to as the friction coefficient, is determined by dividing tensile force by weight force. The tensile force is the pulling force required to slide one of the surfaces across the other. The weight force is the force pushing down on the object being pulled. The equation for calculating the coefficient of friction is as follows:

$$\frac{Ft}{G} = \mu$$

where,

Ft = tensile force in pounds
G = weight force in pounds
μ = coefficient of friction

$$\frac{\textbf{Tensile force}}{\textbf{Weight force}} = \textbf{\textit{Coefficient of friction}}$$

FIGURE 2–3 A replacement clutch is designed to meet the same friction specifications of the original so the new clutch will operate like new.

This equation can be used to show the effect different variables have on the coefficient of friction. For example, if it takes 100 lbs of (tensile) force to pull a 200 lb (weight force) block of wood across a concrete floor, the coefficient of friction is 0.5.

Each vehicle manufacturer specifies the coefficient of friction for each vehicle. The desired coefficient of friction is obtained by using a combination of different friction materials in the manufacture of the clutch disc. If a different clutch friction disc is installed or the lining becomes contaminated, then the coefficient can change and result in slippage or harsh clutch engagement. ● **SEE FIGURE 2–3.**

CLUTCH FACING MATERIAL   The friction facing material of the clutch must be able to withstand the heat generated by the friction during engagement and disengagement. Older clutch friction discs used a mixture of either molded or woven asbestos with various filler and binder materials. Asbestos is nearly an ideal friction material for brake lining and clutch facing because it has a very good coefficient of friction, excellent heat characteristics, and low cost. However, the possibility of technicians getting cancer from inhaling asbestos fibers has greatly reduced its use. Asbestos was replaced with fiberglass, aramid nonmetallic compounds, and/or metallic materials to obtain the desired friction and wear characteristics. Some of the materials used include the following:

- Powdered iron
- Copper
- Graphite
- Ceramics

SURFACE GROOVES   Most nonmetallic facings have a series of radial grooves cut across their surface.

The purpose and function of the grooves include the following:

- Wipe dust and dirt from the surfaces of the flywheel and pressure plate.

- Allow airflow to help cool the friction surfaces.

- Prevent a vacuum that might cause the friction surfaces to stick together during release. Sticking during release will cause clutch drag.

- Some metallic discs have a series of radial slots cut across the facing which allows the disc to expand without warping when it gets hot.

RIVETS   The facing of the clutch disc is attached to the steel cushioning spring by a series of rivets installed in counterbored holes or by bonding which involves attaching the lining to the steel spring by using adhesives (gluing). Some metallic facings are formed directly onto a steel backing. If there is less than 0.015 inch (0.38 mm) of facing above the rivets or backing, a disc is considered worn out.

HUB AND DAMPENER ASSEMBLY   An engine produces uneven power impulses that cause torsional vibration. The damper reduces the torsional vibrations that result from the uneven engine power impulses from the rest of the drivetrain.

- As an engine goes through its power cycle, the crankshaft will speed up and slow down during each revolution.

- If these slight speed fluctuations are not removed by the damper, they could cause "gear rattle," vibration, noise, and increased wear.

The clutch hub has internal splines (from 10 to 26 teeth) that slide on the external splines of the transmission input/clutch shaft. Each time the clutch is applied, the disc must slide forward slightly to contact the flywheel, and it must slide back to prevent drag on the flywheel when the clutch is released.

The damper assembly is composed of the hub with four to eight openings or fingerlike extensions, one or more springs for each extension, a spring washer, and a friction washer. These parts are fitted between the web of the disc and a metal retainer and are held together by a series of rivets called stop pins, which also keep the hub from revolving too far. The damper springs, called **torsional dampers**, are positioned by a series of windows in the web and retainer. The torque must pass through the damper springs on its way from the engine to the transmission, and any power impulses that tend to speed up the clutch hub will compress the springs and help dampen engine firing pulses being transmitted into and through the transmission/transaxle. ● **SEE FIGURE 2–4.**

FIGURE 2–4 A typical stock clutch friction disc that uses coil spring torsional dampers.

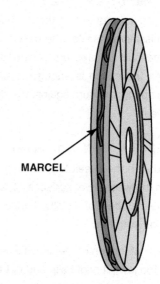

FIGURE 2–5 A marcel is a wavy spring that is placed between the two friction surfaces to cushion the clutch engagement.

In the space between the friction surfaces is a wavy spring steel material called a **cushion spring** or **marcel spring**. The marcel spring helps to absorb the initial shock of rapid engagement and allows for a smooth engagement of the clutch. ● **SEE FIGURE 2–5.**

HIGH-PERFORMANCE CLUTCH DISC   Another type of friction material is a ceramic and metallic mixture. This creates a hard, long-lasting lining, but is more expensive and does not cushion clutch engagement as much as a softer lining. Instead of a full circle of softer friction material, the disc may have only a few segments or buttons of this ceramic-metallic material. Clutches that use these discs, which are sometimes called "button clutches," are found in racing applications where strength and durability are a greater concern than smooth engagement. ● **SEE FIGURE 2–6.**

FIGURE 2–6 A racing or high-performance clutch disc lacks the features of a stock clutch disc that help provide smooth engagement.

FIGURE 2–7 A coil spring (lever style) clutch pressure plate.

PRESSURE PLATES

PURPOSE AND FUNCTION The purpose of the pressure plate is to exert a force on the clutch disc so that engine torque can be transmitted from the engine to the transmission/transaxle. The required strong clamping force is provided by the pressure plate spring(s).

COMPONENT PARTS The pressure plate assembly is a combination of

- The *cover* (also called a *hat*)
- The *pressure springs* and *release levers* (also called *fingers*)
- The cast iron *pressure ring* (*driving plate*) that contacts the friction disc

The strong pressure plate spring force must be released by the force of the driver's foot to engage the clutch. Most pressure plates are made of stamped steel with a nodular cast iron pressure ring, also called a driving plate. A smooth, machined area on one side forms the friction disc contact surface. When the clutch engages, spring force pushes the pressure plate toward the flywheel so the friction disc is clamped between the flywheel and the pressure plate.

STYLES OF PRESSURE PLATES Several styles of pressure plates have been used, including the following:

- **Coil spring style**—This style of pressure plate uses coil springs and three or four release levers. A coil spring-style pressure plate is also called the *lever style* because it uses levers to compress the coil springs. This type of pressure plate is often called a "three finger" pressure plate. ● **SEE FIGURE 2–7.**

FIGURE 2–8 Typical diaphragm-style pressure plate that uses a Belleville spring.

Two types of coil spring-style include the following:

1. *Borg and Beck:* This style uses a round closed cover with three wide-stamped-steel release levers and up to 12 springs with six evenly spaced mounting holes.

2. *Long:* This style uses a triangular-shaped cover with three narrow, forged-steel release levers, which extend through the cover and often have weights on them. This style also usually uses nine springs and has mounting bolt holes in three groups of two.

- **Diaphragm spring style**—This style is the most commonly used pressure plate design. It uses one large, round, steel spring, called a **Belleville spring** to apply even force on the clutch disc. ● **SEE FIGURE 2–8.**

ADVANTAGES OF A DIAPHRAGM-TYPE CLUTCH

Diaphragm-type pressure plates have several advantages over the other types including the following:

1. Diaphragm-type clutch pressure plates tend to be smaller assemblies, weigh less, and have fewer parts than coil spring assemblies. The one-piece diaphragm spring does the job of all the release levers and coil springs in a coil spring clutch.

2. The driver pedal effort required for a diaphragm-type plate is less than that required in a coil spring type. The typical diaphragm-type clutch requires just 35 pounds of force (156 Newtons) to depress the clutch pedal compared to 60 pounds of force (267 Newtons) for a typical coil spring–type clutch. The pedal effort for a coil spring clutch increases the farther down the pedal is pushed.

3. The pedal effort for a diaphragm spring clutch decreases during the second half of pedal travel. As the friction disc wears, coil springs expand and lose some of their clamping force. In contrast, the design of the diaphragm spring tends to increase its clamping force as the friction disc wears to half its original thickness. Then, as the friction disc continues to wear, the clamping force of the spring gradually returns to its original level. This happens without any obvious change in clutch pedal effort.

4. The relatively low height of the diaphragm design is highly favored for transverse engine vehicles where engine and transaxle lengths are critical.

PRESSURE PLATE RING

Pressure plate diameter is measured at the outside diameter of the *pressure plate ring*. It should always be the same size or slightly larger than the disc diameter. A pressure ring is simply a flat, fairly heavy ring usually made from nodular cast iron. The heavy weight is necessary to dissipate heat and provides a heat sink so as not to warp. It also provides sufficient strength so it will spread the spring force evenly onto the disc. For high RPM use, the ring is made from cast steel because centrifugal force can cause a cast iron ring to fail.

- When a clutch slips, heat is generated at the friction surfaces, and this heat will warm the facing, the pressure ring, and the flywheel.

- Excess heat will cause the pressure ring to expand to the point of warpage, destroying its flatness and causing poor ring-to-disc facing contact.

- The greater the mass of the pressure ring, the less the temperature will rise because the heat will spread through more metal which will hold the heat longer.

TECH TIP

Use a "Bent Finger" Pressure Plate

Centrifugal force can affect a diaphragm clutch. During a very high RPM disengagement, the fingers can be moved far enough forward by centrifugal force so that they pass over center (beyond flat). Some people have experienced this during a shift at high RPM when the pedal stays on the floor while the engine overrevs. To prevent this, "bent finger" diaphragms are used for installations where high RPM shifts might occur. The shape of the fingers keeps them from traveling over center. ● **SEE FIGURE 2–9.**

Torque enters the pressure ring from the cover, either through a drive strap or a boss where the release levers extend through openings in the cover. Torque passes out through the friction contact with the facing on the disc.

COVER (HAT) The cover (hat) is the stamped-steel housing that transmits the torque from the flywheel to the pressure ring. It also provides a mounting place for the springs and release levers, and it must be strong enough to contain the various forces without distorting.

RELEASE LEVERS/FINGERS In a coil spring-type clutch, the release levers provide a means of compressing the spring(s) and pulling the pressure ring away from the disc. This movement is called *plate lift*. Along with the leverage of the clutch linkage, release levers provide a lever that will produce the necessary 500 to 1500 pounds (230 to 700 kg) of force needed at the pressure plate from the 20 pounds (9 kg) or so used to push the clutch pedal. A diaphragm-type clutch has multiple fingers formed as part of the Belleville spring that radiate to the center of the clutch. The release bearing presses on these fingers to lift the pressure ring.

DOUBLE DISC CLUTCHES A relatively inexpensive method of increasing clutch torque capacity is to use two or more clutch discs. All that is required is another disc (much like the first) and a floater plate, located between the two friction discs and a lengthened pressure plate cover with provision for the floater plate. ● **SEE FIGURE 2–10.**

The floater plate must be able to move forward to squeeze the front disc against the flywheel and rearward during release to provide air gaps. The pressure plate provides the clamping force for both discs, and has enough movement to provide air gaps at both discs when released.

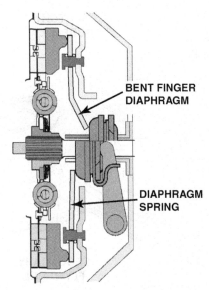

FIGURE 2-9 A bent finger diaphragm clutch. The shape of the fingers keeps the fingers and release bearing from going past center during clutch release.

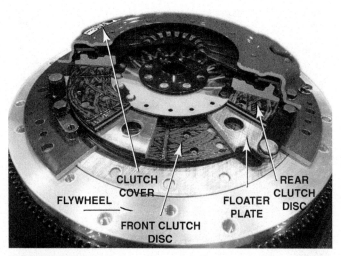

FIGURE 2-10 A double disc clutch that uses a floater plate between the two discs. The second disc doubles the clutch torque capacity.

FIGURE 2-11 The ring gear, which is attached to the outer rim of the flywheel, provides the teeth needed to mesh with the starter pinion gear.

FLYWHEELS

PURPOSE AND FUNCTION The engine flywheel serves four basic purposes:

1. Smooths out or dampens engine power pulses.
2. Absorbs some of the heat created by clutch operation.
3. Provides the connection point for the starter motor to rotate the engine.
4. Provides the friction surface for the clutch friction disc.

INERTIA A flywheel is heavy, or has a large mass, which creates **inertia**. Inertia is the tendency of a moving object to remain in motion, because of its weight, unless forced to slow. This inertia acts upon crankshaft rotation to smooth out or dampen engine power pulses. On a running engine, the crankshaft speeds up as a cylinder fires, then slows due to internal engine friction until the next cylinder fires. The inertia provided by the flywheel mass tends to keep crankshaft speed more constant. The flywheel also absorbs some of the heat created by clutch operation by acting as a heat sink for the clutch friction disc.

STARTER RING GEAR An external ring gear is commonly cast and machined as part of the flywheel, or pressed or welded onto the flywheel, along its outer circumference. The starter-drive gear meshes with the flywheel ring gear. Through gear reduction, the flywheel transfers starter motor rotation to the crankshaft to crank the engine. When the starter motor is engaged, the starter

motor will spin but the engine will not crank if the ring gear on the flywheel is broken. Some ring gears can be replaced separately without having to replace the flywheel in the event of a failure. ● **SEE FIGURE 2-11.**

CONSTRUCTION The flywheel is constructed of cast iron and attaches to the end of the engine crankshaft. The carbon content of the cast iron (about 3%) provides a suitable surface for the clutch disc.

The carbon, in the form of graphite, acts as a lubricant to help provide a smooth engagement of the clutch. The face on the transmission side of the flywheel has a smooth, machined area that creates the application surface for the clutch friction disc. This surface must be properly finished to allow adequate slippage as the clutch engages and disengages, and to prevent

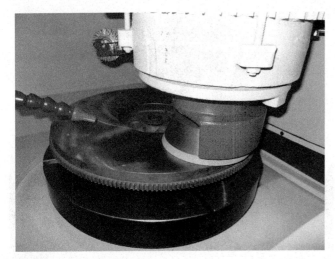

FIGURE 2–12 A flywheel being machined (ground) to provide the correct surface finish for the replacement clutch disc.

FIGURE 2–13 A stepped flywheel has more mass on the outer edge which helps smooth out the impulses from a four-cylinder engine especially at idle speed.

slippage when the clutch is engaged. Being made from cast iron makes resurfacing easy. ● **SEE FIGURE 2–12.**

STEPPED FLYWHEELS Some manufacturers use a stepped flywheel. These are combined with a pressure plate that has either a flat or almost flat cover. Stepped flywheels have more of the mass at the outer edge, which increases the rotational inertia. ● **SEE FIGURE 2–13.**

DUAL-MASS FLYWHEELS

PURPOSE AND FUNCTION Some vehicles, especially high-performance vehicles and vehicles equipped with diesel engines, use a dual-mass flywheel. The purpose of a **dual-mass**

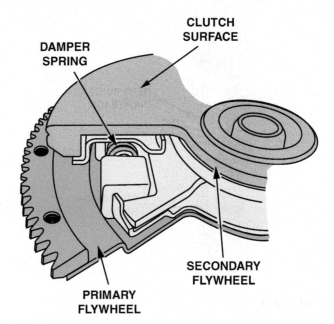

FIGURE 2–14 A dual-mass wheel consists of two flywheels connected between with a spring to help absorb engine pulsations.

flywheel is to dampen engine vibrations and keep them from being transmitted to the passenger compartment through the transmission and shift linkage.

PARTS AND OPERATION A dual-mass flywheel consists of two separate flywheels attached with damper springs, friction material, and ball bearings to allow some movement between the primary and secondary flywheel. By allowing a slight amount of movement between the two flywheels, the damper springs absorb engine torque peaks and normal vibration to provide smoother drivetrain operation. The damper assembly is completely sealed, because it also contains a fluid or lubricant, typically silicone based, which also helps absorb vibration and transmit torque. Typically, the two flywheels twist out of phase with each other by up to about 60° to absorb torsional oscillations.

- The starter ring gear mounts on the primary flywheel. Power from the starter motor does not have to flow through the damper assembly to reach the engine crankshaft.
- The pilot bearing is also attached to the primary flywheel.
- The clutch friction surface is usually on the secondary flywheel. ● **SEE FIGURE 2–14.**

NOTE: If the dual-mass flywheel fails, the symptom is the same as a slipping clutch. The torque-limiting friction material connecting the primary and secondary flywheels can fail. This failure requires the replacement of the flywheel assembly.

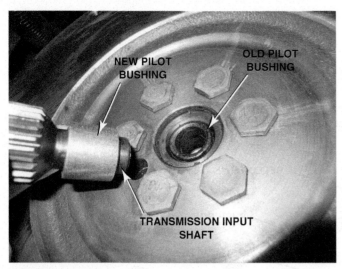

FIGURE 2–15 A pilot bearing or bushing, such as one being used on the rear-wheel-drive pickup truck, is pressed into the end of the engine crankshaft and supports the input shaft of the transmission.

PILOT BEARINGS

PURPOSE AND FUNCTION The engine end of a transmission input (clutch) shaft is supported by a **pilot bearing** that is pressed into the end of the crankshaft. ● **SEE FIGURE 2–15.**

The transmission input shaft goes all the way from the transmission, through the clutch assembly, to the engine. Transmission bearings support the transmission end of the shaft. The pilot bearing or bushing supports it at the engine end. A front-wheel-drive vehicle has a transaxle with an input shaft supported by a pair of bearings and a short input shaft which may not reach all the way to the flywheel. This design does not need a pilot bushing or bearing to support the engine end of the input shaft.

Other designs, such as a rear-wheel-drive vehicle with a flat flywheel, have a much longer transmission input shaft and require the use of a pilot bearing to support the end of the shaft.

CONSTRUCTION Pilot bearings can be constructed using

- Sintered bronze Oilite® bushing, which is impregnated with oil to lubricate it
- Needle bearing
- Sealed ball bearing

● **SEE FIGURE 2–16.**

OPERATION At the engine, the transmission input shaft rests inside a small bore in the flywheel or crankshaft flange. The pilot bearing or bushing supports the engine end of the

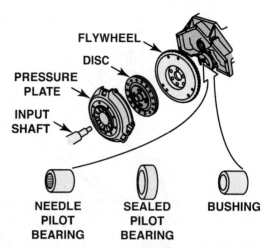

FIGURE 2–16 Pilot bearings (bushings) are made in several different designs depending on the application.

input shaft and provides a low-friction surface for the shaft to ride on. This keeps the shaft and friction disc perfectly aligned with the flywheel and pressure plate. The pilot bearing or bushing rotates with the crankshaft while the engine is running. When the clutch is released, the input shaft does not rotate when the engine is running. The pilot bearing or bushing lowers the friction between these two moving parts.

CLUTCH PEDAL LINKAGE

PURPOSE AND FUNCTION The purpose and function of the clutch pedal linkage are to transfer the force the driver exerts on the clutch pedal to the release bearing.

MECHANICAL CLUTCH LINKAGE Mechanical clutch linkages use either a lever and rod mechanism or a cable release system.

- **Levers and rods.** Mechanical linkages use a series of levers and rods to move the release fork against the throw-out bearing. This method was commonly used on many older vehicles. If a change in direction is needed, *bell cranks* are mounted on pivot shafts to reverse the direction of the force. This type of linkage ends at the clutch fork after it passes through an equalizer shaft that pivots from both the engine/bell housing and the vehicle body. Clutch assembly and engine are on rubber mounts, the engine can move relative to the body and clutch pedal, and any movement during clutch operation can cause an unwanted apply, release, or chatter. ● **SEE FIGURE 2–17.**
- **Cable operation.** A cable is used similar to a brake cable used on a bicycle. Cable linkage consists of a steel cable

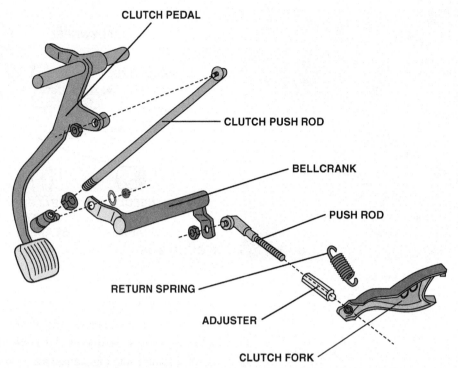

CLUTCH PEDAL

CLUTCH PUSH ROD

BELLCRANK

PUSH ROD

RETURN SPRING

ADJUSTER

CLUTCH FORK

FIGURE 2–17 Older vehicles may use a lever and rod clutch linkage. (Courtesy of General Motors.)

attached to the clutch pedal. The clutch cable is routed to the engine/bell housing, where it can pull on the clutch fork/lever. Much of the cable is enclosed in a housing or conduit so that it can be routed around corners or obstacles. Although simple and inexpensive, cables have a drawback in that they develop internal friction through time, which makes them harder to operate.

ADJUSTMENT. Mechanical linkage includes an adjustment at some point so that *free travel* can be adjusted. Free travel, also called *free play,* is the slight clearance (about 1 inch [25 mm]) measured at the pedal, or is measured at the clutch fork between the throw-out bearing and the pressure plate (about 1/16 inch [2 mm]).

Many vehicles include a *self-adjuster mechanism* at the clutch pedal. Older vehicles include a method of manual adjustment, at the end of either the cable or cable housing. The self-adjuster is usually a spring-loaded cam that is mounted onto the pedal when a spring-loaded pawl engages it. The pawl is lifted each time the clutch is released so that the cam spring can rotate and remove any slack or clearance in the cable. When the pedal is applied, the pawl's spring returns it to lock the cam to the pedal. ● **SEE FIGURE 2–18.**

HYDRAULIC CLUTCH LINKAGE A small master cylinder is located on the bulkhead and operated by the clutch pedal and a **slave cylinder** located near the release (throwout) bearing. This is the most common method of connecting the

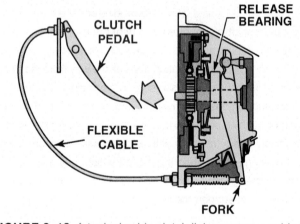

CLUTCH PEDAL

RELEASE BEARING

FLEXIBLE CABLE

FORK

FIGURE 2–18 A typical cable clutch linkage uses a cable to transmit motion from the pedal to the release bearing.

clutch pedal to the release fork on vehicles equipped with a manual transmission. ● **SEE FIGURE 2–19.**

A hydraulic system transmits force using a fluid and is the most commonly used clutch linkage system used. Liquids cannot be compressed, and if a force is put on liquid at one end of a passage, liquid at the other end of the passage will exert the same force.

In a foot-operated system, force is exerted on a piston in the input cylinder, or pump, and leaves at the output cylinder. If these pistons are the same size, they will have equal force and movement. Whatever movement goes in one end will be transmitted to the other end. If the input and output pistons are of different sizes, a hydraulic lever is created. If the input

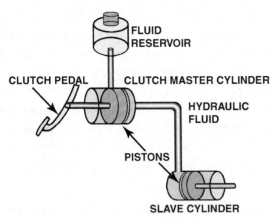

FIGURE 2–19 Simple hydraulic clutch system. The hydraulic fluid will transmit force and motion from the clutch pedal to the slave cylinder.

piston is smaller than the output piston (which is normal), force will increase, but travel of the output piston will be reduced.

In a hydraulic clutch system, the input piston is located in the clutch master cylinder and will be connected to the clutch pedal. The output piston is located in the slave cylinder, and it will operate the clutch fork/lever. The master cylinder and slave cylinder pistons are connected by metal, reinforced rubber, or plastic tubing.

- When the clutch pedal is depressed, the master cylinder piston forces fluid through the tubing to the slave cylinder, where the pressure forces the slave cylinder piston to move the clutch fork/lever.

- When the pedal is released, the pressure plate forces the slave cylinder piston to return the fluid to the master cylinder.

- When the master cylinder is released, a compensating port is opened up between the cylinder bore and the fluid reservoir. This port allows for fluid expansion or contraction due to temperature changes, for any air to leave the fluid, and provides self-adjustment for disc wear.

- Because air can be compressed, any air trapped in a hydraulic system will cause a mushy, spongy pedal, or incomplete operation. DOT 3 brake fluid is generally used in clutch hydraulic systems.

The slave cylinder may be mounted on the exterior of the bell housing. Most systems use a slave cylinder that is concentric to the transmission front bearing retainer or input shaft and has the release bearing connected directly to it. ● SEE FIGURE 2–20.

OVERCENTER SPRING
The clutch pedal may include an overcenter, or assist, spring. This spring is mounted to pull the pedal upward during the first half of pedal travel and downward during the second half. This last action reduces pedal effort and helps release the clutch. This can be demonstrated by carefully

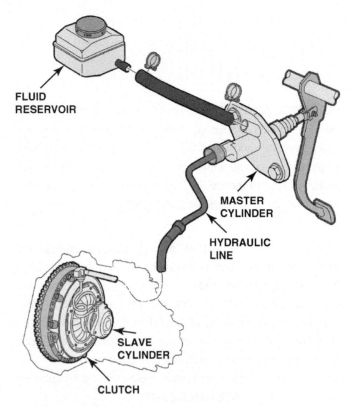

FIGURE 2–20 The slave cylinder of some systems is concentric to the transmission input bearing retainer. When the clutch pedal is depressed, pressurized fluid is forced from the clutch master cylinder to the slave cylinder to release the clutch. (Courtesy of General Motors)

FIGURE 2–21 The overcenter spring is located near the clutch pedal fulcrum. (Courtesy of Jeffrey Rehkopf)

pushing on the clutch pedal with the linkage disconnected. ● SEE FIGURE 2–21.

CAUTION: In most cases, the pedal will move downward rather violently as the spring passes over center.

RELEASE (THROWOUT) BEARING

PURPOSE AND FUNCTION The release bearing, also called a *throwout bearing*, rides on the transmission front bearing retainer and when the clutch pedal is pushed down, it pushes against the fingers of the pressure plate. The clutch operating system moves the clutch release bearing when the driver presses or releases the clutch pedal.

OPERATION The release bearing presses against the diaphragm spring fingers or coil spring levers. This takes spring force off the pressure plate so that it no longer clamps the friction disc against the flywheel. The diaphragm spring fingers or coil spring levers rotate at crankshaft speed, but the clutch operating system is a part of the vehicle chassis and does not rotate. The release bearing is the point where the fixed, stationary clutch operating system meets the rapidly spinning clutch assembly. ● **SEE FIGURE 2–22.**

RELEASE BEARING CONSTRUCTION Most clutch release bearings are ball bearings. The bearing absorbs a thrust load when its outer race presses against the diaphragm spring fingers or coil spring levers. When the outer race contacts the spring fingers or levers, it must rotate with them at engine crankshaft speed. The inner bearing race is pressed onto an iron hub, or sleeve. In some designs, the inner bearing race and sleeve are machined as one piece. The inner bearing race and sleeve are stationary and do not spin when the outer race spins.

RELEASE BEARING LOCATION The transmission front bearing retainer has a long hollow tube extending toward the engine.

The release bearing sleeve slides on the outer surface of this tube, which is also commonly called (slang)

- *Quill*
- *Quill shaft*
- *Candlestick*

In a typical system, the outside of the release bearing sleeve has grooves or raised flat surfaces that fit into the clutch

(a)

(c)

(b)

FIGURE 2–22 (a) A release (throw-out) bearing on a transmission that uses a clutch fork and a mechanical or cable-operated linkage. (b) A style of release bearing that includes the slave cylinder, sometimes called a *concentric slave cylinder.* (c) A combination release bearing and slave cylinder showing the two hydraulic lines. The lower line is from the master clutch cylinder and the upper line is used to bleed air from the hydraulic system.

release fork. A snap ring, spring clips, or lock pins secure the release bearing to the release fork. The clutch operating system pivots the release fork back and forth when the driver presses and releases the clutch pedal. The pivoting motion of the fork slides the release bearing away from or toward the engine to engage or disengage the clutch.

TYPES OF RELEASE BEARINGS   If the clutch operating system self-adjusts, then there is no clearance between the release bearing outer race and the diaphragm spring fingers or coil spring levers.

- The release bearing outer race constantly turns at engine crankshaft speed. This is called a *constant-running release bearing.* In some self-adjusting systems, a snap ring holds the outer race to the spring fingers. This design is typical of pull-type clutch operating systems that move away from the flywheel to disengage the clutch.

- If the clutch operating system does not self-adjust, then there must be some clearance between the release bearing outer race and the spring fingers when the clutch is engaged. The outer race does not contact the spring fingers and so it does not turn. As the driver depresses the clutch pedal, the release bearing moves into contact with the fingers and the outer race begins to rotate with them. This type of release bearing is not designed to rotate constantly. If the clutch is not adjusted properly and there is no clearance, the release bearing spins constantly and wears out quickly.

RELEASE BEARING LUBRICATION   The ball bearing portion of the release bearing is usually permanently lubricated and sealed during manufacture. This part of the bearing should not be lubricated during service. The sleeve, or quill shaft, often needs lubrication during clutch service. Typically, a thin film of high-temperature grease coats the sliding surfaces. Always follow the vehicle manufacturer's recommendations for release bearing lubrication, and avoid overlubricating.

CLUTCH PEDAL SWITCHES

PURPOSE AND FUNCTION   A clutch pedal position switch is used to signal the starter circuit that the clutch is released, which prevents starter operation unless the clutch pedal is depressed. ● **SEE FIGURE 2–23.**

OPERATION   The switch is normally electrically open, and it closes when the pedal is completely depressed. This completes the circuit from the ignition switch to the starter solenoid or relay, and when the circuit is completed, the starter relay energizes the starter, cranking the engine. This safety feature prevents the vehicle from moving accidentally when the starter is engaged.

CAUTION: Older vehicles may not be equipped with a clutch safety switch, so it is very important that the transmission be placed in neutral and/or the clutch fully depressed before starting the engine. ● SEE FIGURE 2–24.

NOTE: On most vehicles, the clutch pedal switch is an input to the engine control module (ECM), rather than being directly inserted into the starter control circuit. On other vehicles, the switch provides the ground for the starter relay coil circuit. Some vehicles use a three-wire pedal position sensor instead of a switch. Always refer to service information (SI) for operational details of the vehicle being serviced. ● SEE FIGURE 2–25.

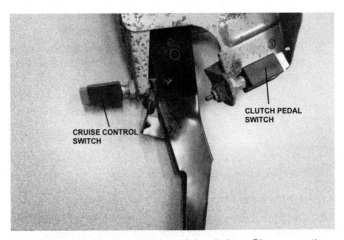

FIGURE 2–23 Typical clutch pedal switches. Shown are the starter safety switch and the cruise control cut-out switch.

<table>
<tr><td>❓</td><td>**FREQUENTLY ASKED QUESTION**</td></tr>
</table>

What Is a Pull-Type Release Bearing?

The pressure plate used on a few FWD vehicles is bolted directly onto the engine's crankshaft, and the flywheel is bolted onto the pressure plate. This allows the release bearing to be placed inside the pressure plate and operated by a pull rod through the transmission input shaft. It is often called a *pull-type clutch.* The mounting of the diaphragm spring is moved in the cover and at the pressure ring so a pulling force is used to release the clutch instead of the normal pushing force. This change produces an improvement in clutch system efficiency and a lower clutch pedal effort.

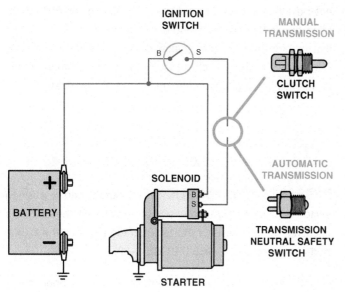

FIGURE 2-24 To prevent the engine from cranking, an electrical switch is usually installed to open the circuit between the ignition switch and the starter solenoid. When the clutch pedal is depressed, the switch closes and completes the circuit to the starter.

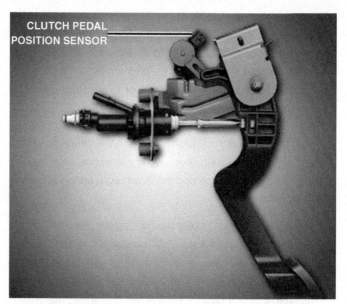

FIGURE 2-25 The clutch pedal position sensor is a 3-wire, 5-volt sensor that returns a voltage signal to the ECM indicating pedal movement and position. (Courtesy of General Motors.)

SUMMARY

1. The purpose and function of a clutch include the following:
   - To disconnect the engine torque from the transmission/transaxle to permit the engine to remain running when the vehicle is stopped and to permit the transmission/transaxle to be shifted.
   - To connect and transmit engine torque to the transmission/transaxle.
   - To dampen and absorb engine power impulses and drivetrain vibration.
   - To provide a smooth engagement and disengagement of torque between the engine and the transmission/transaxle.

2. The clutch assembly includes the flywheel, clutch disc, release (throw-out) bearing, and pressure plate.

3. The purpose of the clutch disc is to transfer engine torque from the flywheel to the input shaft of the transmission/transaxle.

4. The engine flywheel serves four basic purposes:
   - Smooths out or dampens engine power pulses.
   - Absorbs some of the heat created by clutch operation.
   - Provides the connection point for the starter motor to rotate the engine.
   - Provides the application surface for the clutch friction disc.

5. The engine end of a transmission input (clutch) shaft is supported by a pilot bearing that is pressed into the end of the crankshaft.

6. The purpose and function of the clutch pedal linkage are to transfer the force the driver exerts on the clutch pedal to the release bearing.

REVIEW QUESTIONS

1. List the parts of a typical clutch assembly.

2. Describe the sequence of events that happen in the clutch system when the driver depresses the clutch pedal.

3. Explain why a dual-mass flywheel is used on some vehicles.

1. Which part does *not* rotate when the engine is running and the clutch is depressed?
   a. Pilot bearing (bushing)
   b. Pressure plate
   c. Input shaft
   d. Flywheel

2. What part is often *not* used on a front-wheel-drive vehicle with a manual transaxle?
   a. Flywheel
   b. Clutch fork
   c. Release (throwout) bearing
   d. Pilot bearing

3. A dual-mass flywheel is used to_____.
   a. Reduce clutch effort
   b. Reduce vibration
   c. Increase torque holding ability of a clutch
   d. Decrease vehicle weight

4. Most hydraulic clutch systems use what hydraulic fluid?
   a. DOT 3 Brake fluid
   b. Mineral (hydraulic) oil
   c. SAE 80W-90 Gear oil
   d. ATF

5. Flywheels are constructed of cast iron because _____.
   a. They contain about 3% carbon, which acts as a lubricant for the clutch
   b. They have a lot of inertia
   c. Can be resurfaced
   d. All of the above

6. The most commonly used clutch linkage is_____.
   a. Mechanical (rods and levers)
   b. Hydraulic
   c. Cable
   d. Electrically controlled

7. The release bearing sleeve slides on the outer surface of a tube, which is commonly called the_____.
   a. Quill
   b Front bearing retainer
   c. Candlestick
   d. Any of the above

8. A clutch switch is used to_____.
   a. Disengage the clutch
   b. Engage the clutch
   c. Prevent the engine from starting unless the clutch pedal is depressed
   d. Provide an input signal for the PCM to disengage the clutch

9. Springs are mounted at the center of a clutch disc. Technician A says they help cushion clutch engagement. Technician B says they absorb engine torsional vibrations. Which technician is correct?
   a. Technician A only
   b. Technician B only
   c. Both technicians A and B
   d. Neither technician A nor B

10. When the clutch is released (clutch pedal down) _____.
    a. Springs force the pressure ring toward the clutch cover.
    b. Springs force the pressure ring toward the flywheel.
    c. The release (throwout) bearing is used to move the pressure ring toward the clutch cover
    d. The pilot bearing is pressed toward the engine

chapter 3
CLUTCH DIAGNOSIS AND SERVICE

INTRODUCTION

Most automotive technicians perform three different levels of clutch service.

1. Preventive maintenance: Check pedal free travel and fluid levels and make the necessary inspections and adjustments to ensure proper operation.

2. Troubleshooting and diagnosis: Determine the cause of a clutch concern and make recommendations for repair.

3. Replacement: Replace the clutch components to get the vehicle back in proper operation.

CLUTCH INSPECTION

The typical maintenance and service items for a clutch include the following steps. These operations are normally performed along with the other routine service checks.

1. Checking clutch pedal free travel, or free play (older vehicles)

2. Inspecting mechanical linkage systems (older vehicles)

3. Checking the fluid level in hydraulic systems

CLUTCH PEDAL FREE TRAVEL When diagnosing a clutch or transmission concern, the first step is always a clutch pedal free travel check.

- Excessive free travel will cause the clutch to not release completely.

- Too little free travel will not allow the clutch to engage completely, which is more common because clutch pedal free travel will decrease as the clutch disc facing wears.

Note: Not all vehicle clutch systems have pedal free travel. Always check with service information for the exact procedures to follow on the vehicle being checked.

CLUTCH PEDAL FREE TRAVEL TEST PROCEDURE To check and adjust clutch pedal free travel, perform the following steps:

STEP 1 Push the clutch pedal downward by hand. As the pedal moves, there should be a light resistance from the clutch pedal return spring. A much greater resistance is felt as the release bearing contacts the release levers of the pressure plate assembly. The free travel is the distance the pedal moves before the greater resistance

of the release levers is felt. Some manufacturers recommend checking and measuring free travel at the clutch fork or lever. In this case, push on the end of the fork in the direction of release. Some resistance should be felt for a short distance, which is the free travel.

STEP 2 Measure the free travel with a ruler or tape measure. Compare the distance measured with the specifications. Free travel that is more or less than the specifications indicates the need for a clutch adjustment. It should be noted that some manufacturers recommend measuring free travel with the engine running. If no specifications are available, many technicians will use 3/4 to 1 inch (20 to 25 mm) at the clutch pedal and 1/8 to 1/4 inch (3 to 6 mm) at the clutch fork as a rule thumb. ● **SEE FIGURE 3–1.**

STEP 3 If an adjustment is necessary, locate the adjuster and shorten or lengthen the linkage as necessary to correct the free travel. As a final check, operate the clutch pedal through its full range of travel. It should operate smoothly without any unusual lags, skips, binding, roughness, or noise.

Note: On most non-self-adjusting clutch systems, as the clutch disc wears, the free-pedal distance will decrease.

CLUTCH FLUID LEVEL Clutch hydraulic fluid level is checked by looking at the fluid level at the clutch master cylinder reservoir. Many reservoirs will be marked to indicate

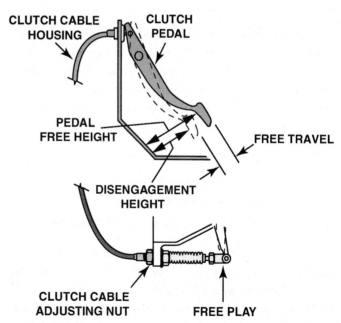

FIGURE 3–1 A typical cable-operated clutch adjustment location.

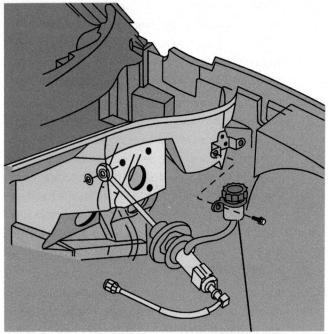

FLUID RESERVOIR

FIGURE 3–2 A typical clutch master cylinder and reservoir mounted on the bulkhead on the driver's side of the vehicle. Brake fluid is used in the hydraulic system to operate the slave cylinder located on the bell housing. (Courtesy of General Motors.)

the correct fluid level. If there are no markings, assume that the fluid level should be between 1/4 and 1/2 inch (6 and 13 mm) from the top. Normally, the fluid level will rise slightly as the clutch facing wears. A low fluid level usually indicates a leak in the system. ● **SEE FIGURE 3–2.**

TYPES OF BRAKE FLUID Brake fluid meeting the DOT 3 designated specification is the most commonly used fluid in hydraulic clutch systems. However, there are several fluids that may be specified depending on vehicle manufacturer, model, and year. The fluids that may be specified include the following types:

- DOT 3 brake fluid (Clear; amber)
- DOT 4 brake fluid (Clear; amber)
- DOT 4+ brake fluid (Clear; amber) (European vehicles)
- Brake hydraulic fluid (clear/amber) ● **SEE FIGURE 3–3.**

Clutch hydraulic fluid is *hygroscopic* and absorbs water directly from the moisture in the air. This means that the hydraulic system may need to be drained, and refilled with new fluid to prevent corrosion and increase the service life of the components. Always follow the vehicle manufacturers' recommend procedures and service intervals.

FIGURE 3–3 Clutch fluid is similar to brake fluid.

CLUTCH PROBLEM DIAGNOSIS

SYMPTOMS OF A DEFECTIVE CLUTCH The following symptoms will occur if there is a fault in the clutch or in the linkage or hydraulic system that could prevent the clutch from being fully disengaged:

- The transmission will be difficult (or impossible) to shift into reverse.
- The transmission will be difficult (or impossible) to shift between forward gears.

LEAK DETECTION A drop in fluid level at the reservoir indicates a fluid leak. Normally, facing wear will cause an increase, or rise, in the fluid level, so topping off the reservoir is not necessary or recommended. The cause of a fluid leak is usually found through visual inspection of the cylinders and lines to locate the wetness. Fluid leak repair is done by correcting the fault which could include the following:

- Tightening a loose line fitting
- Replacing an O-ring, fluid line or hose
- Replacing the clutch master cylinder or slave cylinder

SLAVE CYLINDER TRAVEL Inability to release the clutch completely can be checked by observing slave cylinder travel as the clutch pedal is depressed. The slave cylinder should begin moving immediately and travel in a smooth, steady manner.

Stuck in Gear

A manual shift vehicle sometimes got stuck in first or reverse, and the only way to get it out of gear is to shut the engine off. The transmission shifted okay most of the time.

Thinking that clutch or related components were the most likely cause, the transmission was removed, and an inspection revealed a seizing pilot bushing. Replacement of the bushing fixed this problem. The pilot bushing did not allow the input shaft to move independently of the flywheel when the clutch was depressed.

Some manufacturers provide slave cylinder travel or extension specifications. For example, one manufacturer specifies 0.5 inch (13 mm) of slave cylinder motion for one complete stroke of the clutch pedal. Insufficient slave cylinder travel indicates air in the system or a faulty slave or master cylinder.

CLUTCH SLIPPAGE DIAGNOSIS

Clutch slippage can be checked easily in a shop; however, a more thorough check can be made during a road test.

To check for slippage in a shop, perform the following steps:

STEP 1 Check and adjust clutch pedal free travel.

STEP 2 Warm up the engine to operating temperature, block the wheels, and apply the parking brake completely.

STEP 3 Shift the transmission into high gear and let out the clutch pedal smoothly. The engine should stall immediately. A delay indicates slow engagement and slipping.

To check for slippage on a road test, perform the following steps:

STEP 1 Check and adjust clutch pedal free travel.

STEP 2 Drive to an area with very little traffic. Accelerate slowly and drive at 15 to 20 mph (24 to 32 km/h) in the highest transmission gear. Use the lowest speed at which the vehicle will operate smoothly.

STEP 3 Depress the accelerator completely to wide-open throttle and listen to the engine RPM or watch the tachometer. The engine speed should increase steadily as the vehicle accelerates. If the engine speed flares upward, the clutch is slipping and needs service. Slipping becomes even more evident if this test is made while driving up a hill.

CLUTCH SPIN-DOWN TEST Hard shifting into gear from neutral, sometimes accompanied by gear clash, can be caused by a clutch that is not releasing completely. This is called drag and is easily checked by a spin-down test. **Clutch spin-down** is the time it takes for the clutch disc and transmission gears to spin to a stop when the clutch is released. This time will vary depending on clutch disc diameter and transmission drag.

To check clutch spin-down, perform the following steps:

STEP 1 Check and adjust clutch pedal free travel.

STEP 2 Warm up the engine and transmission to operating temperatures.

STEP 3 With the engine running at idle speed and the transmission in neutral, push in the clutch pedal, wait 9 seconds, and shift the transmission into reverse (a nonsynchronized gear). The shift should occur silently. Gear clash or grinding indicates a dragging clutch that has not released completely. The 9-second time period is very long. Some vehicles that will shift quietly and cleanly into reverse in 3 or 4 seconds. If a clutch fails the spin-down check, it likely needs to be replaced.

CLUTCH SYMPTOM GUIDE

CLUTCH SLIPS Possible causes include the following:

1. Clutch is worn or out-of-adjustment.
2. Clutch disc has oil on the surface.
3. Flywheel height is out-of-specifications.

CLUTCH GRABS Possible causes include the following:

1. Clutch disc has oil on the surface.
2. Clutch linkage is binding.

CLUTCH NOISES Possible causes include the following:

1. Pilot bearing is defective or worn.
2. Release bearing is defective or worn.

NOTE: A squeal that begins as the clutch pedal is depressed about 1 inch (25 mm) is probably caused by a defective or worn release (throw-out) bearing.

CLUTCH REPLACEMENT

PARTS INVOLVED Clutch replacement, commonly called a *clutch job*, is a fairly expensive and labor-intensive repair. During disassembly, each part should be checked to determine if it

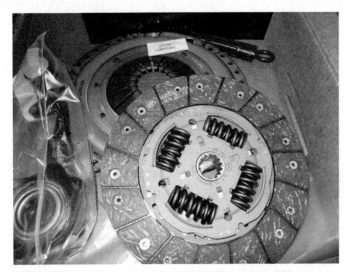

FIGURE 3–4 A typical clutch kit, which includes the clutch disc, pressure plate, and release (throw-out) bearing, as well as grease for the spline and a clutch disc alignment tool.

is the cause of the failure and if it is suitable for reuse. During reassembly, each phase is normally accompanied by checks for proper clearances or operation so that any faulty parts or assemblies can be corrected as early in the assembly as possible.

Clutch replacement normally involves replacing four items:

1. Pressure plate assembly
2. Clutch disc
3. Release bearing
4. Pilot bearing ● **SEE FIGURE 3–4.**

CLUTCH REMOVAL The clutch replacement for a typical rear-wheel-drive vehicle includes the following steps.

1. Hoist the vehicle safely and mark and remove the driveshaft. This step ensures that the driveshaft will be reinstalled correctly and in phase.
2. Disconnect the shift linkage, speedometer connections, and reverse light switch connection as well as the clutch linkage or cable or slave cylinder.
3. Support the transmission with a transmission jack and then remove the rear cross member and bell housing bolts.
4. Carefully move the transmission toward the rear. Try to keep the transmission level to avoid causing damage to the pilot bearing or clutch components. A slight wiggling of the transmission is usually necessary to allow the input shaft to slide over the spline of the clutch disc.
5. After the transmission has cleared the clutch, it can be lowered and inspected before being reinstalled after the clutch assembly has been replaced.

TECH TIP

Old School Removal Tool

A somewhat messy alternative method to remove a pilot bearing is to fill the cavity behind the bearing with chassis grease and drive a close-fitting round rod or dowel into the grease. This will create a hydraulic force behind the bearing, forcing it outward. Soap or wet tissue can also be used. Note that this is NOT a manufacturer approved method; hammering on the end of the crankshaft could possibly cause damage to the thrust bearings.

6. Mark the pressure plate and flywheel if they are to be reused to allow them to be reinstalled in the same location to maintain assembly balance.
7. Remove the clutch pressure plate retaining bolts, and remove the clutch assembly including the release bearing, pressure plate, and clutch disc.

PILOT BEARING REMOVAL A commonly used pilot bushing removal method is to thread a coarse bolt into the bushing so it bottoms against the crankshaft. Further tightening will move the bushing outward. Some vehicle manufacturers recommend the use of a special puller. One type of puller uses a bridge piece and puller legs that lock in behind the bearing to pull it out. ● **SEE FIGURE 3–5.**

CLUTCH COMPONENT INSPECTION

IMPORTANCE OF INSPECTION Technicians should check each part as it is disassembled to determine if it is reusable or why it failed. This identifies any condition that needs special attention before the clutch is reassembled. If the clutch is slipping,

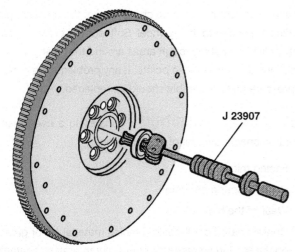

FIGURE 3–5 A slide hammer and special adapter are used to remove the pilot bearing. (Courtesy of General Motors)

FIGURE 3–6 Using an abrasive disc to remove the glaze and to restore the proper surface finish to a flywheel.

the disc and the pressure plate should be replaced. The following sections explain the normal checks to be made during a clutch job.

FLYWHEEL INSPECTION The friction surface of the flywheel should be checked for

- Grooves
- Nicks
- Heat damage (discoloration or cracks caused by excessive heat)

Any of these indicates that the flywheel needs to be resurfaced or replaced.

NOTE: In order to maintain the proper component balance and contact surface taper, flywheels on some vehicles (Corvette) are NOT to be machined. The flywheel friction disc contact surface is tapered (not flat) for improved disc contact. Always refer to service information.

FLYWHEEL RESURFACING. Blanchard grinding moves a spinning grinding stone around the flywheel surface. This is the recommended method of resurfacing because it leaves a truly flat surface with a circular, nondirectional pattern. A nondirectional finish promotes rapid disc facing-to-flywheel break-in.

If the friction surface is flat and smooth but highly polished or glazed, some technicians will sand the friction surface using a disc sander with 80- to 120-grit paper. When doing this, the sander is kept in motion while attempting to duplicate the ground finish of a new unit without cutting grooves. ● **SEE FIGURE 3–6.**

FLYWHEEL RUNOUT AND END PLAY. Many flywheels are forged steel, which tends to warp (potato chip shape) or dish if overheated. This is checked by placing a straightedge across the flywheel in several locations. Over 0.0005 inch (0.013 mm) of warpage per inch of diameter is considered excessive. This

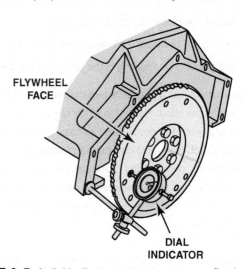

FIGURE 3–7 A dial indicator set up to measure flywheel face or axial runout.

means that a 12-inch-diameter flywheel can have 0.006 inch (12 × 0.0005) of warpage error.

If there is a vibration concern or an odd wear pattern at the hub of the disc or pressure plate release levers, the flywheel should be checked for excessive runout. Face or axial runout is checked by positioning a dial indicator with the indicating stylus at the outer edge of the flywheel face. ● **SEE FIGURE 3–7.**

To measure flywheel **axial runout**, perform the following steps:

STEP 1 Mount the dial indicator so the measuring stem is parallel to the crankshaft and pointing directly toward the flywheel contacting the disc friction area, and adjust the indicator to read zero.

STEP 2 Rotate the flywheel while watching the dial indicator. Maintain an even pressure, either inward or outward, to maintain zero crankshaft end play. The variation in reading is the amount of axial runout.

Follow these instructions to measure flywheel and crankshaft end play:

Set up the dial indicator to measure lengthwise flywheel/crankshaft motion, and push and pull on the flywheel and crankshaft in a direction that is parallel to the crankshaft. The dial indicator is measuring crankshaft end play. Normal crankshaft end play should be about 0.002 to 0.010 inch (0.05 to 0.25 mm). Movement greater than specified indicates worn engine crankshaft thrust bearings.

To measure flywheel **radial runout**, perform the following steps:

STEP 1 Mount the dial indicator so it is at the edge of the flywheel, pointing directly toward the center of the flywheel.

STEP 2 Adjust the dial indicator to read zero.

STEP 3 Rotate the flywheel while watching the dial indicator.

STEP 4 The variation in reading is the amount of radial runout.

Radial runout has a greater effect on balance and vibration than on clutch operation. Runout in either direction greater than 0.010 inch (0.25 mm) is considered excessive axial runout; as little as 0.005 inch (0.1 mm) can cause chatter. If the flywheel is to be removed, place index marks at the crankshaft flange for faster alignment during reassembly. Also inspect the starter ring gear teeth. If they are damaged, replace either the starter gear or the flywheel.

PRESSURE PLATE ASSEMBLY INSPECTION   A used pressure plate assembly should be inspected visually for all of the following.

- Friction surface damage
- Release lever wear
- Lever pivot wear
- Cover distortion

Like the flywheel, the friction surface will tend to polish or glaze from normal use. If there is excessive slippage, grooves, heat checks, and warping can occur. Warpage can be checked by placing a straightedge across the friction surface and will show up as a gap between the straightedge and the inner portion of the pressure plate ring. Set the pressure plate on the flywheel without the clutch disc in place. All of the mounting points should meet the flywheel evenly and completely. Any air gaps indicate a distorted clutch cover. Release lever wear occurs at the contact surface with the release bearing, and this area should appear smooth and polished with no metal removed.

Release lever height should be checked after the pressure plate and disc are bolted to the flywheel. Soft reddish-brown rust and highly polished or shiny rough areas around the lever pivots are indications of wear at these points. If any problems are noticed, the pressure plate assembly should be replaced.

CLUTCH DISC INSPECTION   If installing a used disc, it should be checked for all of the following:

- Facing thickness
- Damper spring condition
- Wear of the hub splines
- Contaminated or oil-soaked facing material (oil or grease on the friction surface can cause clutch grab or chatter)
- Warpage or axial runout

The thickness of the facing can be checked by two different methods.

Method 1 This method involves placing cardboard or a shop cloth over the facing to keep it clean and squeezing the facings together to compress the marcel spring. If specifications are not available, the minimum thickness of the compressed disc should be 0.280 inch (7.1 mm). ●**SEE FIGURE 3–8.**

Method 2 Another method is to measure the height of the facing surface above the rivets, which is also called *rivet head depth*. With a new disc, rivet head depth will be about 0.050 inch (1.2 mm). A disc with less than 0.015 to 0.020 inch (0.38 to 0.5 mm) should be replaced. ●**SEE FIGURE 3–9.**

The damper springs and hub splines are checked visually for reddish rust, often called "rust dust," and shiny worn areas as well as loose, broken, or missing springs. Disc runout warpage is checked by making an axial runout check. This usually

FIGURE 3–8 The thickness of the clutch disc facing can be measured using a dial caliper by first compressing the marcel spring using pliers.

requires a pair of tapered centers or an expanding arbor at true center to the hub splines. The disc is rotated while watching for runout or wobbling of the facing surfaces. More than 0.020 inch (0.5 mm) is excessive, and the disc should be replaced. ● SEE FIGURE 3–10.

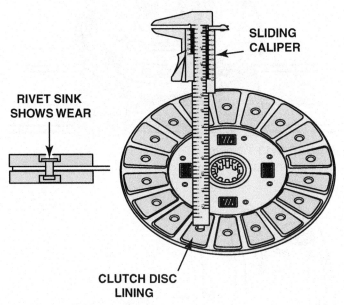

FIGURE 3–9 Measure the rivet depth using a vernier caliper.

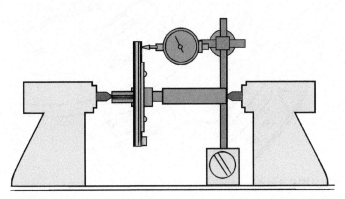

FIGURE 3–10 Check the disc for runout. (Courtesy of General Motors.)

A quick check for warpage is to set the disc against the flywheel. The facing should contact the flywheel evenly all around the disc.

CLUTCH/BELL HOUSING INSPECTION There should not be any oil or grease residue inside the bell housing. If oil is present, check for a leaking front bearing retainer seal or oil galleys plugs or back of the intake manifold. If there has been early failure of the pilot or release bearings, clutch pedal vibration, or the transmission is jumping out of gear, the face and bore surfaces of the bell housing should be checked for excessive runout. Check for excessive runout with a dial indicator attached to the crankshaft, flywheel, pressure plate, or disc, depending on the equipment available and how far the clutch is disassembled.

BELL HOUSING INSPECTION The bell housing should be thoroughly degreased and checked for signs of distortion,

---

?   **FREQUENTLY ASKED QUESTION**

Why Does the New Clutch Disc Use a Thinner Band of Friction Material?

Sometimes a replacement clutch disc looks totally wrong compared to the original. The wise technician always checks that the new part is the correct part before installing it. By using a thinner band of friction material, the centerline of the disc is further from the center. This distance is called the **active radius**. The more the distance between the centerline of the friction material and the centerline of the clutch disc, the higher the torque capacity of the clutch disc. Therefore, some replacement clutch discs may have a different appearance compared to the original. Double-check with the supplier that the replacement clutch disc is designed for the vehicle being serviced before installing the new part. ● SEE FIGURE 3–11.

FIGURE 3–11 The active radius determines the torque capacity of a clutch disc. Therefore, a narrower band of friction material at a further distance from the center may have improved torque capacity over a clutch disc that has a wider band but has a shorter active radius.

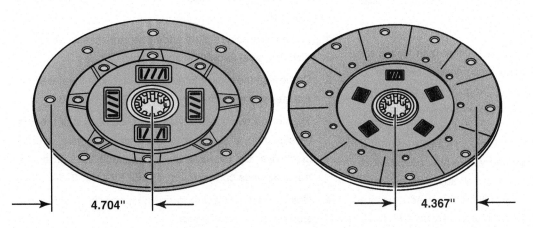

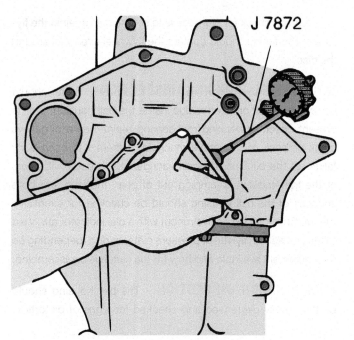

FIGURE 3–12 Use a dial indicator to check block squareness. (Courtesy of General Motors.)

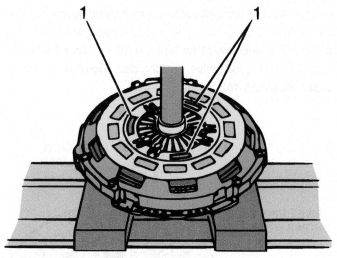

FIGURE 3–13 Compress the fingers with a press. (Courtesy of General Motors.)

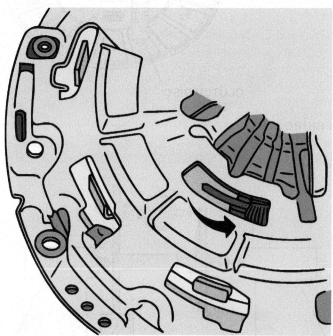

FIGURE 3–14 Push the adjuster until the spring is compressed. (Courtesy of General Motors)

cracks, holes, or damage to its mating surfaces. Although replacement is rarely necessary, thorough evaluation is part of the clutch service procedure. If the clutch fork pivot stud is damaged, it should be replaced.

If engine-to-transmission misalignment is suspected, the bell housing surfaces must be checked. If the bell housing bore is not concentric with the crankshaft or if the rear bell housing surface is not parallel to its front surface, misalignment can occur. Bore concentricity and surface parallelism are checked with a dial indicator.

If the bore runout reading is found to be out of specification, adjustment is possible using offset dowels. If parallelism between front and rear bell housing surfaces is found to be out of specification, the bell housing should be replaced. You can also check the squareness of the area of the engine block where the bell housing portion of the transmission or transaxle attaches to the engine with a dial indicator. ● SEE FIGURE 3–12.

RELEASE BEARING INSPECTION Other than feeling for roughness or seeing obvious wear or discoloration, there are no effective bench checks for release bearings. This is one reason they are normally replaced with the disc and pressure plate.

SELF-ADJUSTING PRESSURE PLATE If a **self-adjusting pressure plate** is not being replaced with a new one, it must be readjusted before installing. A new self-adjusting pressure plate comes already adjusted for installation. A used pressure plate will have self-adjusted to the old clutch disc, so it will have

to be reset before installation. Follow these steps to reset the pressure plate:

1. Place the pressure plate under the arbor press. The clutch disc (flat side) should be acing down.

2. Compress the clutch fingers until pressure is released on the stepped adjusting ring. ● SEE FIGURE 3–13.

3. Then insert two screwdrivers and push on two of the three tension ring stops to rotate the adjusting ring counterclockwise. Do this until the stops reach the end of their travel (springs compressed). ● SEE FIGURE 3–14.

4. Hold the adjusting ring in position, and then release tension on the clutch fingers.

CLUTCH INSTALLATION

PRECAUTIONS   During replacement, the clutch components must be kept clean and dry. All grease and oil that contacts the friction surfaces must be cleaned off. Small amounts of oil on the clutch facing will cause the clutch to grab or chatter.

CLUTCH ASSEMBLY INSTALLATION   To reinstall the clutch assembly perform the following steps:

STEP 1   Check the flywheel bolts to make sure that they are tight and torqued to specifications.

STEP 2   Check the pilot bearing recess to ensure that it is clean, and drive the new pilot bearing into place. The best tool for this is a commercial or shop-made driver with a stem the same size as the bearing bore and a face that is larger than the diameter of the bearing. The new pilot bearing is driven in until it is fully seated or has entered completely into the crankshaft. Most pilot bearings do not require lubrication. Roller bearings with exposed rollers should be lubricated with a thin film of grease or a few drops of engine oil is all that is needed on a sintered bushing.

STEP 3   Place the new clutch disc over the transmission clutch shaft and make sure that it slides freely over the splines. Determine which side of the disc goes against the flywheel which will often be marked *flywheel side*. If not marked, the damper assembly normally faces the pressure plate.

> **Note: To determine the correct clutch disc position, place each side of the disc against the flywheel and rotate it. The side that contacts the flywheel bolts or does not let the clutch facing contact the flywheel is the wrong side.**

STEP 4   Position the *disc alignment tool* or an old transmission shaft or a plastic dummy transmission shaft through the disc and into the pilot bearing to center the disc.

STEP 5   Install the pressure plate over the disc, making sure that it is properly aligned with the dowel pins and mounting bolt holes, and install the mounting bolts.

> **CAUTION: Use only the bolts that were used originally or if replacement bolts are used, be sure that they are grade 8 (high tensile strength) fasteners.**

STEP 6   Tighten the mounting bolts two turns at a time alternating back and forth across the pressure plate. Tighten the bolts to the correct torque.

STEP 7   Remove the alignment device and check to make sure that the pilot bearing is in the exact center of the disc. The height variation of the release levers can be checked after the pressure plate is installed. Use a vernier or dial caliper, and measure from the contact face for the release bearing to the clutch disc. All of the heights should be within 0.020 inch (0.5 mm). The readings will be more accurate after the clutch has been applied a few times.

STEP 8   Check the clutch linkage to make sure that it operates smoothly. On cable-operated clutches, this is a good time to remove, clean, and lubricate the cable.

STEP 9   Fill the groove inside the bore of the release bearing with grease, apply a thin film of the specified high-temperature grease on the fork contact areas, and slide the release bearing onto the transmission quill, making sure that the bearing collar slides smoothly. The quill portion of the transmission bearing retainer should be smooth and unworn. On clutch forks that use pivot balls, a thin film of grease should be put on the ball. On forks mounted on pivot shafts, the pivot bushings should be lubricated.

STEP 10   Replace the transmission/transaxle, being sure to observe the following:

- Place a very thin film of grease on the clutch splines.
- Never let the transmission hang on the clutch disc splines.
- The transmission should be completely seated against the clutch housing or engine before the mounting bolts are tightened.
- Tighten the transmission mounting bolts two turns at a time, working back and forth across the transmission until they are tightened to the correct torque. It should not be necessary to force the transmission into place.
- Adjust the free travel before operating the clutch.

HYDRAULIC CLUTCH SERVICE

PRECAUTIONS   Fluid leaks or failure to release completely indicate the need for hydraulic system service. Clutch hydraulic systems have evolved from the early systems that had free travel adjustment and required clearance at the release bearing to newer systems that maintain a slight preload. Older systems used steel and reinforced rubber lines with threaded fittings,

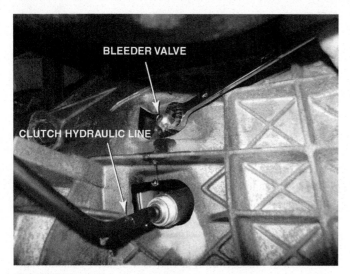

FIGURE 3–15 Gravity bleeding a hydraulic clutch. Opening the bleeder valve should allow air to escape and then fluid should flow.

whereas the newer systems use plastic tubing sealed by O-rings and held together by locking pins at the connections.

HYDRAULIC CLUTCH BLEEDING
In many cases, a clutch hydraulic system can be bled by **gravity bleeding,** while in others, a helper may be needed. To bleed a clutch hydraulic system using the gravity method, perform the following steps:

STEP 1   Clean the bleeder valve at the slave cylinder and place a shop cloth under it to catch escaping fluid. ● **SEE FIGURE 3–15.**

STEP 2   Open the bleeder valve by loosening the bleeder screw and observe the flow. If no flow occurs, have a helper depress the clutch pedal in a smooth, slow manner. Air bubbles coming from the bleed valve indicate that the system needed bleeding. After the air bubbles stop and a constant flow of fluid occurs, close the bleed valve. An alternative method is reverse, or back-bleeding. This is done by forcing fluid through the slave cylinder bleed valve and upward to the reservoir.

STEP 3   Check the fluid level and correct it, if necessary.

Some master and slave cylinders are mounted so that the cylinder portion is above the line connection, which makes it extremely difficult to bleed air from them.

- In some cases, it is possible to bench bleed them to remove all the air before installing on the vehicle. An alternative bleeding method is to have a helper partially apply the clutch while reverse bleeding using pressure surges from the fluid injector.

- Some clutch hydraulic systems will partially self-bleed if the clutch pedal is held completely depressed overnight using a brake pedal depressing tool.

VACUUM BLEEDING PROCEDURE
This alternative procedure can be used anytime air is introduced into the hydraulic system. This procedure may also reduce the number of unnecessary parts replaced for low clutch pedal reserve and high shift effort. The procedure uses a hand vacuum pump and adapter to apply a vacuum to the top of the master cylinder. Follow these steps to vacuum bleed the clutch master cylinder.

1. Verify that all the lines and fittings are dry and secure.
2. Clean the dirt and grease from the reservoir cap in order to ensure that no foreign substances enter the system.
3. Remove the reservoir cap.
4. Fill the reservoir to the proper level with the required fluid.
5. Attach the J 43485 (Adapter) to the J 35555 (Mighty Vac), or equivalent.

   NOTE: Brake fluid will deteriorate the rubber on the J 43485 adapter. Use a clean shop cloth to wipe away the fluid after each use.

6. Place and hold the adapter on the reservoir filler neck to ensure a tight fit. In some cases, the adapter will fit into the reservoir opening.
7. Apply and hold a vacuum of 15–20 hg (51–68 kPa). At this time, air bubbles will be seen rising up into the reservoir.
8. Release the vacuum and remove the adapter.
9. Refill the reservoir to the proper level.
10. Repeat Steps 6, 7, and 8. If needed, refill the reservoir and continue to pull a vacuum until no more bubbles can be seen in the reservoir or until the fluid level no longer drops.
11. Pump the clutch pedal until firm (to refill slave cylinder).
12. Add additional fluid if needed.
13. Test-drive vehicle to ensure proper operation.

1 The first step in the process of replacing the clutch on this Chevrolet S-10 pickup truck is to remove the negative battery cable.

2 Remove the shifter mechanism inside the vehicle. This step may involve removing the center console and other components.

3 Mark and then remove the driveshaft.

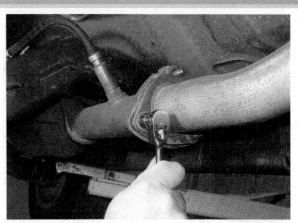

4 Remove the exhaust pipe if needed. It was needed in this case, according to service information.

5 Remove the transmission mount fasteners.

6 Using a transmission jack, support the transmission and remove the bell housing bolts.

CONTINUED ▶

7 A view of the bell housing and throw-out bearing as the transmission assembly is removed from the engine.

8 Removing the fasteners holding the pressure plate to the flywheel.

9 Removing the pressure plate and clutch disc.

10 Using a special puller, remove the pilot bearing.

11 The flywheel is being removed to be refinished or replaced as needed.

12 With the flywheel removed, check to see if the rear main seal is leaking and replace if needed. A wise technician will always replace the seal during a clutch replacement.

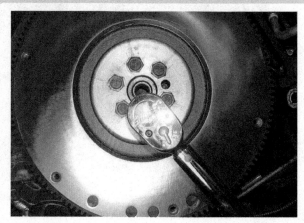

13 Installing a reconditioned flywheel and torquing new bolts to factory specifications.

14 Installing a new pilot bearing and lubricate as per instructions in service information.

15 Using a pilot tool to align the clutch disc with the pilot bearing through the center opening of the pressure plate.

16 Installing the transmission assembly with a new throw-out bearing.

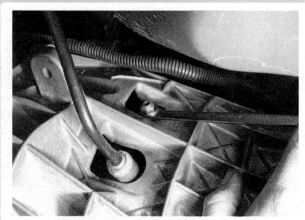

17 Bleeding the air from the hydraulic clutch circuit.

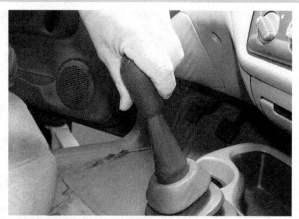

18 Finish the clutch replacement by reinstalling all components removed and check for proper operation.

1 The first step in almost all major service work is to disconnect the negative battery cable from the battery.

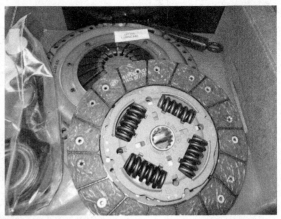

2 A new clutch kit, including the pressure plate, release bearing, and clutch disc, was purchased making sure that all of the needed information was compiled before ordering to help insure that the correct parts were purchased.

3 A holding fixture was attached to support the engine when the transaxle was removed from underneath the vehicle.

4 The "K" (lower support) member was removed to get access to the transaxle.

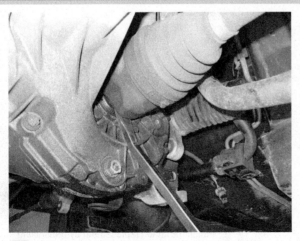

5 Both drive axle shafts (half shafts) were removed.

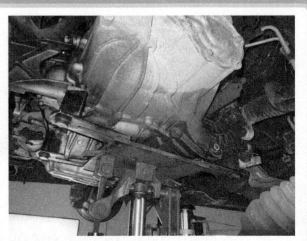

6 The transaxle is supported by a transmission jack as it is being removed from underneath the vehicle.

7 The transaxle assembly is lowered from underneath the vehicle.

8 The original pressure plate shows normal wear. The problem with this clutch was a leaking slave cylinder/release bearing assembly.

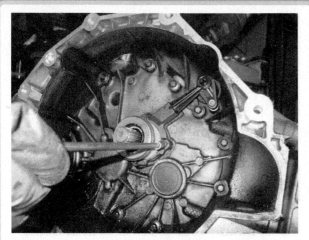

9 The new slave cylinder/release bearing assembly is being installed.

10 The pressure plate is being removed from the flywheel.

11 The flywheel is cleaned using an abrasive pad to remove the glaze on the surface.

12 The flywheel was thoroughly cleaned after being de-glazed.

CONTINUED ▶

13 The spline grease that was included with the clutch kit is being applied to the splines of the clutch disc.

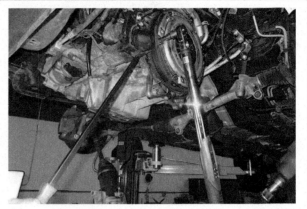

14 The pressure plate retaining bolts are torqued to factory specification while an assistant uses a pry bar to keep the flywheel from turning.

15 The transaxle is then reinstalled from underneath the vehicle.

16 The engine and transaxle mounts are reattached and the half shafts reinstalled.

17 The hydraulic clutch master cylinder is filled with DOT3 brake fluid and allowed to gravity bleed.

18 All fasteners were torqued to factory specification and the vehicle was test driven to confirm proper operation.

SUMMARY

1. Clutch system preventive maintenance ensures proper clutch pedal free travel and/or proper master cylinder fluid level.

2. Excessive slippage, grab, chatter, and unusual noise are common indications of clutch problems.

3. A clutch job requires transmission/transaxle removal to replace the pressure plate, disc, release bearing, and pilot bearing.

4. The flywheel as well as the bell housing should be checked whenever replacing a clutch.

5. Abnormal clutch failure requires additional checks to locate the root cause of the failure.

6. The clutch disc must be kept clean and centered to the pilot bearing during installation.

7. Newer hydraulic systems are replaced as an assembly. They are prefilled with fluid, eliminating the need for system bleeding.

REVIEW QUESTIONS

1. How is clutch pedal free travel measured?

2. How is a clutch spin-down test performed?

3. What parts are normally replaced as part of a clutch job?

4. What should be lubricated during clutch replacement?

CHAPTER QUIZ

1. A cable-operated clutch is being adjusted. Technician A says that free travel is measured at the clutch pedal and should be between 3/4 and 1 inch (19 and 25 mm). Technician B says that the clutch spin-down time should be less than two seconds. Which technician is correct?
   a. Technician A only
   b. Technician B only
   c. Both technicians A and B
   d. Neither technician A nor B

2. A vehicle has a slipping clutch. Technician A says slippage will be most noticeable when accelerating in first gear. Technician B says a clutch slip test can be performed in the shop. Which technician is correct?
   a. Technician A only
   b. Technician B only
   c. Both technicians A and B
   d. Neither technician A nor B

3. Clutch chatter can be caused by_____.
   a. Grease or oil on the clutch friction material
   b. Broken engine mount(s)
   c. Low hydraulic clutch fluid level
   d. Too little free play in the clutch pedal

4. Technician A says that clutch slipping can be caused by a warped clutch disc. Technician B says that slippage is the result of too little free travel. Which technician is correct?
   a. Technician A only
   b. Technician B only
   c. Both technicians A and B
   d. Neither technician A nor B

5. A squeal begins as the clutch pedal is depressed about 1 inch (25 mm). This is probably caused by a _____.
   a. Defective or worn release (throw-out) bearing
   b. Worn clutch disc
   c. Weak pressure plate
   d. Worn pilot bearing

6. What should be lubricated when replacing a clutch assembly?
   a. Disc splines
   b. Pivot bushings (if equipped)
   c. Pilot bearing
   d. All of the above

7. A clutch disc is being installed. Technician A says the damper assembly of the clutch disc normally faces the pressure plate. Technician B says that the disc splines should be lightly lubricated. Which technician is correct?
   a. Technician A only
   b. Technician B only
   c. Both technicians A and B
   d. Neither technician A nor B

8. Technician A says that a pilot bearing should be removed with a puller. Technician B says that some pilot bearings may need a thin coating of grease after installation. Which technician is correct?
   a. Technician A only
   b. Technician B only
   c. Both technicians A and B
   d. Neither technician A nor B

9. During clutch installation, the clutch disc can be aligned to the pilot bearing using _____.
   a. A commercial clutch disc alignment tool
   b. An old transmission shaft
   c. A plastic dummy transmission shaft
   d. Any of the above

10. While discussing the installation of a pressure plate, Technician A says that grade 8 bolts be used for the mounting bolts. Technician B says to move from bolt to bolt at least two times while tightening the bolts. Which technician is correct?
   a. Technician A only
   b. Technician B only
   c. Both technicians A and B
   d. Neither technician A nor B

chapter 4

MANUAL TRANSMISSIONS PARTS AND OPERATION

LEARNING OBJECTIVES

After studying this chapter, the reader should be able to:

1. Explain the construction of a manual transmission.
2. Discuss synchronizer operation.
3. Explain torque flow through a five-speed transmission.
4. Discuss shifter operation.
5. Explain the construction of manual transmission gears.
6. Discuss the purpose of the transmission case and bearings.

This chapter will help you prepare for ASE Manual Drive Train and Axles (A3) certification test content area "B" (Transmission Diagnosis and Repair) and area "C" (Transaxle Diagnosis and Repair).

KEY TERMS

Blocker ring 57
Clutch shaft 54
Constant mesh gears 55
Double cone 59
Hub 56
Idler gear 56
Input shaft 54
Main drive gear 54
Main shaft 54
Manual transmission fluid (MTF) 69
Output shaft 54
Reverse idler shaft 54
Shift fork 64
Sliding Sleeve 56
Speed gears 55
Struts 57
Synchronizer Keys 57
Synchronizer rings 57
Viscosity 68

GM STC OBJECTIVES

GM Service Technical College topics covered in this chapter are as follows:

1. Characteristics of manual transmissions as used in General Motors vehicles.
2. Operation of internal shift shafts, forks, and related components.
3. Operation of synchronizer assemblies.
4. Power flow through a manual transmission.

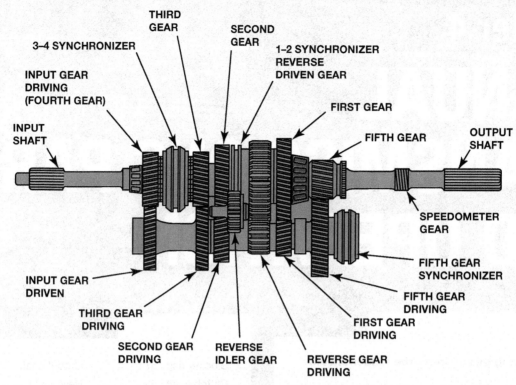

FIGURE 4–1 A five-speed transmission gear set. Power enters through the input shaft and leaves through the transmission output shaft.

Labels in figure:
- THIRD GEAR
- 3–4 SYNCHRONIZER
- SECOND GEAR
- INPUT GEAR DRIVING (FOURTH GEAR)
- 1–2 SYNCHRONIZER REVERSE DRIVEN GEAR
- INPUT SHAFT
- FIRST GEAR
- FIFTH GEAR
- OUTPUT SHAFT
- SPEEDOMETER GEAR
- INPUT GEAR DRIVEN
- FIFTH GEAR SYNCHRONIZER
- THIRD GEAR DRIVING
- FIFTH GEAR DRIVING
- SECOND GEAR DRIVING
- REVERSE IDLER GEAR
- FIRST GEAR DRIVING
- REVERSE GEAR DRIVING

PURPOSE OF MANUAL TRANSMISSONS

The purpose of the transmission is to provide neutral, forward gear speeds or ranges, and reverse. It must be able to provide a gear ratio that is low enough, when multiplied by the final drive ratio, to increase the engine's torque sufficiently to accelerate the vehicle at the desired rate. The highest gear ratio should allow the vehicle to cruise at an engine speed that is low enough to conserve fuel and decrease noise. There also needs to be intermediate ratios that are spaced so that the engine will not overrev before a shift or lug after a shift. Reverse must be roughly the same ratio as first since the vehicle will be starting from a stop in both cases.

CONSTRUCTION

POWER PATHS A transmission has several different paths through which power can flow. These paths provide the required forward gear ranges and a reverse. In a rear-wheel-drive (RWD) transmission, power enters the input shaft and passes through at least two gear sets before transferring to the main shaft. The power will exit through the main shaft and will then pass on to the driveshaft. The transmission main shaft, the output shaft, is directly in line with the input shaft. ● SEE FIGURE 4–1.

PARTS INVOLVED A rear-wheel-drive (RWD) manual transmission includes the following four shafts:

1. A cluster gear, countershaft gear, or *layshaft* (a British term)
2. The **input shaft**, also called a **main drive gear** or **clutch shaft**
3. The **output shaft**, also called a **main shaft**
4. The **reverse idler shaft**

The main shaft is piloted into the rear of the input shaft gear with a bearing. It is also supported at the rear of the transmission case by another large bearing, and by the universal joint slip yoke, which in turn is supported by a bushing at the rear of the extension housing. The input shaft gear is supported by a bearing at the front of the transmission case and the pilot bearing at the end of the crankshaft. Most transmissions support the cluster gear directly by a bearing set. Some transmissions with very long cluster gears and main shaft gear groups use a support in the middle of the transmission with bearings for the cluster gear and main shaft. ● SEE FIGURE 4–2.

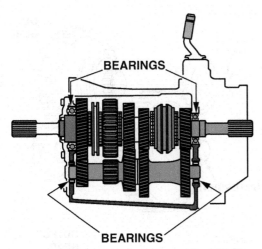

FIGURE 4–2 Bearings support the input shaft, countershaft, main shaft, and speed gears.

SHIFTING GEARS
Constant mesh gears are always engaged with their mating gear and are mounted so that one of them, called a **speed gear**, can freewheel on its shaft. The gears are shifted by connecting the freewheeling gear to its shaft. This is done through a synchronizer assembly. The synchronizer is splined to the shaft and has a sleeve that can be slid into place to engage the gear to the synchronizer. The power will then be able to flow from the gear to the synchronizer and then to the shaft. The advantage of constant mesh gears is that the synchronizer will allow shifts to be made while the vehicle is moving and without the driver doing any extra clutching.

SPEED GEARS
All gears on the countershaft are permanently attached to the shaft. When the countershaft rotates, all gears on the countershaft rotate. The input shaft gear is also part of the input shaft. However, the gears on the main shaft are free to move on the shaft and are connected to the main shaft through the synchronizer hub when a shift is made. The gears that rotate on the main shaft are called speed gears and are free to rotate on a film of oil or on bearings.

GEAR RATIOS
In all gear speeds but one, the power flows from the main drive gear (input) to the cluster gear and then from the cluster gear to the main shaft (output).

The power passes through two gear sets. The exception is a 1:1 ratio, where the power flows directly from the main drive gear to the main shaft.

- All the forward gears are normally in constant mesh so they always rotate at their designed speed relative to engine speed.
- The gears of the cluster gear rotate as an assembly.
- The output (speed) gears usually are mounted on the main shaft so they float or rotate freely.

? **FREQUENTLY ASKED QUESTION**

What Is a Non-synchronized Transmission?

Older vehicles often transmission gears that were engaged by sliding the gears on a shaft, using spur-type gear teeth. The shift fork would slide the selected gear into mesh with a mating gear on the countershaft, literally "shifting gears." If the gear speeds were not perfectly matched, grinding would occur; briefly engaging the clutch in the middle of the shift, if carefully done, would match up the gear speeds (double clutching).

It was common up through the 1960s and early 1970s for some vehicles to have a nonsynchronized first and reverse gear and synchronized (constant mesh) gears for second, third, and fourth gear. Even today, some vehicles still have a nonsynchronized reverse gear that requires the driver to wait a few seconds after releasing the clutch to prevent grinding when selecting reverse.

- The speed gears complete the ratio for each gear speed when they become coupled to the main shaft.
- The main shaft includes synchronizer assemblies for each pair of gear speeds and can lock the individual speed gears to the main shaft. This is done for each shift.

Because the gears in most transmissions are in constant mesh, they will always rotate at their gear ratio speed relative to the input shaft gear.

TORQUE CAPACITY
A transmission is designed to be strong enough to handle the torque output of the engine. High torque requires large input shafts, even larger output shafts, wide gears, and large bearings. This increases the weight of the transmission and also increases the drag and power loss. Smaller transmissions improve fuel mileage, but they can break under load. Using an engine that has a higher torque output than the transmission is designed to handle will cause failure of the transmission. To handle more torque, the following two factors are designed into the transmission:

Factor 1 The diameters of the input and output shafts of a transmission are enlarged.

Factor 2 The distance between the main shaft and the countershaft is increased. This is needed to allow the space in the case for the larger gears and shafts. ● **SEE FIGURE 4–3.**

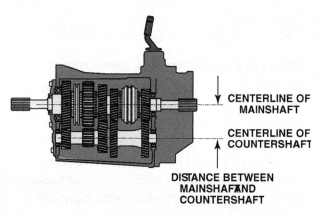

FIGURE 4–3 The torque capacity of a transmission is determined by the size of the gear and bearings used. The greater the distance, usually measured in millimeters such as 77 mm, between the main shaft and the countershaft, the greater the torque capacity.

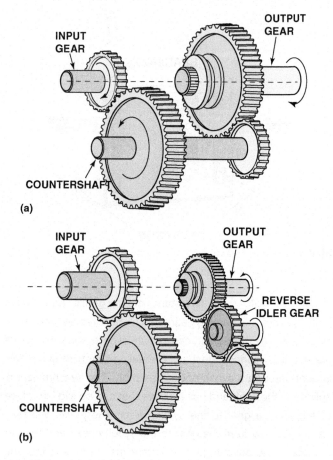

(a)

(b)

FIGURE 4–4 (a) The input shaft rotates in a clockwise direction; the countershaft rotates in a counter-clockwise direction and the first-reverse gear drives the output shaft in a clockwise direction. (b) When meshed with the idler gear, the first-reverse gear will be driven in a counter-clockwise direction. A simple (single) idler is shown.

REVERSE

PRINCIPLES Because the engine is not able to operate backward, the transmission has to reverse the direction of rotation, requiring one more gear in the gear train. When one external gear drives another, they will rotate in opposite directions. In a transmission

- The input shaft gear rotates in a clockwise direction the same as the engine as viewed from the front of the engine (accessory drive belt end).
- The cluster gear rotates in a counter clockwise direction.
- The main shaft rotates clockwise when driven either through the gear train or by the direct coupling.

REVERSE IDLER NEEDED To make the vehicle back up, the main shaft must rotate counter-clockwise. To accomplish this, an **idler gear** is meshed between the cluster gear and the reverse gear on the main shaft. ●SEE FIGURE 4–4.

A simple idler will not change the ratio, but it will cause a reversal of rotation. The idler gears used in some transmissions are long, with a gear of one size meshed with the cluster gear and a different-sized gear to mesh with the reverse gear. This idler gear will affect the ratio.

SYNCHRONIZERS

PURPOSE AND FUNCTION Synchronizers are used in manual transmissions/transaxles to make shifting easier. To synchronize means to make two or more events occur at the

same time. When the driver depresses the clutch pedal, torque is no longer being transmitted to the input shaft and the drive wheels are "driving" the main shaft of the transmission/transaxle. To achieve a clash-free (no grinding sound) shift, the two gears to be meshed must be rotating at the same speed.

The real "shifting" in a synchromesh transmission takes place in the synchronizer assemblies, not the gears. Most synchronizer assemblies ride on the output shaft between two gears. A synchronizer assembly is named for the gears on either side of it, which are the two speeds that it engages. For example, a five-speed transmission with constant-mesh reverse uses a 1–2 synchronizer, a 3–4 synchronizer, and a 5-reverse synchronizer.

SYNCHRONIZER CONSTRUCTION Although there are number of design variations, all are similar and include the following:

- A **hub**
- A **sliding sleeve**

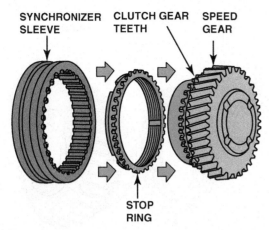

SYNCHRONIZER SLEEVE   CLUTCH GEAR TEETH   SPEED GEAR

STOP RING

FIGURE 4–5 The shifter fork fits into the groove of the synchronizer sleeve. When a shift is made, the sleeve is moved toward the speed gear. The sleeve presses the stop ring (synchronizer ring) against the cone area of the speed gear. The friction between the stop ring and the speed gear causes the speed of the two to become equal, permitting the sleeve to engage the gear clutch teeth of the speed gear. When this engagement occurs, the shift is complete.

- A **blocker ring**, also called *stop ring* or **synchronizer ring**
- **Keys**
- **Springs**

In addition, the tapered cone and coupling teeth machined on the speed gear are part of the synchronizer assembly. **SEE FIGURE 4–5.**

In a typical synchronizer

- Splines attach the center hub of the synchronizer to the output shaft, so the hub and output shaft rotate together. There are also splines machined on the outer circumference of the hub.

- An outer sliding sleeve rides on the external hub splines with enough clearance so that it slides freely. The splines on the sleeve also match the small coupling teeth of the stop ring and speed gear. Coupling teeth are also called engagement or clutch teeth. The sleeve is splined to the hub, so it rotates with the output shaft.

- A **blocker ring** sits between the speed gear and the sleeve. The coupling teeth on the stop ring match those on both the sleeve and the speed gear. The stop ring also has a tapered cone to match the cone machined on the speed gear.

- Small, spring-loaded detent keys, also called **synchronizer keys** or **struts**, ride in slots on the outer sleeve. The stop ring has slots to match these keys. This allows the stop ring to rotate slightly, relative to the sleeve, before the keys hit the sides of their slots and stop the stop ring. As the sleeve moves, the synchronizer keys move with it, which pushes the blocking ring onto the tapered cone of the speed gear.

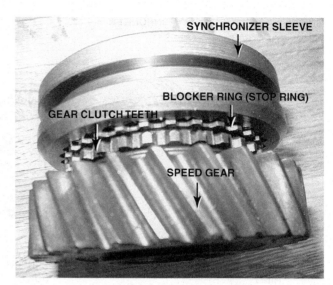

SYNCHRONIZER SLEEVE

BLOCKER RING (STOP RING)

GEAR CLUTCH TEETH

SPEED GEAR

FIGURE 4–6 Typical synchronizer assembly.

SYNCHRONIZER OPERATION   When the synchronizer sleeve is centered on the hub, the synchronizer is in its neutral position—it does not contact either of the speed gears. **SEE FIGURE 4–6.**

To shift into gear, the driver disengages the clutch and moves the shift linkage. The shift linkage, which is described later in this chapter, pushes the sleeve toward one of the speed gears. As the sleeve moves, the detent keys help guide the stop ring toward the speed gear. This causes the ring cone to slide onto the tapered cone of the speed gear.

The speed gear is turning because it is in constant mesh with a countershaft gear. However, the gear may not be turning at the same speed as the synchronizer assembly even though both are on the same shaft. When the clutch is disengaged, the engine is no longer driving the transmission, so there is no torque applied to the input shaft, and the countershaft, or cluster gear, simply freewheels. As the shift is made, the stop ring acts as a brake to slow down the gear so that its speed matches the speed of the synchronizer assembly. That is, it synchronizes the shift. This matched speed allows the internal hub splines to easily engage the coupling teeth on the stop ring and speed gear. When the clutch disengages, the crankshaft drives the input shaft, which drives the countershaft, which in turn drives the output shaft through the selected gear.

The synchronizer goes through three stages during a shift:

1. As the shift is selected, the synchronizer sleeve moves toward the speed gear. If the speeds of the sliding sleeve (main shaft) and the speed gear (counter shaft) are not identical, the speed difference will cause the tapered cone to "misalign" the teeth of the sleeve, the stop

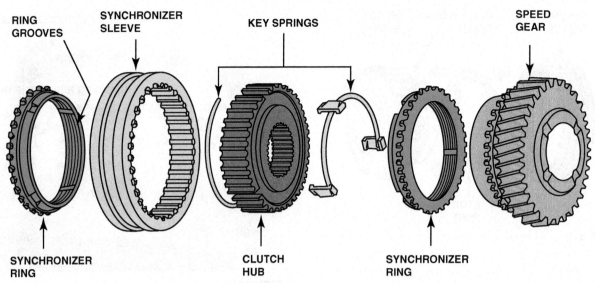

RING GROOVES

SYNCHRONIZER SLEEVE

KEY SPRINGS

SPEED GEAR

SYNCHRONIZER RING

CLUTCH HUB

SYNCHRONIZER RING

FIGURE 4–7 Synchronizer keys are attached to the clutch hub and push against the synchronizer ring when the sleeve is being moved during a shift. Notice the grooves on the synchronizer ring. These grooves prevent lubricating oil from becoming trapped between the ring and the cone surface of the speed gear. The grooves also help the ring release from the cone surface when a shift is made out of a gear.

ring, and the speed gear. This "blocks" the shift. Now, the tapered teeth of the sliding sleeve push against the teeth of the stop ring, which in turn pushes the stop ring tapered surface up against the tapered surface of the speed gear. This causes the speed gear to either speed up or slow down based on the difference between the main shaft speed (hub) and the counter gear speed (speed gear). When the speeds are equal, the thrust is released on the tapered surface, which now allows the "alignment" of the sliding sleeve teeth, the stop ring teeth, and the speed gear teeth, which allows the shift to be completed. ● **SEE FIGURE 4–7.**

2. The sleeve overcomes the force of the detent key springs as the shift linkage continues to move it toward the gear. This allows the stop ring to relax and move slightly so that the sleeve splines begin to engage the coupling teeth on the stop ring. At this point, the coupling teeth on the stop ring and the speed gear may not line up with each other. However, friction continues to build between the ring and the cone, so the gear continues to slow down.

3. Once the sleeve, stop ring, and gear are all turning at the same speed, it takes just a small movement between the stop ring and gear to align the coupling teeth and allow the sleeve to slip completely over both sets. The speed gear is now locked to the output shaft through the synchronizer stop ring and sleeve. ● **SEE FIGURE 4–8.**

Synchronizer stop rings are a simple type of clutch, called a cone clutch for the shape of the mating surfaces.

Some manufacturers refer to the synchronizer action as "clutching." Synchronizer sleeves and hubs are gear-quality steel. Stop rings are a softer metal—usually brass, copper, or a sintered metal—to absorb the friction of synchronizer operation. The tapered cone is relieved; that is, grooves are machined into its contact surface. These grooves serve two purposes:

1. They channel excess lubricant out from between the two pieces for better contact.

2. They retain a small amount of lubricant. This decreases wear when the cone clutch must slip slightly during coupling tooth alignment.

The internal splines on the synchronizer sleeve and the coupling gear teeth on stop rings and speed gears have a special shape that works to hold the gear engaged once the driver releases the shift lever. The ends of the gear teeth are chamfered, giving them a triangular shape. These pointed ends allow easier sleeve-to-gear alignment as the angles tend to center the splines between the teeth. Once aligned, a back taper machined behind the chamfered end of the teeth and splines tends to keep the sleeve in place until the linkage pushes the sleeve away for another shift. Back taper is an angle cut opposite to the chamfer so that spline or tooth narrows just behind the chamfered end. ● **SEE FIGURE 4–9.**

The back taper creates resistance to motion to keep the splines from sliding off the coupling teeth. This is especially important when there is no torque load, such as coasting, to help keep the parts meshed. Worn back taper may cause

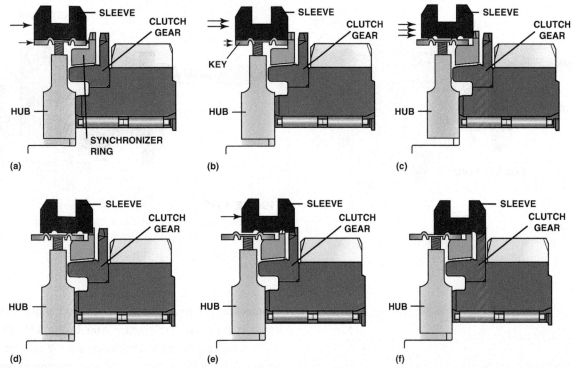

FIGURE 4–8 A shift sequence starts when the shift fork is moved by the driver. (a) Applying a force on the sleeve that moves it toward the speed gear. (b) The sleeve and the inserts (keys) contact the synchronizer ring (blocking ring). (c) The synchronizer ring (stop ring) engages the cone on the speed gear. (d) This causes both assemblies to reach the same speed. (e) The sleeve engages the clutch gear teeth. (f) The shift is completed when the internal teeth of the sleeve mesh with the gear clutch teeth of the speed gear. The detent of the shift key helps to hold the sleeve in position. (Courtesy of General Motors.)

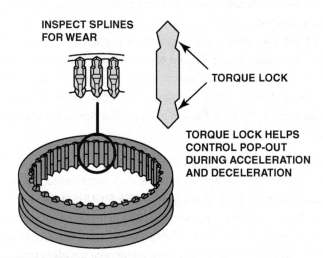

FIGURE 4–9 The shape of the splines helps prevent the transmission/transaxle from jumping out of gear during acceleration and deceleration.

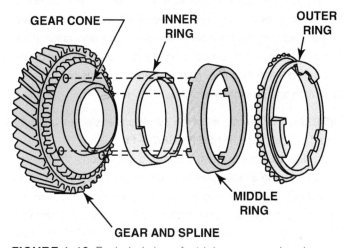

FIGURE 4–10 Exploded view of a triple-cone synchronizer. The inner and outer rings rotate with the synchronizer sleeve while the middle ring rotates with the speed gear.

the transmission to jump out of gear, usually when the throttle is released. Some synchronizer stop rings have friction material on the cone surface. This paper friction material is the same as used on automatic transmission clutch plates, and provides a smoother synchronizing action than metal-to-metal contact. A manual transmission with paper stop rings must use automatic transmission fluid (ATF). Other lubricants damage the paper ring surface. Some synchronizers use a **double cone**, with an outer cone and an inner cone along with the blocker ring. The multiple cones provide more surface area for better synchronization and longer service life. ● **SEE FIGURE 4–10.**

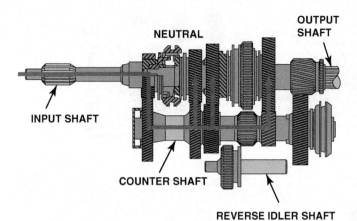

FIGURE 4–11 In neutral, the input shaft and the countershaft are rotating if the clutch is engaged (clutch pedal up), but no torque is being transmitted through the transmission.

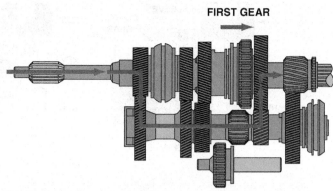

FIGURE 4–12 In first gear, the 1–2 synchronizer sleeve is moved rearward, locking the first speed gear to the output shaft. Torque is transmitted from the input shaft to the countershaft and then to the output shaft.

FIVE-SPEED TRANSMISSION TORQUE FLOW

BORG-WARNER FIVE SPEED A five-speed transmission has six gear sets that provide five forward speeds and one reverse speed. Either a sliding gear or constant mesh gears may be used for reverse. All forward gears are the constant-mesh type. The Borg-Warner T5 manual transmission serves as an example of a contemporary five-speed design. In addition to reverse, the T5 provides three gear reduction ratios (first, second, and third), direct drive (fourth), and an overdriven ratio (fifth). A sliding idler gear is used to change output shaft direction and provide reverse.

NEUTRAL. In neutral, all of the synchronizer sleeves are centered on their hubs. ● **SEE FIGURE 4–11.**

Note that in this and the following illustrations, the reverse idler shaft and sliding gear have been repositioned for clarity. In actuality, the assembly is positioned so it meshes with the reverse gears of the countershaft and output shaft simultaneously. With the clutch engaged, the drive gear of the input shaft turns the cluster gear, or countershaft. The speed gears are driven by the cluster gears, but rotate freely, on the output shaft. The output shaft may turn if the vehicle is moving or coasting, but no engine torque being transferred through the transmission.

FIRST GEAR. In first gear, the shift linkage slides the 1–2 synchronizer sleeve rearward toward the first speed gear. ● **SEE FIGURE 4–12.**

The synchronizer assembly locks the speed gear to the output shaft. With the clutch engaged, the input shaft drives the

countershaft, delivering engine torque to the gearbox. Torque transfers from the first counter gear to the first speed gear, which drives the output shaft through the 1–2 synchronizer hub splines. Torque flows through the transmission in gear reduction at the first gear ratio.

SECOND GEAR. In second gear, the shift linkage slides the 1–2 synchronizer sleeve forward, away from the first speed gear and toward the second speed gear. ● **SEE FIGURE 4–13.**

The synchronizer assembly releases first gear, and then locks the second speed gear to the output shaft. With the clutch engaged, the input shaft is driven at crankshaft speed and turns the countershaft. Engine torque transfers from the second counter gear to the second speed gear, which drives the output shaft through the 1–2 synchronizer hub splines. Torque flows through the transmission in gear reduction at the second gear ratio.

THIRD GEAR. In third gear, the shift linkage centers the 1–2 synchronizer sleeve and moves the 3–4 synchronizer sleeve back toward the third speed gear. ● **SEE FIGURE 4–14.**

The synchronizer assembly locks the third speed gear to the output shaft. With the clutch engaged and the input shaft driving the countershaft, the third counter gear transfers torque to the third speed gear. The speed gear drives the output shaft through the 3–4 synchronizer hub splines. Torque flows through the transmission in gear reduction at the third gear ratio.

FOURTH GEAR. In fourth gear, the shift linkage moves the 3–4 synchronizer sleeve forward, away from the third speed gear and toward the input shaft drive gear. ● **SEE FIGURE 4–15.**

The synchronizer assembly locks the input shaft drive gear to the output shaft. With the clutch engaged, the input shaft drives the output shaft through the 3–4 synchronizer hub

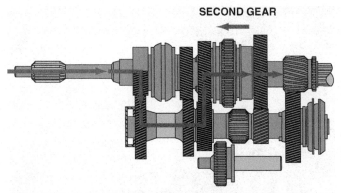

FIGURE 4–13 In second gear, the 1–2 synchronizer sleeve is moved forward, which locks the second speed gear to the output shaft.

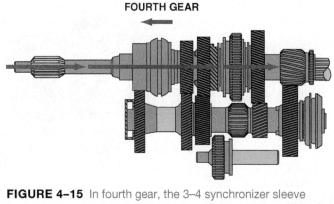

FIGURE 4–15 In fourth gear, the 3–4 synchronizer sleeve is moved forward, which locks the fourth speed gear to the output shaft.

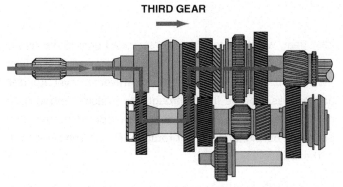

FIGURE 4–14 To achieve third gear, the shaft linkage first centers the 1–2 synchronizer sleeve and then moves the 3–4 synchronizer sleeve rearward, locking third speed gear to the output shaft.

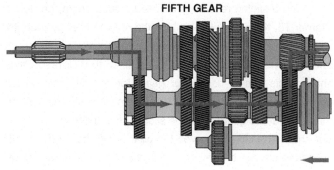

FIGURE 4–16 To achieve fifth gear, the shift linkage first centers the 3–4 synchronizer sleeve and then moves the fifth synchronizer sleeve toward the fifth speed gear, locking it to the output shaft.

splines and both shafts rotate at crankshaft speed. Torque flows straight through the transmission at a 1:1 ratio, delivering engine torque to the drive shaft. This is called *direct drive* because there is no gear reduction through the transmission. The counter gears also turn because they are in constant mesh, but they do not affect torque flow because all of the speed gears are freewheeling on the output shaft.

FIFTH GEAR. In fifth gear, the shift linkage centers the 3–4 synchronizer sleeve and moves the fifth synchronizer sleeve toward the fifth speed gear. ● **SEE FIGURE 4–16.**

Note that on the T5 transmission the synchronizer assembly locks the fifth speed gear to the countershaft. The speed gear drives a fixed gear on the output shaft. With the clutch engaged, the input shaft drives the countershaft. The fifth synchronizer hub is splined to the countershaft, so it is driven and driving the fifth speed gear when fifth gear is engaged. This transfers engine torque to the output shaft through the fixed fifth gear. Note the countershaft gear is larger than the output shaft gear. Therefore, fifth gear is

overdriven. Torque flows through the transmission at the fifth gear, or overdrive, ratio. Typical overdrive gear ratios are between 0.6:1 and 0.8:1. This lowers engine speed for economical highway cruising.

On some five-speed transmissions, the fifth speed gear is on the output shaft with the other speed gears. This type of arrangement is typically used with constant-mesh reverse gears. In these designs, fifth and reverse gears share a synchronizer assembly. The fixed countershaft gear drives the speed gear, which drives the output shaft through the hub splines when the sliding sleeve is engaged. Torque flow through the transmission is similar to any of the gear reduction forward speeds but the fifth speed gear is generally overdriven.

REVERSE. There are two common reverse gear designs used on transmissions:

1. Sliding gear
2. Constant mesh gear

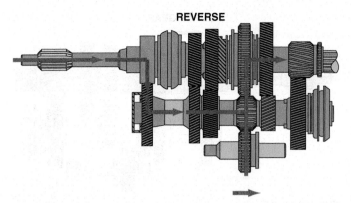

REVERSE

FIGURE 4-17 Torque flows through the transmission in reverse gear. Note that the idler gear drives the 1–2 synchronizer sleeve gear, which is splined to the output shaft.

FIGURE 4-18 Cutaway of a T56 six-speed transmission showing all of its internal parts.

With a sliding reverse gear design, such as on the Borg-Warner T5, the shift linkage slides the reverse idler gear on its shaft until it engages the reverse gears on the countershaft and output shaft gear. Both gears are fixed to their respective shafts. This design uses spur gears for reverse, not helical gears, because the gear teeth must move into and out of mesh. On some gearboxes, the sliding gear splines to the output shaft. The linkage moves the gear along the output shaft splines to engage the reverse idler gear. An unusual feature of the Borg-Warner T5 is that it does not have a separate reverse output shaft gear. ● **SEE FIGURE 4-17.**

Instead, spur teeth machined around the outside of the 1–2 synchronizer sleeve act as the reverse output gear. When the T5 is shifted into reverse, the linkage moves the reverse idler gear rearward so it simultaneously meshes with the countershaft reverse gear and the gear on the synchronizer sleeve. When the clutch is engaged, the countershaft is driven and the reverse gear drives the idler gear, which rotates in the opposite direction of the countershaft. The idler gear drives the 1–2 synchronizer sleeve, so there is another directional change in rotation. Although the sleeve is not engaged to a speed gear, it remains splined to the output shaft, so the sleeve drives the output shaft when the idler gear is engaged. The output shaft rotates in the opposite direction of the input shaft because the idler gear is between them. With constant mesh gears, the shift linkage moves the 5-reverse synchronizer sleeve away from the fifth speed gear and toward the reverse speed gear when reverse is selected. Typically, no stop ring is used between the synchronizer sleeve and the reverse gear, so the output shaft must be stopped to engage reverse without grinding the sleeve splines against the coupling teeth of the reverse gear. The synchronizer assembly locks the reverse speed gear to the output shaft.

With the clutch engaged, the input shaft drives the countershaft. The reverse counter gear drives the reverse idler gear, which drives the reverse speed gear in the direction opposite normal rotation. The reverse speed gear drives the output shaft through the 5-reverse synchronizer hub splines. Torque flows through the transmission in gear reduction at the reverse gear ratio. The output shaft turns opposite its normal direction of rotation, so the vehicle moves to the rear.

SIX-SPEED TRANSMISSIONS A six-speed transmission requires one more gear on the cluster, an additional speed gear, and one-half of a synchronizer assembly. This increases the weight, length, and cost of the unit. The additional gear is usually another overdrive ratio. Some six-speeds have low and high gear ratios similar to those of a five-speed, with the ratios closer together. ● **SEE FIGURE 4-18.**

SEVEN-SPEED TRANSMISSION In the seven-speed Tremec TR6070 transmission, fifth, sixth, and seventh gears are overdrive gears. The fully synchronized gearing has an enhanced synchronizer cone arrangement, with some of the synchronizers made from a bronze/carbon composite material. This arrangement provides improved wear characteristics that include the following:

- Triple-cone rings of first and second
- Double-cone rings of third, fourth, fifth, sixth, seventh, and reverse
- Double cone sintered bronze ring for reverse

ACTIVE REV MATCHING (ARM). Corvettes with this transmission feature active rev matching (ARM) (auto-blip) to assist with smoother shifting. By monitoring the gear position sensor and the clutch pedal position sensor, ARM adjusts engine speed

FIGURE 4–19 The seven-speed transmission has a gear position sensor located at the top rear of the housing. (Courtesy of General Motors.)

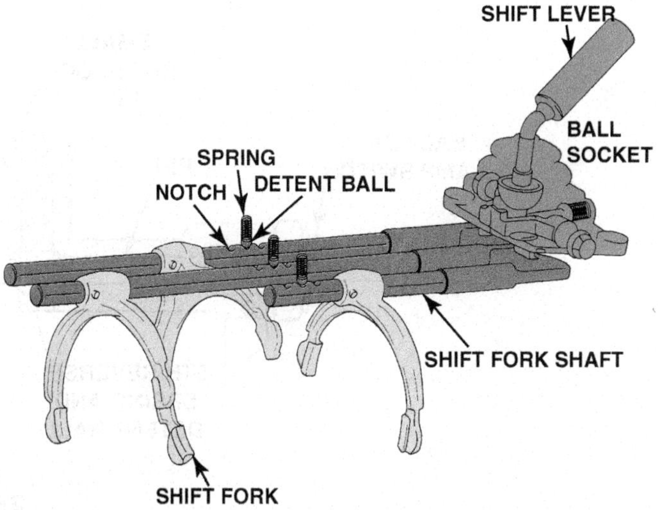

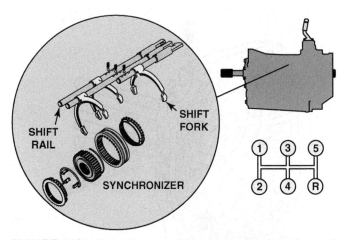

FIGURE 4–20 A typical shift mechanism showing the shift detents designed to give the driver a solid feel when shifting. The shifter also prevents shifting into reverse except from the neutral position.

to match a calibrated value based on gear selection. On up-shifts and downshifts, engine speed increases and decreases to match vehicle road speed and transmission gear position. The ARM system activates and deactivates by pressing either of the paddles marked REV MATCH on the steering wheel and must be activated with each new ignition cycle. Part of the ARM system is a four-wire gear position sensor that mounts to the top of the transmission housing and interfaces directly with the ECM.[1] ● SEE FIGURE 4–19.

SHIFT MECHANISMS

PURPOSE AND FUNCTION   The purpose and function of shift mechanisms are to transfer the action of the driver to the shifting forks inside the transmission or transaxle.

Most vehicles today equipped with a manually shifted transmission use a floor-mounted shifter to change gears. The shifting lever either moves cables that transfer the shifting motion to the transmission or moves the shift forks directly. Inside the transmission/transaxle are shift forks that control shifts between two gears. Interlocks either in the shifter linkage itself or inside the transmission/transaxle prevent the accidental selection of reverse except when shifting from neutral and also prevent selecting two gears at the same time. Detents and interlocks hold the shift mechanism in position ● SEE FIGURE 4–20.

SHIFTER OPERATION   As the gearshift lever moves, the shifter mechanism moves one or two synchronizer sleeves or gears to engage the desired gear speed. The standard shift lever moves in an H pattern for a four-speed or a double

FIGURE 4–21 When the gearshift lever is moved, the internal linkage (shift rails) moves the shift fork and synchronizer sleeve to shift gear speeds.

H pattern for a five-speed. As the lever is moved across the H, the transmission is in neutral and a shift lever is being selected. Moving the shifter into one of the arms of the H moves a shift fork to engage a gear. ● SEE FIGURE 4–21.

During upshift or downshift, one synchronizer sleeve is moved to neutral before the sleeve of the desired gear is moved to engage the desired gear.

Transmissions use two basic types of linkages:

1. Internal linkage (most commonly used)

2. External linkage, where the shift motion is transmitted from the shift lever to the transmission by a group of two or three metal rods mount on the side of the transmission

[1]GM Course # 17440.14D.

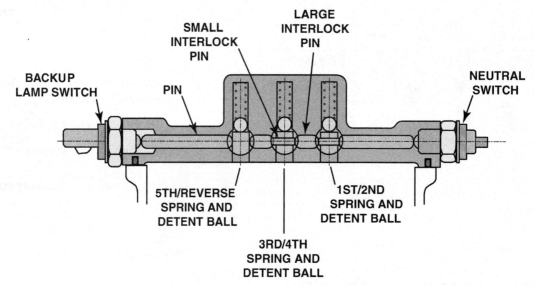

FIGURE 4–22 The internal shift mechanism includes the shift detents and the interlock to keep the shifter from selecting two gear ratios at the same time.

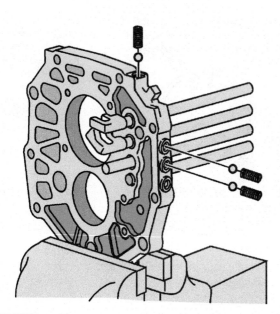

FIGURE 4–23 The detent balls and springs are inserted into threaded holes and are retained by threaded plugs. (Courtesy of General Motors.)

INTERLOCKS AND DETENTS
A shift mechanism must include two features:

1. An interlock system
2. A series of detents

Some transmissions also include a reverse lockout. The interlock prevents engagement of more than one gear at a time. It is impossible for the transmission to transmit power through two different ratios and have two different output shaft speeds at the same time. If two gears are engaged, the transmission

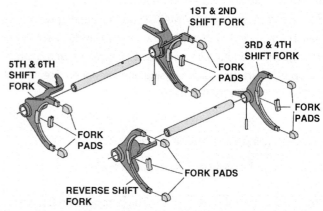

FIGURE 4–24 Some shift forks have nylon pads added to reduce friction. (Courtesy of General Motors.)

will lock up, and both the input and output shafts will become stationary. ● SEE FIGURE 4–22.

Detents are used to locate the internal shift forks in one of their three positions—neutral plus a gear to each side. A detent is usually a spring-loaded ball or bullet-shaped rod that is pushed into one of a series of three notches. ● SEE FIGURE 4–23.

SHIFT FORKS
As a shift of gears is made, the action of the detents can be felt as they engage and disengage the shift rails or cams. The synchronizer sleeve is moved by a **shift fork** that is mounted on either a rail or a cam. A rail is a metal rod that slides lengthwise. A cam usually pivots on its shaft, which extends out the side of the case or side cover. Since it must contact and move the spinning synchronizer sleeve, the contact surfaces of the fork are made of hardened steel, bronze, or a low-friction plastic/nylon pad attached to the fork. ● SEE FIGURE 4–24.

FIGURE 4–25 Getting into reverse requires extra effort to overcome a strong centering spring.

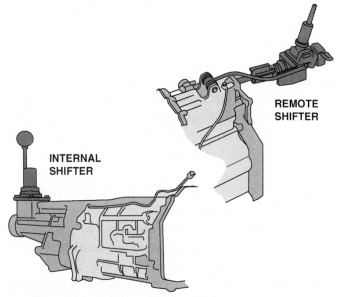

FIGURE 4–26 A remote shifter (upper unit) is used to locate the shifter inside the vehicle in the same location of another type used in a similar vehicle.

After the sleeve/gear has been positioned, there should be little contact between the fork and the sleeve/gear. At this time, the fork is located by the detent. The sleeve is located by the synchronizer keys when in neutral and by the dog clutch teeth on the mating gear when it is shifted. The detents, shift rails, and forks are not designed to hold the gear or sleeve into mesh, only to position it completely into mesh. The cut of the sleeve or gear is what actually keeps it into mesh during the different driving situations. Holding a gear into mesh with the fork will cause rather rapid wear of the fork and fork groove.

REVERSE LOCKOUT A reverse lockout mechanism is used to prevent accidental engagement of reverse while making an upshift. This mechanism requires the driver to perform an additional operation to shift into reverse. This might require that the shift lever be pushed downward or lifted up, or there may be an additional lever or button to be pushed. Most transmissions use a stronger shift lever centering spring so it takes extra effort to move the shifter to select the reverse shift rail. ● **SEE FIGURE 4–25.**

Some six-speed transmissions include a reverse lockout to prevent shifting into reverse gear while the vehicle is moving forward. The six-speed shift pattern along with a synchronized reverse gear make a shift into reverse quite possible, and powertrain damage could easily occur. This mechanism uses a solenoid that is electronically controlled by the powertrain control module (PCM).

MANUAL TRANSMISSION GEARS

TYPES USED All forward gears in a transmission are helical gears with spur gears sometimes used for reverse. When driving in reverse, a whine or light growl from transmissions that use spur gears can often be heard.

The end thrust created by a helical gear requires a thrust surface on the side of the gear that is loaded. This is especially true at the side loaded during forward motion. During deceleration, the thrust direction will reverse, and a helical gear will thrust in the opposite direction. Gear side or end float should be limited to reduce noise or possible damage, especially in the gears used at cruising speeds where throttle change is normal.

A helical gear can also be made with the helix cut at different angles. As the angle is increased, the gear will run more quietly, but end thrust will increase. Some transmissions use fine-pitched gears with a greater helix angle for the top gears. This produces quiet operation at cruising speeds where low torque loading is encountered. ● **SEE FIGURE 4–27.**

MAIN SHAFT Close inspection of a main shaft reveals specific areas that serve specific purposes. For example, the positioning of the snap ring grooves is very exacting to locate parts in precise locations. The snap rings may be available in different widths to adjust thrust clearance/gear end play. The main shaft itself is located by the rear bearing, bearing surface, and retaining ring. Each synchronizer assembly has a set of splines so that torque can transfer to the shaft. Each gear location has a bearing surface, or journal, which often has a special provision for lubricating the floating speed gear. A main shaft will have a surface for the pilot bearing to the main drive gear at the front and the splines to match the U-joint splines at the rear. Close to the rear of the shaft, there will be provision for mounting a speedometer drive gear or vehicle speed sensor (VSS) or the worm teeth for the speedometer drive gear will be cut into the shaft.

COUNTERSHAFT AND CLUSTER GEAR The cluster gear is supported by the rod-like countershaft with a set of needle bearings at each end in older transmissions. The countershaft has a press fit into the case. Units with high torque loading use a double set of needle bearings at each end to support the cluster gear. A thrust washer is used between the gear and the case at each end to control end thrust. The thrust washer or a wear plate is keyed into the case so that it will not spin and wear into the case.

The fit between the countershaft and the case is tight enough to prevent lubricant leaks. At one end of the shaft, there is normally a locating device to prevent shaft rotation.

Some newer transmissions support the countershaft assembly, which includes the cluster gear, with a pair of tapered roller bearings. Tapered bearing design is capable of absorbing thrust loads along with the normal side loads. Tapered roller bearings are normally adjusted during installation to obtain free running with a very slight clearance.

Most cluster gears are one-piece units, and if one of the gears is damaged, the entire unit must be replaced. In some transmissions, the cluster gear is a three-piece unit. ● **SEE FIGURE 4–28.**

The two gears at the front of the cluster gear have a press fit onto the main cluster gear. Woodruff keys help the assembly transfer torque. Another type of cluster gear is used in the six-speed, T56 transmission. The cluster gear/countershaft fits in the main case and has the gears needed for first through fourth. A countershaft extension drives fifth, sixth, and reverse, and it fits in the extension housing. The back of the cluster gear and the front of the extension have matching splines to transfer torque.

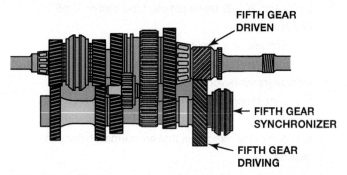

FIFTH GEAR DRIVEN

← FIFTH GEAR SYNCHRONIZER

← FIFTH GEAR DRIVING

FIGURE 4–27 Notice the gear teeth in this transmission that those on the fifth gears have a finer pitch and a greater helix angle, to produce quieter operation while cruising.

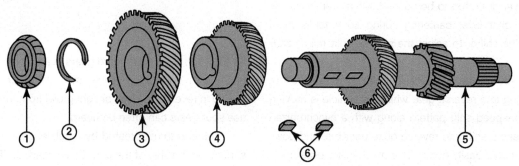

FIGURE 4–28 Two gears, (3) and (4), are press fit onto the cluster gear in a Tremec TR-3550 transmission. The Woodruff keys (6) lock the gears to the shaft.

TRANSMISSION CASE AND BEARINGS

TRANSMISSION CASE   The main case and extension housing are usually made from aluminum castings, whereas older transmissions use cast iron cases. Most cases have openings for access to the gear train. The term *open case* is sometimes used for a case in which the side or top cover is removable and includes the shifting forks and other mechanisms. ● **SEE FIGURE 4–29.**

A cover that includes the shift mechanism is normally located by dowel pins so that the shift motions do not cause movement of the cover, which could cause incomplete gear engagement. Closed case refers to a case that might have access openings, but the shift mechanism is located entirely within the case. In a split case design, the case has two halves that are bolted together. Many five- and six-speed transmissions use a *center plate* design. The center plate has bearings that support the main shaft and cluster gear.

FIGURE 4–29 A Borg-Warner T5 five-speed transmission shown with the shifter cover removed.

BEARINGS   Transmissions use a variety of bearings, depending on the particular design. The types used can include the following:

- Needle bearings
- Ball bearings
- Tapered roller bearings
- Bushings

● **SEE FIGURE 4–30.**

- Needle bearings, either caged or free, can carry large side loads but are unable to control end thrust loads. Free needle bearings are used to support the cluster gear in older transmissions. The speed gears in many transmissions are mounted over caged needle bearings.
- Ball bearings can carry moderate to high side loads and thrust loads. Therefore, they are commonly used for the main drive gear and main shaft. A "maxi" version of the ball bearing can carry even greater side loads. A maxi bearing can be identified by the increased number of balls as well as loading notches at one side of the inner and outer races.
- Tapered roller bearings can carry large side and thrust loads and are generally used in pairs with the cones and cups facing in opposite directions. This bearing is normally installed with a method (usually shims) for adjusting end play or, in a few cases, preload. In some transmissions, tapered roller bearings are used to support the main drive gear, the main shaft, and the countershaft.
- A bushing is used to support the driveshaft slip yoke in the extension housing. A bushing can support a large side load and allows free in-and-out movement.

MANUAL TRANSMISSION LUBRICATION

PURPOSE AND FUNCTION   Manual transmissions, transfer cases, and drive axles must be lubricated to reduce heat and friction. Lubricants can be either refined petroleum

FIGURE 4–30 The types of frictionless bearings are ball bearings (a), straight roller bearings (b), needle bearings (c), and tapered roller bearings (d).

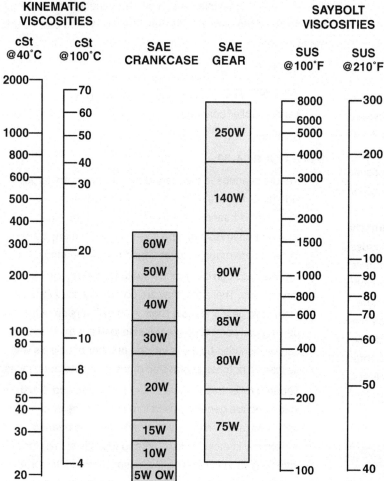

KINEMATIC VISCOSITIES

cSt @40°C | cSt @100°C | SAE CRANKCASE | SAE GEAR

SAYBOLT VISCOSITIES

SUS @100°F | SUS @210°F

FIGURE 4–31 Gear oil and crankcase (engine oil) are shown together on this viscosity chart.

or synthetic products. The job of the lubricant includes the following:

- Reduce friction
- Transfer heat away from the gears and bearings
- Reduce corrosion and rust
- Flush dirt and wear particles away from the moving parts

Two rating systems are used to select the proper lubricant:

1. Society of Automotive Engineers (SAE) viscosity rating
2. American Petroleum Institute (API) Service Classification

The lubricant can be any of the following, depending on vehicle manufacturer, model, and year:

- Gear oil such as SAE 80W-90
- Engine oil such as SAE 5W-30
- ATF such as Dexron III/VI
- Manual transmission fluid

VISCOSITY **Viscosity** is a measurement of fluid thickness. Viscosity is determined by observing how fast the fluid runs through a precisely sized orifice at a particular temperature.

All oils are thicker, and flow slower when cold and thinner and flow faster when hot. The *viscosity index (VI)* is an indication of the flow difference between hot and cold. Viscosity index numbers are low, such as 80, if the lubricant is not able to maintain a consistent viscosity and high, such as 150, if the lubricant has a more stable viscosity throughout a wide temperature range.

- In a gearbox, a lubricant that is too thick will deliver poor lubrication when cold because the thick fluid will not flow into smaller areas. Too-thick gear oil might channel, which means that it flows in a rope-like pattern. It also increases drag between parts so they do not turn as easily, and shift collars will not slide as easily. Synchronizer cones will not work very well because they cannot break through the thick oil film. This can cause hard shifting until the fluid warms.

- A too-thin lubricant will not provide the lubricating film under hot conditions. Thin fluids also cause more gear noise. The viscosity numbers used for gear oils are higher than those for engine oils, but the actual viscosity is similar. ● **SEE FIGURE 4–31.**

FIGURE 4–32 When selecting the specified lubricant to be used in a manual transmission, always check that the viscosity and the rating match factory specifications.

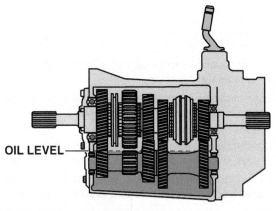

OIL LEVEL

FIGURE 4–33 The fluid level of most transmissions is at the bottom of the fill plug opening. Always check service information because some vehicle manufacturers specify that the correct full level is one inch (25 mm) below the bottom of the fill hole.

FIGURE 4–34 The transmission gears rotating in the case is what forces the oil throughout the transmission as shown in this cutaway that is powered by an electric motor to show the action.

GEAR OIL CLASSIFICATIONS The API gear oil classifications are as follows:

GL-1 Straight mineral oil and not suitable for current passenger car transmissions

GL-2 A designation for worm gear drives used mostly in industrial applications

GL-3 Contains mild extreme pressure (EP) additives and specified for use in manual transmissions and transaxles with spiral bevel final drives

GL-4 Formulated for use in manual transmissions and transaxles with hypoid final drives and contains about half the additives used in GL-5

GL-5 Enough EP additive to lubricate hypoid gears in drive axles

GL-6 An obsolete designation

An additional classification, GLS (Gear Lubricant Special), is sometimes used to indicate a proprietary set of specifications determined by the vehicle or gearbox manufacturer. **Manual transmission fluid (MTF)** usually is in this category. An MTF might contain a friction modifier to give proper synchronizer action and long life. ● **SEE FIGURE 4–32.**

LUBRICATION INSIDE THE TRANSMISSION The transmission cluster gears run in a bath of lubricant, and as they spin, their motion will throw the lubricant throughout the case.

The fluid level is normally at the bottom of the check/fill plug in the side of the case. ● **SEE FIGURE 4–33.** This is usually at a level just below the rear bushing and seal.

The lubricant reduces friction so that the parts spin more easily and transfers heat away from the gear contact and rubbing parts. Floating gears on the main shaft or cluster gears have special paths and provisions for getting the lubricant into their bearings, and some transmissions have troughs or oiling funnels to get lubricant into the critical areas.

Each transmission includes a vent, normally located at the top of the case. This relieves internal pressure that would occur as the gears and oil warm up while operating. If not relieved, the pressure would force the oil out past the input and output shaft seals.

CAUTION: A transmission is lubricated by oil thrown off the cluster gear. If a vehicle is towed in neutral, the cluster gear does not rotate and wear can occur between the rotating main shaft and the stationary gears that float on it. A transmission with the synchronizer on the cluster gear will receive some lubrication through its gear action. ● SEE FIGURE 4–34.

1. Transmissions provide gear sets for forward speeds and reverse as well as neutral.

2. Transmissions normally have four shafts: cluster gear (countershaft), input shaft, output shaft, and reverse idler shaft.

3. Synchronizer assemblies normally have a hub, sleeve, a set of keys, two blocker rings, and a speed gear on each side.

4. Early blocker rings were a single, brass ring, whereas newer blocker rings are double, paper-lined rings.

5. Transmissions torque capacity is determined by the size of the gears and shafts.

6. Transmissions shifts use external or internal linkages that include detents, interlocks, and shift forks.

7. Transmissions are lubricated with gear oil, engine oil, or manual transmission fluid (MTF).

8. Special transmission design features include gear tooth pitch and helix angle, cluster gear variations, case construction, and bearing type.

REVIEW QUESTIONS

1. What are the two types of gear sets used in standard transmissions?

2. Synchronizer assembly includes what parts?

3. How does a synchronizer work?

4. What does a detent do?

CHAPTER QUIZ

1. The input and output shafts of a rear-wheel-drive transmission are called _____ and _____.
   a. Input and output
   b. countershaft and main shaft
   c. Clutch shaft and main shaft
   d. Both a and c are correct

2. What is designed into a transmission so that it can handle more engine torque?
   a. Longer length
   b. Input and output shafts are larger
   c. The case is made from cast steel
   d. Needle bearings are used in all locations

3. Which gear is most likely to use a spur gear?
   a. First
   b. Second
   c. Fourth
   d. Reverse

4. To achieve a clash-free (no grinding sound) shift, what is used in a manual transmission?
   a. Large diameter gears
   b. Synchronizers
   c. Roller bearings
   d. Internal shift linkage

5. A _____ is used to prevent accidental engagement of reverse while making an upshift.
   a. Reverse lockout
   b. Internal shift linkage
   c. External shift linkage
   d. Detent

6. Most manual transmissions use a case made from _____.
   a. Cast steel
   b. Cast aluminum
   c. Pressed steel
   d. Cast iron

7. The idler gear is used for which gear?
   a. First gear
   b. Second gear
   c. Third gear
   d. Reverse

8. The type of bearing used in a manual transmission is _____
   a. Needle bearing
   b. Ball bearing
   c. Tapered roller bearing
   d. Any of the above

9. The lubricant used in a manual transmission is _____
   a. Gear oil
   b. ATF
   c. Manual transmission fluid
   d. Any of the above depending on the make and model of vehicle

10. The detent mechanism inside a transmission is used to _____.
    a. Locate the synchronizer sleeves in the correct position
    b. Prevent more than one shift fork from moving at one time
    c. Hold a gear into mesh
    d. All of these

TRANSAXLE PARTS AND OPERATION

BACKGROUND The development of the transaxle has, in part, made the modern, fuel-saving front-wheel-drive (FWD) vehicle possible. Early FWD vehicles included the American Cord of the 1930s ● **SEE FIGURE 5–1**.

A large majority of the vehicles sold today are front-wheel drive. The engine and transaxle are either transverse or longitudinally mounted.

- A **transverse engine** points across the vehicle also called *East-West* positioning.

- A **longitudinal engine** is commonly used in rear-wheel-drive vehicles and is often called *North-South* positioning.

Many features of the transmission part of a transaxle are similar to those of a rear-wheel-drive transmission. There are differences, however, in the number of shafts and the power flow. There is also the addition of the final drive gears and the differential.

TRANSAXLES DESIGNS Most front-wheel-drive vehicles have transverse-mounted engines, and the engine-transmission package must fit in the vehicle between the suspension components. Many transaxles have the differential mounted off center, which results in unequal-length drive shafts. ● **SEE FIGURE 5–2**.

Unequal-length drive shafts can cause the vehicle to pull to one side during acceleration, which is called **torque steer**. Torque steer is caused by the following:

- Unequal CV joint angles
- Unequal length of the shafts
- The tendency for the longer drive shaft to twist

(a)

(b)

FIGURE 5–1 (a) The Cord was one of the first front-wheel-drive vehicles. (b) The Cord did not use a transaxle but instead drove the front wheels through a transmission and drive axle through constant velocity (CV) joints.

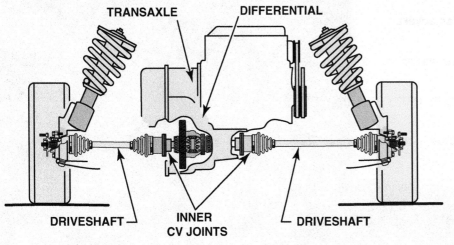

FIGURE 5–2 A transaxle is a transmission plus the final drive and differential. The inner CV joints of the front drive shafts connect to the side gears in the transaxle differential.

The vehicle has a tendency to pull toward the side that has the longer drive shaft. Most front wheel drive vehicles use a short intermediate drive shaft to shorten the length of the long axle. This makes both axles the same length and helps to equalize the CV joint angles. Making the drive axles the same length minimizes or eliminates torque steer. ● SEE FIGURE 5–3.

TRANSAXLE CONSTRUCTION

A transaxle may be made with two or three shafts, depending on the manufacturer and the number of forward gear ratios. At each gear pair, one gear is secured solidly to the shaft and the other floats on the shaft, right next to a synchronizer assembly. Some transaxles secure all the gears on the input shaft to form a cluster gear. These can be either a single cluster gear or a group of gears pressed onto a splined shaft. Other designs float all or some of the driving gears on the input shaft and secure the driven gears onto the main shaft. ● SEE FIGURE 5–4.

Most engines rotate in a clockwise direction (viewing the drive rotation from the right, or passenger, side of the vehicle). The input shaft rotates clockwise, the main shaft rotates counterclockwise in forward gears, and the differential rotates clockwise to drive the wheels in a clockwise direction. ● SEE FIGURE 5–5.

The transaxle used on older vehicles had four forward speeds with most vehicles later using a five-speed transaxle. Newer vehicles may have a six-speed design in a compact housing. ● SEE FIGURE 5–6.

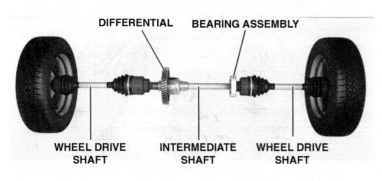

FIGURE 5–3 Using an intermediate axle shaft allows both wheel drive shafts to be the same length. The bearing assembly is bolted with a mount to the side of the lower engine block. (Courtesy of General Motors.)

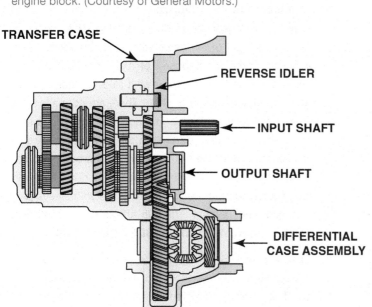

FIGURE 5–4 This five-speed transaxle is a two-shaft design; that is, the main gear set assembly has two shafts. A three shaft design will, in addition, have an intermediate shaft.

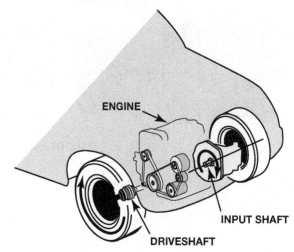

FIGURE 5–5 The engine and the transaxle input shaft rotate in a clockwise direction in most FWD vehicles (viewed from the right side). The intermediate shaft will rotate counterclockwise and drive the ring gear, differential, and drive shafts in a clockwise direction.

FIGURE 5–6 A six-speed manual transaxle. (Courtesy of General Motors.)

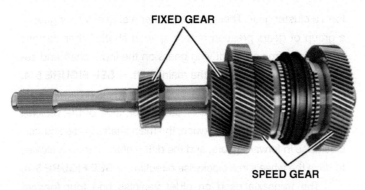

FIXED GEAR

SPEED GEAR

FIGURE 5–7 The input shaft may include both speed gears and fixed gears. (Courtesy of General Motors.)

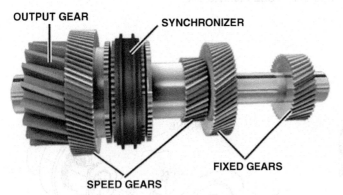

OUTPUT GEAR

SYNCHRONIZER

FIXED GEARS

SPEED GEARS

FIGURE 5–8 The output shaft includes the output gear (drive pinion gear) that drives the differential ring gear. (Courtesy of General Motors.)

TRANSAXLE COMPONENTS Typical components include the following.

1. **Input shaft**—The input shaft is the primary input from the clutch to the transmission gears. It is sometimes called the **clutch shaft** because it provides a splined end for the clutch disc to ride on. The opposite end contains the gears. Front and rear bearings support the input shaft. Depending on the application, either speed gears or fixed gears mount on the input shaft. For speed gears, a synchronizer assembly is included to enable gear selection. Bushings, spacers, and bearing collars support the gears and control end play. ● **SEE FIGURE 5–7.**

2. **Output shaft**—The output shaft, also called a **countershaft** in some applications, provides the power to the differential assembly. Case bearings support the output shaft. The output gear at the end of the output shaft is in mesh with the differential ring gear. The output shaft contains fixed and speed gears. The speed gears have a synchronizer associated with them and the output **drive pinion gear** drives the differential ring gear by way of a machined gear at the end of the shaft. ● **SEE FIGURE 5–8.**

FIGURE 5–9 This intermediate shaft includes two speed gears and one fixed gear. (Courtesy of General Motors.)

3. **Intermediate shaft**—Intermediate shafts are incorporated in three-shaft design transmissions. The use of an **intermediate shaft** allows for the addition of gear sets. Manufacturers of transmissions with three shafts have various ways of identifying the shafts. For instance, a configuration may be an input shaft, an intermediate shaft, and an output shaft, or another may be an input shaft, an upper shaft, and a lower shaft. The intermediate shaft components are the same as the input and output components; however, the sole purpose of the intermediate shaft is to provide additional gear sets to the input and output shafts. The intermediate shaft does not have a splined end, nor does it provide an output to the differential. ● **SEE FIGURE 5–9.**

4. **Synchronizers**—Synchronizers are used to speed up or slow down gear speed during shifting. This allows for the engagement of the gears with minimum interference. A synchronizer is composed of many different components, which include inserts, a shift sleeve, blocking rings with coned surfaces, and a hub. There are normally three inserts, which are installed in machined slots in the lock ring hub to provide pressure on the shift sleeve. A shift sleeve has a machined groove around the outer circumference, providing a slot for the shift rail/fork assembly to ride. Clutching teeth on each side of the shift sleeve provide gear engagement. The hub affixes to the shaft with one shift sleeve riding on it. ● **SEE FIGURE 5–10.**

5. **Speed gears**—Speed gears ride on bushings on a shaft and spin freely. The speed gears are almost always helical cut. They provide clutching teeth and a coned surface for synchronizer operation.

6. **Idler gear**—Idler gears provide reverse gear operation and ride on a reverse gear idler shaft.

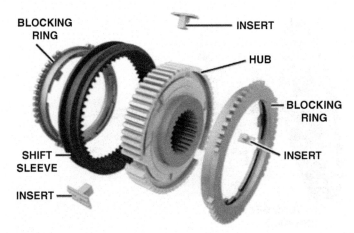

FIGURE 5–10 A synchronizer assembly. (Courtesy of General Motors.)

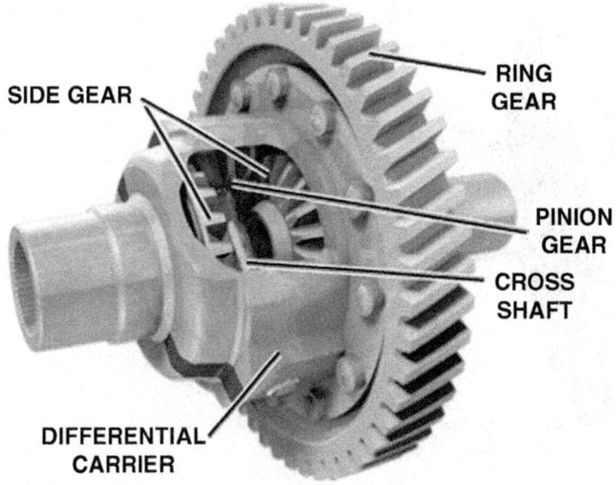

FIGURE 5–11 The final drive assembly, also called the differential assembly. The ring gear is driven by the output gear. (Courtesy of General Motors.)

7. **Differential assembly**—The differential assembly transmits power to the axle shafts. The differential ring gear mounts to the differential carrier and receives input from the transmission output shaft gear. The **differential** divides the power flow between the two CV joints coupled to the drive shafts and on to the wheels. The differential **pinion gears** and side (axle) gears in the differential allow for speed differences when the vehicle turns a corner. This gear arrangement also splits the power from a single source to two sources with, typically, 50/50 torque distribution. ● **SEE FIGURE 5–11.**[1]

TRANSAXLE OPERATION

POWER FLOW   The power flow through the transmission section of a transaxle is essentially the same in all the forward gears. The power (torque) passes

- From the driving gear on the input shaft
- To the driven gear on the main shaft and then
- Through the synchronizer assembly to the main shaft itself
- The power leaves the transaxle main shaft through the drive pinion, which drives the final drive ring gear

Because the power passes through only one set of gears, the ratio for that gear speed is determined by that pair of gears. The smallest gear on the input shaft drives the largest gear on the main shaft for first gear, and the largest gear on the input shaft drives the smallest gear on the main shaft for highest gear. For example, the power flow through a commonly used five-speed transaxle is shown in ● **FIGURE 5–12.**

The synchronizers are the same as those used in a rear-wheel-drive transmission and their parts and operation are identical.

The power flow for reverse gear is also similar to that of a rear-wheel-drive transmission. In most cases, the reverse idler is shifted into mesh with the reverse gear on the input shaft and the sleeve of the 1–2 synchronizer assembly, which has the spur gear teeth for reverse on the outer diameter. The idler gear will rotate in a counterclockwise direction viewed from the right side, the 1–2 synchronizer assembly will rotate clockwise, and the differential and drive wheels will rotate counterclockwise to drive the vehicle backward. ● **SEE FIGURE 5–13.**

FINAL DRIVE AND DIFFERENTIAL   The power leaves the transaxle main shaft through the drive pinion, which drives the final drive ring gear. The drive pinion and ring gear are a pair of helical gears. This gear set operates rather quietly and does not require critical adjustments like a hypoid gear set. ● **SEE FIGURE 5–14.**

TRANSAXLE GEARS   Like manual transmissions, manual transaxles use helical gears for all the forward speeds and spur gears for reverse. To allow for engine length in the cramped width of the engine compartment, the speed gears, synchronizer assemblies, and bearings are kept as narrow and compact as practical. This design factor is much more critical with transaxles than with transmissions.

TRANSAXLE BEARINGS   The bearing surfaces on many transaxles are made with lubrication slots to compensate for the reduced gear width, whereas on other units the speed gears

---

[1] This section is adapted from GM Center of Learning Course # 17043.38W1.

FIRST GEAR
ENGAGED

(a)

SECOND GEAR
ENGAGED

(b)

THIRD GEAR
ENGAGED

(c)

FOURTH GEAR
ENGAGED

(d)

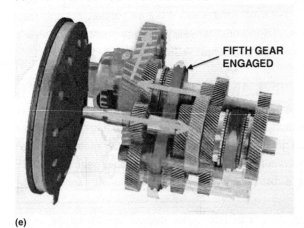

FIFTH GEAR
ENGAGED

(e)

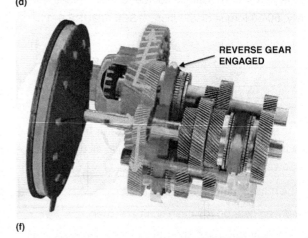

REVERSE GEAR
ENGAGED

(f)

FIGURE 5–12 (a) First gear power flow through a five-speed transaxle. (b) Second gear. (c) Third gear. (d) Fourth gear. (e) Fifth gear. (f) Reverse. (Courtesy of General Motors)

are mounted on roller or needle bearings. These features also improve the efficiency of the transaxle and fuel economy. Some transaxles use a roller bearing at the engine end of the input shaft and main shaft and a ball bearing at the other end of the shaft.

The ball bearing supports one end and also positions the shaft to the case as the roller bearing supports the end with the greater side loading from the final drive. This feature makes for

easy servicing, as the roller bearing can slide through the openings when the cover is removed or installed.

On transaxles that use tapered roller bearings, bearing clearance or preload is adjusted by selecting the correct size of shim to place at the bearing or bearing cup. The *selective shim* is positioned under the bearing cup in the case. A selective shim means that there are several different thickness shims available that can be inserted behind the bearing to provide the

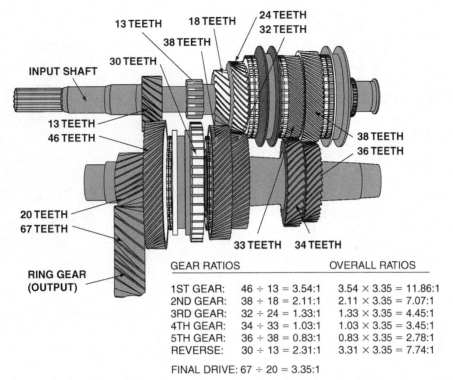

INPUT SHAFT

13 TEETH
38 TEETH
30 TEETH
18 TEETH
24 TEETH
32 TEETH

13 TEETH
46 TEETH

38 TEETH
36 TEETH

20 TEETH
67 TEETH

RING GEAR
(OUTPUT)

33 TEETH   34 TEETH

GEAR RATIOS			OVERALL RATIOS
1ST GEAR:	46 ÷ 13 = 3.54:1		3.54 × 3.35 = 11.86:1
2ND GEAR:	38 ÷ 18 = 2.11:1		2.11 × 3.35 = 7.07:1
3RD GEAR:	32 ÷ 24 = 1.33:1		1.33 × 3.35 = 4.45:1
4TH GEAR:	34 ÷ 33 = 1.03:1		1.03 × 3.35 = 3.45:1
5TH GEAR:	36 ÷ 38 = 0.83:1		0.83 × 3.35 = 2.78:1
REVERSE:	30 ÷ 13 = 2.31:1		3.31 × 3.35 = 7.74:1

FINAL DRIVE: 67 ÷ 20 = 3.35:1

FIGURE 5–13 The gear ratios of a transaxle are determined by dividing the tooth count of the driven gear by that of the driving gear. Multiplying the transaxle gear ratio by the final drive ratio gives us the overall ratio.

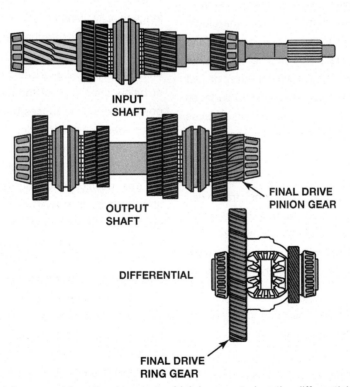

INPUT
SHAFT

OUTPUT
SHAFT

FINAL DRIVE
PINION GEAR

DIFFERENTIAL

FINAL DRIVE
RING GEAR

FIGURE 5–14 The final drive pinion gear drives the ring gear, which is mounted on the differential case.

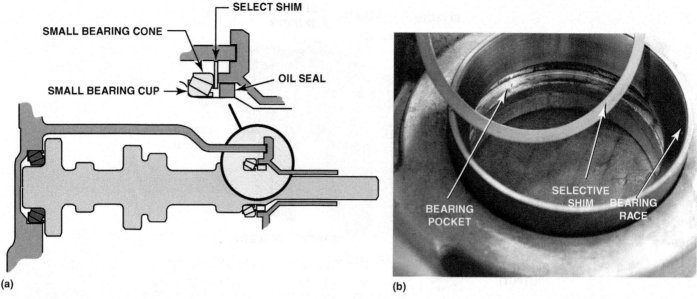

(a) **(b)**

FIGURE 5–15 (a) This transaxle uses tapered roller bearings at the input shaft. To adjust these bearings, the selective shim is located at each bearing set. (b) The selective shim is used under the bearing race and placed into the bearing pocket (bearing counter-bore) before the race is pressed into the transaxle case.

specified bearing preload. In loaded areas where shaft movement can create a problem, the bearings are adjusted to a slight preload. ● **SEE FIGURE 5–15**.

TRANSAXLE CASE DESIGN   Transaxle cases are made from cast aluminum. Many cases use a two-part assembly with a right-hand case or cover that also forms the clutch housing and a left-hand or main case that contains the gears. Some units have a separate side case or side cover that encloses the fifth gear set and the synchronizer or just the left-side bearings. The case provides machined surfaces that allow the case to attach to the engine. Machined surfaces on the case, used in a conjunction with a sealer, seal in the lubricating fluids.

SPLASH LUBRICATION   Like transmissions, transaxles use a supply of oil in the sump at the bottom of the case that is circulated by gear rotation. This type of lubrication is called *splash lubrication*. The oil is directed to critical areas by troughs and oiling funnels. The fluid level is normally checked at a fill-level plug or with a dipstick.

- Most transaxles have a common case, so the transmission and final drive share the same lubricant.
- Some units separate the two and different oils may be used for each gear set, and there will be two fluid-level plugs.

LONGITUDINAL TRANSAXLES

A few front-wheel-drive vehicle manufacturers place the engine longitudinally (lengthwise) rather than placing transversally. This requires a major change in the transaxle. In these units, the power must turn 90° to align with the front drive. Some units use a hypoid gear set that mounts the drive pinion above or below the center of the ring gear. This gear set turns the power flow as it produces the necessary final drive reduction. The power flow from the ring gear through the differential to the CV joints is the same as described previously.

Hypoid gears require adjustments for proper ring and pinion gear positioning during assembly procedures. This transaxle lends itself to AWD or 4WD because of the longitudinal position of the main shaft. It is a fairly simple matter for the manufacturer to install a clutch at the rear end of the main shaft and extend an output shaft to connect to a driveshaft for the rear wheels. ● **SEE FIGURE 5–16**.

Another longitudinal configuration is used in the Chevrolet Corvette. The design is not actually a transaxle but may be referred to as a transaxle in some publications. The transmission is placed at the rear of the vehicle and attached with a flange assembly to the final drive axle to make up a rigid assembly for driving the rear wheels. ● **SEE FIGURE 5–17**.

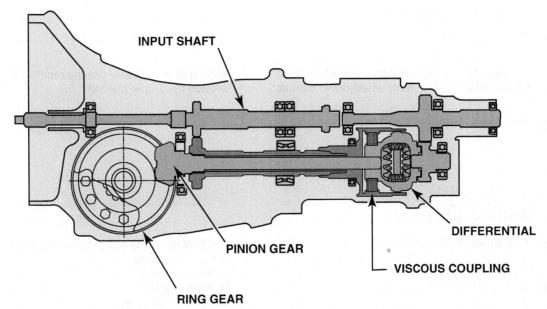

FIGURE 5–16 This transaxle is used with an engine that is mounted lengthwise in the vehicle. Note how the final drive is through a ring and pinion gear set. Also note the center differential and extension to drive the rear wheels of an all-wheel-drive vehicle.

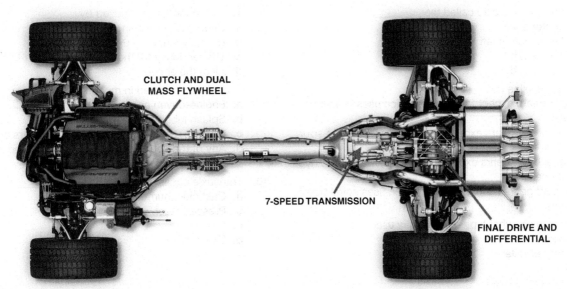

FIGURE 5–17 The rear-mounted seven-speed transmission is mated to the final drive assembly and may sometimes be referred to as a transaxle. (Courtesy of General Motors.)

SUMMARY

1. Transaxles combine a transmission with the final drive gear set and differential.

2. Some transaxles are mounted in a longitudinal position and use a hypoid final drive gear set.

3. Transaxles use helical cut gears except for reverse where straight cut spur gears are often used.

1. What is the major difference between a rear-wheel-drive manual transmission and a front-wheel-drive manual transaxle?

2. The final drive gears of a typical transaxle use what type of gears?

3. What type of transaxle bearing requires selective shims to provide the proper preload?

CHAPTER QUIZ

1. An early front-wheel vehicle was a _____.
   a. Cord
   b. Ford Model T
   c. Cadillac
   d. Mercedes

2. The inboard CV joints on the driveshaft are splined to the _____.
   a. Differential pinion gears
   b. Differential case
   c. Differential side gears
   d. Output shaft

3. The main shaft is also called the _____.
   a. Counter shaft
   b. Intermediate shaft
   c. Clutch shaft
   d. Either a or b

4. Most transaxles use _____
   a. Spur gears except for reverse, which uses helical-cut gears
   b. Helical-cut gears except for reverse, which uses spur gears
   c. Spiral bevel gears except for reverse, which uses hypoid gears
   d. Hypoid gears except reverse, which uses spiral bevel gears

5. In a transaxle, what type of bearing is used?
   a. Roller
   b. Tapered roller
   c. Ball
   d. All of the above

6. The final drive ring and pinion gears in a typical transaxle are _____ type.
   a. Hypoid gears
   b. Helical gears
   c. Spiral bevel gears.
   d. Both b and c.

7. A typical transaxle has how many shafts?
   a. Four
   b. Three
   c. Two
   d. One

8. Torque steer can be caused by _____.
   a. Unequal CV joint angles
   b. Unequal length of the shafts
   c. The tendency for the longer drive shaft to twist
   d. All of the above

9. The lubrication used in most transaxles uses _____.
   a. Engine-driven an oil pump
   b. Splash lubrication
   c. Oil from the engine to lubricate the gears and bearings
   d. Any of the above depending on make and model of the vehicle

10. Transaxle cases are made from _____.
    a. Cast aluminum
    b. Pressed steel
    c. Cast iron
    d. Either a or b

chapter 6
MANUAL TRANSMISSION/ TRANSAXLE DIAGNOSIS AND SERVICE

LEARNING OBJECTIVES

After studying this chapter, the reader should be able to:

1. Explain how to perform transaxle/transmission maintenance operations.
2. Explain manual transaxle/transmission diagnosis.
3. Discuss the procedure for transaxle/ transmission removal and replacement.
4. Discuss the procedure for transaxle/ transmission overhaul.

This chapter will help you prepare for ASE Manual Drive Train and Axles (A3) certification test content area "B" (Transmission Diagnosis and Repair) and area "C" (Transaxle Diagnosis and Repair).

KEY TERMS

Anaerobic sealants 102
Blocker ring clearance 97
Brinelling 95
Contamination 95
Dynamic shift test 88
Electric arcing 95
End play 100
Formed-in-place gaskets (FIPG) 102
Fretting 95
Lubricant checks 82

Misalignment 95
Peeling 95
Preload 100
Room-temperature vulcanizing (RTV) 102
Rust dust 86
Seizing 95
Shim 100
Spalling 95
Static shift test 88
Visual inspection 86

GM STC OBJECTIVES

GM Service Technical College topics covered in this chapter are:

1. Diagnose unusual fluid usage, level, and condition concerns to determine necessary repairs.
2. Diagnose shift concerns related to the shift mechanisms (rails, cables, and detents).
3. Diagnose shift concerns related to the internal gears and clutch system.
4. Describe the proper road test procedure including all of the steps involved.
5. Properly perform a manual gearbox dynamic and static test.

6. Inspect, adjust, or replace shifter mechanism and linkage.
7. Perform an accurate visual inspection.
8. Perform fluid drain and refill using the appropriate procedure and fluids.
9. Remove and install a manual gearbox assembly.
10. Properly disassemble and reassemble, clean, and inspect all manual gearbox internal components.
11. Perform end play measurements to determine correct selective components.

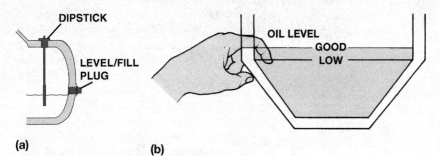

(a)   **(b)**

FIGURE 6–1 (a) Transaxles and transmissions use either a dipstick or level plug to check the oil level. (b) To determine the fluid level, insert a finger into the opening and feel for the fluid level. Some vehicle manufacturers specify that the fluid level be 1 inch (25 mm) below the fill plug opening.

PREVENTIVE MAINTENANCE

MAINTENANCE ITEMS   In-vehicle service, also called *on-vehicle service*, in most cases is a normal maintenance operation and includes the following:

- Periodic check of the lubricant level
- Linkage/shifter adjustment
- Mount inspection or replacement as needed
- Visual inspection for leaks and other abnormal conditions

When a problem such as hard shifting occurs, the shift linkage is also checked and readjusted, if necessary. If possible, service and repair operations are done with the transaxle/transmission in the vehicle. Transmission removal and replacement (R&R) takes about 2.5 hours and transaxle removal and replacement may take up to 5 hours. This varies greatly depending on the vehicle and the experience of the technician, but in any case, transmission/transaxle removal and replacement is time consuming.

LUBRICANT CHECK   Often, the **lubricant check** is a neglected operation. It is recommended to check the lubricant level at each engine oil change. When the fluid level is correct, most transaxle/transmissions will operate for the life of the vehicle. Gears and bearings can be damaged in just a few minutes if operated with low lubricant level. A transmission/transaxle usually requires the vehicle be raised to gain access to the filler/level plug. The way the fluid level is checked depends on whether the unit has a dipstick (rare) or just a sight plug. Check service information for the exact procedure to follow.

- If equipped with a dipstick, remove the dipstick, wipe it clean, reinsert it making sure it goes completely into the opening, remove it again, and read both sides. The fluid level should be between the "full" and "low" marks.
- If equipped with a level plug, be sure the engine is off before removing the plug. Be prepared for a fluid spill due to a high fluid level. The fluid level should be even with

the bottom of the opening. If the fluid is not running out, carefully insert a finger into the opening to feel the level of the fluid. ● **SEE FIGURE 6–1.**

CAUTION: Always properly identify the filler/check plug. For example, on the case of the Tremec 5 speed there is a large screw that looks like a check plug. If this plug is removed, it will cause a shift lever to fall inside the transmission. Always check service information for the exact location of the drain and fill plugs of the vehicle being serviced.

If the fluid level is low, add the recommended fluid to bring it to the correct level. Also, check for leaks or the reason for the low fluid level. If the level is high, drain out the excess fluid.

While checking fluid level, the condition of the fluid should also be noted.

- Color and smell in case of manual transmission fluids should be like new fluid.
- Dirty fluid should be changed.
- Fluid with silver or gold metallic flakes indicates severe wear and repair is required.
- Also check that the vent for the transmission/transaxle is free and clear.

   REAL WORLD FIX

A Hard-to-Shift Transmission

A vehicle came in with a hard shifting concern. A road test confirmed that the car shifted hard into every gear. There was no grinding that would indicate a clutch problem. The fluid level was OK, but the fluid appeared to be about 30 weight engine oil.

The technician drained, flushed, and filled the transaxle with the correct manual transmission fluid (MTF), and this fixed the hard shift problem. Always check service information to determine the specified fluid to use.

TRANSMISSION LUBRICANT REPLACEMENT

Some vehicle manufactures specify that the fluid be replaced at regular intervals. To change transaxle/transmission fluid, perform the following steps:

STEP 1 If possible, drive the vehicle to bring the lubricant up to operating temperature.

STEP 2 Raise and securely support the vehicle on a hoist or safety (jack) stands.

STEP 3 Check service information for the exact location of the fill and drain plugs. Then locate and loosen the fill plug to make sure that it can be removed before draining the fluid from the transmission or transaxle.

STEP 4 Locate the drain plug at the bottom of the transaxle/ transmission, place a drain pan under it, and remove the drain plug.

STEP 5 Allow the lubricant to drain out completely before replacing the plug. Check for any steel particles on the magnetic drain plug, which could indicate serious internal problems.

STEP 6 Inspect the old lubricant for any contamination, and dispose of it in the proper manner.

STEP 7 Check the owner's manual or service information to determine the correct lubricant type and refill quantity.

STEP 8 Refill the transaxle/transmission to the correct level.

NOTE: When DEXRON-III is indicated as the fluid fill for manual transmissions and transfer cases, DO NOT use DEXRON-VI. Instead, use GM Manual Transmission Fluid p/n 88861800 in these components. (Refer to PIP3836B.) If the manual transmission or transfer case indicates use of DEXRON-VI, then, of course, it should be used.

TRANSAXLE LINKAGE ADJUSTMENT

The exact method of adjusting transaxle shift linkage varies. Some have no adjustment, whereas others provide adjustments

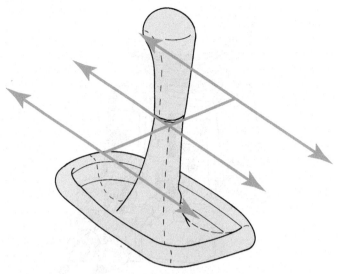

CHECK SHIFTER MOVEMENT

(a)

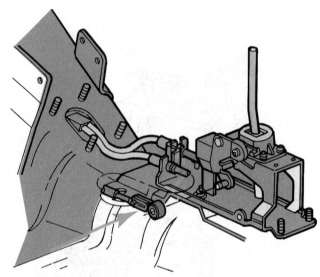

ADJUST SHIFTER LINKAGE

(b)

FIGURE 6–2 (a) Operate the shift levers through all of the gears with the engine off and again with it running. (b) If necessary, adjust the shift linkage following the vehicle manufacturer's specified procedure.

with gauging methods. Always follow the procedures found in service information for the vehicle being serviced. ● **SEE FIGURE 6–2.**

For example, to adjust the shift cables on a Chevrolet Cavalier or Cobalt:

1. Set the parking brake and remove the console.

2. Lift and unlock the shift cable retainers. ● **SEE FIGURE 6–3.**

3. Push the shifter neutral lock clip. Move the shifter slightly in order to center the lock clip. This will lock the shifter in

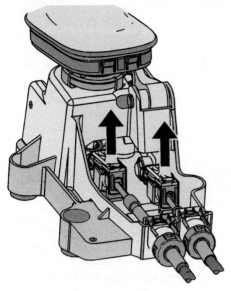

FIGURE 6–3 Unlock the shift cable retainers. (Courtesy of General Motors.)

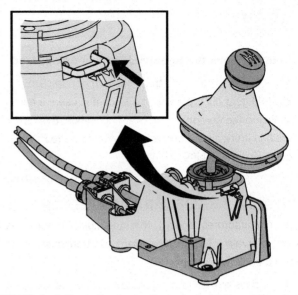

FIGURE 6–4 Push the lock clip in to hold the shifter in the neutral position. (Courtesy of General Motors.)

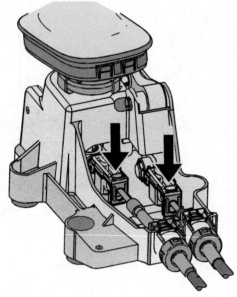

FIGURE 6–5 Lock the cables in position. (Courtesy of General Motors.)

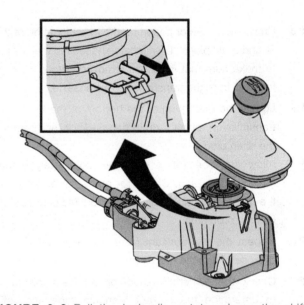

FIGURE 6–6 Pull the lock clip out to release the shifter. (Courtesy of General Motors.)

the neutral position. At the transaxle, make sure that the transmission is in neutral. ● **SEE FIGURE 6–4.**

4. Press and lock the shift cable retainers. ● **SEE FIGURE 6–5.**

5. Pull the shifter neutral lock clip to its original position and install the console. ● **SEE FIGURE 6–6.**

TRANSMISSION MOUNT INSPECTION Raise the vehicle on a hoist and secure it using safety stands or a lift-locking mechanism.

Using a pry bar or suitable tool, lift on the rear of the transmission at the mount to see if the mount has separated.

TRANSMISSION MOUNT REPLACEMENT

1. Raise and suitably support the vehicle.

2. Remove the transmission mount-to-cross member nut.

3. Remove the transmission mount bolts to the transmission.

4. Raise the transmission, using a suitable trans mission jack, just enough in order to permit the removal of the mount. ● **SEE FIGURE 6–7.**

5. Remove the transmission mount.

6. Install the new rear transmission mount.

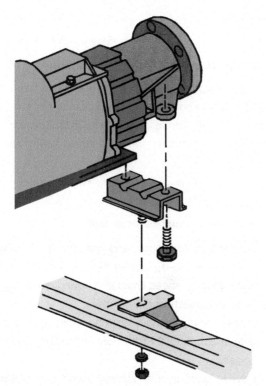

FIGURE 6–7 Lift the rear of the transmission slightly and remove the mount. Install the new mount in the reverse order. (Courtesy of General Motors.)

NOTE: Use the correct fastener in the correct location. Replacement fasteners must be the correct part number for that application. Fasteners requiring replacement or fasteners requiring the use of thread-lock¬ing compound or sealant are identified in the service procedure. Do not use paints, lubricants, or corrosion inhibitors on fasteners or fastener joint surfaces unless specified. These coatings affect fastener torque and joint clamping force and may damage the fastener. Use the correct tightening sequence and specification, when installing fasteners in order to avoid damage to parts and systems.

MANUAL TRANSMISSION/ TRANSAXLE DIAGNOSIS

DIAGNOSTIC PROCESS The process of diagnosing manual transmission/transaxle faults or concerns includes the following steps:

STEP 1   Verify the customer concern by performing a road test.

STEP 2   Perform a visual inspection.

STEP 3   Follow service information and follow pinpoint tests to determine the root cause.

STEP 4   Perform the needed repair.

STEP 5   Verify the repair.

 **REAL WORLD FIX**

The Worn Shift Fork Mystery

A vehicle equipped with a manual transmission had to be repaired several times for worn shift forks. Even though the vehicle warranty paid for the repair, both the customer and the service department personnel were concerned about the repeated failures. All technical service bulletins (TSBs) were checked to see if there was an updated, improved shift fork. No luck. Even the manufacturer's technical assistance personnel were unable to determine why the shift forks were wearing out. After the third repair, the service technician rode with the customer to see if the cause could be determined. As the woman driver got into the driver's seat, she placed the handle of her purse over the shifter on the floor and allowed the purse to hang from the shifter. The technician asked the owner if she always placed her purse on the shifter and when she said yes, the technician knew immediately the cause of the worn shift forks. The purse exerted a force on the shifter all the time. This force pushed the shift forks against the synchronizer sleeve. Because the sleeve rotates all the time the vehicle is in motion, the shift forks were quickly worn. The service technician should have determined the root cause of the problem after the first repair. The customer agreed to find another location for her purse so that the transmission problem would not reoccur.

 **TECH TIP**

Take the Owner on the Test Drive

Everyone drives differently. By having the vehicle owner along, he or she can better point out when the fault occurs and under what conditions. Sometimes, the owner should drive so the technician can verify the concern.

VERIFY CUSTOMER CONCERN The first step is to verify the customer concern. The customer should be asked the following questions in an effort to determine as much about the problem as possible.

- What exactly seems to be the concern? (Ask the customer to be as detailed as possible.)
- When did the problem first appear?
- Is there a problem between forward gears and reverse?

FIGURE 6–8 Check the clutch pedal for proper operation and be sure that the floor mat or carpet is not interfering with the operation of the clutch.

- Under what conditions do the symptoms occur? (Do they occur first thing in the morning? After the vehicle has been driven for a while?) Describe under what driving conditions the problem is noticed, such as when accelerating or while coasting to a stop or some other condition. Has the vehicle been serviced recently, such as a fluid change?

TEST DRIVE The vehicle should be test driven and the technician should check the following:

- The quality of the upshifts and downshifts.
- Listen for any unusual noises.
- Feel for any unusual movements or vibrations as the vehicle accelerates or decelerates in each gear.
- In cases where there is doubt about proper operation, the operation can be compared with that of a similar vehicle.

A typical test drive procedure includes the following operations:

- Check clutch pedal free play. ● **SEE FIGURE 6–8.**
- Warm up transmission before testing (drive aluminum case units for about 20 minutes).
- With vehicle stationary, engine idling, clutch depressed, and in neutral:
  a. Release clutch and listen for noise, and depress pedal noting any noises.
  b. Release clutch, depress pedal, wait 3 seconds, and shift into reverse, then first gear, and then back to reverse. Repeat, but wait 20 seconds. Note any differences in noise or shifting ability.
  c. Shift into reverse, release pedal, and while carefully backing, increase engine speed to 2500 RPM, and note any noises.

TECH TIP

Too High Viscosity Oil Can Hurt Shifting

During a shift, the synchronizer ring must cut through the lubricant to contact the speed gear cone. Hard shifts can result from a lubricant that is too thick or from worn synchronizer rings (the threadlike grooves are no longer sharp).

- Drive vehicle on road with little traffic:
  a. Start in first, accelerate, and upshift at 4000 RPM (1–2, 2–3, and 3–4). Upshift 3–4 and 4–5 as possible depending on speed limits and driving conditions. Note shift quality and any noises.
  b. Decelerate using engine braking, downshifting in each gear at about 3000 RPM. Note shift quality and any noises.
  c. Drive in fourth gear at highway speed, accelerate (if speed limit allows), and shift to fifth gear.
  d. Drive in fifth gear for a moment, and downshift to fourth gear and note any problems.

TYPICAL PROBLEM AREAS ● **SEE CHART 6–1** for a list and possible causes of most transaxle/transmission problems.

VISUAL INSPECTION Hoist vehicle safely and perform a thorough **visual inspection** of the driveline including the following:

- Examine the driveshaft for damage or mud that could affect its balance.
- Examine U-joints for damage or looseness. Check for **"rust dust,"** which is a reddish dust found around areas that have rusted and is a likely location where wear has occurred. ● **SEE FIGURE 6–9.**
- Examine engine and transmission mounts for damage.
- Check electrical and mechanical connections.
- Check for leaks at the transmission/transaxle.
- Check clutch master cylinder fluid level or mechanical clutch linkage.
- Check broken or damaged motor mounts.
- Examine transaxle/transmission and bell housing bolt tightness.
- Check for damage to the transaxle/transmission case, mounts, and support.
- Check for worn, bent, or sloppy shift linkage.

TRANSMISSION/ TRANSAXLE FAULT	DESCRIPTION OF FAULT	POSSIBLE CAUSE(S)
Leaks	Fluid escapes from the transaxle/ transmission	Leaking gaskets or seals
Hard shifts	Requires an abnormally high amount of force to shift into gear	Possible incorrect lubricant in the transmission and/or shifter/ linkage/shift fork problems
Shift block-out	Will not shift into one or more gears	Possible shift linkage and/or interlock concerns. Can be caused by the "shift skip" system which forces a shift to 4th instead of 2nd at lower vehicle speeds to improve fuel economy
Locked into gear	Transmission/transaxle will not shift out of a gear	Shifter/linkage/shift fork problems
Jumps out of gear	Will shift into neutral on its own	Often caused by worn synchronizer assemblies
Clash/grinding during a shift	Gear clash/grinding noise occurs as shift is made	Often caused by worn synchronizer assemblies
Noisy	A grinding, growling noise while in neutral	Worn or defective bearings
No gear at all	Sometimes the teeth are sheared and there is no gear at all (usually second gear)	Usually caused by driver abuse

CHART 6–1

Typical manual transmission/transaxles faults and some possible causes.

FIGURE 6–9 When performing a visual inspection, check for "rust dust," which is evidence of worn components such as universal joints.

- Check loose or missing transaxle/transmission or clutch housing mounting bolts.
- Check for fluid leaks from the transaxle/transmission or clutch area.

TRANSMISSION NOISE DIAGNOSIS Manual transmission noises will vary greatly between makes and models. Some older transmission models normally were noisy, especially in reverse or first gear. The Muncie "Rock Crusher" four-speed transmission is an example where the transmission was very noisy because it used spur gears instead of the quieter

TECH TIP

How to Pin Down the Source of a Vibration

A noise concern that occurs with the vehicle at idle speed in neutral can be caused by harmonic vibrations. Slowly increase engine speed to about 2500 RPM. If the noise goes away, it is engine harmonics. The problem is not in the transmission and it could be caused by a faulty clutch disc damper, bad dual-mass flywheel, or an engine fault.

helical-cut gears. The variations in noise levels are due to manufacturing variations, transmission type (heavy duty trucks are usually noisier), clutch disc damper, flywheel type, and amount of vehicle noise insulation. Some transmission noises are caused by the uneven power flow pulses from the engine.

- A bearing noise problem while in neutral with the clutch disengaged is related to clutch bearing noises.
- Noises can travel. For example, the driveshaft can transmit rear drive axle noises so they seem to be coming from the transmission. A helpful diagnostic tool, called a "Chassis Ears," consists of a headset and six sensors that can be attached to various locations under the vehicle. The vehicle is then driven for a road test while the technician listens to each of the six different locations. This should help locate the exact location of the noise.

COMMONLY HEARD NOISES	USUALLY HEARD WHEN	POSSIBLE CAUSES
Gear rattle	Most noticeable while accelerating at low RPM and lugging the engine	Possible defective clutch disc (broken damper springs) or a defective dual mass flywheel, if equipped
Neutral rattle	Occurs with the engine running in neutral with the clutch engaged	These vibrations can occur in the engine with balance shafts and dual-mass flywheels, and proper clutch-disc hub damper springs
Backlash	Occurs when the driveline load or direction is changed, for example, when the throttle is changed abruptly or when the vehicle is brought to a stop and shifted into reverse	Often caused by worn U-joints or lack of lubrication on the splines on the output shaft of a rear-wheel-drive transmission
Gear clash	The grinding that occurs if the clutch is released too quickly while making a shift or a shift is made too quickly with nonsynchronized gears	Clash can be the result of improper shifts (rushed too quickly), wrong gear oil, worn synchronizers, or a misadjusted clutch

CHART 6–2

Typical noises and their causes plus possible items to look for to solve these noise concerns.

TECH TIP

Drips Run Downhill

If a leak is noted and the source cannot be seen, remember that a fluid normally runs downward and that the wind under the vehicle will move the fluid to the rear, so the point of leakage is normally above and forward of the fluid drips.

● **SEE CHART 6–2** for some of the more common noise problems to look for when the transmission/transaxle is disassembled.

ENGINE-OFF SHIFT TEST

The engine-off shift test, also called a **static shift test** or a *shift effort test*, measures the effort required to move the synchronizer sleeve or gear, fork, and shift rail past the neutral detent and into mesh.

To perform a static shift test, the engine must be off. Slowly move the shift control lever into every gear position. Take note of any feeling in the shift control lever that may feel like a blockage. A blockage may feel like the shift control lever cannot move into a certain gear. Also, check for excessive movement or a binding condition when shifting into all of the gear ranges.

- The shift effort will vary with transmission and synchronizer design, and heavy-duty transmissions usually require greater shift effort. Shift effort also varies with temperature and is usually higher at cold temperature because the transmission fluid is thicker. It is also greater if the shifts are rushed and slower shift speeds usually require less effort.

- Try comparing the effort to shift into one gear with the effort to shift into the gears on a similar transaxle/transmission. As the test is made, listen for any unusual noises that might occur in the transaxle/transmission or linkage.

ENGINE-RUNNING SHIFT TEST

The engine-running shift test, also called a **dynamic shift test**, is almost a repeat of the engine-off check except that it checks for clutch drag as well as transaxle/transmission problems. A dragging clutch will cause the gears to rotate, and the synchronizer action will block shifts until equal speeds occur.

To perform a dynamic shift test, the engine must be running and the clutch must be engaged. Start with the shift control lever in the neutral position, disengage the clutch, and move the shift control lever into first gear. Repeat this operation for all gears, including reverse. This test checks for binding of internal transmission components with the engine running and the possibility of gear clashing in more than the suspected gear.

REVERSE GEAR LOCKOUT OPERATION

Verify that the reverse gear lockout feature is properly operating by driving the vehicle above 4.8 kilometers per hour (km/h) or 3 miles per hour (mph). During the drive, attempt to place the transmission into reverse. If the transmission will not go into reverse, it is functioning properly. If the transmission allows a shift into reverse, further diagnosis is needed.

CAUTION: Don't actually shift it into reverse; just test to see if it could shift into reverse.

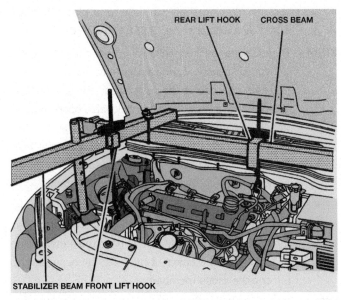

STABILIZER BEAM FRONT LIFT HOOK

REAR LIFT HOOK   CROSS BEAM

FIGURE 6–10 Most front-wheel-drive (FWD) vehicles require the use of a fixture to support the engine before removing the transaxle. (Courtesy of General Motors.)

REVERSE LAMP OPERATION

To check the operation of the reverse lamps, bring the vehicle to a stop. Then, move the shift control lever into reverse. Have another technician watch the reverse lamps at the back of the vehicle. The reverse lamps should illuminate when the shift control lever moves into the reverse position. If the lamps do not illuminate, perform further diagnosis to determine the root cause of the problem.

TRANSAXLE/ TRANSMISSION REMOVAL

EQUIPMENT NEEDED Removal and replacement of a transaxle/transmission is required to repair internal transaxle/transmission problems or gain access to the clutch assembly. The exact operation varies somewhat between vehicle models, so it is highly recommended that service information covering the particular vehicle model be used when removing and replacing a transaxle/transmission. In some vehicles, the transmission or transaxle can only be removed along with the engine. With most four-wheel-drive vehicles, the transfer case is removed before or along with the transmission.

Some transaxles/transmissions are quite heavy and awkward to handle and therefore the shop should have available the following:

- A transmission jack

FIGURE 6–11 A transaxle being removed from underneath a vehicle and being supported by a transmission jack.

- A tall safety stand to support the vehicle or the engine
- An engine support fixture must be used to support and move the unit in and out of the vehicle

TRANSAXLE REMOVAL   To remove a transaxle, perform the following steps:

STEP 1   Disconnect the negative (–) battery cable.

STEP 2   Disconnect the following accessible parts: shift cables or rods, clutch linkage, backup light switch or wires, speedometer cable or speed sensor connections, and any hose or cable brackets with connections to the body or engine.

STEP 3   Many front-wheel-drive (FWD) vehicles require the installation of an *engine support tool* to keep the engine in the proper location as the transaxle and its mounts are removed. ● **SEE FIGURE 6–10.**

STEP 4   Remove the upper clutch housing bolts and install a guide pin into one or two of the bolt holes.

STEP 5   Raise and securely support the vehicle on a hoist or on jack stands.

STEP 6   If a drain opening is provided, drain the transaxle oil. Be sure to check the condition and the amount of fluid that comes out.

STEP 7   Position a transmission jack to support the transaxle, remove any transaxle mounts or supports, remove the remaining clutch housing bolts, and install the second guide pin (if not already installed). Slide the transaxle away from the engine to clear the clutch and right driveshaft. Carefully lower it from the vehicle. ● **SEE FIGURE 6–11.**

FIGURE 6–12 A tail shaft housing plug is being used to help keep the transmission fluid from leaking as the transmission is being removed from the vehicle.

CAUTION: Do not depress the clutch pedal while the transaxle is being removed.

TRANSAXLE INSTALLATION Replacement of the transaxle usually follows the procedure just described, only in reverse. The following points should be observed during transaxle installation:

- Use guide pins and/or a transmission jack to support the unit to eliminate the possibility of hanging the transaxle on the clutch shaft.
- Be sure that wires, cables, and hoses are positioned correctly as the transaxle is slid into place.
- Install the mounts, mounting bolts, and supports before removing the transmission jack.
- Tighten all nuts and bolts to the correct torque.
- If the front suspension mounting points were disturbed, perform a wheel alignment to ensure proper vehicle operation.
- Fill the transaxle to the correct level with the correct lubricant before starting the engine.
- If necessary, check and adjust clutch pedal free travel and the shift linkage.

TRANSMISSION REMOVAL The procedure usually includes the following steps:

STEP 1 Disconnect the negative (–) battery cable.

STEP 2 Raise and securely support the vehicle.

STEP 3 Drain the fluid, noting the amount and condition of fluid that comes out. If the fluid is not drained, install a stop-off tool into the rear seal. This can be a commercial tool, an old driveshaft slip yoke, or a plastic bag secured by a rubber band. ● **SEE FIGURE 6–12.**

STEP 4 Remove the backup light wires, speedometer cable or speed sensor connections, any hose or cable brackets attached to the vehicle, and the shift linkage. Check under any switches for removable operating pins or balls. On transmissions with internal linkage, it is usually necessary to remove the boot and shift lever from inside the vehicle before it is lifted. On some vehicles it is necessary to remove part of the exhaust system.

STEP 5 Position a transmission jack to support the transmission. Remove the transmission support bolts, raise the transmission slightly, and remove the transmission support. In some cases, it may also be necessary to remove the cross-member.

STEP 6 Remove the transmission-to-clutch housing or transmission-to-engine bolts. On many vehicles the transmission can be lowered enough to gain access to the upper mounting bolts.

STEP 7 Move the transmission and jack to the rear to clear the clutch shaft, and lower the unit out of the vehicle.

TRANSMISSION INSTALLATION Transmission replacement usually follows the procedure just described, only in reverse.

TRANSAXLE/ TRANSMISSION OVERHAUL

TYPICAL PROCEDURE The overhaul operations for most transaxles/transmissions are very similar. The steps involved are as follows:

- Disassembly of the unit
- Cleaning and identifying the unit so that the correct parts and specifications can be found
- Gear inspection
- Bearing inspection
- Reconditioning of the subassemblies
- Checking gear end float and adjusting bearing clearances as the unit is reassembled

The exact procedure for carrying out each of these steps will vary depending on the make and model. It is highly recommended that the procedure specified in service information be followed along with the clearances and torque specifications.

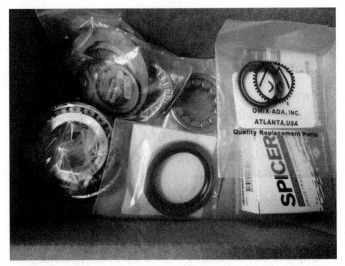

FIGURE 6–13 A service parts kit for a Borg-Warner T5 manual transmission which includes bearings, seals, and snap rings.

FIGURE 6–14 Using a holding fixture is a great way to support the transaxle during disassembly and reassembly.

As the transaxle/transmission is disassembled, the experienced technician will look for the possible causes of the problem. For example, if a transaxle/transmission jumps out of fifth gear, the technician would check for a worn internal shift linkage, fork, or synchronizer sleeve, burred fifth-gear clutching teeth, or excessive fifth-gear end float. Experienced technicians diagnose the problem and usually know what is wrong before the transmission is removed from the vehicle.

WEAR ITEMS TO BE CHECKED The following are normally checked during disassembly:

- The internal shift linkages for rough operation and wear
- Clearance between all shift forks and sleeves
- All shafts for excessive end play and rough operation
- All floating gears for excess end float or rough rotation
- All blocker rings for free motion and excessive or insufficient clearance or damaged lining
- All gears for chipped or broken teeth

PARTS NEEDED A transmission/transaxle kit is recommended for every transmission/transaxle overhaul. These kits contain most of the normal wear items but not any hard parts. A typical kit includes the following items:

- New snap rings
- Thrust washers
- Slingers
- Synchronizer rings
- Synchronizer springs
- Special clips

- Bushings
- Roller bearings
- Gaskets and seals
- Strut keys

Check local parts suppliers or do Internet searches for manual transmission repair kits. ● **SEE FIGURE 6–13.**

What is required to remove a part is found in service information. A hydraulic press and special pullers may be required. Many bearings, synchronizer assemblies, and some countershafts will slide out of and into the proper location using only light force. For example, when a shift rail will not slide out of the case, it is usually held by a detent or interlock. If it is necessary to force parts, use a "soft" hammer (plastic, brass, or lead) or a soft punch made from either brass or aluminum.

Worn parts are normally replaced with new ones. When purchasing parts, sometimes upgraded parts, which are stronger than the original, should be purchased to solve problems with particular units.

TRANSAXLE DISASSEMBLY To disassemble a transaxle, perform the following steps:

STEP 1 Install a holding fixture to support the unit during disassembly and reassembly, ● **SEE FIGURE 6–14.**

STEP 2 Remove the drain plug, and check the quantity and condition of the fluid. Also, remove the fill plug to ensure that it is not seized or has damaged threads.

STEP 3 On some transaxles, the differential bearing retainer, extension housing, and differential are removed first. On some transaxles, the disassembly begins with the removal of the left side case cover, fifth-gear synchronizer assembly, and the fifth counter gear. Sometimes service information specifies that the disassembly begin with the removal of the backup light switch, reverse idler shaft retaining bolt, detent plunger retaining screw, interlock sleeve retaining pin, and fill plug.

STEP 4 Remove the case-to-clutch housing or end-cover-to-case attachment bolts. As these bolts are removed, note their length so that they can be replaced in the proper location. It will usually be necessary to tap the case with a plastic hammer or pry upward using a small prybar to break the seal between the two parts.

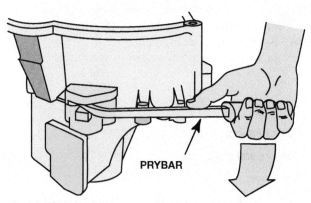

PRYBAR

FIGURE 6–15 Most transaxles use formed-in-place gaskets that tend to glue the case and covers together. This unit has a slot to allow prying without damaging the gasket surfaces.

If using a prying tool, try not to scratch the sealing surfaces. ● **SEE FIGURE 6–15**.

STEP 5 After removing the cover, remove the shift mechanism, the reverse idler gear, and its shaft, if necessary.

STEP 6 Remove the input and main shaft assemblies together, holding them so that the gears stay in mesh until the shafts leave their bearings.

STEP 7 Remove the ring gear and differential assembly. ● **SEE FIGURE 6–16**.

The side gears of some differentials have rounded thrust faces so that they will rotate easily to the windows of the differential case and fall out. These gears are normally held in place by a special tool or wooden or plastic plug inserted into them when the drive shafts are removed.

TRANSMISSION DISASSEMBLY

TYPICAL PROCEDURE As with a transaxle, the procedure given here is general and intended to familiarize the service procedures and how they are performed. The exact procedure for disassembling a specific transmission is found in service information.

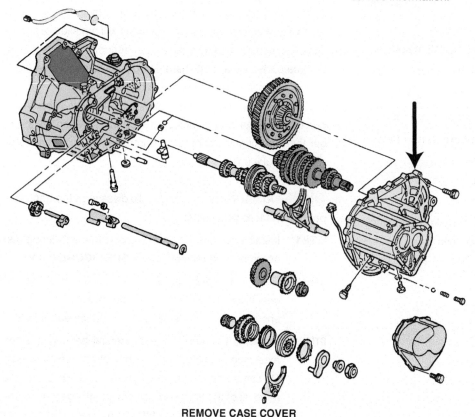

REMOVE CASE COVER

FIGURE 6–16 Removing the side cover allows access to the shift forks and differential assembly.

FIGURE 6–17 The Borg-Warner T5 five-speed manual transmission is used in many makes and models of vehicles and they vary with the number of splines for either the input shaft or output shaft or both.

FIGURE 6–18 Drain the fluid into a suitable container and dispose of the old fluid accruing to local, state, and federal regulations.

Synchronizer assemblies are normally left assembled until it is time to inspect the parts. Most sleeves and hubs are factory-matched sets and should be kept in their same position relative to each other. An experienced technician will use a permanent marker or small grinder to place index marks on both the sleeve and hub to speed up reassembly and prevent future problems. In most cases, if any part of this assembly is damaged, except for the blocker rings, replacement of the entire synchronizer assembly will be required.

To disassemble a typical transmission, perform the following steps:

STEP 1 Clean and identify the unit so that the correct parts and specifications can be found. ● **SEE FIGURE 6–17.**

STEP 2 Remove the drain plug and check the quantity and condition of the fluid. ● **SEE FIGURE 6–18.**

STEP 3 Remove the case cover or case cover with shift mechanism. On some units, it is necessary to disconnect the shift shaft in the extension housing, remove the extension housing, and then remove the case cover and shift mechanism.

STEP 4 On units that use tapered roller bearings, remove the shims and bearing cup. The input shaft/main drive gear can now be removed.

STEP 5 Remove the extension housing. The countershaft extension with the fifth and sixth drive gears and the synchronizer assembly along with the shift fork can now be removed.

STEP 6 Remove the rear bearing and then remove the main shaft assembly. This usually involves using a puller to remove a ball bearing or sliding the cup of a tapered roller bearing out of the case and then moving the main shaft forward, upward, and out of the case.

FIGURE 6–19 A rear bearing being removed using a gear/bearing puller.

STEP 7 Remove the cluster gear and countershaft. On one-piece tapered roller bearing units, remove the rear bearing retainer and slide the countershaft to the rear of the case to remove the rear bearing cup, then move the shafts forward and upward for removal. ● **SEE FIGURE 6–19.**

STEP 8 Locate and remove the reverse idler gear shaft locking device, and remove the shaft, gear, and any thrust washers or O-rings. On some units, the idler gear shaft must be driven out using a long tapered punch. On other units, the idler gear shaft must be pressed out.

PARTS CLEANING The first step in cleaning is to check the debris attached to the magnet located in the bottom of the case.

This will provide an important clue to the internal damage that may be found. Large, irregular-shaped particles are probably chips from gear teeth. Small, fine, sand-like or powder like particles indicate material worn off a bearing, gear, or synchronizer assembly.

CAUTION: Parts should *not* be wiped dry with shop towels because this could leave lint, which later could block an oiling funnel or passage.

The cleanup of most of the internal parts is done using safety solvent while scrubbing them with a cleaning brush or by running them through a hot-water washer. After cleaning, the parts are dried using compressed air and if necessary, then rewashed and redried until they are clean.

CAUTION: Do not allow the bearing to spin which will damage the bearing because it is being spun without any lubrication.

GEAR INSPECTION In some cases, gear damage is quite obvious and easy to locate. With other gears, however, a close inspection is necessary to determine if there is a problem with the teeth or thrust or bearing surfaces. ● **SEE FIGURE 6–20.**

Each of the gears should be inspected for wear or damage. Close inspection of a gear tooth will often show a smooth metallic sheen with a duller, cleaner area and this indicates the gear contact with its mating gear. Many gear teeth will also show underlying machine marks from when the gear was originally made and these marks are normal. The contact area should occur in the vertical center of the tooth and be almost as long as the tooth. Improper contact patterns are especially important when checking for gear noise problems. ● **SEE FIGURE 6–21.**

NOTE: If one gear of a set has a broken tooth, be aware that a tooth on the mating gear encountered the same load and is probably damaged. The broken gear and its mate are replaced as a set.

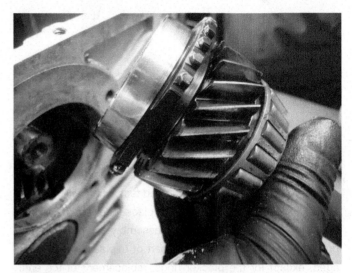

FIGURE 6–20 Visually check the condition of all gears and bearings.

DESCRIPTION	ACCEPTABLE	REJECT
DESIRED CONTACT PATTERN	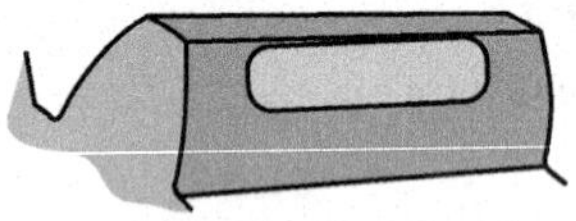	
END CONTACT PATTERN		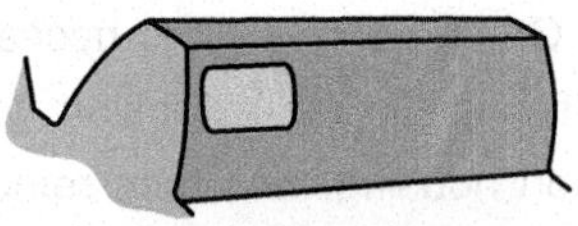
TRAVELING CONTACT (MOVES FROM SIDE TO SIDE)		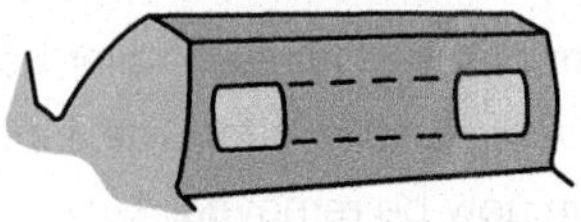
HIGH CONTACT	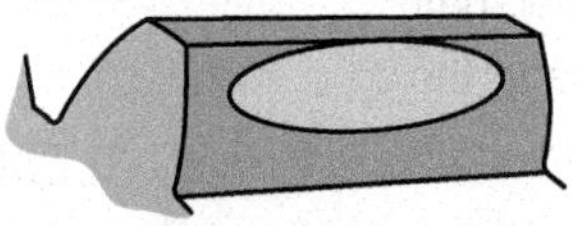	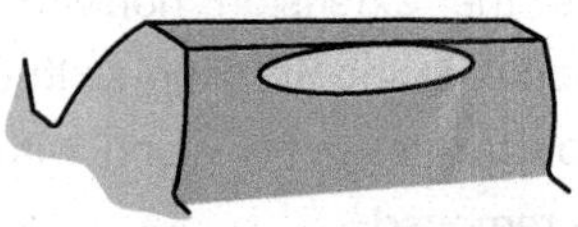
LOW CONTACT	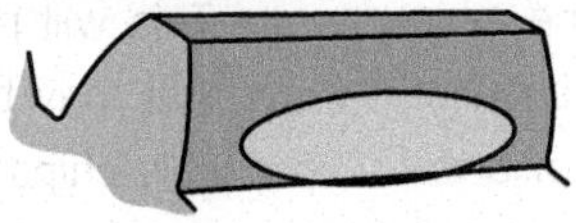	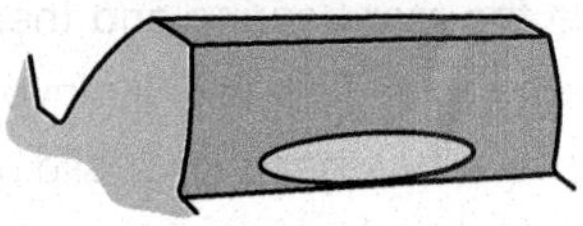

FIGURE 6–21 Worn gears will often show a contact pattern on close inspection. Good and bad patterns are shown.

FIGURE 6–22 Carefully inspect all bearings before reassembling the unit. If one is worn or damaged, then many experts recommend that all of the bearings be replaced because they all share the same lubricating oil and any wear metal will be thrown throughout the assembly.

 TECH TIP

Reuse Old or Replace?

A technician often has to decide whether to reuse or replace slightly worn or damaged parts. Some cluster gears, for example, are very expensive, and replacement can raise the cost of a rebuild significantly. Normally, chips that do not extend into the contact area do not require gear replacement. They can, however, cause a slight noise or be the base of a stress crack or further chipping. Small burrs and chips can be removed or blended into the gear surface using a high-speed grinder with a small abrasive stone. Worn, rounded, or burred clutching teeth can also be corrected by grinding.

BEARING INSPECTION Immediately after cleaning an antifriction (ball, roller, or needle) bearing, it should be dipped in a clean, lightweight lubricant and covered to keep it clean and dust free. Inspection of a bearing is normally done by sight, feel, and sound. Visual inspection of a worn bearing can reveal a broken cage or pitted races. ● **SEE FIGURE 6–22.**

Bearing damage occurs in many forms. The terms commonly used to describe bearing damage are as follows:

- **Brinelling:** a series of indentations pressed or worn into a race
- **Contamination:** scratches, pitting, or scoring in a scattered pattern on the ball or roller surfaces
- **Electric arcing:** a series of small burn marks or grooves across the raceways

 **TECH TIP**

Bearing Failure? Check the Body Grounds

Premature bearing failure that results in a pitted bearing can be caused by poor electrical grounds. The pits are often completely around the bearing races. Current flow for the electrical systems must return to battery ground. Poor engine ground straps will force this current to pass through the transmission and across the bearings, and this can cause an arc at the bearing races. If arcing of bearings is discovered, check and repair the factory ground wiring and connections at the body, engine block, and the transmission/transaxle itself.

 TECH TIP

Bearing Checks

Holding the bearing in a vertical position by the outer race while spinning the inner race by hand allows damage to be felt or heard. Many technicians place the shaft inside the inner race, giving it a slight load and a much better turning handle. The weight of the shaft also makes any bearing problem more evident.

- **Fretting:** small particles that decay and break off the bearing races
- **Misalignment:** a diagonal polish of the stationary race while excess wear occurs all over the rotating raceway from a bore and shaft that are not correctly aligned
- **Peeling:** a light scraping away of the surface of the bearing race
- **Seizing:** caused when balls or rollers fail to roll and this causes damage to cage and end of rollers with evidence of excessive heat
- **Spalling:** an advanced stage of decay with flaking away of particles from the bearing race

BEARING REMOVAL AND INSTALLATION The inner races of bearing are often pressed onto the shaft and the pressing force should be transmitted only to the inner race. ● **SEE FIGURE 6–23**.

When pressing a bearing, an experienced technician will always place some form of a shield over the bearing to contain possible flying parts. It is often possible to remove a bearing with a gear so that the gear will press against the inner race, saving

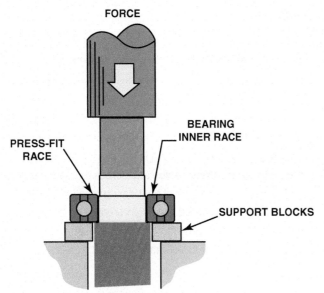

FORCE

PRESS-FIT
RACE

BEARING
INNER RACE

SUPPORT BLOCKS

APPLY FORCE ONLY TO PRESS-FIT RACE

FIGURE 6–23 When a ball bearing is pressed off a shaft, the bearing should be supported by the inner race (if possible) so the force is not exerted on the outer race by the balls.

FIGURE 6–24 Use caution when pressing parts onto the main shaft. Always follow the specified assembly procedures as found in service information.

 TECH TIP

Take a Photo Before Disassembling

Many technicians have learned that it is helpful to have a photo available of a part that is together before it is disassembled. Take a photo of the main shaft with a phone or camera to use just in case it is needed to insure proper assembly.

TECH TIP

Heat or Cool for Best Results

When installing a tight-fitting bearing over a shaft, heat the bearing in an oven or hot oil. A temperature of 300° to 400°F (150° to 200°C) will expand the bearing about 0.001 inch per inch of bearing diameter. If external part cannot be heated, sometimes the internal part can be cooled to make it smaller. Parts can be chilled by placing them in a freezer or immersing them in a container with dry ice and acetone. Either of these methods can change a press fit into a slip fit.

To disassemble a main shaft, a typical procedure includes the following steps:

STEP 1 In some cases, the end gear will simply slide off the shaft. In other cases, the end gear will be held in place by a bearing that must be pressed off the shaft. Use a bearing separator and press the shaft out of the gear and bearing. ● **SEE FIGURE 6–24**.

Because the gear will contact the inner bearing race, this should remove the bearing with no damage to it. A puller can also be used.

STEP 2 Remove the blocker ring and the synchronizer hub retaining ring and install a bearing separator onto the gear next to the synchronizer assembly and then press the shaft out of the gear, blocker ring, and synchronizer assembly.

STEP 3 Continue this disassembly procedure to remove any remaining gears, thrust washers, synchronizer assembly, and bearings.

the bearing. Some shops make it a practice to heat any bearing that is pressed onto a shaft because the expansion makes installation easier, with less possibility of damage to the bearing.

MAIN SHAFT DISASSEMBLY Transaxle/transmission main shafts are disassembled to allow a thorough inspection of the journals and bearings where the gears are mounted and for access to the synchronizer assemblies. In some cases, this is simply a matter of removing snap rings and sliding the various parts off the shaft, but in most cases, the parts must be removed using a press or puller. All of these parts have a front and back and some technicians place a small index mark using a die grinder on the front of each part as it is removed. This mark will ensure that the part is positioned correctly during reassembly.

SYNCHRONIZER DISASSEMBLY, INSPECTION, AND REASSEMBLY Synchronizer assemblies are disassembled for cleaning, inspection, and occasionally for deburring the ends of the splines in the sleeve.

FIGURE 6–25 When the cone is pushed against the gear, there should be a minimum amount of clearance between the blocker ring and gear clutching teeth. Use a feeler gauge to determine this measurement.

NOTE: The sleeve and hub are matched at the factory and should be marked before it is disassembled.

Some synchronizer sleeves have notches for the inserts only in certain areas, and some assemblies include a detent ball and spring in addition to the inserts and energizer springs. Other assemblies use winged inserts or keys, which remain in place as the sleeve is removed. Most inserts have straight sides and pop out of place as the sleeve is slid off.

To disassemble a synchronizer assembly, remove the energizer springs and slide the sleeve off the hub. The inserts will either fall or slide out of their grooves.

Inspection includes checking the inserts for wear or breakage, checking the sleeve for burrs, and checking the fit of the sleeve to the hub. A hub should fall freely through the sleeve. A tight-fitting sleeve will cause hard shifts. Usually, a fault with any part of the assembly will require replacement with a new synchronizer assembly.

Reassembling a synchronizer assembly usually includes the following steps:

STEP 1 Place the sleeve over the hub with the index marks aligned. If there are no index marks, locate the sleeve over the hub in a position where it moves freely and in the correct front-to-rear position. When aligned properly, the sleeve should free-fall over the hub. Many technicians set the sleeve and hub on the bench top with the front/engine ends upward.

STEP 2 Slide an insert into each of the grooves.

STEP 3 Set an energizer spring in place. A common spring style has a tang that enters one of the inserts and a tail that is placed under the other inserts in a clockwise direction. Other spring styles are positioned in a similar manner.

STEP 4 Turn the assembly over and place the tang of the second spring into the other end of the same insert, and place the spring under the other insert in a clockwise direction. In this way, the two springs are running in opposite directions. It should be noted that some manufacturers recommend placing the spring tangs into different inserts.

The purpose of the energizer spring placement is to obtain equal spring pressure under each of the inserts. When other spring styles are used, they are also positioned so as to distribute their force equally.

Although separate from the assembly, also check the blocker rings and cone clutch area of the gear. Blocker ring problems commonly encountered include the following:

- Burred clutching teeth
- Broken rings
- Worn insert grooves
- Wear on the inner cone surface

Then, place the ring over the gear's cone and measure the clearance. Some manufacturers specify a minimum clearance of about 0.020 inch (0.5 mm). **Blocker ring clearance** is also called *ride height* or *synchronizer reserve*. ● **SEE FIGURE 6–25.**

Each gear next to a synchronizer assembly has a center bearing and a thrust surface on each side of it. The center

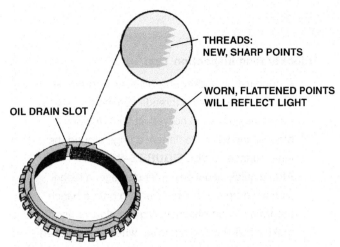

FIGURE 6–26 The thread-like grooves of a new blocker ring are sharp so that they cut through the lubrication film. They become flattened as they wear, and the flat edges will reflect light.

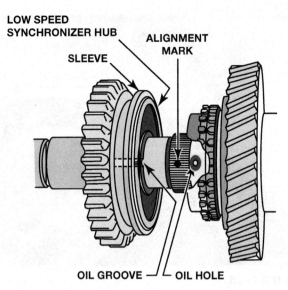

FIGURE 6–27 This synchronizer hub has an oil groove that must be aligned with the oil hole in the main shaft during assembly.

bearing is either the smooth bore of the gear, a sleeve, or a set of needle bearings and operates on the main shaft journals. The thrust surfaces are the smooth sides of the gears that can run against the smooth side of the synchronizer hub or a thrust washer. The parts should be washed in solvent and air dried.

BLOCKER RING INSPECTION There are several ways to check a blocker ring. If specifications are not available, measure the clearance using a new ring as a guide.

- The cone surface of the gear should be smooth and polished with no metal buildup (usually brass from the old ring). Metal buildup can be removed using fine emery cloth and polished using crocus cloth.
- Another check is to push the ring onto the cone as the gear is rotated. The ring should lock to the gear and rotate, but it should also pull right off the gear without sticking.

MAIN SHAFT REASSEMBLY After the used parts are cleaned and checked and any new parts needed are made available, the main shaft is ready for reassembly.

To reassemble a main shaft, perform the following steps:

STEP 1 Place the first gear to be installed (with its sleeve, bushing, or bearing, if used) onto the main shaft along with its blocker ring. Set the synchronizer assembly in place, making sure that it is facing the proper direction. Turn the main shaft so that the gear is above the synchronizer, align the blocker ring so that its notches engage the inserts, and shift the synchronizer sleeve to engage the gear's clutching teeth to keep the

blocker ring aligned. Some synchronizer hubs have oiling grooves that must be aligned with an oil hole in the shaft. ● SEE FIGURE 6–27.

STEP 2 Press the shaft into the synchronizer hub and install the snap ring to retain it. Place wooden blocks or a shop cloth onto the press plates to protect the hub from becoming burred.

STEP 3 Shift the synchronizer sleeve to neutral, and check the gear and blocker ring for *end float* and free movement. In some cases, *selective-fit* snap rings or thrust washers are available to adjust the clearance, if necessary.

STEP 4 Place the next blocker ring and gear in place, making sure the blocker ring notches engage the inserts, and shift the sleeve to keep them aligned. Depending on the main shaft, this will be followed by a thrust washer(s) and retaining ring or snap ring or a bearing and snap ring. The retaining/snap ring will often be the base for a thrust washer and another gear set. Pressing the shaft into a bearing normally completes the buildup of that end of the shaft.

STEP 5 After installing all the parts, check the assembly by shifting the synchronizer sleeves into neutral.

TRANSAXLE FINAL DRIVE SERVICE Transaxle final drives (differentials) need to be partially or completely disassembled to replace the bearing cones, ring gear, or differential gears. The differential should be inspected and serviced whenever major transaxle service is performed ● SEE FIGURE 6–28.

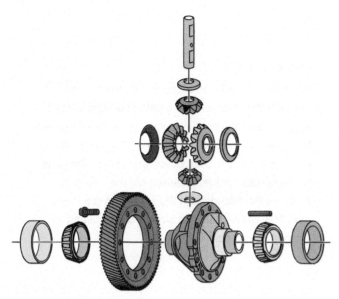

FIGURE 6–28 Disassemble the final drive and inspect for wear and damage. Pay close attention to the side and pinion gear thrust washers. (Courtesy of General Motors.)

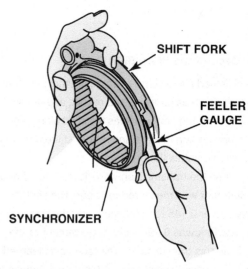

FIGURE 6–29 There should be a specified clearance, usually about 0.030 inch (0.8 mm), between the fork and the groove in the sleeve. Excess clearance indicates a worn fork or groove.

SHIFT MECHANISM

TYPES   Each mechanism set contains a fork for each synchronizer sleeve or gear to be shifted, and each fork is mounted on a rail or lever that moves it through its travel. Each shifter includes one or more spring loaded detent balls or cams and some form of interlock that allows only one shift fork to move at a time.

When visually inspecting the shift mechanisms, check the following:

- *Shift forks:* inspect for distortion, bends, cracks, broken or worn inserts, and step wear at both the sleeve and cam contact areas. ● **SEE FIGURE 6–29.**
- *Shift rails:* inspect for distortion, bends, burrs, scores, grooves, and elongated pinholes.
- *Detent springs*: breakage.
- *Detent cam:* (sometimes part of a rail): wear and scoring.
- *Interlock plates:* burrs, wear, and scoring.
- *Selector plates*: burrs, wear, and scoring.
- *Reverse lockout mechanism/solenoid:* proper operation.

Always have service information available as the transaxle/transmission is assembled, so each of these parts should be checked for complete movement and smooth operation. ● **SEE FIGURE 6–30.**

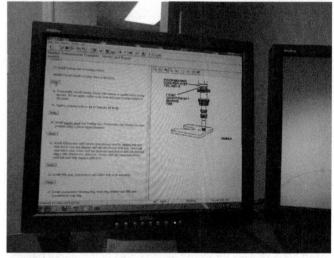

FIGURE 6–30 Having service information readily available is important so that each step can be checked as the unit is being reassembled.

CASE AND COVERS

CLEANING AND INSPECTION   The case and all covers should be thoroughly cleaned and carefully checked for cracks, and distortion or wear of bearing bores, stripped bolt threads, and worn release (throwout) bearing supports. Damaged cases are normally replaced. Some rebuilders machine the case and

The Case of the Worn Shift Fork

A vehicle had a problem of first-gear jump-out. The transmission was removed and rebuilt, and a new 1–2 guide sleeve and first gear was installed along with new transmission mounts and rubber shifter mounts. But, this did not fix the problem.

When the transmission was disassembled again, the shift fork was measured for wear. The shift fork measured at 0.145 to 0.170 inch, and the dimension of a new fork was 0.190 inch. Replacement of the fork fixed this transmission. The technician learned to check all possible parts involved that could cause the customer concern when the unit is apart.

TECH TIP

The Solder Trick

An alternative method of measuring the distance between the case and the bearing cup is to place two very thin strips of solder in place of the shim between the case and the bearing cup, install the shaft and bearing, install the case cover, and tighten the bolts to the correct torque. Disassemble the unit, and measure the thickness of the solder using a micrometer. This will be the shim size before adjusting for preload or end play.

☠ **WARNING**

Keep open flames away from transmission/transaxle cases. Most gear cases are cast from aluminum and, in a few cases, magnesium. Aluminum and magnesium have very similar properties except that magnesium burns. The metal will ignite at approximately 1600°F (870°C) and burn with an intense white flame. Once combustion begins, it is extremely difficult to stop. Unpainted magnesium cases can be identified by a dull battleship-gray coating of magnesium oxide.

END PLAY/PRELOAD CHECKS During the reassembly of a transaxle/transmission that uses tapered roller bearings, the **preload** or **end play** of each shaft should be checked. A selective **shim** is located at a bearing at one end of each shaft, and the thickness of this shim controls the amount of preload or end play.

- Preload causes a slight drag as a shaft is rotated and it is usually measured using a torque wrench or spring scale.
- End play is a free, lengthwise movement of the shaft and is usually measured using a dial indicator or feeler gauge. ● **SEE FIGURE 6–31.**

Gauging fixtures are available for some transaxles that allow for setting the clearance on all three of the shafts at one time. Without special fixtures, most shops will need to check the clearance on each shaft, one at a time. This must be done if a bearing, shaft, bearing retainer/case cover, or case has been replaced.

To check and adjust bearing clearance/preload on a transaxle, perform the following steps:

STEP 1 Place the shaft to be checked with its bearings in the case. If new parts are used, adjustment is necessary. Use an adjusting shim that is too small, so there will be end play. A shim that is about 0.010 inch (0.25 mm) smaller than the one that was originally used, or the smallest one available, is normally used as a starter.

STEP 2 Install the bearing retainer or case cover, and tighten all bolts to the correct torque. Rotate the shaft several times as the bolts are tightened to seat the bearings.

insert steel sleeves for worn bearing bores or throw-out bearing supports to return them to the original diameter and provide stronger-than-new material.

SEAL INSTALLATION Most cases include one or more seals, which are normally replaced during a rebuild. These seals include the following:

- Each shift shaft that passes through the case
- One or two output shaft seals
- Sometimes an input shaft seal

Old seals are normally removed by prying them out using a seal puller or prybar, or by driving them out from behind. New seals are driven into place using a seal driver that fits against the entire outer surface of the seal to prevent seal distortion.

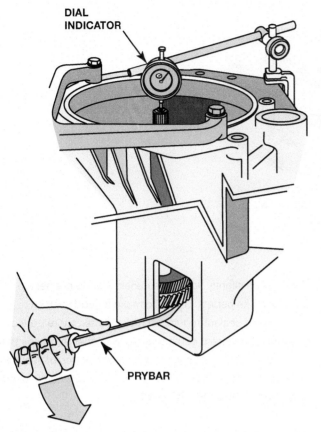

FIGURE 6–31 The dial indicator is set up to measure input shaft endplay as it is lifted and dropped using the prybar.

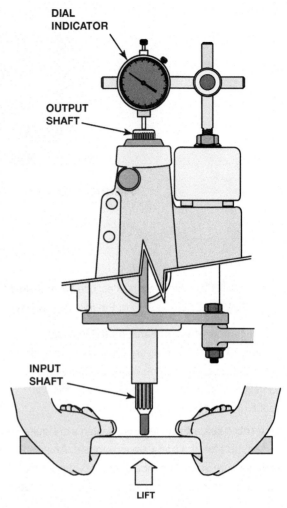

FIGURE 6–32 A dial indicator has been set up to measure the end play that occurs as the cluster gear is lifted and dropped.

STEP 3 Install a dial indicator with the indicating stylus at the end of and parallel to the shaft. Move the shaft up and down through its free travel several times while reading the end play or clearance on the dial indicator. ● **SEE FIGURE 6–32.**

NOTE: Check end play at least three times or until consistent readings are obtained.

STEP 4 Compare the measured travel to the specifications.

STEP 5 If a shim change is required, remove the bearing retainer/case cover and remove the old shim. Measure the thickness of the shim. Add that size to the amount of change measured in the last step. Select and install a shim of the correct size, replace the bearing retainer/case cover, tighten the bolts, rotate the shaft to seat the bearings, and feel for end play. On preloaded shafts, there should not be any end play.

STEP 6 Using a torque wrench or spring scale and adapter, measure the torque required to keep the shaft rotating, not the breakaway or starting torque.

NOTE: An oversized socket can be used on splined shafts by placing cardboard or cloth over the shaft so a pressure is required to slide the socket in place.

Compare the preload reading to the specifications; if they are within the specifications, the shim is correct. Readings that are too high or too low indicate the wrong shim. In these cases, use the next larger or smaller shim to correct preload.

STEP 7 When the clearance/preload is correct, remove this shaft, and repeat this check on the next shaft.

FIGURE 6–33 When using RTV to seal a transmission/transaxle case, be sure to surround each bolt hole to help prevent leakage.

CASE SEALANTS   Most transaxles use **formed-in-place gaskets (FIPG)**. These are usually of the following two types:

- **Room-temperature vulcanizing (RTV)** liquid sealant. RTV is thick and very viscous as it comes out of the tube. Depending on temperature and humidity, it will set up to a rubber-like material in about 15 minutes.

- **Anaerobic sealants**. Anaerobic sealants are quite fluid and set up after the parts are assembled. Anaerobic sealants cure in the absence of air. RTV sealants are commonly used on covers that are less than perfectly flat, or on slightly flexible materials that do not necessarily make perfect joints. To make a good seal, an anaerobic sealant requires a wider, flatter, more perfect surface because it cures to a much thinner thickness than that of RTV. To make a good seal, both types of sealants require surfaces that are clean and oil-free when they are applied. ● **SEE FIGURE 6–33.**

FINAL CHECKS   In neutral, both input and output shafts should turn freely of each other without drag. Shifts into each gear should be smooth, and the shafts should rotate easily and smoothly in each gear.

1 Start any transmission/transaxle removal procedure by disconnecting the negative battery cable.

2 Mark the position of the driveshaft, and then remove the driveshaft from underneath the vehicle.

3 Use to tape or a rubber glove over the U-joint to keep the end caps from falling off and use a plug at the extension housing of the transmission to help keep transmission fluid from leaking.

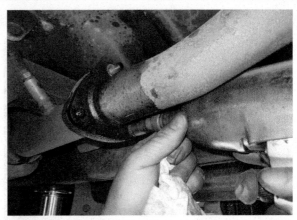

4 Removing the exhaust system was needed to be done to provide the clearance to remove the transmission.

5 Removing the bolts for the rear cross member by using an impact and extension to get to the fasteners inside the frame rail.

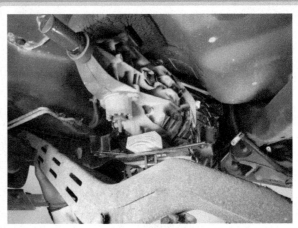

6 Removing the rear cross member but not before supporting the transmission with a transmission jack.

CONTINUED ▶

7 When the hydraulic clutch line was removed, hydraulic fluid (brake fluid) leaked out and into a catch pan.

8 The transmission was lowered enough to disconnect the shifter from the transmission. This step helps save time by eliminating the need to remove the shifter and boot from inside the vehicle.

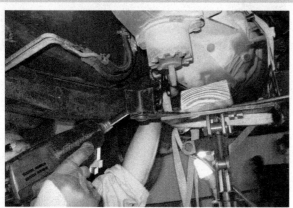

9 The bell housing bolts are removed using a long extension on the impact wrench.

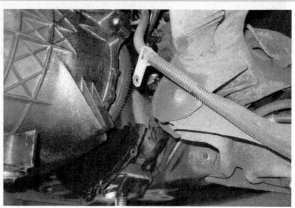

10 The engine is being supported by a tall safety stand as the transmission is being removed.

11 The transmission is lowered using the transmission jack and safety strap to help prevent it from falling off the jack.

12 The original release bearing and clutch assembly is going to be replaced.

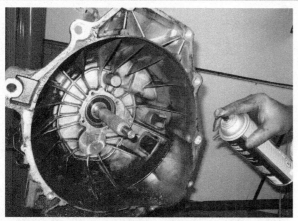

13 The bell housing area was cleaned after removing the release bearing.

14 The old pressure plate being removed from the flywheel.

15 After installing the new clutch assembly, the transmission was reinstalled and all of the fasteners tightened to factory specifications.

16 The worn rear U-joint was replaced and then the driveshaft was installed.

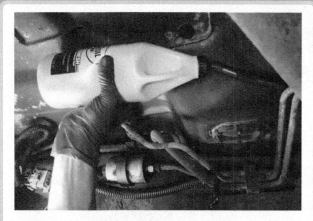

17 The specified gear lube was added to the manual transmission after it was fully installed.

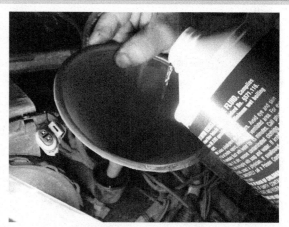

18 The clutch fluid is being added, and then the system bled and the truck was test driven to verify proper operation.

CONTINUED ▶

1 A NV-1500 five-speed manual transmission is used in two-wheel drive applications only.

2 The shifter assembly has been removed. Note the roll pin in the center of the shift lever socket.

3 Snap-ring pliers are being used to remove the snap ring retaining the input shaft bearing.

4 The upside down case is being separated showing the countershaft (top) and shift forks.

5 Before further disassembly can be accomplished, the shift lever socket roll pin must be driven out using a punch and a hammer.

6 The shift shaft and forks can now be removed.

7 The reverse idle gear is unbolted from the case and removed.

8 The output shaft assembly fifth gear (far left) and the synchronizer assemblies.

9 The bearing is being removed using a bearing splitter and a hydraulic press.

10 A speed gear (bottom) along with the double row needle bearing used between the shaft and the speed gear. The hub (center) is splined and rotates with the output shaft.

11 A synchronizer assembly being reassembled. It often takes several hands to hold the hub (center) and the sleeve (outer ring).

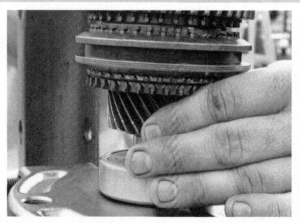

12 A hydraulic press is used to reassemble output shaft and bearing.

CONTINUED ▶

13 The assembled output shaft is held against the counter shaft to double check that all of the gears have been correctly assembled.

14 The assembled output shaft and counter shaft are being reinstalled in the transmission case.

15 The case halves are bolted together.

16 The last step is to assembly the shift lever and check for proper operation in all gear positions.

1 After the transaxle has been removed from the vehicle and the fluid drained, place the transaxle on a work surface.

2 The bell housing case half containing the large output shaft front bearing (center) and the input shaft front bearing (smaller bearing on the left).

3 The differential assembly is lifted out of half of the case.

4 The input and output shafts are a press fit into the bearings and are also retained with a snap ring, which must be removed.

5 Using a special tool, the input and output shafts are pressed out of the housing using a hydraulic press.

6 The input shaft can be disassembled using a bearing splitter and a press, or sliding the gears off the shaft.

7 This transaxle uses both brass and powdered metal synchronizer rings with a fiber (paper) inner cone surface.

8 Synchronizer ring gaps are being measured using a feeler (thickness) gauge. The factory specifications are usually 0.040 inch to 0.069 inch.

9 The gear clutch teeth should be inspected for wear.

10 An assembled synchronizer assembly containing a sleeve, keys, springs, and detent.

11 The input shaft (left) and the output shaft (right) are checked for proper assembly before being installed into the case.

12 The differential bearing preload is determined by measuring for zero end play; then adding the thickness shim under the bearing cup.

CONTINUED ▶

13 The bearing cup is being installed using an installation tool and a hammer.

14 All of the shift forks and shift arms must be aligned properly before installing the components into the case.

15 All of the components, including the differential (upper right), the output shaft (center), and the input shaft (left), plus the shift linkage are installed and checked for proper positioning.

16 The case halves being reinstalled. The bearings (top) must be pressed back onto the input and output shafts using a press.

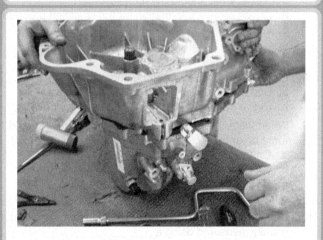

17 The bell housing case being reattached.

18 The completed assembly. Notice the bearing cover (top) has already been installed.

SUMMARY

1. Transmissions must have clean gear oil at the proper level and of the proper type.

2. Faulty shift linkage can cause problems.

3. The cause of improper transmission operation is determined using several diagnostic steps.

4. Internal transmission problems require that the transmission be removed from the vehicle. Transaxle removal is generally more difficult.

5. Transmission and transaxle disassembly and reassembly varies between different makes and models.

6. Presses and pullers are often required for complete disassembly.

7. A thorough cleanup is done so parts can be inspected.

8. Gears, bearings, synchronizer assemblies, shift forks, and transaxle differentials are the major wear components.

9. Synchronizer assemblies require careful assembly.

10. Shafts that use tapered roller bearings require end play adjustments as the unit is assembled.

REVIEW QUESTIONS

1. Where can the type and viscosity of transmission/transaxle lubricant be found?

2. How is the transmission fluid level determined?

3. What is a typical shifter adjustment procedure?

4. How should bearings be removed and installed on transmission/transaxle shafts?

5. What problems can a worn shift fork cause?

CHAPTER QUIZ

1. A transaxle lubricant level is being checked. Technician A says that the fluid level should be even with the bottom of the filler hole. Technician B says that it should be in the hatch-marked area of the dipstick. Which technician is correct?
   a. Technician A only
   b. Technician B only
   c. Both technicians A and B
   d. Neither technician A nor B

2. "Rust Dust" is an indication of what fault?
   a. Broken blocker rings
   b. Worn steel parts such as U-joints
   c. A slipping clutch
   d. Fluid leak

3. A transaxle shifts easily through all the gear ranges with the engine shut off, but with the engine running, the shifts into all forward gears are hard and there is a clash when shifting into reverse. Technician A says this problem could be caused by a worn shift fork. Technician B says there could be worn countershaft bearings. Which technician is correct?
   a. Technician A only
   b. Technician B only
   c. Both technicians A and B
   d. Neither technician A nor B

4. A typical transaxle repair kit includes _____.
   a. Seals
   b. Snap rings
   c. Gaskets
   d. All of the above

5. A transmission is noisy when driving in most gears. What is the most likely cause?
   a. A clutch that is not fully released
   b. Worn or defective bearing(s)
   c. Defective synchronizer blocker ring(s)
   d. Worn shift fork

6. All of the following should be observed carefully when checking bearings except:
   a. Bearings should be air-dried by spinning them with compressed air
   b. A rough bearing should be cleaned, dried, and rechecked
   c. A bearing is checked by rotating it feel and listen for roughness
   d. Bearing should be lightly oiled before checking

7. Before checking the fluid level in a manual transmission or transaxle, what should the technician do?
   a. Check service information for the specified procedure
   b. Loosen the fluid fill hole plug
   c. Check for the specified fluid type and viscosity
   d. All of the above

8. Blocker ring clearance can be checked using a _____.
   a. Dial bore gauge
   b. Feeler gauge
   c. Dial indicator
   d. Plastigauge

9. When installing a bearing over a shaft, where should the force be applied?
   a. On the outer (outside) race
   b. On the inner (inside) race
   c. On both the inner and outer races
   d. On the ball bearing themselves

10. Preload causes a slight drag as a shaft is rotated and it is usually measured using a _____.
    a. Feeler gauge
    b. Torque wrench
    c. Spring scale
    d. Either b or c

chapter 7

DRIVESHAFTS AND CV JOINTS

LEARNING OBJECTIVES

After studying this chapter, the reader should be able to:

1. Describe driveshaft design and balance.
2. Describe the function and operation of U-joints.
3. Describe how CV joints work.
4. Discuss the two types of CV joints.

This chapter will help you prepare for ASE Manual Drive Train and Axles (A3) certification test content area "D" (Drive Shaft/Half Shaft and Universal Joint/Constant Velocity (CV) Joint Diagnosis and Repair (Front and Rear Wheel Drive).

KEY TERMS

Cardan joints 117
Center support
 bearing 114
CV joint boot 122
CV joints 117
Double-Cardan
 joints 118
Drive axle shaft 121
Driveshaft 114

Fixed joint 119
Half shaft 121
Plunge joint 120
Propeller shaft 114
Rzeppa joint 119
Spider 117
Trunnions 117
Universal joints 117

STC OBJECTIVES

GM Service Technical College topics covered in this chapter are as follows:

1. Characteristics and theory of propeller shafts and U-joints used on rear-wheel-drive-type drive trains.
2. Characteristics and theory of half shafts and CV joints used on front-wheel-drive-type drive trains (04510.01W).

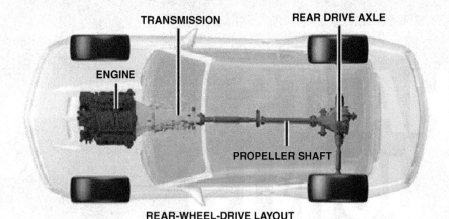

FIGURE 7–1 Typical rear-wheel-drive powertrain arrangement. The engine is mounted longitudinal (lengthwise). (Courtesy of General Motors.)

TRANSMISSION

REAR DRIVE AXLE

ENGINE

PROPELLER SHAFT

REAR-WHEEL-DRIVE LAYOUT

ENGINE

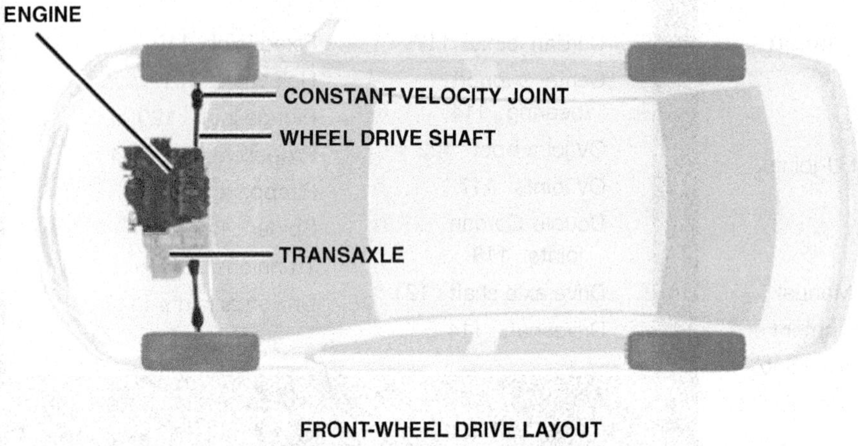

FIGURE 7–2 Typical front-wheel-drive powertrain arrangement. The engine is usually mounted transversely (sideways). (Courtesy of General Motors.)

CONSTANT VELOCITY JOINT

WHEEL DRIVE SHAFT

TRANSAXLE

FRONT-WHEEL DRIVE LAYOUT

DRIVESHAFTS

PURPOSE AND FUNCTION A driveshaft transmits engine torque from the transmission or transaxle (if front-wheel drive) to the rear axle assembly or drive wheels. ● **SEE FIGURES 7–1 AND 7–2**.

Driveshaft is the term used by the Society of Automotive Engineers (SAE) to describe the shaft between the transmission and the rear axle assembly on a rear-wheel-drive vehicle. General Motors and some other manufacturers use the term **propeller shaft** or *prop shaft* to describe this same part. The SAE term will be used throughout this textbook.

A typical driveshaft is a hollow steel tube. A splined end yoke is welded onto one end that slips over the splines of the

output shaft of the transmission. ● **SEE FIGURE 7–3**. An end yoke is welded onto the other end of the driveshaft. Some driveshafts use a center support bearing.

DRIVESHAFT DESIGN Most driveshafts are constructed of hollow steel tubing. *The forces are transmitted through the surface of the driveshaft tubing.* The surface is therefore in tension, and cracks can develop on the outside surface of the driveshaft due to metal fatigue. Driveshaft tubing can bend and, if dented, can collapse. A dented driveshaft should be replaced and no attempt should be made to repair the dent. ● **SEE FIGURE 7–4**.

Most rear-wheel-drive cars and light trucks use a one or two-piece driveshaft. A steel tube driveshaft has a maximum *length of about 65 inches (165 cm)*. Beyond this critical length, a **center support bearing** must be used, as

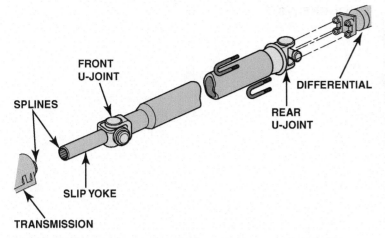

FIGURE 7–3 Typical driveshaft (also called a *propeller shaft*). The driveshaft transfers engine power from the transmission to the differential.

FIGURE 7–4 This driveshaft was found to be dented during a visual inspection and has to be replaced.

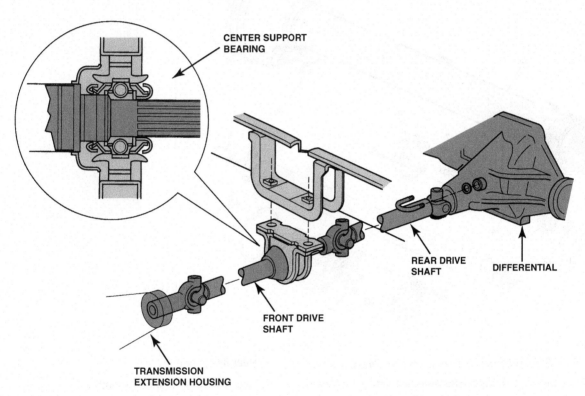

FIGURE 7–5 A center support bearing is used on many vehicles with long driveshafts.

shown in ● **FIGURE 7–5**. A center support bearing is also called a steady bearing or hanger bearing.

Some vehicle manufacturers use aluminum driveshafts; these can be as long as 90 inches (230 cm) with no problem. Many extended-cab pickup trucks and certain vans use aluminum driveshafts to eliminate the need (and expense) of a center support bearing. Composite-material driveshafts are also used in some vehicles. These carbon-fiber-plastic driveshafts are very strong yet lightweight, and can be made in extended lengths without the need for a center support bearing.

To dampen driveshaft noise, it is common to line the inside of the hollow driveshaft with cardboard or rubber. This helps eliminate the tinny sound whenever shifting between drive and reverse in a vehicle equipped with an automatic transmission. ● **SEE FIGURE 7–6**.

FIGURE 7–6 Some driveshafts use rubber between an inner and outer housing to absorb vibrations and shocks to the drive line.

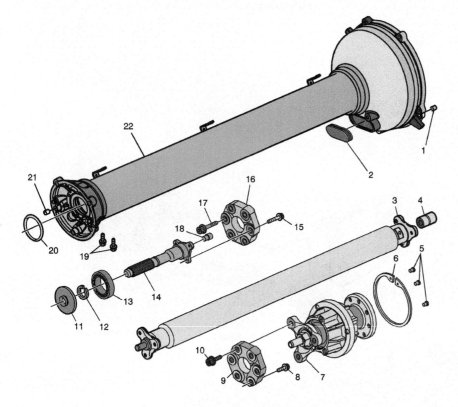

FIGURE 7–7 Driveline support assembly and driveshaft. (Courtesy of General Motors.)

TORQUE TUBE DRIVELINE Torque tube drivelines, used on some vehicles with a rear-mounted transmission, virtually eliminate the effects of rear-end torque on the rear axle. The driveshaft turns inside a steel or aluminum tube bolted to the rear-mounted transmission, transaxle, or rear axle. ● **SEE FIGURE 7–7.**

This type of driveline assembly is called a driveline support assembly by General Motors and is used on Corvette and Cadillac XLR. The driveshaft rotates inside of the tube. Referring to FIGURE 7–7, some of the components are as follows:

- Front input shaft and flex coupling (14, 16)
- Driveline support tube (22)
- Driveshaft (3)

- Rear flex joint (9)
- Rear yoke and bearing assembly (7)

A flex joint transfers power from the engine flywheel and bell housing to the front of the driveshaft; a flexible coupler or splined connection at the rear of the shaft transfers power to the rear-mounted flex plate and torque converter.

DRIVESHAFT BALANCE

All driveshafts are balanced. Generally, any driveshaft whose rotational speed is greater than 1000 RPM must be balanced. Driveshaft balance should be within 0.5% of the driveshaft

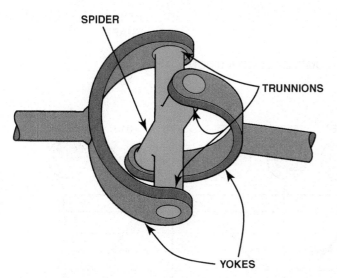

FIGURE 7–8 A simple universal joint (U-joint).

SPIDER

TRUNNIONS

YOKES

weight. (This is one of the biggest reasons why aluminum or composite driveshafts can be longer because of their light weight.)

Driveshafts are often not available by make, model, and year of the vehicle. There are too many variations at the factory, such as transmission type, differential, or U-joint type. To obtain a replacement driveshaft, it is usually necessary to know the series of U-joints (type or style of U-joint) and the center-to-center distance between the U-joints.

U-JOINT DESIGN AND OPERATION

UNIVERSAL JOINTS **Universal joints (U-joints)** are often used at both ends of a driveshaft. U-joints allow the wheels and the rear axle to move up and down, remain flexible, and still transfer torque to the drive wheels. A simple universal joint can be made from two Y-shaped yokes connected by a crossmember called a cross or **spider**. The four arms of the cross are called **trunnions**. ● SEE FIGURE 7–8 for a line drawing of a simple U-joint with all part names identified. A similar design is the common U-joint used with a socket wrench set.

Most U-joints are called cross-yoke joints or **Cardan joints**. *Cardan* is named for a sixteenth-century Italian mathematician who worked with objects that moved freely in any direction. Torque from the engine is transferred through the U-joint. The engine drives the U-joint at a constant speed, but the output speed of the U-joint changes because of the angle of the joint.

The speed changes twice per revolution. *The greater the angle, the greater the change in speed (velocity).* ● SEE FIGURE 7–9.

If only one U-joint were used in a driveline, this change in speed of the driven side (output end) would generate vibrations in the driveline. To help reduce vibration, another U-joint is used at the other end of the driveshaft. If the angles of both joints are nearly equal, the acceleration and deceleration of one joint is offset by the alternate deceleration and acceleration of the second joint. *It is very important that both U-joints operate at about the same angle to prevent excessive driveline vibration.* ● SEE FIGURE 7–10.

ACCEPTABLE WORKING ANGLES Universal joints used in a typical driveshaft should have a *working angle* of 1/2 to 3 degrees. ● SEE FIGURE 7–11. The working angle is the angle between the driving end and the driven end of the joint. If the driveshaft is perfectly straight (0 degree working angle), then the needle bearings inside the bearing cap are not revolving because there is no force (no difference in angles) to cause the rotation of the needle bearings. If the needle bearings do not rotate, they can exert a constant pressure in one place and damage the bearing journal. If a two-piece driveshaft is used, one U-joint (usually the front) runs at a small working angle of about 1/2 degree, just enough to keep the needle bearings rotating. The other two U-joints (from the center support bearing and rear U-joint at the differential) operate at typical working angles of a single-piece driveshaft.

If the U-joint working angles differ by more than a 1/2 degree between the front and the rear joint, a vibration is usually produced that is *torque sensitive.* As the vehicle is first accelerated from a stop, engine torque can create unequal driveshaft angles by causing the differential to rotate on its suspension support arms. This vibration is most noticeable when the vehicle is heavily loaded and being accelerated at lower speeds. The vibration usually diminishes at higher speeds due to decrease in the torque being transmitted. If the driveshaft angles are excessive (over 3 degrees), a vibration is usually produced that increases as the speed of the vehicle (and driveshaft) increases.

CONSTANT VELOCITY JOINTS

PURPOSE AND FUNCTION Constant velocity joints, commonly called **CV joints**, are designed to rotate without changing speed. Regular U-joints are usually designed to work up to 12 degrees of angularity. If two Cardan-style U-joints

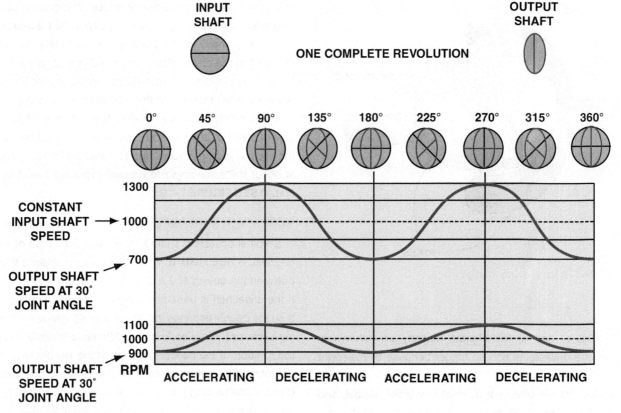

INPUT SHAFT

OUTPUT SHAFT

ONE COMPLETE REVOLUTION

0°   45°   90°   135°   180°   225°   270°   315°   360°

CONSTANT INPUT SHAFT SPEED → 1000

OUTPUT SHAFT SPEED AT 30° JOINT ANGLE

1300
1000
700

OUTPUT SHAFT SPEED AT 30° JOINT ANGLE

1100
1000
900
RPM

ACCELERATING   DECELERATING   ACCELERATING   DECELERATING

FIGURE 7–9 How the speed difference on the output of a typical U-joint varies with the speed and the angle of the U-joint. At the bottom of the chart, the input speed is a constant 1000 RPM, while the output speed varies from 900 to 1100 RPM when the angle difference in the joint is only 10°. At the top of the chart, the input speed is a constant 1000 RPM, yet the output speed varies from 700 to 1200 RPM when the angle difference in the joint is changed to 30°.

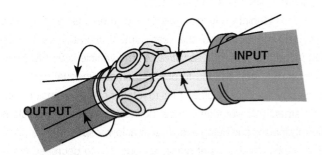

INPUT

OUTPUT

FIGURE 7–10 The joint angle is the difference between the angles of the joint.

FIGURE 7–11 The angle of this rear Cardan U-joint is noticeable.

are joined together, the angle at which this **double-Cardan joint** can function is about 18 to 20 degrees. ● **SEE FIGURE 7–12**.

Double-Cardan U-joints were first used on large rear-wheel-drive vehicles to help reduce driveline-induced vibrations, especially when the rear of the vehicle was fully loaded and driveshaft angles were at their greatest. As long as a U-joint (either single or double Cardan) operates in a straight line, the driven shaft will rotate at the same constant speed (velocity) as the driving shaft. As the angle increases, the driven shaft speed or velocity varies during each revolution. This produces pulsations and a noticeable vibration or surge.

NOTE: Many four-wheel-drive light trucks use standard Cardan-style U-joints in the front drive axles. If the front wheels are turned sharply and then accelerated, the entire truck often shakes due to the pulsations created by the speed variations through the U-joints. This vibration is normal and cannot be corrected. It is characteristic of this type of design and is usually not noticeable in normal driving.

FIGURE 7-12 A double-Cardan U-joint.

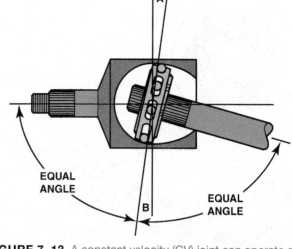

FIGURE 7-13 A constant velocity (CV) joint can operate at high angles without a change in velocity (speed) because the joint design results in equal angles between input and output.

RZEPPA JOINTS The first constant velocity joint was designed by Alfred H. Rzeppa (pronounced shep'pa) in the mid-1920s. The **Rzeppa joint** transfers torque through six round balls that are held in position midway between the two shafts. This design causes the angle between the shafts to be equally split regardless of the angle. ● **SEE FIGURE 7-13.** Because the angle is always split equally, torque is transferred equally without the change in speed (velocity) that occurs in Cardan-style U-joints. This style of joint results in a constant velocity between driving and driven shafts. It can also function at angles greater than simple U-joints can, up to 40 degrees.

NOTE: CV joints are also called LOBRÖ joints, the brand name of an original equipment manufacturer.

While commonly used today in all front-wheel-drive vehicles and many four-wheel-drive vehicles, its first use was on the front-wheel-drive 1929 Cord. Built in Auburn, Indiana, the Cord was the first front-wheel-drive car to use a CV-type drive axle joint.

OUTER CV JOINTS The Rzeppa-type CV joint is most commonly used as an outer joint on most front-wheel-drive vehicles. ● **SEE FIGURE 7-14.** The outer joint must do the following:

1. Allow up to 40 degrees or more of movement to allow the front wheels to turn.
2. Allow the front wheels to move up and down through normal suspension travel in order to provide a smooth ride over rough surfaces.
3. Be able to transmit engine torque to drive the front wheels.

Outer CV joints are called **fixed joints.** The outer joints are also attached to the front wheels. They are more likely to suffer from road hazards that often can cut through the protective outer flexible boot. ● **SEE FIGURE 7-15.** Once this boot has been split open, the special high-quality grease is thrown out and contaminants such as dirt and water can enter. Some joints cannot be replaced individually if worn. ● **SEE FIGURE 7-16.**

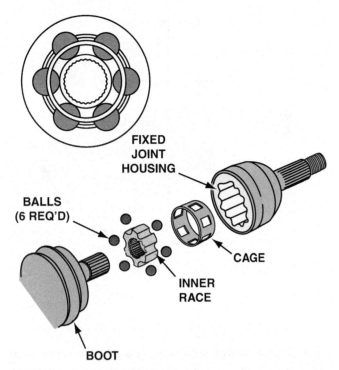

FIXED JOINT HOUSING

BALLS (6 REQ'D)

CAGE

INNER RACE

BOOT

FIGURE 7–14 A Rzeppa fixed joint. This type of CV joint is commonly used at the wheel side of the drive axle shaft. This joint can operate at high angles to compensate for suspension travel and steering angle changes.

FIGURE 7–15 The protective CV joint boot has been torn away on this vehicle and all of the grease has been thrown outward onto the brake and suspension parts. The driver of this vehicle noticed a "clicking" noise, especially when turning.

NOTE: Research has shown that in as few as eight hours of driving time, a CV joint can be destroyed by dirt, moisture, and a lack of lubrication if the boot is torn. The technician should warn the owner as to the possible cost involved in replacing the CV joint itself whenever a torn CV boot is found.

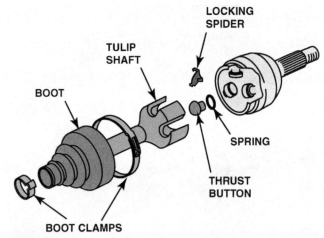

LOCKING SPIDER

TULIP SHAFT

BOOT

SPRING

THRUST BUTTON

BOOT CLAMPS

FIGURE 7–16 A tripod fixed joint. This type of joint is found on some Japanese vehicles. If the joint wears out, it is to be replaced with an entire drive axle shaft assembly.

? FREQUENTLY ASKED QUESTION

What Is That Weight for on the Drive Axle Shaft?

Some drive axle shafts are equipped with what looks like a balance weight. ● SEE FIGURE 7–18. It is actually a dampener weight used to dampen out certain drive line vibrations. The weight is not used on all vehicles and may or may not appear on the same vehicle depending on engine, transmission, and other options. The service technician should always try to replace a defective or worn drive axle shaft with the exact replacement. When replacing an entire drive axle shaft, the technician should always follow the manufacturer's instructions regarding either transferring or not transferring the weight to the new shaft.

INNER CV JOINTS Inner CV joints attach the output of the transaxle to the drive axle shaft. Inner CV joints are therefore inboard, or toward the center of the vehicle. ● SEE FIGURE 7–17.

Inner CV joints have to be able to perform two very important movements:

1. Allow the drive axle shaft to move up and down as the wheels travel over bumps.

2. Allow the drive axle shaft to change length as required during vehicle suspension travel movements (lengthening and shortening as the vehicle moves up and down; same as the slip yoke on a conventional RWD driveshaft). CV joints are also called **plunge joints**.

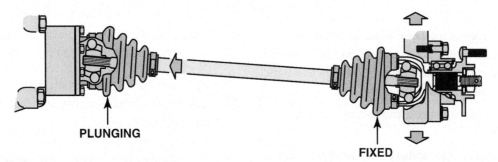

PLUNGING   **FIXED**

FIGURE 7–17 The fixed outer joint is required to move in all directions because the wheels must turn for steering as well as move up and down during suspension movement. The inner joint has to be able to not only move up and down but also plunge in and out as the suspension moves up and down.

DAMPENER WEIGHT

FIGURE 7–18 A typical drive axle shaft with dampener weight.

TRIPOD-TYPE PLUNGE JOINT

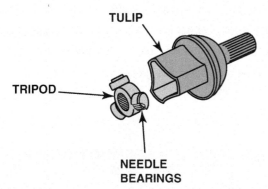

TULIP

TRIPOD

NEEDLE BEARINGS

FIGURE 7–19 A tripod joint is also called a tripot, tripode, or tulip design.

DRIVE AXLE SHAFTS   Unequal-length **drive axle shafts** (also called **half shafts**) result in unequal drive axle shaft angles to the front drive wheels. This unequal angle often results in a pull on the steering wheel during acceleration. This pulling to one side during acceleration due to unequal engine torque being applied to the front drive wheels is called torque steer. To help reduce the effect of torque steer, some vehicles are manufactured with an intermediate shaft that results in equal drive axle shaft angles. Both designs use fixed outer CV joints with plunge-type inner joints.

Typical types of inner CV joints that are designed to move axially, or *plunge,* include the following:

CROSS-GROOVE PLUNGE JOINT

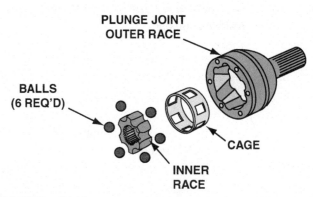

PLUNGE JOINT OUTER RACE

BALLS (6 REQ'D)

CAGE

INNER RACE

FIGURE 7–20 A cross-groove plunge joint is used on many German front-wheel-drive vehicles and as both inner and outer joints on the rear of vehicles that use an independent-type rear suspension.

DOUBLE-OFFSET BALL-TYPE PLUNGE JOINT

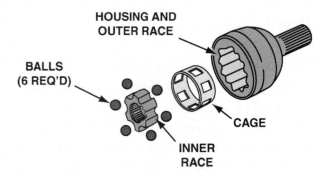

HOUSING AND OUTER RACE

BALLS (6 REQ'D)

CAGE

INNER RACE

FIGURE 7–21 Double-offset ball-type plunge joint.

1. Tripod. ● **SEE FIGURE 7–19.**
2. Cross groove. ● **SEE FIGURE 7–20.**
3. Double offset. ● **SEE FIGURE 7–21.**

CV joints are also used in rear-wheel-drive vehicles and in many four-wheel-drive vehicles.

CV JOINT BOOT MATERIALS

The pliable boot surrounding the CV joint, or **CV joint boot**, must be able to remain flexible under all weather conditions and still be strong enough to avoid being punctured by road debris. There are four basic types of boot materials used over CV joints:

1. *Natural rubber* (black) uses a bridge-type stainless steel clamp to retain.

2. *Silicone rubber* (gray) is a high-temperature-resistant material that is usually used only in places that need heat protection, such as the inner CV joint of a front-wheel-drive vehicle.

3. *Hard thermoplastic* (black) is a hard plastic material requiring heavy-duty clamps and a lot of torque to tighten (about 100 lb-ft!).

4. *Urethane* (usually blue) is a type of boot material usually found in an aftermarket part.

NOTE: Some aftermarket companies offer a split-style replacement CV joint boot. Being split means that the boot can be replaced without having to remove the drive axle shaft. Vehicle manufacturers usually do *not* recommend this type of replacement boot because the joint cannot be disassembled and properly cleaned with the drive axle still in the vehicle. The split boots must also be kept perfectly clean (a hard job to do with all the grease in the joint) in order to properly seal the seam on the split boot.

It is important that boot seals be inspected regularly and replaced if damaged. The inboard (plunging joint) can often pump water into the joint around the seals or through small holes in the boot material itself because the joint moves in and out. Seal retainers are used to provide a leakproof connection between the boot seal and the housing or axle shaft.

CV JOINT GREASE

CV joints require special greases. Grease is an oil with thickening agents. Greases are named for the thickening agents used.

Most CV joint grease is molybdenum-disulfide-type grease, commonly referred to as *moly* grease. The exact composition of grease can vary depending on the CV joint manufacturer. *The grease supplied with a replacement CV joint or boot kit should be the only grease used.*

The exact mix of chemicals, viscosity (thickness), wear, and corrosion-resistant properties varies from one CV joint application to another. Some technicians mistakenly think that the *color* of the grease determines in which CV joint it is used. The color—such as black, blue, red, or tan—is used to identify the grease during manufacturing and packaging as well as to give the grease a consistent, even color (due to blending of various ingredients in the grease).

The exact grease to use depends on many factors, including the following:

1. The type (style) of CV joint. For example, outer (fixed) and inner (plunging) joints have different lubricating needs.

2. The location of the joint on the vehicle. For example, inner CV joints are usually exposed to the greatest amount of heat.

3. The type of boot. The grease has to be compatible with the boot material.

TECH TIP

CV Joint Boots Are in a Hot Place

While the outer CV boots move when the front wheels are steered, the inner boots are also subjected to possible damage because they are often near the exhaust system where the high temperatures can damage the boot material. Then, if there is an engine oil leak, the engine oil could harm the CV boot too. Try to fix all leaks to help prevent premature CV boot failure. ● **SEE FIGURE 7–22**.

FIGURE 7–22 Many CV joints are close to the exhaust system where they are exposed to higher than normal temperatures.

SUMMARY

1. The driveshaft of a rear-wheel-drive vehicle transmits engine torque from the transmission to the differential.

2. Driveshaft length is usually limited to about 65 inches due to balancing considerations unless a two-piece or a composite-material shaft is used.

3. Universal joints (U-joints) allow the driveshaft to transmit engine torque while the suspension and the rear axle assembly are moving up and down during normal driving conditions.

4. Acceptable working angles for a Cardan-type U-joint fall within 1/2 to 3 degrees. Some angle is necessary to cause

the roller bearings to rotate; a working angle of greater than 3 degrees can lead to driveline vibrations.

5. Constant velocity (CV) joints are used on all front-wheel-drive vehicles and many four-wheel-drive vehicles to provide a smooth transmission of torque to the drive wheels regardless of angularity of the wheel or joint.

6. Outer or fixed CV joints commonly use a Rzeppa design, while inner CV joints are the plunging or tripod type.

REVIEW QUESTIONS

1. Explain why Cardan-type U-joints on a driveshaft must be within 1/2 degree working angles.

2. What makes a constant velocity joint able to transmit engine torque through an angle at a constant velocity?

3. What type of grease must be used in CV joints?

CHAPTER QUIZ

1. The name most often used to describe the universal joints on a conventional rear-wheel-drive vehicle driveshaft is _____.
   a. Trunnion
   b. Cardan
   c. CV
   d. Spider

2. A rear-wheel-drive vehicle shudders or vibrates when first accelerating from a stop. The vibration is less noticeable at higher speeds. The most likely cause is _____.
   a. Driveshaft unbalance
   b. Excessive U-joint working angles
   c. Unequal U-joint working angles
   d. Brinelling of the U-joint

3. All driveshafts are balanced.
   a. True
   b. False

4. The maximum difference between the front and rear working angle of a driveshaft is _____.
   a. 1/4 degree
   b. 1/2 degree
   c. 1 degree
   d. 3 degrees

5. Which series U-joint has the greatest torque capacity?
   a. 1260
   b. 1310
   c. 1350
   d. 1480

6. Two technicians are discussing torque steer on a front-wheel-drive vehicle. Technician A says that equal-length drive axle shafts help reduce torque steer. Technician B says that equal drive axle shaft angles help reduce torque steer. Which technician is correct?
   a. Technician A only
   b. Technician B only
   c. Both Technicians A and B
   d. Neither Technician A nor B

7. The outer CV joints used on front-wheel-drive vehicles are _____.
   a. Fixed type
   b. Plunge type

8. The proper grease to use with a CV joint is _____.
   a. Black chassis grease
   b. Dark blue EP grease
   c. Red moly grease
   d. The grease that is supplied with the boot kit

9. Drive axle shafts are also called _____.
   a. Double-Cardan shafts
   b. Half shafts
   c. Driveshafts
   d. Propeller shafts

10. Two technicians are discussing a dented driveshaft. Technician A says that it should be repaired. Technician B says that it should be replaced. Which technician is correct?
    a. Technician A only
    b. Technician B only
    c. Both Technicians A and B
    d. Neither Technician A nor B

chapter 8

DRIVE AXLE SHAFT AND CV JOINT SERVICE

U-JOINT DIAGNOSIS

BACKGROUND The driveshaft of a typical rear-wheel-drive (RWD) vehicle rotates about three times faster than the wheels. This is due to the gear reduction that occurs in the differential. The differential not only provides gear reduction but also allows for a difference in the speed of the rear wheels that is necessary whenever turning a corner.

The driveshaft rotates at the same speed as the engine if the transmission ratio is 1 to 1 (1:1). The engine speed, in revolutions per minute (RPM), is transmitted through the transmission at the same speed. In lower gears, the engine speed is many times faster than the output of the transmission. Most transmissions today, both manual and automatic, have an overdrive gear. This means that at highway speeds, the driveshaft is rotating faster than the engine (the engine speed is decreased or over-driven to help reduce engine speed and improve fuel economy).

SYMPTOMS OF DEFECTIVE U-JOINTS The driveshaft must travel up and down as the vehicle moves over bumps and dips in the road while rotating and transmitting engine power to the drive wheels. The driveshaft and universal joints should be carefully inspected whenever any of the following problems or symptoms occur:

1. Vibration or harshness at highway speed

2. A clicking sound whenever the vehicle is moving either forward or in reverse

3. A clunking sound whenever changing gears, such as moving from drive to reverse

NOTE: A click-click-click sound while moving in reverse is usually the first indication of a defective U-joint. This clicking occurs in reverse because the needle bearings are being forced to rotate in a direction opposite the usual.

DRIVESHAFT AND U-JOINT INSPECTION

The driveshaft should be inspected for the following:

1. Any dents or creases caused by incorrect hoisting of the vehicle or by road debris.

   CAUTION: A dented or creased driveshaft can collapse, especially when the vehicle is under load. This collapse of the driveshaft can cause severe damage to the vehicle and may cause an accident.

FIGURE 8–1 Notice how the needle bearings have worn grooves into the bearing surface of the U-joint. This type of wear is caused by loss of lubricant or improper working angles.

 REAL WORLD FIX

The Squeaking Pickup Truck

The owner of a pickup truck complained that a squeaking noise occurred while driving in reverse. The "eeee eeee eeee" sound increased in frequency as the truck increased in speed, yet the noise did not occur when driving forward.

Because there was no apparent looseness in the U-joints, the driveshaft was removed to further investigate the problem. The U-joint needle bearings had worn the cross-shaft bearing surface of the U-joint. ● **SEE FIGURE 8–1.** The noise occurred only in reverse because the wear had occurred in the forward direction, and therefore only when the torque was applied in the opposite direction did the needle bearing become bound up and start to make noise. A replacement U-joint solved the squeaking noise in reverse.

2. Undercoating, grease, or dirt buildup on the driveshaft can cause vibrations.

3. Undercoating should be removed using a suitable solvent and a rag. Always dispose of used rags properly.

The **U-joints** should be inspected every time the vehicle chassis is lubricated. Original equipment (OE) U-joints are

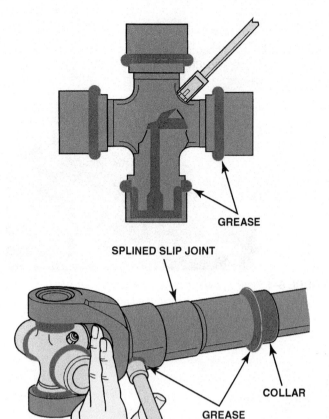

FIGURE 8–2 All U-joints and spline collars equipped with a grease fitting should be greased as part of a regular lubrication service. (Courtesy of Dana Corporation.)

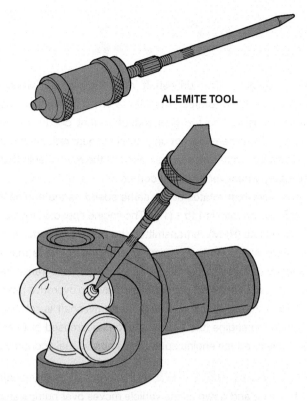

FIGURE 8–3 Some U-joints require a special grease gun tool to reach the grease fittings. (Courtesy of Dana Corporation.)

FIGURE 8–4 Always mark the original location of U-joints before disassembly.

permanently lubricated and may have no provision for greasing. If there is a grease fitting, the U-joint should be lubricated by applying grease with a grease gun. ● SEE FIGURES 8–2 AND 8–3.

In addition to periodic lubrication, the driveshaft should be grabbed and moved to see if there is any movement of the U-joints. If *any* movement is noticed when the driveshaft is moved, the U-joint is worn and must be replaced.

U-joints can be defective and still not show noticeable free movement. *A proper U-joint inspection can be performed only by removing the driveshaft from the vehicle.*

Before removing the driveshaft, always mark the position of all mating parts to ensure proper reassembly. White correction fluid, also known as "White Out" or "Liquid Paper," is an easy and fast-drying marking material. ● SEE FIGURE 8–4.

To remove the driveshaft from a rear-wheel-drive vehicle, remove the four fasteners at the rear U-joint at the differential. ● SEE FIGURE 8–5.

Push the driveshaft forward toward the transmission and then down and toward the rear of the vehicle. The driveshaft should slip out of the transmission spline and can be removed from underneath the vehicle.

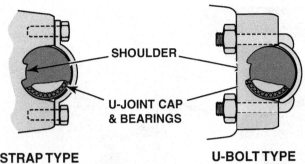

SHOULDER

U-JOINT CAP
& BEARINGS

STRAP TYPE   U-BOLT TYPE

FIGURE 8–5 Two types of retaining methods that are commonly used at the rear U-joint at the differential.

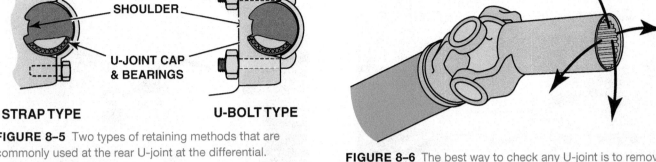

FIGURE 8–6 The best way to check any U-joint is to remove the driveshaft from the vehicle and move each joint in all directions. A good U-joint should be free to move without binding.

 TECH TIP

Spline Bind Cure

Driveline "clunk" often occurs in rear-wheel-drive vehicles when shifting between drive and reverse or when accelerating from a stop. The cause of this noise can be a worn out U-joint or excessive clearances in the rear axle. Another cause is called **spline bind**, where the changing rear pinion angle causes the driveshaft slip splines to move as the shaft length changes.

For example, when a pickup truck stops, the weight transfers toward the front and unloads the rear springs. The front of the differential noses downward and forward as the rear springs unload. When the driver accelerates forward, the rear of the truck squats downward, causing the driveshaft to be pulled rearward when the front of the differential rotates upward. This movement on poorly lubricated spline often causes the spline to bind and make a loud clunk when the bind is finally released.

The method recommended by vehicle manufacturers to eliminate this noise is to disassemble and clean the splines on both the driveshaft yoke and the slip joint. Apply grease to the spline teeth of the yoke and reassemble. Finish by lubricating the slip joint with a grease gun.

NOTE: With the driveshaft removed, transmission lubricant can leak out of the rear extension housing. To prevent a mess, use an old spline the same size as the one being removed or place a plastic bag over the extension housing to hold any escaping lubricant. A rubber band can be used to hold the bag onto the extension housing.

FIGURE 8–7 Typical U-joint that uses an outside snap ring. This style of joint bolts directly to the companion flange that is attached to the pinion gear in the differential.

To inspect U-joints, move each joint through its full travel, making sure it can move (articulate) freely and equally in all directions. ● **SEE FIGURE 8–6.**

U-JOINT REPLACEMENT

All movement in a U-joint should occur between the trunnions and the needle bearings in the end caps. The end caps are press-fit to the yokes, which are welded to the driveshaft. Three types of retainers are used to keep the bearing caps on the U-joints: the outside snap ring (● **SEE FIGURE 8–7**), the inside retaining ring, and injected synthetic (usually nylon). (● **SEE FIGURE 8–8.**)

FIGURE 8–8 A U-joint that is held together by nylon and usually requires that heat be applied to remove from the yoke.

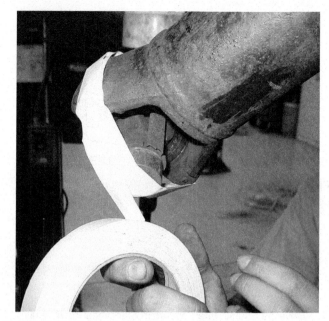

FIGURE 8–10 Taping the U-joint to prevent the caps from coming off.

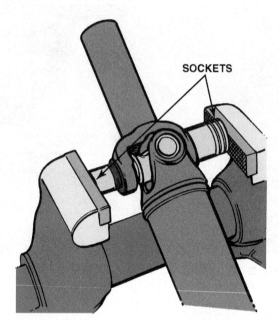

SOCKETS

FIGURE 8–9 Use a vise and two sockets to replace a U-joint. One socket fits over the bearing cup and the other fits on the bearing to press-fit the cups from the crosspiece.

After removing the retainers, use a press or a vise to separate the U-joint from the yoke. ● SEE FIGURE 8–9.

U-joints that use **synthetic retainers** must be separated using a press and a special tool to press onto both sides of

TECH TIP

Use Tape to Be Safe

When removing a driveshaft, use tape to prevent the rear U-joint caps from falling off. If the caps fall off the U-joint, all of the needle bearings will fall out and scatter over the floor. ● SEE FIGURE 8–10.

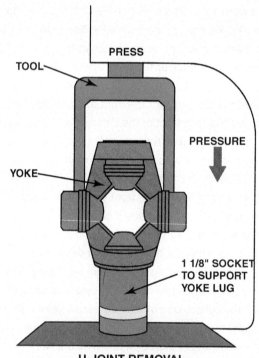

PRESS

TOOL

PRESSURE

YOKE

1 1/8" SOCKET TO SUPPORT YOKE LUG

U-JOINT REMOVAL SYNTHETIC RETAINERS

FIGURE 8–11 A special tool being used to press apart a U-joint that is retained by injected plastic. Heat from a propane torch may be necessary to soften the plastic to avoid exerting too much force on the U-joint.

the joint in order to shear the plastic retainer, as shown in ● FIGURE 8–11.

Replacement U-joints use spring clips instead of injected plastic. Remove the old U-joint from the yoke, as shown in ● FIGURE 8–12, and replace with a new U-joint.

FIGURE 8–12 Removing the yoke from the worn cross.

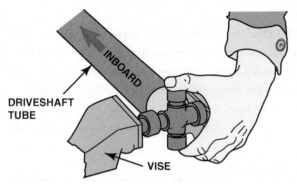

FIGURE 8–13 When installing a new U-joint, position the grease fitting on the inboard side (toward the driveshaft tube) and in alignment with the grease fitting of the U-joint at the other end.

Replacement U-joints usually have a grease fitting so that the new replacement U-joint can be properly lubricated. ● SEE FIGURE 8–13.

After removing any dirt or burrs from the yoke, press in a new U-joint. Rotate the new joint after installation to make sure it moves freely, without binding or stiffness. If a U-joint is stiff, it can cause a vibration.

NOTE: If a U-joint is slightly stiff after being installed, strike the U-joint using a brass punch and a light hammer. This often frees a stiff joint and is often called "relieving the joint." The shock aligns the needle bearings in the end caps.

U-JOINT WORKING ANGLES

Unequal or incorrect U-joint working angles can cause severe vibrations. Driveshaft and U-joint angles may change from the original factory setting due to one or more of the following:

FIGURE 8–14 A transmission oil pan gasket leak allowed automatic transmission fluid (ATF) to saturate the rear transmission mount rubber, causing it to collapse. After replacing the defective mount, proper driveshaft angles were restored and the driveline vibration was corrected.

1. Defective or collapsed engine or transmission mounts
2. Defective or sagging springs, especially the rear springs due to overloading or other causes
3. Accident damage or other changes to the chassis of the vehicle
4. Vehicle modification that raises or lowers the ride height

Replace any engine or transmission mount that is cracked or collapsed. When a mount collapses, the engine drops from its original location. Now the driveshaft angles are changed and a vibration may be felt. ● SEE FIGURE 8–14.

Rear springs often sag after many years of service or after being overloaded. This is especially true of pickup trucks. Many people carry as much as the cargo bed can hold, often exceeding the factory-recommended carry capacity or gross vehicle weight (GVW) of the vehicle.

MEASURING AND ADJUSTING WORKING ANGLES

To measure U-joint and driveshaft angles, the vehicle must be hoisted using an axle contact or drive-on-type lift so as to maintain the same driveshaft angles as the vehicle has while being driven.

The working angles of the two U-joints on a driveshaft should be within 1/2 degree of each other in order to cancel out speed changes. ● SEE FIGURE 8–15.

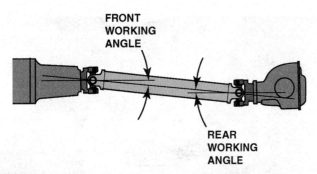

FIGURE 8–15 The working angle of most U-joints should be at least 1/2 degree (to permit the needle bearing to rotate in the U-joints) and should not exceed 3 degrees or a vibration can occur in the driveshaft, especially at higher speeds. The difference between the front and rear working angles should be within 1/2 degree of each other.

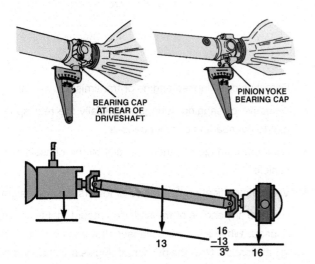

FIGURE 8–16 An inclinometer with a magnetic base is being used to measure the angle of the driveshaft at the rear U-joint. (Courtesy of General Motors.)

To measure the working angle of a U-joint, follow these steps:

STEP 1 Place an **inclinometer** (a tool used to measure angles) on the rear U-joint bearing cap. Level the bubble and read the angle. ● **SEE FIGURE 8–16**; the pictured reading is 16 degrees.

STEP 2 Rotate the driveshaft 90 degrees and read the angle of the rear yoke. For example, this reading is 13 degrees.

STEP 3 Subtract the smaller reading from the larger reading to obtain the working angle of the joint. In this example, it is 3 degrees (16 degrees – 13 degrees = 3 degrees).

Repeat the same procedure for the front U-joint. The front and rear working angles should be within 0.5 degrees. If the two working angles are not within 0.5 degrees, shims can be added to bring the two angles closer together. The angle of the rear joint is changed by installing a tapered shim between the leaf spring and the axle, as shown in ● **FIGURE 8–17**.

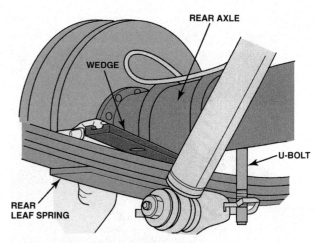

FIGURE 8–17 Placing a tapered metal wedge between the rear leaf spring and the rear axle pedestal to correct rear U-joint working angles.

CAUTION: Use caution whenever using wedges between the differential and the rear leaf spring to restore the correct U-joint working angle. Even though wedges are made to raise the front of the differential, the tilt often prevents rear-end lubricant from reaching the pinion bearing, resulting in pinion bearing noise and eventual failure.

🔧 **TECH TIP**

Quick and Easy Backlash Test

Whenever a driveline clunk is being diagnosed, one possible cause is excessive backlash (clearance) between the ring gear teeth and differential pinion teeth in the differential. Another common cause of excessive differential backlash is too much clearance between differential carrier pinion teeth and side gear teeth. A quick test to check backlash involves three easy steps:

STEP 1 Hoist the vehicle on a frame contact lift, allowing the drive wheels to be rotated.

STEP 2 Have an assistant hold one drive wheel and the driveshaft to keep them from turning.

STEP 3 Move the other drive wheel, observing how far the tire can rotate. This is the amount of backlash in the differential; it should be less than 1 inch (25 mm) of movement measured *at the tire*.

If the tire can move more than 1 inch (25 mm), then the differential should be inspected for wear and parts should be replaced as necessary. If the tire moves *less* than 1 inch (25 mm), then the backlash between the ring gear and pinion is probably *not* the cause of the noise.

The angle of the front joint is changed by adding or removing shims from the mount under the transmission.

CV JOINT DIAGNOSIS

When a CV joint wears or fails, the most common symptom is noise while driving. An outer fixed CV joint will most likely be heard when turning sharply and accelerating at the same time. This noise is usually a clicking sound. While inner joint failure is less common, a defective inner CV joint often creates a loud clunk while accelerating from rest. To help verify a defective joint, drive the vehicle in reverse while turning and accelerating. This almost always will reveal a defective outer joint.

REPLACEMENT SHAFT ASSEMBLIES

Front-wheel-drive vehicles were widely used in Europe and Japan long before they became popular in North America. The standard repair procedure used in these countries is the replacement of the entire drive assembly if there is a CV joint failure. Replacement boot kits are rarely seen in Europe because it is felt that even a slight amount of dirt or water inside a CV joint is unacceptable. Vehicle owners simply wait until the joint wear causes severe noise, and then the entire assembly is replaced.

Normally, the entire drive axle shaft assembly is replaced and the defective unit is returned for remanufacturing. Since the parts supplier or repair shop does not have to stock every type, size, and style of boot kit and CV joint, replacement with a remanufactured axle assembly is usually the best option. Service procedures and practices vary according to location and the availability of parts.

NOTE: Some drive axle shafts have a weight attached between the inner and outer CV joints. This is a dampener weight. It is not a balance weight, and it need not be transferred to the replacement drive axle shaft (half shaft) unless instructed to do so in the directions that accompany the replacement shaft assembly.

CV JOINT SERVICE

The hub nut must be removed whenever servicing a CV joint or shaft assembly on a front-wheel-drive vehicle. Since these nuts are usually torqued to almost 200 lb-ft (260 N-m), keep the

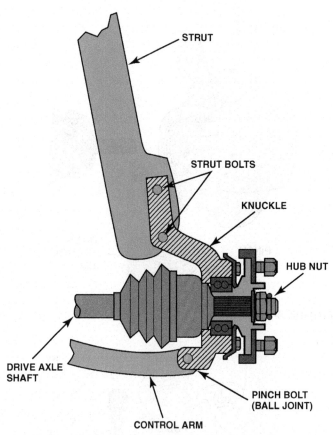

FIGURE 8–18 The hub nut must be removed before the hub bearing assembly or drive axle shaft can be removed from the vehicle.

vehicle on the ground until the hub nut is loosened and then follow these steps (● **SEE FIGURE 8–18**):

STEP 1   Remove the front wheel and hub nut.

NOTE: Most manufacturers warn against using an air impact wrench to remove the hub nut. The impacting force can damage the hub bearing.

STEP 2   To allow the knuckle room to move outward enough to remove the drive axle shaft, some or all of the following will have to be disconnected:

a. Lower ball joint or **pinch bolt** (● **SEE FIGURE 8–19**)
b. Tie rod end (● **SEE FIGURE 8–20**)
c. Stabilizer bar link
d. Front disc brake caliper

STEP 3   Remove the splined end of the axle from the hub bearing. Sometimes a special puller may be necessary, but in most cases the shaft can be tapped inward through the hub bearing with a light hammer and a brass punch can be used. To protect the threads of the drive axle shaft, install the hub nut temporarily. ● **SEE FIGURES 8–21 AND 8–22.**

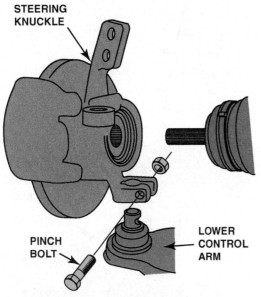

FIGURE 8–19 Many knuckles are attached to the ball joint on the lower control arm by a pinch bolt.

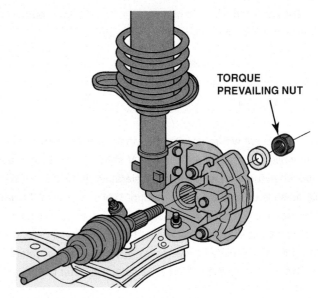

FIGURE 8–21 Many drive axles are retained by **prevailing torque nut** that must not be reused. Prevailing torque nuts are slightly deformed or contain a plastic insert that holds the nut tight (retains the torque) to the shaft without loosening.

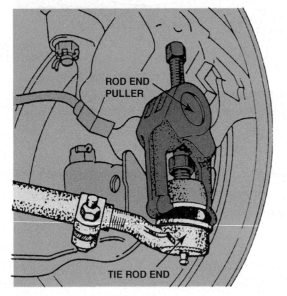

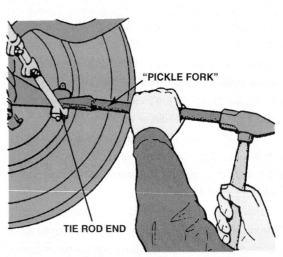

FIGURE 8–20 The preferred method for separating the tie rod end from the steering knuckle is to use a puller such as the one shown. A "pickle-fork"-type tool should be used only if the tie rod is going to be replaced. A pickle-fork-type tool will damage or tear the rubber grease boot.

STEP 4 Use a prybar or special tool with a slide hammer, as shown in ● FIGURE 8–23, and remove the inner joint from the transaxle.

STEP 5 Disassemble, clean, and inspect all components. ● SEE FIGURES 8–24 THROUGH 8–30.

STEP 6 Replace the entire joint if there are *any* worn parts. Pack *all* the grease that is supplied into the assembly or joint. ● SEE FIGURE 8–31. Assemble the joint and position the boot in the same location as marked. Before clamping the last seal on the boot,

🔧 **TECH TIP**

REPAIR OR REPLACE?

After removing the axle a decision must be made to replace the axle assembly or only the CV joint. If replacing the complete axle skip to step 7. If replacing or repacking the CV joint continue with steps 5 through 7. The technician should be aware that a noisy CV joint will NOT be repaired by just repacking and installing a new boot. It will still be noisy and the job will have to be done again (maybe for free).

FIGURE 8–22 A special General Motors tool is being used to separate the drive axle shaft from the wheel hub bearing.

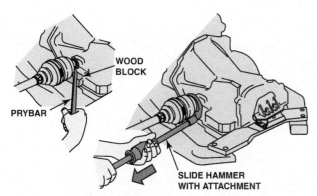

FIGURE 8–23 Most inner CV joints can be separated from the transaxle with a slide hammer and attachment or a prybar. Use caution when using the prybar.

FIGURE 8–24 When removing a drive axle shaft assembly, use care to avoid pulling the plunge joint apart.

FIGURE 8–25 If other service work requires that just one end of the drive axle shaft be disconnected from the vehicle, be sure that the free end is supported to prevent damage to the protective boots or allowing the joint to separate.

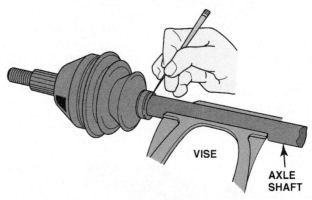

FIGURE 8–26 With a scribe, mark the location of the boots before removal. The replacement boots must be in the same location.

be sure to release trapped air to prevent the boot from expanding when heated and collapsing when cold. This is sometimes called *burping the boot.* Clamp the boot according to the manufacturer's specifications.

STEP 7 Reinstall the drive axle shaft in the reverse order of removal, and torque the drive axle nut to factory specifications. ● **SEE FIGURE 8–32.**

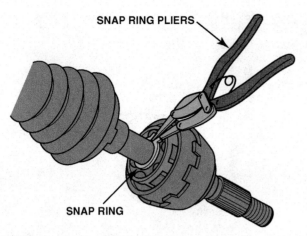

FIGURE 8–27 The CV joint may use a snap ring to retain the joint on the drive axle shaft.

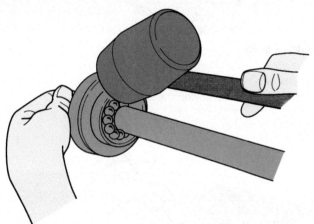

FIGURE 8–28 After releasing the snap ring, most CV joints can be tapped off the shaft using a brass or shot-filled plastic (dead-blow) hammer.

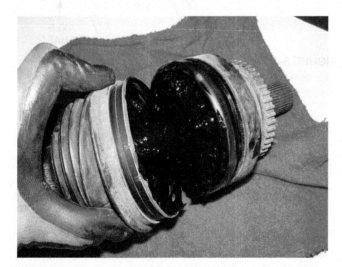

FIGURE 8–29 Typical outer CV joint after removing the boot and the joint from the drive axle shaft. This joint was removed from the vehicle because a torn boot was found. After disassembly and cleaning, this joint was found to be OK and was put back into service. Even though the grease looks terrible, there was enough grease in the joint to provide lubrication to prevent any wear from occurring.

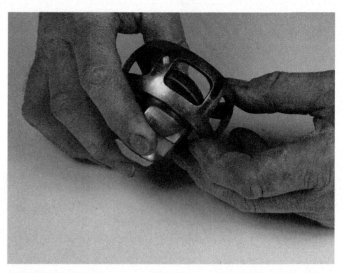

FIGURE 8–30 The cage of this Rzeppa-type CV joint is being carefully inspected before being reassembled.

FIGURE 8–31 Be sure to use *all* of the grease supplied with the replacement joint or boot kit. Use only the grease supplied and do not use substitute grease.

 REAL WORLD FIX

The Vibrating Buick

The owner of a front-wheel-drive Buick complained that it vibrated during acceleration only. The vehicle would also pull toward one side during acceleration. An inspection discovered a worn (cracked) engine mount. After replacing the mount, the CV joint angles were restored and both the vibration and the pulling to one side during acceleration were solved. ● **SEE FIGURE 8–33**.

FIGURE 8–32 A punch being used to keep the rotor from rotating while torquing the axle shaft spindle nut.

FIGURE 8–33 The engine had to be raised to get the new (non-collapsed) engine mount installed.

DRIVE AXLE SHAFT REPLACEMENT

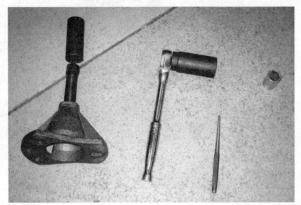

1 Tools needed to replace a drive axle shaft on a General Motors vehicle include a drift, sockets, plus a prybar bearing/axle shaft special tool.

2 The drive axle shaft retaining nut can be loosened with the tire on the ground, or use a drift inserted into the rotor cooling fins before removing the nut.

3 Use a special tool to push the drive axle splines from the bearing assembly.

4 Remove the disc brake caliper and support it out of the way. Then, remove the disc brake rotor.

5 To allow for the removal of the drive axle shaft, the strut is removed from the steering knuckle assembly.

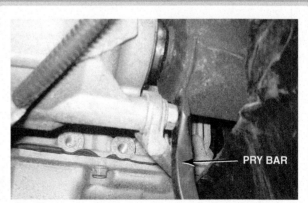

PRY BAR

6 A prybar is used to separate the inner drive axle shaft joint from the transaxle. Do not pry against the transmission case.

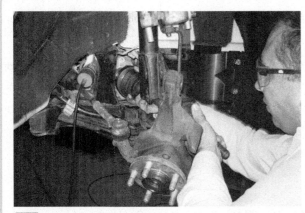

7 After the inner joint splines have been released from the transaxle, carefully remove the drive axle shaft assembly from the vehicle.

8 To install, reverse the disassembly procedure and be sure to install the washer under the retainer-nut, and always use a new prevailing torque nut.

9 Reinstall the disc brake rotor and caliper and then torque the drive axle shaft retaining nut to factory specifications.

1. A defective U-joint often makes a *clicking* sound when the vehicle is driven in reverse. Severely defective U-joints can cause driveline vibrations or a *clunk* sound when the transmission is shifted from reverse to drive or from drive to reverse.

2. Incorrect driveshaft working angles can result from collapsed engine or transmission mounts.

3. Driveline clunk noise can often be corrected by applying high-temperature chassis grease to the splines of the front yoke on the driveshaft.

4. CV joints require careful cleaning, inspection, and lubrication with specific CV joint grease.

REVIEW QUESTIONS

1. List two items that should be checked when inspecting a driveshaft.

2. List the steps necessary to measure driveshaft U-joint working angles.

3. Describe how to replace a Cardan-type U-joint.

4. Explain the proper steps to perform when replacing a CV joint.

CHAPTER QUIZ

1. Two technicians are discussing U-joints. Technician A says that a defective U-joint could cause a loud clunk when the transmission is shifted between drive and reverse. Technician B says a worn U-joint can cause a clicking sound only when driving the vehicle in reverse. Which technician is correct?
   a. Technician A only
   b. Technician B only
   c. Both Technicians A and B
   d. Neither Technician A nor B

2. Incorrect or unequal U-joint working angles are most likely to be caused by _____.
   a. A bent driveshaft
   b. A collapsed engine or transmission mount
   c. A dry output shaft spline
   d. Defective or damaged U-joints

3. A defective outer CV joint will usually make a _____.
   a. Rumbling noise
   b. Growling noise
   c. Clicking noise
   d. Clunking noise

4. The last step after installing a replacement CV boot is to _____.
   a. "Burp the boot"
   b. Lubricate the CV joint with chassis grease
   c. Mark the location of the boot on the drive axle shaft
   d. Separate the CV joint before installation

5. A Cardan-type U-joint may require what tool(s) to replace? _____
   a. A special tool
   b. A torch
   c. A press or a vise
   d. Any of the above

6. What needs to be removed to replace a drive axle shaft from a front-wheel-drive vehicle?
   a. Tie rod end
   b. Lower control arm or ball joint
   c. Hub nut
   d. All of the above

7. The splines of the driveshaft yoke should be lubricated to prevent _____.
   a. A vibration
   b. Spline bind
   c. Rust
   d. Transmission fluid leaking from the extension housing

8. It is recommended by many experts that an air impact wrench *not* be used to remove or install the drive axle shaft nut because the impacting force can damage the hub bearing.
   a. True
   b. False

9. Front and rear driveshaft U-joint working angles should be within _____ degrees of each other.
   a. 0.5
   b. 1.0
   c. 3.0
   d. 4.0

10. A defective (collapsed) engine mount on a front-wheel-drive vehicle can cause a vibration.
    a. True
    b. False

After studying this chapter, the reader will be able to:

1. Discuss the various types, designs, and parts of automotive antifriction wheel bearings.
2. Describe the symptoms of defective wheel bearings.
3. Explain wheel bearing inspection procedures and causes of spalling and brinelling.
4. List the installation and adjustment procedures for front wheel bearings.
5. Explain how to inspect, service, and replace rear wheel bearings and seals.

This chapter will help you prepare for ASE Manual Drive Train and Axles (A3) certification test content area "D" (Drive Shaft/Half Shaft and Universal Joint/Constant Velocity (CV) Joint Diagnosis and Repair (Front and Rear Wheel Drive) and Suspension and Steering (A4) area "C" (Related Suspension and Steering Service).

Antifriction bearings 140
Axial load 141
Ball bearings 140
Brinelling 155
Cage 141
C-lock axle 150
Cone (inner ring) 141
Cup (outer ring) 141
Dynamic seals 143
Garter spring 143
GC-LB 143

Grease 142
Grease seal 147
Hub assemblies 141
Needle rollers 140
NLGI 142
Radial load 141
Retainer plate-type axles 150
Roller bearings 140
Spalling 155
Static seal 143
Tapered roller bearings 141

GM Service Technical College topics covered in this chapter are as follows:

1. Inspect and service wheel bearings following GM specifications and procedures.

FIGURE 9–1 Rolling contact bearings include (left to right) ball, roller, needle, and tapered roller.

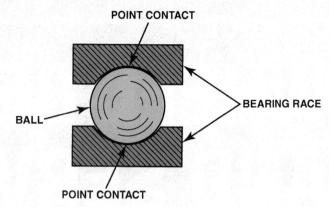

FIGURE 9–2 Ball bearing point contact.

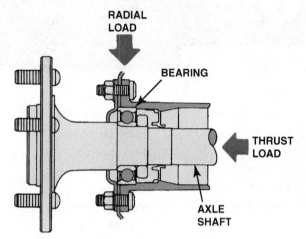

FIGURE 9–3 Radial load is the vehicle weight pressing on the wheels. The thrust load occurs as the chassis components exert a side force during cornering.

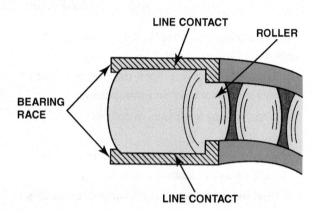

FIGURE 9–4 Roller bearing line contact.

ANTIFRICTION BEARINGS

PURPOSE AND FUNCTION Bearings allow the wheels of a vehicle to rotate and still support the weight of the entire vehicle. **Antifriction bearings** use rolling parts inside the bearing to reduce friction. Four styles of rolling contact bearings include ball, roller, needle, and tapered roller bearings, as shown in ● **FIGURE 9–1**. All four styles convert sliding friction into rolling motion. All of the weight of a vehicle or load on the bearing is transferred through the rolling part. In a ball bearing, the entire load is concentrated into small spots where the ball contacts the inner and outer race (rings). ● **SEE FIGURE 9–2**.

BALL BEARINGS **Ball bearings** use hardened steel balls between the inner and outer race to reduce friction. While ball bearings cannot support the same weight as roller bearings, there is less friction in ball bearings and they generally operate at higher speeds. Ball bearings can control thrust movement of

an axle shaft because the balls ride in grooves on the inner and outer races. The groove walls resist lateral movement of the wheel on the spindle. The most frequent use of ball bearings is at the rear wheels of a rear-wheel-drive vehicle with a solid rear axle. These bearings are installed into the axle housing and are often press fitted to the axle shaft. Many front-wheel-drive vehicles use sealed double-row ball bearings as a complete sealed unit and are nonserviceable except as an assembly. ● **SEE FIGURE 9–3**.

ROLLER BEARINGS **Roller bearings** use rollers between the inner and outer race to reduce friction. A roller bearing having a greater (longer) contact area can support heavier loads than a ball bearing. ● **SEE FIGURE 9–4**.

A needle bearing is a type of roller bearing that uses smaller rollers called **needle rollers**. The clearance between the diameter of the straight roller is manufactured into the bearing to provide the proper radial clearance and is not adjustable.

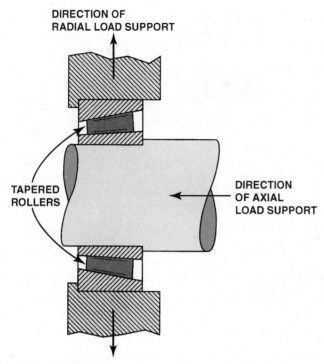

FIGURE 9–5 A tapered roller bearing will support a radial load and an axial load in only one direction.

FIGURE 9–6 Many tapered roller bearings use a plastic cage to retain the rollers.

TAPERED ROLLER BEARINGS The most commonly used automotive wheel bearing is the **tapered roller bearing**. Not only is the bearing itself tapered, but the rollers are also tapered. By design, this type of bearing can withstand **radial loads** (up and down) as well as **axial loads** (thrust) in one direction. ● **SEE FIGURE 9–5**.

Many non-drive-wheel bearings use tapered roller bearings. The taper allows more weight to be handled by the friction-reducing bearings because the weight is directed over the entire length of each roller rather than concentrated on a small spot, as with ball bearings. The rollers are held in place by a **cage** between the inner race (also called the **inner ring or cone**) and the outer race (also called the **outer ring or cup**). Tapered roller bearings must be loose in the cage to allow for heat expansion. Tapered roller bearings should always be adjusted for a certain amount of free play to allow for heat expansion. On non-drive-axle vehicle wheels, the cup is tightly fitted to the wheel hub and the cone is loosely fitted to the wheel spindle. New bearings come packaged with the rollers, cage, and inner race assembled together with the outer race wrapped with moisture-resistant paper. ● **SEE FIGURE 9–6**.

INNER AND OUTER WHEEL BEARINGS Many rear-wheel-drive vehicles use an inner and an outer wheel bearing on the front wheels. The inner wheel bearing is always the larger bearing because it is designed to carry most of the vehicle weight and transmit the weight to the suspension through to the spindle. Between the inner wheel bearing and the spindle, there is a grease seal, which prevents grease from getting onto the braking surface and prevents dirt and moisture from entering the bearing. ● **SEE FIGURE 9–7**.

STANDARD BEARING SIZES Bearings use standard dimensions for inside diameter, width, and outside diameter. The standardization of bearing sizes helps interchangeability. The dimensions that are standardized include bearing bore size (inside diameter), bearing series (light to heavy usage), and external dimensions. When replacing a wheel bearing, note the original bearing brand name and number. Replacement bearing catalogs usually have cross-over charts from one brand to another. The bearing number is usually the same because of the interchangeability and standardization within the wheel bearing industry.

SEALED FRONT-WHEEL-DRIVE BEARINGS Most front-wheel-drive (FWD) vehicles use a sealed nonadjustable front wheel bearing. This type of bearing can include either two preloaded tapered roller bearings or a double-row ball bearing. This type of sealed bearing is also used on the rear of many front-wheel-drive vehicles and are usually called **hub assemblies**.

Double-row ball bearings are often used because of their reduced friction and greater seize resistance. ● **SEE FIGURES 9–8 AND 9–9**.

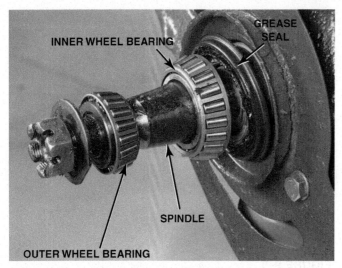

FIGURE 9–7 Non-drive-wheel hub with inner and outer tapered roller bearings. By angling the inner and outer in opposite directions, axial (thrust) loads are supported in both directions.

FIGURE 9–9 Sealed bearing and hub assemblies are serviced as a complete unit as shown. This assembly includes the wheel speed sensor.

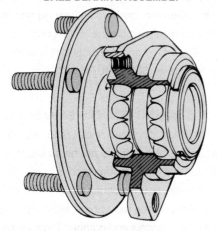

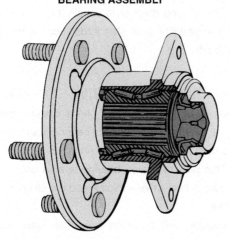

FIGURE 9–8 Sealed bearing and hub assemblies are used on the front and rear wheels of many vehicles.

BEARING GREASES

DEFINITION OF GREASE Vehicle manufacturers specify the type and consistency of grease for each application. The technician should know what these specifications mean. **Grease** is oil with a thickening agent to allow it to be installed in places where a liquid lubricant would not stay. Greases are named for their thickening agent, such as aluminum, barium, calcium, lithium, or sodium.

GREASE ADDITIVES Commonly used additives in grease include the following:

- Antioxidants
- Antiwear agents
- Rust inhibitors
- Extreme pressure (EP) additives such as sulfurized fatty oil or chlorine

Grease also contains a dye to not only provide product identification but also give the grease a consistent color.

The grease contains a solid such as graphite or molybdenum disulfide (moly), which acts as an antiseize additive.

NLGI CLASSIFICATION The **National Lubricating Grease Institute (NLGI)** uses the penetration test as a guide to assign the grease a number. Low numbers are very fluid and higher numbers are more firm or hard. Number 2 grease is the most commonly used. See the chart.

NATIONAL LUBRICATING GREASE INSTITUTE (NLGI) NUMBERS	
NLGI Number	**Relative Consistency**
000	Very fluid
00	Fluid
0	Semi-fluid
1	Very soft
2	Soft (typically used for wheel bearings)
3	Semi-firm
4	Firm
5	Very firm
6	Hard

Grease is also classified according to quality. Wheel bearing classifications include the following:

- GA—mild duty
- GB—moderate duty
- GC—severe duty, high temperature (frequent stop-and-go service)

GC indicates the highest quality. Chassis grease, such as is used to lubricate steering and suspension components, includes the following classifications:

- LA—mild duty (frequent relubrication)
- LB—high loads (infrequent relubrication)

LB indicates the highest quality. Most multipurpose greases are labeled with both wheel bearing and chassis grease classifications such as **GC-LB**.

More rolling bearings are destroyed by overlubrication than by underlubrication because the heat generated in the bearings cannot be transferred easily to the air through the excessive grease. Bearings should never be filled beyond one-third to one-half of their grease capacity by volume.

SEALS

PURPOSE AND FUNCTION   Seals are used in all vehicles to keep lubricant, such as grease, from leaking out and to prevent dirt, dust, or water from getting into the bearing or lubricant.

TYPES OF SEALS   Two general applications of seals are static and dynamic.

- **Static seals** are used between two surfaces that do not move.
- **Dynamic seals** are used to seal between two surfaces that move.

Wheel bearing seals are dynamic-type seals that must seal between rotating axle hubs and the stationary spindles or axle housing. Most dynamic seals use a synthetic rubber lip seal encased in metal. The lip is often held in contact with the moving part with the aid of a **garter spring**, as seen in ● **FIGURE 9–10**. The sealing lip should be installed toward the grease or fluid being contained. ● **SEE FIGURE 9–11**.

BEARING DIAGNOSIS

SYMPTOMS OF A DEFECTIVE BEARING   Wheel bearings control the positioning and reduce the rolling resistance of vehicle wheels. Whenever a bearing fails, the wheel may not be kept in position and noise is usually heard. Symptoms of defective wheel bearings include the following:

1. A hum, rumbling, or growling noise that increases with vehicle speed

FIGURE 9–10 Typical lip seal with a garter spring.

2. Roughness felt in the steering wheel that changes with the vehicle speed or cornering

3. Looseness or excessive play in the steering wheel especially while driving over rough road surfaces

4. A loud grinding noise in severe cases, indicating a defective front wheel bearing

5. Pulling during braking

DETERMINING BEARING NOISE FROM TIRE NOISE

A defective wheel bearing is often difficult to diagnose because the noise is similar to a noisy winter tire or a severely cupped tire. Customers often request that tires be replaced as a result of the noise when the real problem is a bad wheel bearing. To help determine if the noise is caused by a wheel bearing or a tire, try these tests:

TEST 1 Drive the vehicle over a variety of road surfaces. If the noise changes with a change in road surface, then the noise is caused by a tire(s). If the noise remains the same, then the cause is a defective wheel bearing.

TEST 2 Try temporarily overinflating the tires. If the noise changes, then the tires are the cause. If the noise is the same, then defective wheel bearings are the cause.

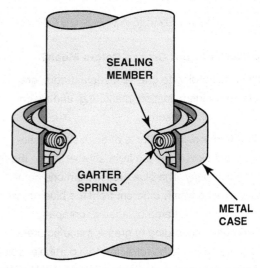

FIGURE 9–11 A garter spring helps hold the sharp lip edge of the seal tight against the shaft.

TESTING A WHEEL BEARING With the vehicle off the ground, rotate the wheel by hand, listening and feeling carefully for bearing roughness. Grasp the wheel at the top and bottom and wiggle it back and forth, checking for bearing looseness.

WHEEL BEARING SERVICE

The steps in a non-drive-wheel bearing inspection include the following:

1. Hoist the vehicle safely.

2. Remove the wheel.

3. Remove the brake caliper assembly and support it with a coat hanger or other suitable hook to avoid allowing the caliper to hang by the brake hose.

4. Remove the grease cap (dust cap). ● **SEE FIGURE 9–12.**

5. Remove the old cotter key and discard.

   NOTE: The term *cotter*, as in cotter key or cotter pin, is derived from the Old English verb meaning "to close or fasten."

6. Remove the spindle nut (castle nut).

7. Remove the washer and the outer wheel bearing. ● **SEE FIGURE 9–13.** Remove the bearing hub from the spindle. The inner bearing will remain in the hub and may

FIGURE 9–12 Removing the grease cap with grease cap pliers.

FIGURE 9–13 Using a seal puller to remove the grease seal.

be removed (simply lifted out) after the grease seal is pried out.

8. Most vehicle and bearing manufacturers recommend cleaning the bearing thoroughly in solvent or acetone. ● **SEE FIGURE 9–14.** If there is no acetone, clean the solvent off the bearings with denatured alcohol or brake cleaner to make certain that the thin solvent layer is completely washed off and dry. *All solvent must be removed or allowed to dry from the bearing because the new grease will not stick to a layer of solvent.*

9. Carefully inspect the bearings and the races for the following:
   a. The outer race for lines, scratches, or pits.

FIGURE 9–14 Cleaning a wheel bearing with a parts brush and solvent.

   b. The cage should be round. If the round cage has straight sections, this is an indication of an overtightened adjustment or a dropped cage. ● **SEE CHART 9–1.**

   If either of the above is observed, then the bearing, including the outer race, must be replaced. Failure to replace the outer race (which is included when purchasing a bearing) could lead to rapid failure of the new bearing. ● **SEE FIGURES 9–15 AND 9–16.** Pack the cleaned or new bearing thoroughly with clean, new, approved wheel bearing grease. Always clean out all of the old grease before applying the recommended type of new grease. *Because of compatibility problems, it is not recommended that greases be mixed.* There are several different ways to pack wheel bearings including the following:

   ■ **By hand.** Place some grease in the palm of the hand and then force the grease through the bearing until grease can be seen out the other side. ● **SEE FIGURE 9–17.**

   ■ **By hand-operated bearing packer.** A hand-operated bearing packer is faster to use and produces excellent results. ● **SEE FIGURE 9–18.**

   ■ **Grease gun-type bearing packer.** This type of bearing packer uses a grease gun to fill the bearing with grease. The grease gun can be hand-operated or powered by electric or air. ● **SEE FIGURE 9–19.**

10. Place a thin layer of grease on the outer race.

11. Apply a thin layer of grease to the spindle, being sure to cover the outer bearing seat, inner bearing seat, and shoulder at the grease seal seat.

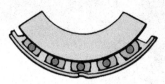

BENT CAGE

CAGE DAMAGE CAUSED BY IMPROPER HANDLING OR TOOL USE

GALLING

METAL SMEARS OR ROLLER ENDS CAUSED BY OVERHEATING, OVERLOADING, OR INADEQUATE LUBRICATION

STEP WEAR

NOTCHED WEAR PATTERN ON ROLLER ENDS CAUSED BY ABRASIVES IN THE LUBRICANT

ETCHING AND CORROSION

EATEN AWAY BEARING SURFACE WITH GRAY OR GRAY-BLACK COLOR CAUSED BY MOISTURE CONTAMINATION OF THE LUBRICANT

PITTING AND BRUISING

PITS, DEPRESSIONS, AND GROOVES IN THE BEARING SURFACES CAUSED BY PARTICULATE CONTAMINATION OF THE LUBRICANT

SPALLING

FLAKING AWAY OF THE BEARING SURFACE METAL CAUSED BY FATIGUE

MISALIGNMENT

SKEWED WEAR PATTERN CAUSED BY BENT SPINDLE OR IMPROPER BEARING INSTALLATION

HEAT DISCOLORATION

FAINT YELLOW TO DARK BLUE DISCOLORATION FROM OVERHEATING CAUSED BY OVERLOADING OR INADEQUATE LUBRICATION

BRINELLING

INDENTATIONS IN THE RACES CAUSED BY IMPACT LOADS OR VIBRATION WHEN THE BEARING IS NOT TURNING

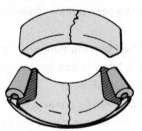

CRACKED RACE

CRACKING OF THE RACE CAUSED BY EXCESSIVE PRESS FIT, IMPROPER INSTALLATION, OR DAMAGED BEARING SEATS

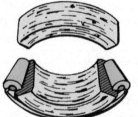

SMEARING

SMEARED METAL FROM SLIPPAGE CAUSED BY POOR FIT, POOR LUBRICATION, OVERLOADING, OVERHEATING, OR HANDLING DAMAGE

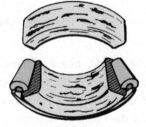

FRETTAGE

ETCHING OR CORROSION CAUSED BY SMALL RELATIVE MOVEMENTS BETWEEN PARTS WITH NO LUBRICATION

CHART 9–1

Wheel bearing inspection chart. Replace the bearing if it has any of the faults shown.

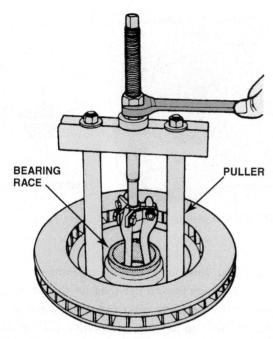

FIGURE 9–15 A wheel bearing race puller.

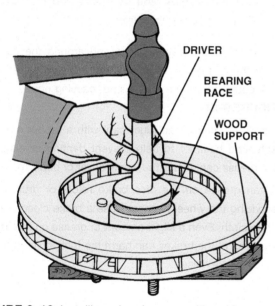

FIGURE 9–16 Installing a bearing race with a driver.

12. Install a new **grease seal** (also called a *grease retainer*) flush with the hub using a seal driver.

13. Place approximately three tablespoons of grease into the grease cavity of the wheel hub. Excessive grease could cause the inner grease seal to fail, with the possibility of grease getting on the brakes. Place the rotor with the inner bearing and seal in place over the spindle until the grease seal rests on the grease seal shoulder.

14. Install the outer bearing and the bearing washer.

15. Install the spindle nut and, while rotating the tire assembly, tighten to about 12 to 30 lb-ft with a wrench to " seat"

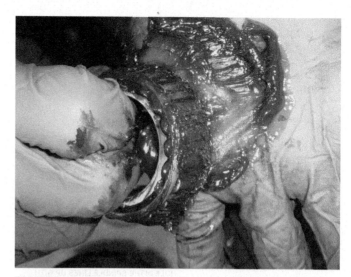

FIGURE 9–17 Notice the new blue grease has been forced through the bearing.

FIGURE 9–18 A commonly used hand-operated bearing packer.

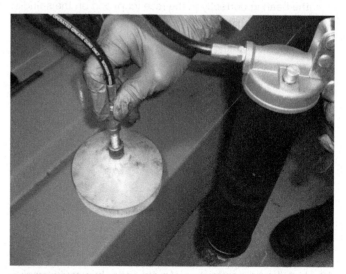

FIGURE 9–19 The wheel bearing is placed between two nylon cones and then a grease gun is used to inject grease into the center of the bearing.

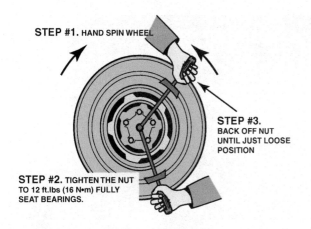

STEP #1. HAND SPIN WHEEL

STEP #2. TIGHTEN THE NUT TO 12 ft.lbs (16 N•m) FULLY SEAT BEARINGS.

STEP #3. BACK OFF NUT UNTIL JUST LOOSE POSITION

STEP #5. LOOSEN NUT UNTIL EITHER HOLE IN THE SPINDLE LINES UP WITH A SLOT IN THE NUT — THEN INSERT COTTER PIN.

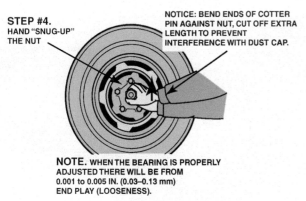

STEP #4. HAND "SNUG-UP" THE NUT

NOTICE: BEND ENDS OF COTTER PIN AGAINST NUT, CUT OFF EXTRA LENGTH TO PREVENT INTERFERENCE WITH DUST CAP.

NOTE. WHEN THE BEARING IS PROPERLY ADJUSTED THERE WILL BE FROM 0.001 to 0.005 IN. (0.03–0.13 mm) END PLAY (LOOSENESS).

FIGURE 9–20 The wheel bearing adjustment procedure as specified for many rear-wheel-drive vehicles. Always check service information for the exact specified procedure for the vehicle being serviced.

the bearing correctly in the race (cup) and on the spindle. ● **SEE FIGURE 9–20.**

16. While still rotating the tire assembly, loosen the nut approximately one-half turn and then *hand tighten only* (about 5 lb-inch).

17. Loosen the adjusting nut slightly (no more than 1/16 inch of a turn) until the cotter pin hole lines up. Never tighten more than hand tight.

    NOTE: If the wheel bearing is properly adjusted, the wheel will have about 0.001 to 0.005 inch (0.03 to 0.13 mm) end play. This looseness is necessary to allow the tapered roller bearing to expand when hot and not bind or cause the wheel to lock up.

18. Install a new cotter key. (An old cotter key could break a part off where it was bent and lodge in the bearing, causing major damage.)

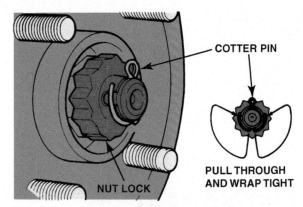

COTTER PIN

PULL THROUGH AND WRAP TIGHT

NUT LOCK

FIGURE 9–21 A properly secured wheel bearing adjust nut.

CAUTION: This is a typical adjustment method. Some vehicles have a pre-load on the wheel bearings when properly adjusted, with no end play. Always refer to service information for the proper procedure. All vehicles are not the same and an incorrect adjustment will overheat and lock up the bearing in a very short time.

19. Bend the cotter key ends up and around the nut, not over the end of the spindle where the end of the cotter key could rub on the grease cap, causing noise. ● **SEE FIGURE 9–21.**

20. Install the grease cap (dust cap) with a rubber mallet or softfaced hammer to help prevent denting or distorting the grease cap. Install the wheel cover or hub cap.

21. Clean grease off the disc brake rotors or drums after servicing the wheel bearings. Use a brake cleaner and a shop cloth. Even a slight amount of grease on the friction surfaces of the brakes can harm the friction lining and/or cause brake noise.

SEALED BEARING SERVICE

Many late-model vehicles use a sealed bearing/hub assembly that is bolted to the steering knuckle or axle and supports the drive axle. The bearing may be part of a hub and bearing assembly on the front or the rear. ● **SEE FIGURE 9–22.**

Diagnosing a defective front bearing on a front-wheel-drive vehicle is sometimes confusing. A defective wheel bearing is usually noisy while driving straight, and the noise increases with vehicle speed (wheel speed). A drive axle shaft U-joint (CV joint) can also be the cause of noise on a front-wheel-drive vehicle, but usually makes more noise while turning and accelerating.

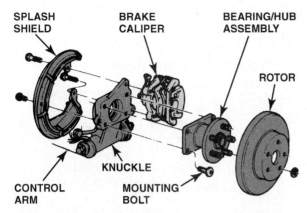

FIGURE 9-22 A rear wheel sealed bearing hub assembly.

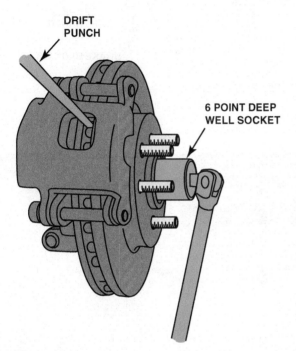

FIGURE 9-23 Removing the drive axle shaft hub nut. This nut is usually very tight and the drift (tapered) punch wedged into the cooling fins of the brake rotor keeps the hub from revolving when the nut is loosened. Never use an impact to remove or install a drive axle shaft hub nut because the hammering action can damage the bearing.

AXLE BEARING/HUB ASSEMBLY REPLACEMENT

As always, refer to the manufacturer's service information for details. The general procedure to replace a front bearing/hub assembly is as follows:

1. Raise and support the vehicle at a comfortable working height.

2. Loosen and remove the drive shaft nut. This can be done before or after the wheel is removed, depending on the vehicle. ● SEE FIGURE 9-23.

3. Remove the brake caliper and rotor.

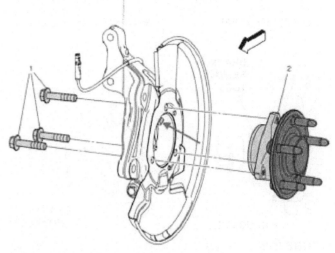

FIGURE 9-24 Remove the bolts (1) and then the hub assembly (2). Be careful not to damage the wheel speed sensor (arrow) when removing the hub. (Courtesy of General Motors.)

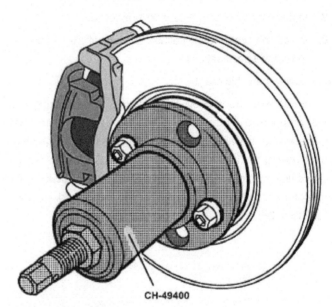

CH-49400

FIGURE 9-25 A special tool may be needed to push the axle out of the hub assembly. (Courtesy of General Motors.)

4. Disconnect the wheel speed sensor wiring connector (if equipped) and move it out of the way. On some vehicles, the sensor stays on the knuckle when the hub is removed. Be careful not to damage the sensor tip.

5. Remove the bearing/hub assembly mounting bolts, and then remove the hub assembly and splash shield. ● SEE FIGURE 9-24.

NOTE: Special tools may be required to push out the axle. ● SEE FIGURE 9-25.

6. Lightly grease the steering knuckle bore. Install the splash shield and new hub assembly.

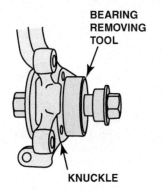
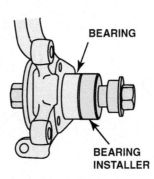

BEARING REMOVAL

BEARING
REMOVING
TOOL

KNUCKLE

BEARING INSTALLATION

BEARING

BEARING
INSTALLER

FIGURE 9–26 A special puller makes the job of removing the hub bearing from the knuckle easy without damaging any component.

7. Torque the mounting bolts to specifications.

8. Install the wheel speed sensor, if removed.

9. Install the brake rotor, caliper, and wheel. Remember to torque to specifications.

10. Lower the vehicle.

Some older front-wheel-drive vehicles use a bearing that must be pressed off the steering knuckle. Special aftermarket tools are also available to remove many of the bearings without removing the knuckle from the vehicle. Check the factory service information and tool manufacturer's instructions for the exact procedures for the vehicle being serviced. ● **SEE FIGURE 9–26.**

REAR AXLE BEARING AND SEAL REPLACEMENT

The rear bearings used on rear-wheel-drive vehicles are constructed and serviced differently from other types of wheel bearings. Rear axle bearings are either sealed or lubricated by the rear-end lubricant. The rear axle must be removed from the vehicle to replace the rear axle bearing. There are two basic types of axle retaining methods:

- **Retainer plate-type**
- **C-lock**

RETAINER PLATE-TYPE REAR AXLES The retainer plate-type rear axle uses four fasteners that retain the axle in the axle housing. To remove the axle shaft and the rear axle bearing and seal, the retainer bolts or nuts must be removed.

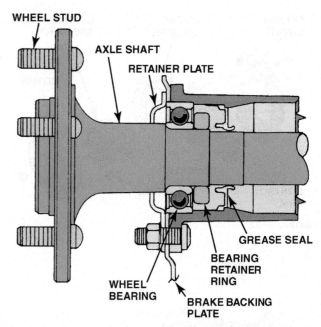

WHEEL STUD

AXLE SHAFT

RETAINER PLATE

GREASE SEAL

BEARING
RETAINER
RING

WHEEL
BEARING

BRAKE BACKING
PLATE

FIGURE 9–27 A retainer plate-type rear axle bearing. Access to the fasteners is through a hole in the axle flange.

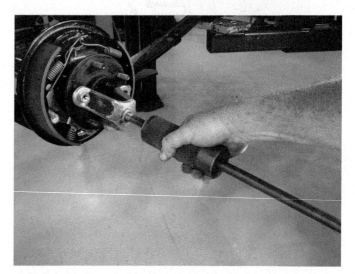

FIGURE 9–28 A slide hammer-type axle puller is used to remove the axle and bearing from the axle housing.

NOTE: If the axle flange has an access hole, then a retainer plate-type axle is used.

The hole or holes in the wheel flange permit a socket wrench access to the fasteners. After the fasteners have been removed, the axle shaft must be removed from the rear axle housing. With the retainer plate-type rear axle, the bearing and the retaining ring are press fit onto the axle and the bearing cup (outer race) is also tightly fitted into the axle housing tube. The axle bearing is a tight fit into the axle tube and usually requires a puller to remove it. ● **SEE FIGURES 9–27 AND 9–28.**

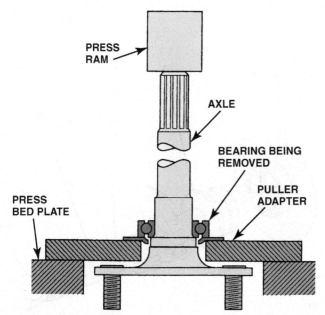

FIGURE 9–29 Using a hydraulic press to press an axle bearing from the axle. When pressing a new bearing back onto the axle, pressure should only be on the inner bearing race to prevent damaging the bearing.

Axle bearings with inner races are pressed onto the axle shaft and must be pressed off using a hydraulic press. A bearing retaining collar should be chiseled or drilled into to expand the collar, allowing it to be removed. ● SEE FIGURE 9–29.

C-LOCK-TYPE AXLES

Vehicles that use C-locks (clips) use a straight roller bearing supporting a semi-floating axle shaft inside the axle housing. The straight rollers do not have an inner race. The rollers ride on the axle itself. If a bearing fails, both the axle and the bearing usually need to be replaced. The outer bearing race holding the rollers is pressed into the rear axle housing. The axle bearing is usually lubricated by the rear-end lubricant and a grease seal is located on the outside of the bearing.

NOTE: Some replacement bearings are available that are designed to ride on a fresh, unworn section of the old axle. These bearings allow the use of the original axle, saving the cost of a replacement axle.

The C-lock-type rear axle retaining method requires that the differential cover plate be removed. After removal of the cover, the differential pinion shaft has to be removed before the C-lock that retains the axle can be removed. ● SEE

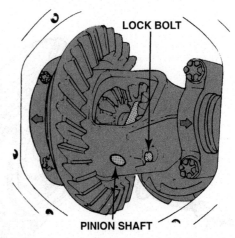

FIGURE 9–30 To remove the C-lock (clip), the lock bolt has to be moved before the pinion shaft.

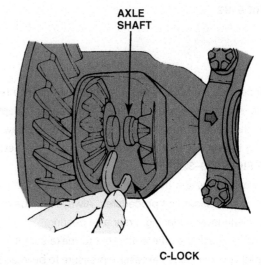

FIGURE 9–31 The axle must be pushed inward slightly to allow the C-lock to be removed. After the C-lock has been removed, the axle can be easily pulled out of the axle housing.

FIGURES 9–30 AND 9–31. Once the C-lock has been removed, the axle simply is pulled out of the axle tube.

NOTE: When removing the differential cover, rear axle lubricant will flow from between the housing and the cover. Be sure to dispose of the old rear axle lubricant in the environmentally approved way, and refill with the proper type and viscosity (thickness) of rear-end lubricant. Check the vehicle specifications for the recommended grade.

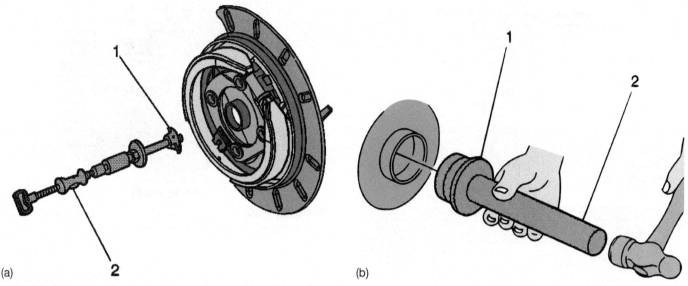

(a)   (b)

FIGURE 9–32 (a) Rotate the adapter (1) and insert it behind the bearing, and then use the slide hammer (2) to pull out the bearing. (b) Using the proper-sized adapter (1), drive in the new bearing with a hammer and the driver handle (2). (Courtesy of General Motors.)

Once the axle is removed, use the seal puller to remove the axle seal. Use a slide hammer and bearing adapter to remove the bearing from the axle tube. Install the new bearing using the proper size driver and then install the new seal. ● **SEE FIGURE 9–32.**

Always follow the manufacturer's recommended bearing removal and replacement procedures. Always replace the rear axle seal whenever replacing a rear axle bearing.

Always check the differential vent to make sure it is clear. A clogged vent can cause excessive pressure to build up inside the differential and cause the rear axle seals to leak. If rear-end lubricant gets on the brake linings, the brakes will not have the proper friction and the linings themselves are ruined and must be replaced.

FIGURE 9–33 This is a normally worn bearing. If it does not have too much play, it can be reused. (Courtesy SKF USA Inc.)

BEARING FAILURE ANALYSIS

Whenever a bearing is replaced, the old bearing must be inspected and the cause of the failure eliminated. ● **SEE FIGURES 9–33 THROUGH 9–39** for examples of normal and abnormal bearing wear.

A wheel bearing may also fail for reasons that include the following.

METAL FATIGUE   Long vehicle usage, even under normal driving conditions, causes metal to fatigue. Cracks often appear, and eventually these cracks expand downward into the metal from the surface. The metal between the cracks can break

(a)

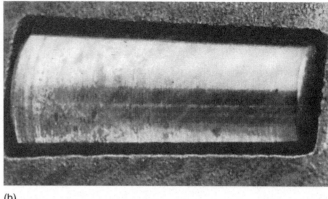
(b)

FIGURE 9–34 (a) When corrosion etches into the surface of a roller or race, the bearing should be discarded. (b) If light corrosion stains can be removed with an oil-soaked cloth, the bearing can be reused. (Courtesy SKF USA Inc.)

(a)

(b)

FIGURE 9–35 (a) When just the end of a roller is scored, it is because of excessive preload. Discard the bearing. (b) This is a more advanced case of pitting. Under load, it will rapidly lead to spalling. (Courtesy SKF USA Inc.)

(a)

(b)

FIGURE 9–36 (a) Always check for faint grooves in the race. This bearing should not be reused. (b) Grooves like this are often matched by grooves in the race (above). Discard the bearing. (Courtesy SKF USA Inc.)

(a)   (b)

FIGURE 9-37 (a) Regular patterns of etching in the race are from corrosion. This bearing should be replaced. (b) Light pitting comes from contaminants being pressed into the race. Discard the bearing. (Courtesy SKF USA Inc.)

(a)   (b)

FIGURE 9-38 (a) This bearing is worn unevenly. Notice the stripes. It should not be reused. (b) Any damage that causes low spots in the metal renders the bearing useless. (Courtesy SKF USA Inc.)

(a)   (b)

FIGURE 9-39 (a) In this more advanced case of pitting, you can see how the race has been damaged. (b) Discoloration is a result of overheating. Even a lightly burned bearing should be replaced. (Courtesy SKF USA Inc.)

(a)

(b)

FIGURE 9–40 (a) Pitting eventually leads to spalling, a condition where the metal falls away in large chunks. (b) In this spalled roller, the metal has actually begun to flake away from the surface. (Courtesy SKF USA Inc.)

out into small chips, slabs, or scales of metal. This process of breaking up is called **spalling**. ● **SEE FIGURE 9–40.**

ELECTRICAL ARCING   Bearings can be damaged caused by poor ground wires or improper welding on the vehicle.

SHOCK LOADING   Dents can be formed in the race of a bearing, which eventually leads to bearing failure. ● **SEE FIGURE 9–41.**

FIGURE 9–41 These dents resulted from the rollers "hammering" against the race, a condition called brinelling. (Courtesy SKF USA Inc.)

 TECH TIP

"Bearing Overload"

It is not uncommon for vehicles to be overloaded. This is particularly common with pickup trucks and vans. Whenever there is a heavy load, the axle bearings must support the entire weight of the vehicle, including its cargo. If a bump is hit while driving with a heavy load, the balls of a ball bearing or the rollers of a roller bearing can make an indent in the race of the bearing. This dent or imprint is called **brinelling**, named after Johann A. Brinell, a Swedish engineer who developed a process of testing for surface hardness by pressing a hard ball with a standard force into a sample material to be tested.

Once this imprint is made, the bearing will make noise whenever the roller or ball rolls over the indent. Continued use causes wear to occur on all of the balls or rollers and eventual failure. While this may take months to fail, the *cause* of the bearing failure is often overloading of the vehicle. Avoid shock loads and overloading for safety and for longer vehicle life.

REAR AXLE BEARING

1 After safely hoisting the vehicle, remove the rear wheels and brake drums.

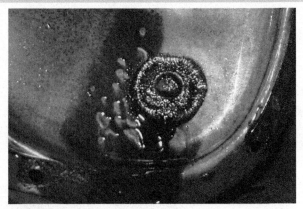

2 Remove the rear differential cover and inspect the magnet for metal particles that would indicate serious wear or damage.

3 Remove the retaining bolt and allow the pinion shaft to be removed.

4 Push the axle inward toward the center of the vehicle to free the axle clip.

5 After removing the clip, the axle can then be removed. Note that the backing plate is wet, indicating that the axle seal has been leaking.

6 A seal removal tool being used to remove the axle seal.

CONTINUED ▶

7 If a retainer-type axle is being serviced, the bearing and seal need to be pressed off of the axle.

8 After installing a new bearing and seal, insert the axle and install the clip, then the pinion shaft.

9 Clean the differential housing before installing the cover gasket and cover. Refill the differential with the specified fluid.

SUMMARY

1. Wheel bearings support the entire weight of a vehicle and are used to reduce rolling friction. Ball and straight roller-type bearings are nonadjustable while tapered roller-type bearings must be adjusted for proper clearance.

2. Most front-wheel-drive vehicles use sealed bearings, either two preloaded tapered roller bearings or double-row ball bearings.

3. Most wheel bearings are standardized sizes.

4. A defective bearing can be caused by metal fatigue that leads to spalling, shock loads that cause brinelling, or damage from electrical arcing due to poor body ground wires or improper electrical welding on the vehicle.

5. Bearing grease is an oil with a thickener. The higher the NLGI number of the grease, the thicker or harder the grease consistency.

6. Tapered wheel bearings must be adjusted by hand tightening the spindle nut after properly seating the bearings. A new cotter key must always be used.

7. Defective wheel bearings usually make more noise while turning because more weight is applied to the bearing as the vehicle turns.

8. All bearings must be serviced, replaced, and/or adjusted using the vehicle manufacturer's recommended procedures as stated in the service manual.

REVIEW QUESTIONS

1. List three common types of automotive antifriction bearings.

2. Explain the adjustment procedure for a typical tapered roller wheel bearing.

3. List four symptoms of a defective wheel bearing.

4. Describe how the rear axle is removed from a C-lock-type axle.

CHAPTER QUIZ

1. Which type of automotive bearing can withstand radial and thrust loads, yet must be adjusted for proper clearance?
   a. Roller bearing
   b. Tapered roller bearing
   c. Ball bearings
   d. Needle roller bearing

2. Most sealed bearings used on the front wheels of front-wheel-drive vehicles are usually which type?
   a. Roller bearing
   b. Single-tapered roller bearing
   c. Double-row ball bearing
   d. Needle roller bearing

3. On a bearing that has been shock loaded, the race (cup) of the bearing can be dented. This type of bearing failure is called _____.
   a. Spalling
   b. Arcing
   c. Brinelling
   d. Fluting

4. The bearing grease most often specified is rated NLGI _____.
   a. #00
   b. #0
   c. #1
   d. #2

5. A non-drive-wheel bearing adjustment procedure includes a final spindle nut tightening torque of _____.
   a. Finger tight
   b. 5 lb-in.
   c. 12 to 30 lb-ft
   d. 12 to 15 lb-ft plus 1/16 in. turn

6. After a non-drive-wheel bearing has been properly adjusted, the wheel should have how much end play?
   a. Zero
   b. 0.001 to 0.005 in.
   c. 0.10 to 0.30 inches
   d. 1/16 to 3/32 in.

7. The differential cover must be removed before removing the rear axle on which type of axle?
   a. Retainer plate
   b. C-lock
   c. Press fit
   d. Welded tube

8. What part(s) should be replaced when servicing a wheel bearing on a non-drive wheel?
   a. The bearing cup
   b. The grease seal
   c. The cotter key
   d. Both the grease seal and the cotter key

9. Technician A says that a defective wheel or axle bearing often makes a growling or rumbling noise. Technician B says that a defective wheel or axle bearing often makes a noise similar to a tire with an aggressive mud or snow design. Which technician is correct?
   a. Technician A only
   b. Technician B only
   c. Both Technicians A and B
   d. Neither Technician A nor B

10. Two technicians are discussing differentials. Technician A says all differentials are vented. Technician B says that a clogged vent can cause the rear axle seal to leak. Which technician is correct?
   a. Technician A only
   b. Technician B only
   c. Both Technicians A and B
   d. Neither Technician A nor B

DRIVE AXLES AND DIFFERENTIALS

LEARNING OBJECTIVES

After studying this chapter, the reader should be able to:

1. Discuss the different drive axle designs.
2. Explain the features of ring and pinion gears.
3. Discuss the types of differential carriers.
4. State the purpose of differentials and identify the parts of a differential assembly.
5. Identify the different types of limited slip differentials.

This chapter will help you prepare for ASE Manual Drive Train and Axles (A3) certification test content area "E" (Rear Axle Diagnosis and Repair).

GM STC OBJECTIVES

GM Service Technical College topics covered in this chapter are as follows:

1. Rear axle identification (14041.18W1).
2. Internal gearing configurations.
3. Differences between different types of ring and pinion gear sets.
4. Characteristics of semi- and full-floating rear drive axle mechanical systems.

KEY TERMS

Backlash 163
Carrier bearings 165
Coast side 163
Dead axle 160
Differential 165
Drive side 163
Electronic traction control (ETC) 172
Face 163
Final drive 161
Flank 163
Float 163
Friction modifier 169
Full-floating axle 161
Heel 163
Hunting gear sets 163
Hypoid gear set 162
Independent rear suspension (IRS) 173
Integral carrier 165
Limited slip differential (LSD) 167

Live axle 160
Locked differential 167
Non-hunting 163
Open differential 167
Overhung pinion 165
Partial non-hunting 163
Pinion gear 161
Pitch line 163
Positraction 168
Removable carrier 165
Retainer-plate-type axle 161
Ring gear 161
Semi-floating axle 161
Side bearings 165
Side gears 166
Straddle mounting 166
Toe 163
Torque bias ratio (TBR) 168
Torsen® 170

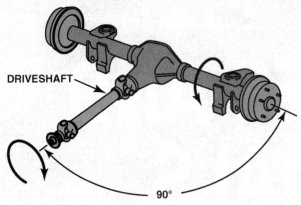

DRIVESHAFT

90°

FIGURE 10-1 The rear axle assembly changes the direction of engine torque and increases the torque to the drive wheels.

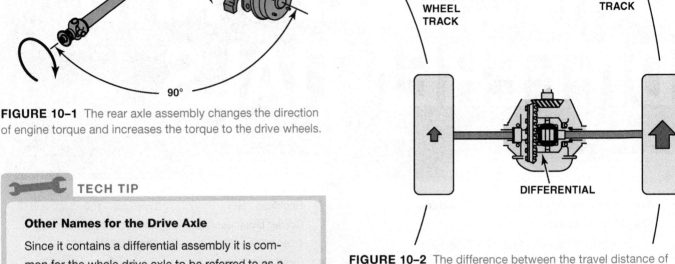

INNER WHEEL TRACK

OUTER WHEEL TRACK

DIFFERENTIAL

FIGURE 10-2 The difference between the travel distance of the drive wheels is controlled by the differential.

● SEE FIGURE 10-1.
● SEE FIGURE 10-2.

TECH TIP

Other Names for the Drive Axle

Since it contains a differential assembly it is common for the whole drive axle to be referred to as a "differential."

Some other terms that may be used are given:

- Third member. With the engine being the first member of the drive train, the transmission, the second member, then the rear axle is the "third member."
- Pumpkin. When removed, a removable final drive/differential assembly resembles a "pumpkin."
- Chunk. When removed, the assembly is quite heavy and rock-looking and could be called a "chunk" by some mechanics.

DRIVE AXLE TERMINOLOGY

All rear-wheel-drive (RWD) vehicles use a drive axle assembly to transfer power from the driveshaft to the drive wheels. Because it is powered, it is sometimes called a **live axle.** Front-wheel-drive (FWD) cars use a non-powered rear axle, sometimes called a **dead axle,** as a rear axle. The major parts of a drive axle include the following:

- The ring and pinion gears
- Differential assembly
- Axle shafts

Many 4WD and AWD vehicles use a similar axle at the front, the major difference being steerable drive wheels.

DRIVE AXLE ASSEMBLY

PURPOSE AND FUNCTION The purpose and function of a drive axle assembly include the following:

1. *Changing the direction and multiplying engine torque*—This is achieved using a ring and pinion gears. ● **SEE FIGURE 10-1.**

2. *Allowing the drive wheels to rotate at different speeds when turning*—This is achieved using a differential assembly. ● **SEE FIGURE 10-2.**

3. *Support the weight of the vehicle*—This is achieved by using a robust drive axle assembly that is capable of supporting the suspension and the carrying the load of the vehicle itself plus the carrying capability of the vehicle.

4. *Drive the wheels through axles*—The drive axles are splined to the differential side gears and attached to the drive wheels at the outer end.

AXLE DESIGNS

AXLE SHAFTS On most rear-wheel-drive vehicles, the axle shafts transfer the torque from the differential side gears to the drive wheels and support the weight of the vehicle. To give

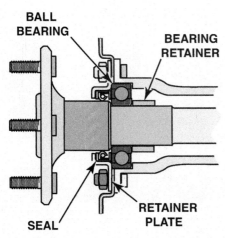

FIGURE 10–3 A typical retainer-plate-type axle, which uses a ball bearing and uses a bearing retainer ring which is a press fit into the axle shaft.

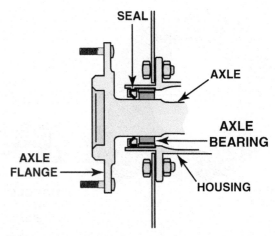

FIGURE 10–4 A C-lock type axle uses a straight roller bearing which is lubricated by the drive axle lube.

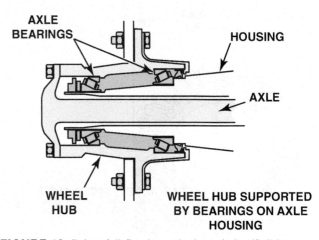

FIGURE 10–5 In a full-floating axle the axle itself slides through the center of the wheel hub assembly and does not support the weight of the vehicle.

them the necessary strength to transfer the torque, axles are made of forged steel. The inner ends are splined to match the splines of the differential side gears.

SEMI-FLOATING AXLES

Axle shafts can be classified by the way the axle is loaded and how the axle is retained in the housing. Currently, all rear-wheel-drive passenger vehicles use **semi-floating axles**.

- The inner end floats because it is supported by a gear, not a bearing.
- The outer end uses a bearing in the end of the housing. This bearing transfers the load of the vehicle to the axle, which, in turn, transfers it to the wheel.
- If the axle were to break outboard of the bearing, the wheel would fall off and the vehicle would drop.

There are two types of semi-floating axles:

1. **Retainer-plate type**—A retainer-plate-type axle usually uses a ball bearing. With a ball bearing axle, the side thrust is transferred from the axle to the axle tube through the bearing and the retainer plate. ● **SEE FIGURE 10–3**.

2. **C-Lock**—A C-lock axle uses a straight roller bearing and uses the axle shaft itself as the inner race. The C-locks keep the axle shafts from moving outward and the differential pinion shafts prevent axle movement inward. ● **SEE FIGURE 10–4**.

FULL-FLOATING AXLES

All heavy trucks use a full-floating axle design. The wheel hub has a pair of large tapered roller bearings that transfer all of the vehicle loads except torque from the axle housing to the wheel. The axle shaft slides into mesh with the axle gear and is bolted to the hub. Even

if the axle shaft is removed, the vehicle will still roll down the road. ● **SEE FIGURE 10–5**.

THREE-QUARTER AXLES

A few older vehicles used three-quarter-floating axles. This design uses a single roller or ball bearing between the hub and axle housing. Vertical loads pass from the hub through this bearing to the housing, but cornering loads, which try to pull the axle out of the housing, act on the axle. If the axle breaks, it can slide out of the housing.

RING AND PINION GEARS

FINAL GEAR RATIO The **ring** and **pinion gears** are the **final drive** reduction gears.

- The final drive gear ratio and tire size are selected to provide the best engine RPM for cruise speed.

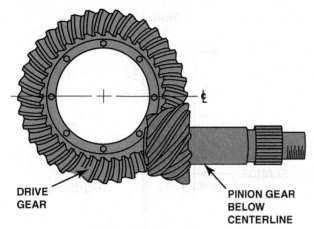

FIGURE 10–6 A hypoid gear set uses a drive pinion that meshes with the ring gear below the center line of the ring gear.

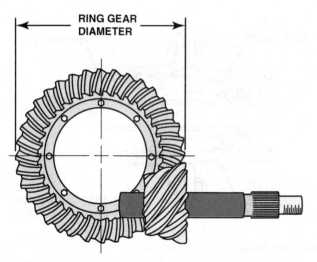

RING GEAR DIAMETER

FIGURE 10–7 A 9-inch axle has a ring gear with a rough diameter of 9 inches.

Sometimes the ratio must be selected so that it will provide sufficient torque for low-speed operation.

- The ring and pinion gear set must also turn the power flow from the driveshaft 90° to align with the axles.

HYPOID GEAR SET
The ring and pinion gear set is a hypoid type. These are similar to spiral bevel gears except for the location of the pinion gear. ● SEE FIGURE 10–6.

A **hypoid gear set** has the pinion gear below the center line. This accomplishes two purposes:

1. Allows a lower the driveshaft so that the tunnel or hump in the floor of the vehicle can be smaller.

2. Allows a larger and stronger drive pinion gear in which the pinion gear teeth slide across the teeth of the ring gear. This also makes a hypoid gear set quieter. The sliding, wiping action of the gear teeth requires a special GL-4 or GL-5 lubricant.

FIGURE 10–8 A 5-cut gear on the left and a 2-cut gear on the right. (Courtesy of General Motors.)

? FREQUENTLY ASKED QUESTION

What Does the 9-Inch Refer to When Describing a Drive Axle?

A 9-inch drive axle actually is referring to the rough diameter of the ring gear. A 9-inch gear set is bigger and stronger than an 8-inch gear set. ● SEE FIGURE 10–7.

HYPOID GEAR SET MANUFACTURING As a gear set is made, after the gears have been cut, hardened, and ground to shape, the ring and pinion are run against each other in a machine with abrasive compound on their teeth. This laps or wears them to match each other perfectly. At this point, they become a matched set, and damage to one will require replacement of both with another matched set. There is normally a mark etched on the head of the pinion gear and on the side of the ring gear to identify a particular set. There is often a stamping that indicates the gear ratio or part number, and sometimes there will also be a marking that indicates the pinion gear depth.

Production drive pinion and ring gear sets are manufactured by using either a 2-cut or a 5-cut method. The 2-cut drive pinions and ring gears can be identified by having a groove cut into the outside edge of the ring gear and a ring on the stem of the drive pinion. The gear tooth contact patterns that are produced from each style of gear set differ slightly. ● SEE FIGURE 10–8.

HYPOID GEAR TOOTH TERMINOLOGY When a hypoid ring and pinion gear set is adjusted, reference is often made

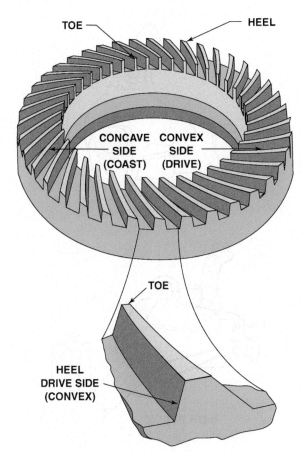

FIGURE 10–9 The drive side is the convex side of the ring gear except for some front axles used in four-wheel vehicles, and they often use the concave side on the drive side.

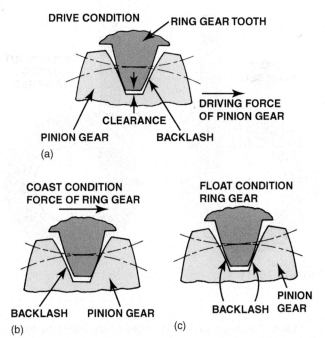

FIGURE 10–10 (a) During a drive condition, the pinion gear is driving the ring gear and there is backlash at the coast side of the ring gear tooth. (b) During a coast condition, this action is reversed. (c) During a float condition, lash is split between both sides of the tooth.

to particular parts of the gears and their teeth. The outer ends of the ring gear teeth are called the **heel** and the inner ends the **toe**. ● SEE FIGURE 10–9.

The **pitch line** is the design center of contact between the two gears and is about halfway up the tooth. The **face** of the tooth is above the pitch line, and the **flank** is below it.

The **drive side** of the ring gear teeth is the vertical, *convex* side of the tooth. This is the side of the tooth that contacts the pinion gear while the engine is driving the vehicle forward.

There should be a clearance at the coast side of the tooth which is called **backlash**. The **coast side** of ring gear teeth is the slanted, *concave* side of the tooth. This surface receives pressure while the vehicle is coasting and the vehicle is driving the engine. While coasting, the backlash will be at the drive side of the tooth. The third tooth-load condition is called **float**. During float there is no load on the gear teeth, and backlash will be on both sides. ● SEE FIGURE 10–10.

HUNTING AND NON-HUNTING GEAR SET
The final drive gear ratio determines how many times a drive pinion tooth will make contact with a particular ring gear tooth during

one revolution. This affects final drive gear set manufacture and service. Final drive gear sets may be divided into three types, depending on the final drive gear ratio.

1. **Hunting gear sets** are gear sets with final drive ratios expressible in a fraction that cannot be reduced to any lower terms. An example of a hunting gear set is one that has 41 teeth on the ring gear and 11 teeth on the drive pinion. This combination creates a 3.73:1 axle ratio. This type of gear set requires no timing marks or alignment during assembly. As the pinion gear drives the ring gear, each pinion tooth will hunt for, or seek, contact with every ring gear tooth.

2. **Non-hunting gear sets** are gear sets with final drive ratios expressible as a whole number. An example of a non-hunting gear set is a differential that uses 39 teeth on the ring gear and 13 teeth on the pinion gear which gives a 3.00:1 gear ratio. Non-hunting gear sets require *timing marks*. As the pinion gear drives the ring gear, each pinion tooth contacts only a few ring gear teeth during each revolution.

3. **Partially non-hunting gear sets** are gear sets with final drive ratios expressible as a reducible fraction not equaling a whole number. An example of a partial non-hunting gear set is an axle ratio of 3.50:1. Partially non-hunting gear sets also require timing marks. During final drive operation, each pinion tooth contacts only some of the ring pinion

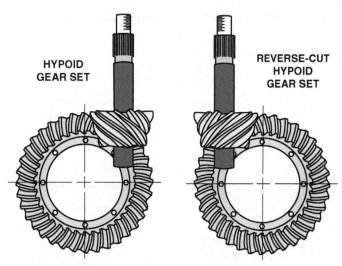

FIGURE 10–11 A reverse-cut gear set is a mirror image of the normal hypoid gear set.

teeth. For the pinion teeth to make contact with the highest number of ring gear teeth, the pinion gear must drive the ring gear more than one revolution. On non-hunting and partially non-hunting gears, manufacturers lap (provide a surface finish) the contacting gear teeth to decrease wear. For this reason, these gear sets are marked to ensure proper alignment during assembly procedures. To preserve the wear patterns, the gear sets should be reassembled using the same alignment. This prolongs the life of the gear set and decreases operational noise.

REVERSE-CUT RING AND PINION GEARS Reverse-cut ring and pinion gears were primarily designed for front-wheel drive applications to take advantage of their increased strength. The gears have the teeth spirally cut in the opposite direction of standard gears. ● **SEE FIGURE 10–11**.

Some 4WD vehicles use a standard rear-drive axle that has been turned around for the front, but this arrangement drives on the coast side of the gear tooth which results in a gear that is 15% to 30% weaker. Reverse-cut gears are stronger when used in the front axle and move the drive pinion above the centerline of the ring gear. When the drive pinion is above the centerline of the ring gear (high-mounted), the angle of the driveshaft will be decreased and this is especially useful when the vehicle has been lifted for additional ground clearance. The housing is especially designed with different oiling passages to properly lubricate the gears. ● **SEE FIGURE 10–12**.

ABS RELUCTOR WHEEL On rear-wheel-drive vehicles with antilock braking system (ABS), the rear wheel speed sensor(s) is attached to the rear axle assembly. Some older vehicles that are equipped with a three-channel ABS will use

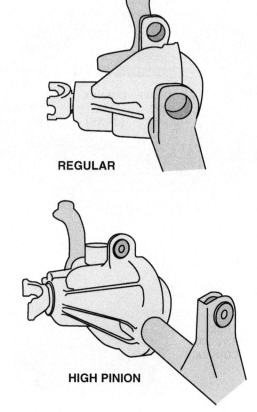

REGULAR

HIGH PINION

FIGURE 10–12 Two front drive axles. The left one has a standard-cut ring and pinion, whereas the one at the right has high-pinion, reverse-cut ring and pinion gears.

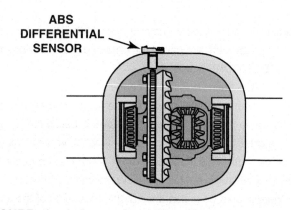

ABS DIFFERENTIAL SENSOR

FIGURE 10–13 Some vehicles with ABS will have a single rear wheel speed sensor at the ring gear or a speed sensor at each axle shaft. Some will use a similar sensor at the drive pinion shaft.

one speed sensor mounted to the driveshaft flange, drive pinion shaft, or ring gear, whereas others use a pair of sensors near the end of the axle at each wheel hub. Because they include a magnetic core, sensors that are in the axle housing can be affected by metal particles worn from the gears or bearings. Sensors at the axle shafts can be affected by worn axle bearings. ● **SEE FIGURE 10–13**.

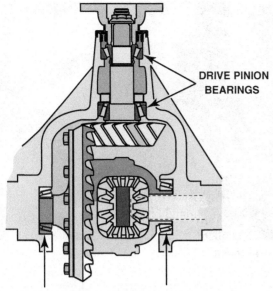

DRIVE PINION
BEARINGS

DIFFERENTIAL CARRIER BEARINGS

FIGURE 10–14 A pair of tapered roller bearings called carrier bearings is used to locate the drive pinion gear and the differential case and ring gear. Another pair of bearings locates the drive pinion gear.

GEAR AND PINION MOUNTING The ring and pinion gears must be mounted securely because of the large torque load involved. Gear separation forces try to move the gears away from each other. The ring gear is bolted or riveted to the differential case. Rivets provide a secure and permanent mounting, but they make it harder to remove the ring gear. The differential case is mounted on a pair of tapered roller bearings, which are commonly called **carrier bearings** or **side bearings**. ● **SEE FIGURE 10–14.**

DIFFERENTIAL CARRIERS

PURPOSE AND FUNCTION The **differential** is responsible for allowing the drive wheels to rotate at different speeds when turning or when the vehicle is traveling over uneven road surface. The *differential carrier* is the heavy cast iron portion of the rear axle assembly that provides mounting points for the drive pinion shaft bearings and the carrier bearings. Many carriers have special reinforcing webs to contain the gear separation forces of the ring and pinion gear set.

TYPES OF CARRIERS

Removable carriers—Most early trucks and passenger vehicle drive axles had removable carriers, which could be

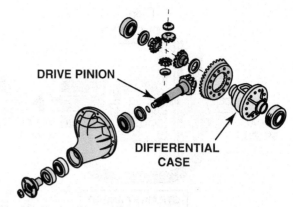

DRIVE PINION

DIFFERENTIAL
CASE

FIGURE 10–15 A removable carrier final drive unit. This older design uses an axle housing that is often called a "banjo" because of the shape of the axle housing, which is similar to the musical instrument.

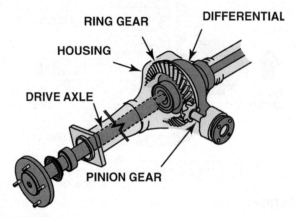

RING GEAR   DIFFERENTIAL

HOUSING

DRIVE AXLE

PINION GEAR

FIGURE 10–16 An integral carrier axle assembly is the most commonly used design of drive axle.

unbolted and removed from the housing for service. They are also known as

- Third member
- Drop-out
- Pumpkin ● **SEE FIGURE 10–15.**

Integral carriers—Most rear-wheel-drive passenger vehicles and light trucks use integral carriers, and the axle tubes are welded to extensions of the carrier. An integral carrier is stronger in the areas around the carrier bearings. An integral carrier axle assembly, sometimes called a *Salisbury* or *Spicer axle*, has a removable rear cover for access to the differential and other internal parts. ● **SEE FIGURE 10–16.**

PINION SHAFTS The pinion shaft is also mounted on a pair of tapered roller bearings. There are two common styles of mounting the shaft and gear.

1. In the first and most common style, called an **overhung pinion**, the pinion gear hangs over from the rear bearing. The two tapered roller bearings are positioned as far apart

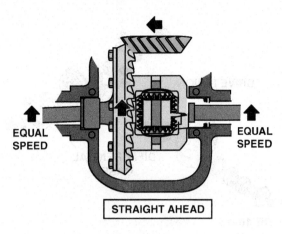

EQUAL SPEED | EQUAL SPEED

STRAIGHT AHEAD

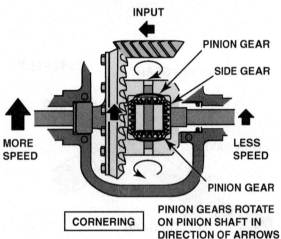

INPUT

PINION GEAR

SIDE GEAR

MORE SPEED | LESS SPEED

PINION GEAR

CORNERING

PINION GEARS ROTATE ON PINION SHAFT IN DIRECTION OF ARROWS

FIGURE 10–17 When the vehicle turns a corner, the inner wheel slows and the outer wheel increases in speed to compensate. This difference in rotational speed causes the pinion gears to "walk" around the slower side gear.

as practical to hold the pinion shaft rigid and not allow any movement of the pinion gear as it tries to climb or move away from the ring gear.

2. In the second style, called **straddle mounting**, the pinion gear is straddled by two bearings where the rear tapered roller bearing is located in front of the gear and a pilot bearing behind the gear. The pilot bearing is usually a smaller roller bearing. Straddle mounting is the strongest, in that the pilot bearing prevents any flexing of the pinion shaft. It also eliminates any gear-to-bearing leverage effects and allows the two tapered roller bearings to be placed fairly close to each other.

DIFFERENTIALS

PURPOSE AND FUNCTION
A differential, inside the drive axle housing, splits torque equally to the drive wheels. The differential allows engine torque to be applied to both drive

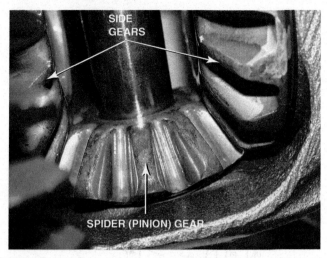

SIDE GEARS

SPIDER (PINION) GEAR

FIGURE 10–18 A close-up view of the side gears and spider (pinion) gear. The axle shafts are splined to the side gears. The pinion shaft drives the pinion gears, which then drive the side gears.

axles, which rotate at varying speeds during cornering and while traveling over bumps and dips in the road.

A differential is a mechanical addition and subtraction assembly. A differential is sometimes referred to as *torque equalizer* because it splits the engine torque equally to the drive wheels. When the vehicle is turning a corner, the torque forces cause the side gear and pinion gears to subtract torque from one side and add torque to the opposite side. ● **SEE FIGURE 10–17.**

PARTS AND OPERATION
A drive axle assembly must include a differential to allow the drive wheels to rotate at different speeds on corners. The differential used in most drive axles includes:

- Two or more differential pinion gears mounted on a differential pinion shaft(s)
- Two side or axle gears which are splined to the axle shafts

The differential pinion shaft runs through the case and has the two differential pinion gears (sometimes called spider gears) floating on it. These gears are not secured to the shaft. They are located between the differential case and the two **side gears**, which are also called *axle gears*. ● **SEE FIGURE 10–18.**

The axle gears also float in the case, but they have internal splines so they can drive the axle shafts. All four of these gears are spur bevel gears. The spur bevel gears can usually be operated by lifting both drive wheels and rotating one wheel by hand. When one wheel is turned, note that the other wheel is rotating in the opposite direction because the pinion gears

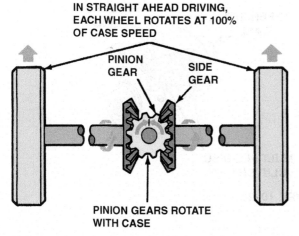

IN STRAIGHT AHEAD DRIVING, EACH WHEEL ROTATES AT 100% OF CASE SPEED

PINION GEAR

SIDE GEAR

PINION GEARS ROTATE WITH CASE

FIGURE 10–19 Differential action while driving straight ahead. (Courtesy of General Motors.)

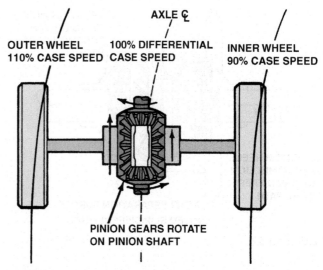

AXLE C̵L

OUTER WHEEL 110% CASE SPEED

100% DIFFERENTIAL CASE SPEED

INNER WHEEL 90% CASE SPEED

PINION GEARS ROTATE ON PINION SHAFT

FIGURE 10–20 During a turn the axles turn at different speeds. (Courtesy of General Motors.)

FREQUENTLY ASKED QUESTION

Why Does One Wheel Spin When the Other Wheel Is on Dry Pavement?

A standard, called an *open differential*, splits torque equally to the drive wheels. If one tire is on a slippery surface and only 50 pounds-feet of torque can be applied to the road, the other side will also have the same 50 pounds-feet. Even if the tire on the other side from the one on a slippery surface is on dry pavement, the force being sent to the drive wheel (50 pounds) is not enough to propel the vehicle.

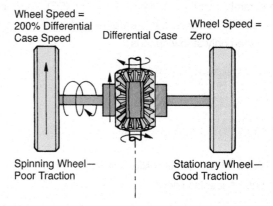

Wheel Speed = 200% Differential Case Speed

Differential Case

Wheel Speed = Zero

Spinning Wheel— Poor Traction

Stationary Wheel— Good Traction

FIGURE 10–21 If one tire has poor traction, it will rotate easily, so the differential pinion gears rotate on their shaft and walk around the other side gear, which offers more resistance. The result will be wheel spin on the side with poor traction.

are acting like idlers between the two side gears. The load of the side gears determines what the differential pinion gears do.

- If both side gears are loaded the same and offer the same resistance, the differential pinion gears remain motionless on their shaft and the entire differential assembly rotates as one unit with no internal gear movement.

- When a vehicle goes around a corner, the side gears are equally loaded, but the one connected to the outer wheel will rotate faster. At this time, the differential pinion gears will rotate on their shafts to compensate for this change in speed. The outer wheel will speed up relative to the vehicle and differential, and the inner wheel will slow down the same amount. For example, if the outer wheel speeds up 10% from 100 RPM to 110 RPM, the inner wheel will slow down by the same percentage. ● **SEE FIGURES 10–19 AND 10–20.**

TYPES OF DIFFERENTIALS Pickups and rear-wheel-drive vehicles encounter more single-wheel traction problems than front-wheel-drive vehicles basically because the weight is over the drive wheels on a front-wheel-drive vehicle. Therefore, rear-wheel-drive vehicles encounter more driving conditions in which the open differential action is not suitable. One tire cannot receive more torque than either tire can transmit to the ground. ● **SEE FIGURE 10–21.**

The three major types of differentials are as follows:

1. **Open differential** This type of differential is used in most passenger vehicles.

2. **Limited Slip differential (LSD)** This type of differential can send more torque to the wheel with traction than the wheel with poor traction.

3. **Locked differential** This type of differential connects both axle shafts together to eliminate differential action,

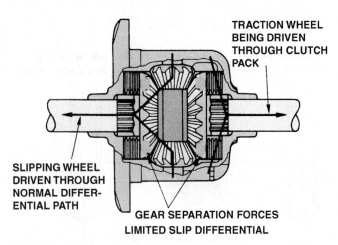

TRACTION WHEEL
BEING DRIVEN
THROUGH CLUTCH
PACK

SLIPPING WHEEL
DRIVEN THROUGH
NORMAL DIFFER-
ENTIAL PATH

GEAR SEPARATION FORCES
LIMITED SLIP DIFFERENTIAL

FIGURE 10–22 Limited slip differentials transfer most of the torque through the pinion shaft and gears like a conventional differential. Some torque is also transferred through the clutch pack going from the case through the clutch to the side gear (right).

but rarely used in original equipment (OE) applications except for vehicles that are designed for off-road travel, and then only at low speeds.

LIMITED SLIP DIFFERENTIALS

TERMINOLOGY Limited slip differential is a generic name for a group of specific vehicle-line units such as:

- **Positraction** is the specific name of the limited slip differential used in Chevrolet vehicles

NOTE: The RPO code "G80" is used to identify any form of limited slip differential on GM products.

DIFFERENTIAL TORQUE BIAS RATIO An open differential has a **torque bias ratio (TBR)** of 1:1. A 1:1 TBR indicates that the torque applied to each wheel is the same. This means that the available torque that can be sent to the two wheels is twice that of the tire with the least traction. Any more torque than this will cause the tire with poor traction to spin. If the poor-traction tire spins at 50 pound-feet of torque, only 50 pound-feet of torque can be sent to the good-traction tire.

Limited slip differentials can deliver as much as five times the torque to the tire with good traction which would be a TBR of 5:1. If the differential has a TBR of 2.5:1 and 50 pounds-feet of torque can be sent to the poor traction tire, then 50 × 2.5 or 125 pounds-feet of torque can be sent to the good traction tire. A total of 175 pounds-feet of torque can be sent to both tires.

NOTE: Limited slip differentials are *torque biasing devices* (TBD) that have been traditionally used to

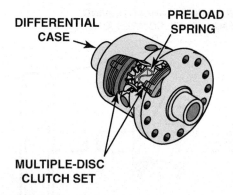

DIFFERENTIAL
CASE

PRELOAD
SPRING

MULTIPLE-DISC
CLUTCH SET

FIGURE 10–23 A limited slip differential showing the preload spring and how the steel plates of the clutch pack are held to the differential case.

improve traction for both off-road and on-road driving. These devices are also used with the recent all-wheel-drive (AWD) vehicle where on-road handling in both good and bad traction conditions is a major priority. Electronic wheel speed, steering, and yaw sensors determine what the vehicle is doing relative to what the driver is requesting it to do, and the TBD is electronically actuated to send more torque to the tire most able to improve the situation.

TYPES OF LIMITED SLIP DIFFERENTIALS There are several different styles of limited slip differentials used in production vehicles including the following:

1. Preloaded clutches
2. Self-applying clutches
3. Viscous couplings
4. Eaton locker differential
5. Hydraulic applied clutches
6. Cone type
7. Electronic locking differential

PRELOADED CLUTCH DIFFERENTIAL Differentials with a preloaded clutch(es) provide two different differential power paths. ● **SEE FIGURE 10–22**.

One path is through the differential gears as in other differentials, and the other path is directly through the clutch pack(s). Most of these units use two clutch packs, one on each side, but a few designs use a single clutch pack. The operation is essentially the same. Flat, hardened-steel plates with various-shaped oiling grooves are used for the clutch plates. Half of them are splined to the axle gear and the other half are splined to the differential case.

To provide the preload force to apply the clutch, spring pressure forces the axle gear against the clutch pack. The spring can be a single coil spring, a group of coil springs, an S-shaped spring, or one or more Belleville springs. ● **SEE FIGURE 10–23**.

This style of differential has a tendency to lock up under high-torque conditions such as during hard acceleration. This is due to the gear separation force between the differential pinions and the side gears. The applied torque will try to move the side gears away from the differential

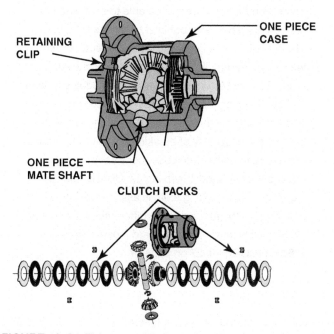

FIGURE 10–24 This type of limited slip differential uses the preload force from a spring and the torque generated by the side gears as the two axles rotate at different rates to apply the clutches and limit the amount of difference in the speed of two axles.

pinion gears. The separation force, also called *torque loading*, will increase the applied force at the clutch packs. ● **SEE FIGURE 10–24.**

CONE CLUTCH DESIGN Some limited slip differentials use a pair of cone clutches in place of the clutch plates. A cone is splined to each axle shaft, and the differential case is machined to form the mating cone surface. ● **SEE FIGURE 10–25.**

EATON LOCKER DIFFERENTIAL The Eaton "locker" differential used in some pickups and light trucks includes a governor, latching mechanism, and differential cam gear. Normally, this unit will operate as a limited slip differential, but if a wheel-to-wheel speed difference of 100 RPM or more occurs, the unit will lock up. Lockup occurs because the spinning cam in the case turns the governor

FIGURE 10–25 Exploded view of a limited slip differential using cone-type clutches.

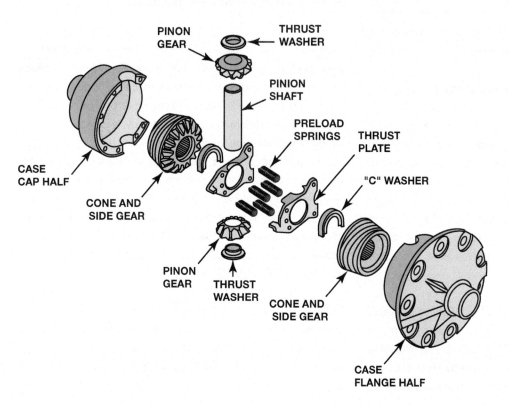

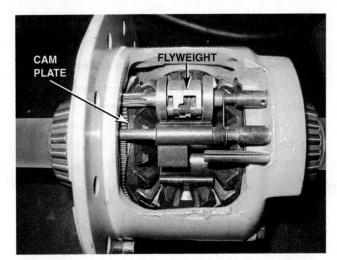

FIGURE 10–26 A locker-type differential operates as a limited slip differential until there is a wheel-to-wheel speed difference of 100 RPM or more. At that point, the governor weights move outward and cause the mechanism to lock the clutch pack.

weights fast enough to fly outward. This, in turn, causes the latching operation, which causes the cam gear to rotate relative to the cam side gear, and locks up the clutch pack. ● SEE FIGURE 10–26.

SELF-APPLYING CLUTCH DIFFERENTIAL Some limited slip differentials use self-applying clutches. They do not maintain a constant preload on the clutch packs, so differential action during normal driving is free of clutch drag. These differentials used a four-pinion differential with two separate differential pinion shafts. The two shafts called *mate shafts* are fitted into the case in an opposing manner, with ramplike attachments to the case.

While going down the road, the two shafts stay centered by pushing toward each other with equal force because of the equal driving loads and differential gear separation forces. If one wheel loses traction, the driving load on one of the pinion shafts drops off. The load on the other pinion shaft causes it to lag behind the differential case and move sideways because of the case ramps. This force from the differential pinion gears through the axle gear applies the clutch on the side with good traction. The result is that this differential applies the clutch needed to drive the other wheel from the one with poor traction. ● SEE FIGURE 10–28.

VISCOUS COUPLING DIFFERENTIAL Viscous coupling differentials use a stack of intermeshed clutch plates that run in a bath of silicone fluid and are not spring loaded. The thickness of the fluid causes a drag that tries to keep the two sets of plates at the same speed. Slippage between the plates heats the fluid

I Used to Have a Limited Slip Differential

An owner of a Chevrolet S-10 pickup truck equipped with a V-6 and five-speed manual transmission complained that he used to be able to spin both rear tires on dry pavement, but lately only one tire spins. The service technician assigned to the repair order was very familiar with what might have occurred. Many General Motors pickup trucks are equipped with an Eaton locking differential that uses a torque limiting disc. The teeth of this disc are designed to shear to prevent the possibility of breaking an axle. The service procedure to correct the customer's concern is to replace the left-hand clutch plates. Usually, the shearing of the torque-linking teeth is associated with a loud bang in the rear axle. The differential will continue to operate normally as a standard (open) differential. ● SEE FIGURE 10–27 on page 171.

causing it to expand. A unique feature of silicone fluid is that the drag increases as the slip speed of the plates increases. Single-wheel spinning tends to lock up the differential. The plates and silicone fluid must be isolated within a chamber inside the differential case and must be kept separate from the gear oil in the axle. ● SEE FIGURE 10–29.

TORSEN® DIFFERENTIAL The **Torsen®** differential is a pure mechanical worm gear differential. The name is derived from *torque sensing*. Two helical gears, called "side gears," are connected to the axle shafts. Three pairs of worm gears are mounted in the differential case, and these are called "element gears." Each element gear has the worm gear in the center and a spur gear at each end. The spur gears mesh with the spur gears of the mating element gear. If one of the element gears rotates in the case, its mate must rotate in the opposite direction. Note that all three pairs of element gears must rotate at the same time. Gleason, the company that developed Torsen® differentials, calls the element and side gears *Invex gearing*. ● SEE FIGURE 10–30.

ELECTRIC LOCKING DIFFERENTIALS A locking differential eliminates any differential action by coupling two of the differential parts together. When the axle shaft or side gear is connected to the differential case, the differential becomes locked.

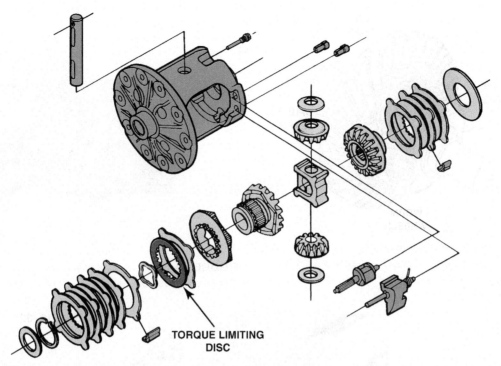

FIGURE 10–27 This Eaton design differential uses a torque-limiting disc to prevent the possibility of breaking an axle in the event of a high-torque demand. When the disc tangs shear, the differential will continue to function but as an open rather than as a limited slip differential.

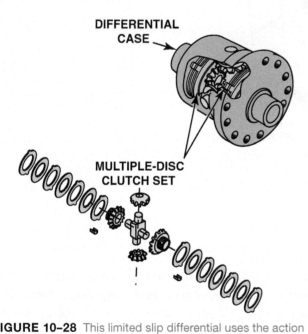

FIGURE 10–28 This limited slip differential uses the action of the pinion mate shafts and ramps in the differential case to apply pressure on the clutch pack and send torque to the wheel with traction.

Electric locking differentials use an electric motor or magnetic clutch assembly to move the locking mechanism. Current flow to the motor can be electronically controlled by the powertrain control module (PCM). Locking differentials are used in both rear and front axles. ● **SEE FIGURE 10–31.**

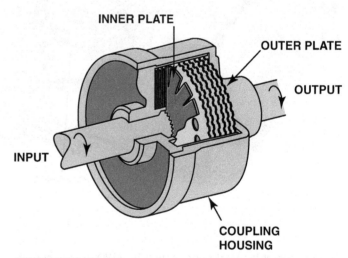

FIGURE 10–29 In a viscous coupling, silicone fluid is placed between the plates in a seal assembly. When the two axles are moving at different speeds, the fluid becomes hot and expands, which forces the clutch plates to rotate together.

ELECTRONIC TORQUE MANAGEMENT Some vehicles are using a variable torque rear drive axle. These are basically front-wheel-drive vehicles that have a rear drive axle with no differential with the ring gear mounted on a spool to drive two clutches.

The pair of electronically controlled wet clutch packs is used to send power to the rear axle shafts. The clutches can

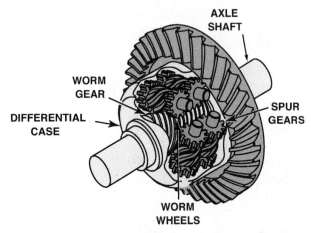

FIGURE 10–30 A torque sensing differential is used in the front drive axle in front-wheel-drive vehicles as well as in the rear in rear-wheel-drive or all-wheel drive vehicles.

FIGURE 10–31 An electrically locking differential unit. (Courtesy of General Motors)

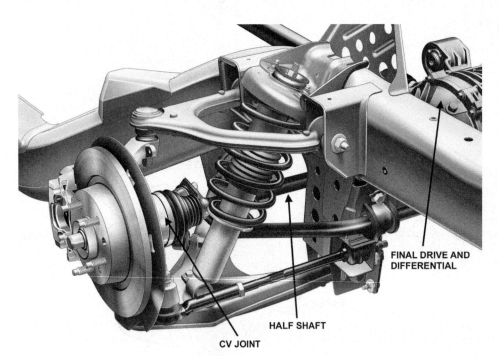

FIGURE 10–32 An independent rear suspension is used to reduce the amount of weight that the suspension has to carry to improve ride and handling. The differential is attached to the frame of the vehicle and does not move when the rear wheels travel over bumps in the road. (Courtesy of General Motors)

be engaged at times of poor traction for AWD or they can be engaged to provide high-speed vehicle stability. The latter is called *automatic yaw control (AYC)* and it drives one or both rear wheels as needed to keep the vehicle under control. Clutch control comes from an electronic control module (ECM), which receives signals from front and rear wheel speed sensors and engine speed and load sensors.

INDEPENDENT REAR SUSPENSION DRIVE AXLES

Vehicles with **independent rear suspension (IRS)** have wheels that are supported by the suspension system and the drive shafts, also called *half shafts*, connect them to the axle assembly. The axle housing is very short, slightly bigger than the carrier, and short output shafts are used to connect the axle gears to the U-joint half shaft flanges. ● **SEE FIGURE 10–32.**

Check Tire Size

A common problem encountered with limited slip differentials is a stick/slip condition in which the plates stick together, break apart, and stick together instead of sliding smoothly over each other. This problem shows up as a series of clunks or chuckle sounds as a vehicle rounds a corner. It is very important to keep the drive tires the same diameter with these differentials. Having tires of different diameters will cause the clutch stacks to slip continuously, which, in turn, will cause early failure.

How Does Electronic Traction Control Work?

Many recent vehicles use **electronic traction control (ETC)** to prevent single-wheel spin. ETC uses the wheel speed sensors, control module, and hydraulic modulator of the antilock brake system (ABS) to sense wheel spin and, if spin occurs, to apply the brake on that wheel. This will transfer torque to the other drive wheel.

SUMMARY

1. A drive axle combines the hypoid final drive gears with the differential and two axle shafts.
2. Hypoid ring and pinion gears must be adjusted correctly for long life and quiet operation.
3. The pinion gear and shaft are supported by two pinion bearings, and the ring gear and differential case are supported by two carrier bearings.
4. Differentials allow two wheels to be driven at different speeds.
5. Limited slip differentials increase torque bias to send more torque to the tire with good traction.
6. Several bearing types are used at the axle wheel ends. Axle shafts can be retained by the axle retainer, a C-lock in the differential, or a full-floating axle is bolted to the hub.

REVIEW QUESTIONS

1. Why is a hypoid gear set used in drive axle assemblies?
2. What is the difference between a hunting and non-hunting gear set?
3. What is the difference between an integral and removal carrier?
4. What are the six types of limited slip differentials?
5. Why is a friction modifier additive required for use in some rear drive axles?

CHAPTER QUIZ

1. In a rear axle, the drive pinion gear works with _____.
   a. A ring gear to change the direction of the power flow
   b. Side gears to provide differential action
   c. A ring gear to provide a gear reduction
   d. All of the above
2. Hypoid ring and pinion gears are used in passenger vehicle drive axles. Technician A says that the concave side of the ring gear tooth is called the drive side. Technician B says that the heel is the smaller, inner end of the ring gear tooth. Which technician is correct?
   a. Technician A only
   b. Technician B only
   c. Both technicians A and B
   d. Neither technician A nor B
3. An overhung pinion uses _____.
   a. One pinion bearing
   b. Two tapered roller pinion bearings
   c. Three roller pinion bearings
   d. Four ball-type pinion bearings

4. Which of the following is not true about a hypoid gear set?
   a. The pinion gear is mounted below the ring gear centerline.
   b. A special type of gear oil is required.
   c. This is an efficient gear set with very little friction.
   d. Special procedures are required to adjust it.

5. Which axle design is used for heavy duty vehicles?
   a. Full floating
   b. C-lock axle
   c. Retainer plate axle
   d. Semi-floating

6. A ring and pinion with a 3.76:1 ratio is classified as _____.
   a. Hunting
   b. Non-hunting
   c. Partial non-hunting
   d. None of the above

7. What is the dimension that is used to identify a 9-inch axle?
   a. The distance between side bearings
   b. The diameter of the inspection cover
   c. The diameter of the ring gear
   d. The diameter of the axle tubes

8. The differential case _____.
   a. Provides a mounting point for the ring gear
   b. Encloses the differential gears
   c. Is supported by the carrier bearings
   d. All of these

9. A removable carrier is also called a _____.
   a. A third member
   b. A drop out
   c. Pumpkin
   d. Any of the above

10. Most limited slip differentials transfer torque through _____.
    a. The differential gears
    b. One or two clutch stacks
    c. Both a and b
    d. Neither a nor b

chapter 11

DRIVE AXLE AND DIFFERENTIAL DIAGNOSIS AND SERVICE

After studying this chapter, the reader should be able to:

1. Perform the maintenance needed to keep a drive axle operating properly.
2. Describe the steps involved in drive axle service.
3. Discuss drive axle lubrication.
4. Discuss drive axle diagnosis.
5. Discuss the procedures for in-the-shop inspections.
6. Explain the on-vehicle service operations.
7. Explain the procedure for differential carrier service and differential assembly service.
8. Explain pinion depth shim selection and drive pinion bearing preload adjustment.
9. Explain the steps to adjust backlash and carrier bearing preload.

This chapter will help you prepare for ASE Manual Drive Train and Axles (A3) certification test content area "E" (Rear Axle Diagnosis and Repair).

Backlash 179
Backlash variation 188
Bearing spacer 191
Carrier bearing
  preload 194
Contact pattern 193
Crush sleeve 191
Differential case
  clearance 189

Gear marking
  compound 193
Pinion bearing
  preload 185
Ring gear runout 187
Service spacer 197

GM Service Technical College topics covered in this chapter are:

1. Rear axle identification. (14041.18W2)
2. Diagnose a semi and full-floating, rear drive axle with the symptom based, the operational test, and the visual inspection.
3. Diagnose a rear drive axle and the rear drive axle differential.
4. Service and repair a rear drive axle using GM specified service procedures.

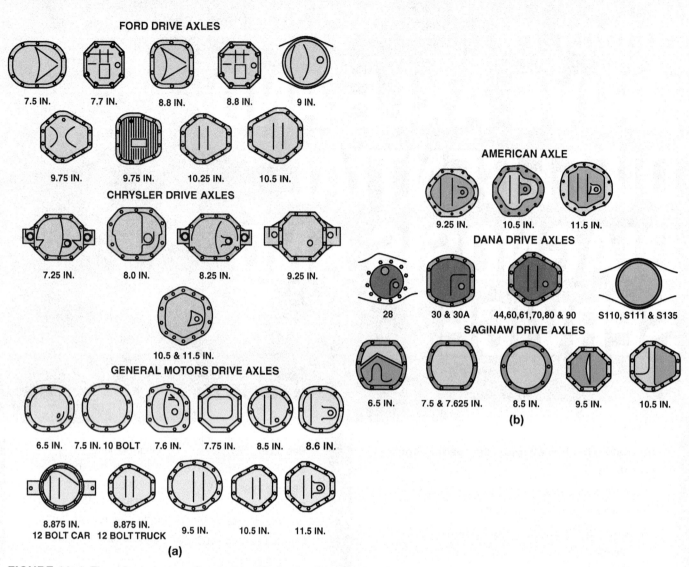

FORD DRIVE AXLES

7.5 IN.   7.7 IN.   8.8 IN.   8.8 IN.   9 IN.

9.75 IN.   9.75 IN.   10.25 IN.   10.5 IN.

CHRYSLER DRIVE AXLES

7.25 IN.   8.0 IN.   8.25 IN.   9.25 IN.

10.5 & 11.5 IN.

GENERAL MOTORS DRIVE AXLES

6.5 IN.   7.5 IN. 10 BOLT   7.6 IN.   7.75 IN.   8.5 IN.   8.6 IN.

8.875 IN. 12 BOLT CAR   8.875 IN. 12 BOLT TRUCK   9.5 IN.   10.5 IN.   11.5 IN.

(a)

AMERICAN AXLE

9.25 IN.   10.5 IN.   11.5 IN.

DANA DRIVE AXLES

28   30 & 30A   44,60,61,70,80 & 90   S110, S111 & S135

SAGINAW DRIVE AXLES

6.5 IN.   7.5 & 7.625 IN.   8.5 IN.   9.5 IN.   10.5 IN.

(b)

FIGURE 11–1 The drive axle can often be identified using the shape and counting the bolts on the inspection cover. This is most helpful if trying to locate a heavy duty drive axle at a wrecking (recycling) yard. (a) Drive axles sorted by the Detroit three vehicle manufacturers. (b) Axles sorted by axle manufacturers such as American Axle and Manufacturing (AAM), who supply axles to many vehicle manufacturers.

DRIVE AXLE SERVICE

STEPS INVOLVED When diagnosing drive axle concerns, perform the following steps:

STEP 1 The first step is to verify the customer complaint. This step usually includes test-driving the vehicle to see if the complaint can be duplicated. If the problem cannot be duplicated, then the repair or service cannot be verified.

STEP 2 Identify the vehicle and the drive axle including the gear ratio so that the proper procedures and specifications will be used. The proper identification can include the following:

- Visual identification (number of bolts used on the cover and the cover design). ● **SEE FIGURE 11–1**.

- *Regular production option* (RPO) code identification or *service parts identification*. This is found on a sticker located in the trunk or glove box in many vehicles. ● **SEE FIGURE 11–2**.

- On GM Global Connect, research "Investigate Vehicle History" > "Vehicle Build".

STEP 3 Check vehicle history and technical service bulletins (TSBs) for the vehicle or axle being serviced.

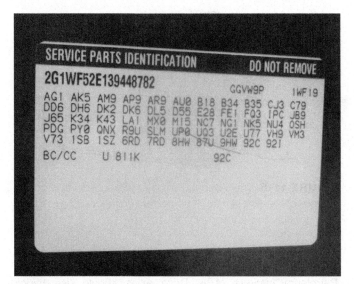

FIGURE 11–2 The service parts identification sticker includes the codes for major components parts and includes the drive axle ratio and other information needed by the parts department to get the correct parts.

STEP 4 Safely hoist the vehicle and remove the wheels. Visually check for the following:
- Proper gear lubricant level
- Leaks
- Obvious problems such a broken or damaged suspension parts that could affect the operation of the drive axle
- The driveshaft and U-joints for damage or excessive wear

STEP 5 Disassembly and inspect all internal components.

STEP 6 Test for proper backlash and correct operation of the limited slip unit, if equipped.

STEP 7 Replace all components that do not meet factory specifications.

STEP 8 Test-drive the vehicle to verify that the repairs did correct the customer concern.

DETERMINING THE AXLE RATIO Sometimes the axle ratio has to be determined, especially if using a wrecking (recycling) yard unit. The axle ratio can often be identified from the tag attached to the axle housing or by the coding on some axles, but not all. The axle ratio can be determined by two other methods.

- **Gear Tooth Count:** The most accurate method of determining gear ratios, if the ring and pinion gears are exposed, is to read the tooth number markings on the ring gear or count the number of teeth on the two gears. Now divide the tooth count of the ring gear by that of the pinion gear, and the result is the ratio.

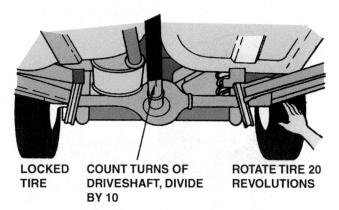

LOCKED TIRE   **COUNT TURNS OF DRIVESHAFT, DIVIDE BY 10**   **ROTATE TIRE 20 REVOLUTIONS**

FIGURE 11–3 The quickest way to check the drive axle ratio is to rotate one wheel with the other wheel locked and count the number of times the driveshaft rotates. If the driveshaft rotates 37 1/3 turns while the free tire rotates 20 turns, the ratio is 3.73:1.

- **Counting Revolutions:** The axle ratio can be determined by counting the number of revolutions of the driveshaft that are required to turn the wheels one revolution. The best way of doing this is to lock one of the tires using the parking brake or a block. Now, turn the driveshaft until the free tire turns 20 revolutions, and divide the driveshaft revolutions by 10. For example, if there are 23 1/3 turns of the driveshaft to 20 turns of the free tire, the gear ratio is 2.33:1. With one wheel locked, the differential will cause the other wheel to turn twice as fast. ● **SEE FIGURE 11–3.**

DRIVE AXLE LUBRICATION

GEAR OIL MOVEMENT A drive axle is normally filled with gear oil to a point just below the filler hole. The action of the ring gear running in the bath of oil distributes the lubricant through the housing. Many carriers provide a trough to ensure adequate oiling of the front pinion shaft bearing. The gear oil is kept in the housing by one or more grease seals in each end of the axle housing and at the drive pinion shaft. ● **SEE FIGURE 11–4.**

VISCOSITY OF GEAR OIL The term "viscosity" means the "resistance to flow" and assigned a number by SAE (Society of Automotive Engineers). The higher the number, the less viscous the oil and is therefore thicker. The first number followed by the letter W is the viscosity rating when the oil is cold. The letter "W" stands for *winter*.

- The second number indicates the viscosity when tested at 212°F (100°C).

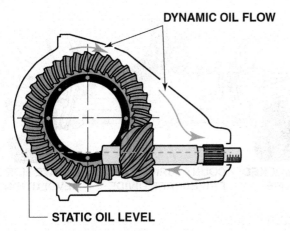

DYNAMIC OIL FLOW

STATIC OIL LEVEL

FIGURE 11–4 In most axles the gear oil level is at the bottom of the filler opening. When the axle operates, the ring gear will produce a dynamic oil flow to lubricate all the parts.

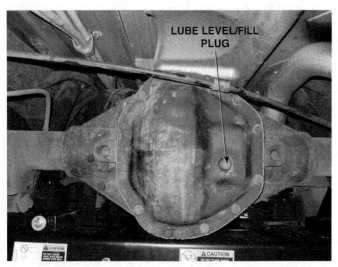

LUBE LEVEL/FILL PLUG

FIGURE 11–5 The fill/level plug may be located on the inspection cover but is more often located on the side of the differential housing.

The gear oil used in drive axles can include the following viscosities:

- SAE 75W-90
- SAE 80W-90
- SAE 85W-90
- SAE 85W-140
- SAE 90

NOTE: Some vehicle manufacturers specify the use of synthetic gear oil of the specified viscosity. Always check service information for the exact gear lubricant to use.

API GEAR OIL GRADE Because all differentials use hypoid gear sets, a special lubricant is necessary because the gears both roll and slide between their meshed teeth. Gear oils

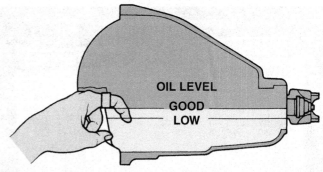

OIL LEVEL
GOOD
LOW

FIGURE 11–6 The lubricant (oil) level is usually even with the bottom of the fill opening. If necessary, a finger can be used as a dipstick to determine the level.

labeled *gear lubricant* (GL) are specified by the American Petroleum Institute (API). Drive axles should use hypoid quality GL-5 (meets military Mil-L2150B requirements) gear lubricant of the specified viscosity. If the axle has a limited slip differential, the gear lubricant must meet the requirements for that differential type. A label is normally located near the filler opening on those axles to indicate the fluid required.

CHECKING DRIVE AXLE GEAR OIL LEVEL To check the gear oil level, perform the following steps.

STEP 1 Raise and securely support the vehicle on a hoist or safety stands to gain access to the axle. The vehicle should be raised so that the drive axle is in its normal position relative to level.

STEP 2 Locate the gear oil level plug, which can be in the side of the case or on the cover. Clean the area around it, and remove the plug. Be prepared for fluid to run out of the opening. ● **SEE FIGURE 11–5**.

STEP 3 In most axles the gear oil level should be even with the bottom of the opening. If the gear oil level cannot be seen, carefully insert a finger into the opening and bend it downward, using it as a level indicator. ● **SEE FIGURE 11–6**.

- The fluid level on some axles should be a specified distance below the opening and requires a special dipstick, which can be shop-made. A high fluid level can flood the axle seals and can cause gear oil to leak into the brake drums or rotors. If the fluid level is too low, gear and bearing wear and overheating will occur.
- Gear oil normally has a mildly unpleasant rotten egg smell because of the additive's sulfur compounds. Its color should be the same as that of new oil. Metal particles in the oil indicate internal problems.

WHEN NOISE OCCURS	POSSIBLE CAUSE
Under all driving conditions	Road and tires; wheel bearings; incorrect driveline angles
Changes with road surface	Tires
Noise becomes louder during cornering	Differential gears; axle bearings
Howling sound	Ring and pinion gears (incorrect adjustment, worn, or runout issues)
Growling sound	Bearing(s)
Whine noise concern	Check ring gear pattern for incorrect backlash or pinion depth
Clunk on speed change or going from forward to reverse or reverse to forward	Worn U-Joints, differential or driveshaft splines
Continuous low pitched whir	Worn U-joints
Low pitch rumble over 20 MPH (32 km/h)	Worn carrier bearings
Chatter during cornering	Incorrect gear oil or worn limited slip clutches

CHART 11–1

A summary chart showing the probable causes of various drive axle-related noise concerns.

DRIVE AXLE DIAGNOSIS

ROAD TEST Most drive axle problems are related to noise, vibration, leaks, and failure to transmit power.

The road test should include the following driving conditions:

- **Drive:** Light-to-moderate throttle acceleration
- **Cruise:** Enough throttle to maintain a constant speed
- **Float:** Just enough throttle to keep engine load off the drivetrain as the vehicle slows
- **Coast:** Closed throttle deceleration
- **Coast while in neutral:** Isolates transmission noises

NOISE DIAGNOSIS Drive axle noise problems normally fall into one of these categories:

- **Gear noise:** Howling or whining and is often torque sensitive but can be continuous.
- **Bearing noise:** Can be a high-pitched, whistlelike sound but is usually a rough growl or rumble. Bearings will often make a "wow-wow" type of sound at the speed frequency of the spinning shaft.

 **TECH TIP**

Noises Can Travel

While diagnosing noise problems, remember that they can come from the exhaust system (both normal air-transmitted noises and noises from metal-to-metal contact between the exhaust system and the vehicle body or frame), tires, and wind. Drivetrain noises can usually be heard while the vehicle is operated and being supported on a hoist or safety stands. Vehicle loads can be simulated by applying the brake for short periods of time.

- **Clunk:** Heavy metallic slapping noise during reversal of power flow or engagement of power from neutral. This fault is caused by excessive slack or excessive clearances in the drivetrain and can be felt in the drive axle.
- **Chuckle:** A rattling noise, similar to a playing card against spinning bicycle spokes, during deceleration below 40 MPH (64 km/h). This fault is often caused by excessive clearance in the differential.
- **Chatter on corners:** A vibration or noise as the vehicle turns a corner, especially after prolonged straight driving. This noise is often called *chatter,* commonly caused by a stick/slip condition at the clutch plates of a limited slip differential. After changing the lubricant in a limited slip differential to cure a chatter problem, drive the vehicle through 10 to 12 figure-8 turns. This procedure will force the new lubricant between the clutch plates.

● **SEE CHART 11–1** for summary of noise-related faults and their possible causes.

IN-THE-SHOP INSPECTIONS

DRIVE AXLE BACKLASH A drivetrain clunk during a power change can be caused by too much internal **backlash.** To quickly determine if the drive axle is the cause of the noise due to backlash, perform the following steps:

STEP 1 Raise and securely support the vehicle on a hoist or jack stands and the wheels are free to turn.

STEP 2 Lock the driveshaft and drive pinion companion flange by clamping a bar to the companion flange and the body or rear suspension. ● **SEE FIGURE 11–7.**

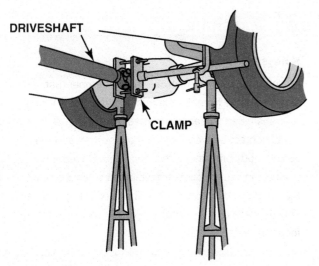

DRIVESHAFT

CLAMP

FIGURE 11–7 A drive axle can be checked for excessive play in the differential by blocking one drive wheel and the driveshaft.

LOCK LEFT REAR WHEEL

FIGURE 11–8 One way to lock one wheel is to lower the vehicle so one tire is resting on a barrel or something similar that will keep the wheel from moving.

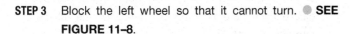

STEP 3 Block the left wheel so that it cannot turn. ● **SEE FIGURE 11–8.**

STEP 4 Turn the right wheel slowly in one direction until it stops, loading the entire lash (clearance) to one side. Using chalk or marking crayon, place a mark on the side of the tire 12 inches (30 cm) from the center of the wheel.

STEP 5 Hold the chalk steady and rotate the tire in the opposite direction until it stops.

STEP 6 Measure the length of the chalk mark; this is the amount of drive axle backlash. More than 1 inch (25 mm) of lash is excessive and indicates that something in the axle is worn. ● **SEE FIGURE 11–9.**

AXLE SHAFT ENDPLAY To check axle shaft endplay, grip each wheel and attempt to move it in and out. If axle shaft endplay seems excessive, place index marks on the tire and the brake drum and remove them. Mount a dial indicator on the brake backing plate and position the stylus on the axle flange. Move the axle shaft in and out while looking at the

CHALK MARK

12"

FIGURE 11–9 The mark should be 1 in. or shorter. If the mark is less than 1 in. and there is a clunk in the driveline, the problem is NOT in the drive axle assembly.

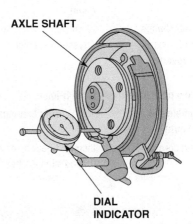

AXLE SHAFT

DIAL INDICATOR

FIGURE 11–10 Axle shaft endplay can be checked by mounting a dial indicator on the brake assembly or axle housing with the indicator stylus on the axle. The indicator will measure the endplay as the axle is moved in and out.

endplay on the dial indicator. Check the results with the vehicle manufacturer specifications. Excessive endplay can mean a worn axle groove for the C-lock or a worn axle bearing. ● **SEE FIGURE 11–10.**

AXLE FLANGE RUNOUT To check wheel mounting flange runout, perform the following steps:

STEP 1 Raise and securely support the vehicle on a hoist or safety stands and remove the tire/wheel assembly and drum/disc.

STEP 2 Install a dial indicator and while pushing the axle inward to remove any end-play, measure lateral (side-to-side) and radial (out-of-round) ends of the axle flange. Lateral runout of 0.005 inch (0.1 mm) or less is acceptable.

- Radial runout of 0.030 inch (0.76 mm) or less is acceptable.
- If the runout is more than the specifications, the axle should be replaced. ● **SEE FIGURE 11–11.**

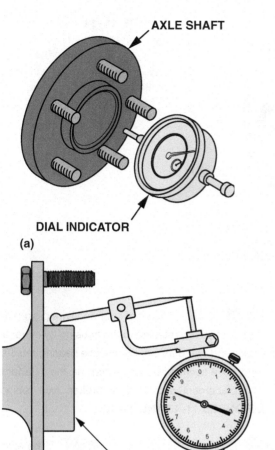

(a)

AXLE SHAFT

DIAL INDICATOR

(b)

AXLE HUB

FIGURE 11–11 (a) This dial indicator is set up to measure axle flange lateral runout, which can cause the wheel to wobble. (b) This dial indicator is set up to measure radial runout of the drum and wheel pilot, which can cause the wheel to run off-center.

LEAK DETECTION   Most gear oil leaks will be found at the following locations:

- Axle shaft seals
- Drive pinion seals
- Rear cover
- Carrier-to-housing gasket (on removable carrier type)

Occasionally, a leak is found in a porous casting or a faulty weld in the housing. A porous casting can be repaired using epoxy. A leaky weld, however, is a sign of a potentially dangerous stress crack or fracture, and the housing should be replaced. ● **SEE FIGURE 11–12.**

LIMITED SLIP DIFFERENTIAL CHECK   To confirm that a limited slip differential is able to drive both drive wheels

FIGURE 11–12 Many leaks are caused by defective gaskets but some axle oil leaks can be caused by a porous casting or cracked welds. A casting problem can be repaired using epoxy sealant, whereas a cracked weld requires housing replacement.

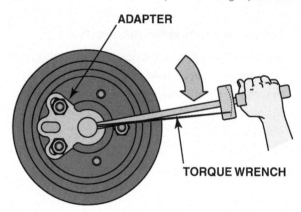

ADAPTER

TORQUE WRENCH

FIGURE 11–13 A special tool has been attached to two wheel studs, allowing a torque wrench to be used to measure the torque required to turn this wheel. The opposite wheel is on the ground with the transmission in neutral. A low reading indicates limited slip differential wear.

requires a special adapter and a torque wrench. ● **SEE FIGURE 11–13.**

To do so, perform the following steps:

STEP 1   Attach an adapter to one of the rear hubs. Some adapters require removal of the wheel and tire.

STEP 2   Raise the wheel with the adapter off the floor and leave the other wheel on the floor and place the transmission in neutral.

STEP 3   Attach a torque wrench to the adapter and read the amount of torque required as the wheel is rotated. Compare the reading to factory specifications. If no torque specifications are available, some technicians will use a rule-of-thumb of 35 to 40 lb-ft (48 to 54 N-m) minimum. Readings lower than this indicate a badly worn clutch pack in the differential.

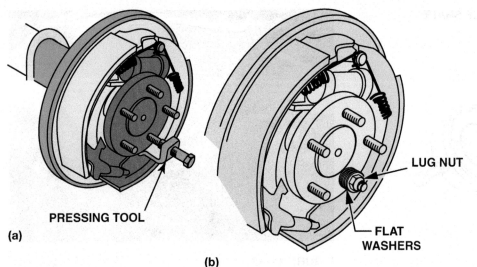

FIGURE 11–14 (a) A tight stud should be removed using a pressing tool so as not to bend the axle flange. (b) A new wheel stud is installed by tightening the lug nut against a stack of flat washers.

LUG NUT

PRESSING TOOL

FLAT WASHERS

(a)

(b)

TECH TIP

Look for the Hole in the Retainer Plate

Most axle flanges include a hole so that a socket and extension bar can be used to remove and replace the retainer bolts. If the axle does not have a hole in the retainer plate, then the axle uses a C-lock-type retaining method.

ON-VEHICLE SERVICE OPERATIONS

ITEMS THAT CAN BE SERVICED   On-vehicle operations include the following:

- Wheel stud replacement
- Axle seal replacement
- Axle shaft
- Axle bearing
- Drive pinion seal replacement

WHEEL STUD REPLACEMENT   Wheel studs are held in the axle flange by an interference fit between a serrated portion of the stud and the hole in the flange. Wheel studs should be carefully inspected and replaced if the threads are stripped or damaged. Damaged wheel studs can be replaced without removing the axle. ● **SEE FIGURE 11–14**.

AXLE REMOVAL   Passenger car and light pickup axles are semi-floating and are retained in the housing by either a C-lock at the inner end of the axle or by the axle bearing retainer at the outer end. Axle service includes removing the axle for bearing or seal replacement and bent or broken axle replacement. ● **SEE FIGURES 11–15 AND 11–16**.

C-LOCK AXLE SEAL REPLACEMENT   The axle seal is located next to the bearing and seals against a smooth area of the axle shaft.

Both the bearing and the seal are removed from the housing using a slide hammer and special adapter. ● **SEE FIGURE 11–17**.

Pull the seal first and then, if needed, remove the bearing. After they are removed, the recesses where they fit should be checked for scratches or gouges that might let gear oil past the seal. Another special tool is required to install the bearing. It should be slightly smaller than the diameter of the bearing and have a face that meets the face of the bearing to prevent damaging the bearing during installation. The new bearing is driven straight into the housing to the end of its recess. The same installation procedure and tool is used to install the new seal.

RETAINER AXLE BEARING AND SEAL REMOVAL AND REPLACEMENT   The retainer bearing-type axle bearing is press fit on the axle and requires a hydraulic press and special adapters to remove and install. Extreme caution should be observed when performing this procedure to avoid serious injuries from possible bearing explosion during the pressing procedure. Most axle bearing removal tools enclose the bearing completely to contain the bearing if it explodes.

CAUTION: When pressing a bearing off an axle, place a brake drum over the bearing as a shatter shield.

C-Lock Retained Axle

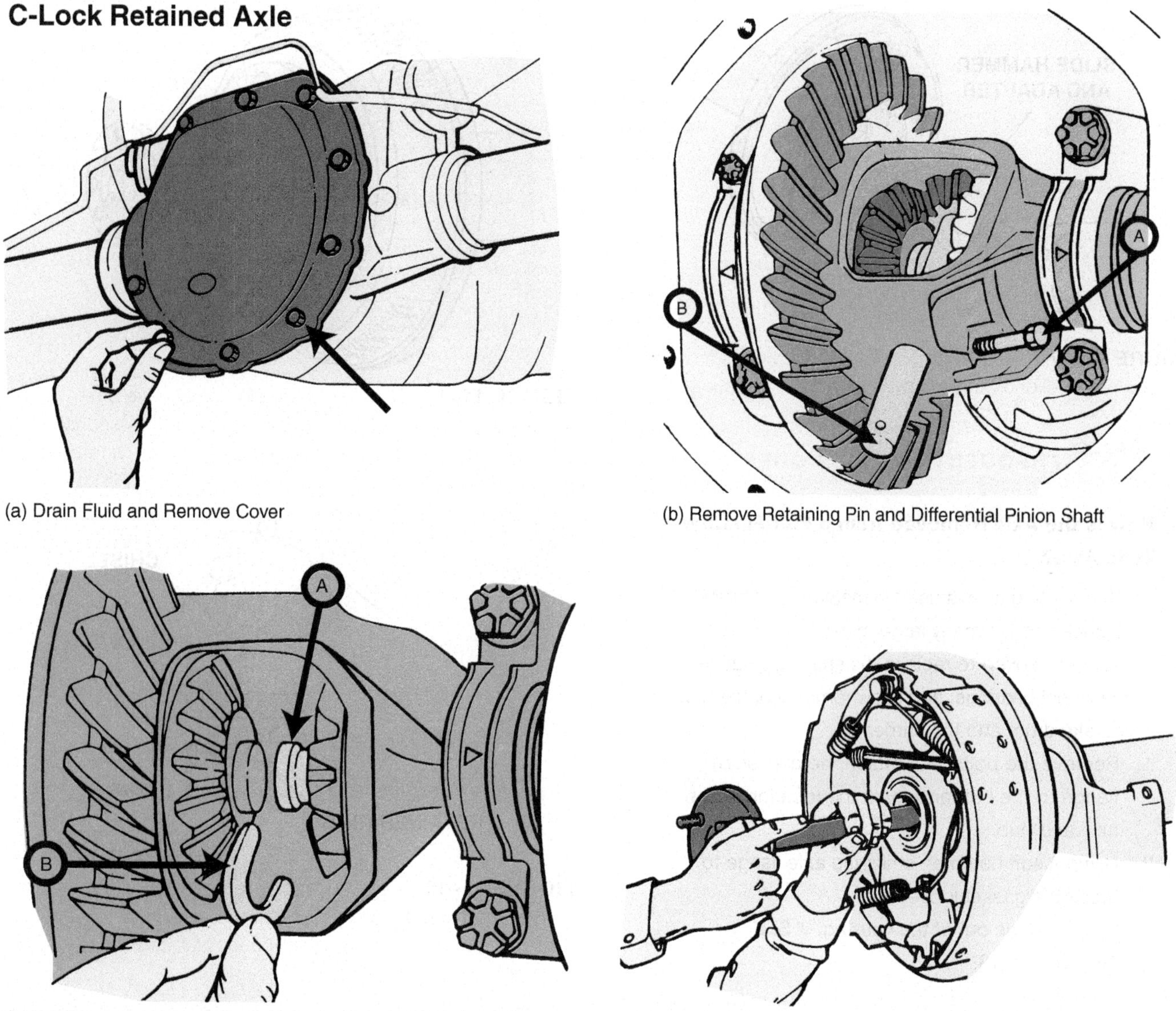

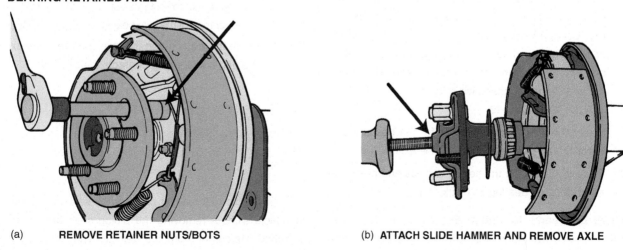

(a) Drain Fluid and Remove Cover

(b) Remove Retaining Pin and Differential Pinion Shaft

(c) Remove C-Lock

(d) Remove Axle

FIGURE 11–15 The differential pinion shaft must be removed to allow the C-lock and axle to be removed.

BEARING RETAINED AXLE

(a) **REMOVE RETAINER NUTS/BOTS**

(b) **ATTACH SLIDE HAMMER AND REMOVE AXLE**

FIGURE 11–16 The retainer nuts/bolts are removed before sliding the bearing-retained axle from the housing.

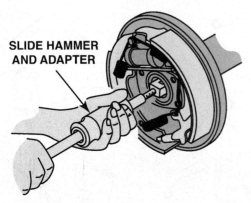

SLIDE HAMMER AND ADAPTER

FIGURE 11-17 The bearing and seal are removed from the housing with a slide hammer and adapter.

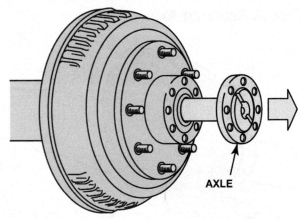

AXLE

FIGURE 11-18 After the axle flange bolts have been removed, a full-floating axle can be slid out of the housing. This permits access to the axle, wheel bearings, and brakes.

 FREQUENTLY ASKED QUESTION

How Is the Axle Removed from a Full-Floating-Type Axle?

The full-floating axle is used in medium and heavy-duty trucks and in many larger pickups and vans. Axles are removed to replace the shaft, gain access to the wheel bearings, and allow removal of the hub and brake drum and the carrier.

1. Remove the bolts that attach the axle shaft flange to the hub and mark the location of the axle and hub.
2. Using a soft hammer, strike the axle flange to break the gasket loose.
3. Slide the axle out of the housing. ● **SEE FIGURE 11-18.**

To remove and replace a bearing pressed on an axle shaft, perform the following steps:

STEP 1 Position the axle so that the lock ring rests on the edge of the anvil portion of a vise or a sturdy bench-top. Using a hammer and cold chisel, make a series of six or eight cuts into the ring. Strike each location once or twice using fairly strong blows to expand the ring slightly so that it will relax its grip on the axle. ● **SEE FIGURE 11-19.**

STEP 2 Select the correct size adapter for the bearing, and install the adapter and fixture on the axle.

STEP 3 Place the fixture in the bed of a press and press the axle out of the bearing and lock ring.

CAUTION: Be ready to catch the axle as it moves through the bearing as it will fall freely after moving about an inch (25 mm).

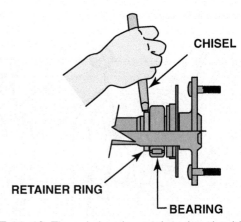

CHISEL

RETAINER RING

BEARING

FIGURE 11-19 The axle bearing retainer ring should be cut or stretched using a drill and a chisel to make six to eight blows before trying to press the bearing off the axle.

To press a bearing onto an axle, perform the following steps:

STEP 1 Clean the bearing retainer and the end of the axle, and place the bearing retainer onto the axle.

STEP 2 Place the bearing on the axle and press the axle into the bearing to the correct position. Be sure to press only on the inner race of the axle bearing. ● **SEE FIGURE 11-20.**

STEP 3 Place the lock ring on the axle and press the axle into the ring until the ring contacts the bearing.

PINION SHAFT SEAL REPLACEMENT

PROCEDURE A leaking pinion shaft seal can be replaced in-vehicle without removing the pinion shaft from the carrier or drive axle/carrier from the vehicle. The driveshaft flange is removed and then the seal is removed and replaced.

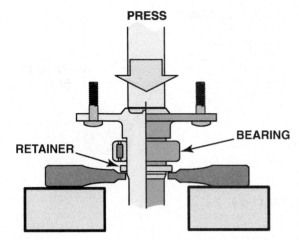

FIGURE 11-20 The axle is being pressed into the bearing and retainer plate.

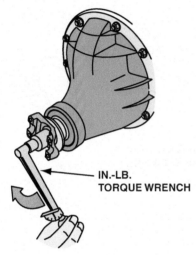

FIGURE 11-21 A leaky drive pinion seal is repaired by first measuring the axle preload. After removing the wheels and eliminating any brake drag, use an inch-pound torque wrench to measure the pinion bearing preload. It should be between 17 and 22 inch-pounds or slightly lower in most applications.

An important requirement while performing this operation is to not disturb the drive **pinion bearing preload** adjustment.

NOTE: Measuring the drive axle preload in step 2 provides the information for tightening the pinion nut in step 7.

To remove and replace a drive pinion seal, perform the following steps:

STEP 1 Disconnect the driveshaft from the companion flange, and support the driveshaft so it does not hang from the front U-joint. Remove the wheels and brake drums or brake pads to eliminate any brake drag.

STEP 2 Measure the torque required to rotate the pinion shaft (pinion and carrier bearing preload) using an inch-pound torque wrench, and record this measurement. ● **SEE FIGURE 11-21.**

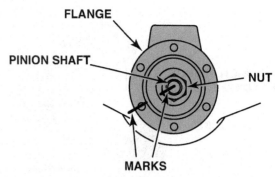

FIGURE 11-22 Mark the pinion flange, pinion nut, and the pinion shaft before removing the pinion nut.

STEP 3 Place index marks on the end of the pinion shaft, pinion nut, and the companion flange so that the flange can be installed back on the same spline. ● **SEE FIGURE 11-22.**

STEP 4 Remove the drive pinion nut, washer, and companion flange. ● **SEE FIGURE 11-23.**

STEP 5 Remove the pinion seal. ● **SEE FIGURE 11-24.**

STEP 6 Check the bearing pocket for damage. Then, apply a thin film of gear oil to the lip of the seal and the sealing surface of the flange. ● **SEE FIGURE 11-25.**

STEP 7 Reinstall the companion flange (align the marks) and install the pinion nut with a washer and tighten the nut until the parts align as per the marks that were made in step 3. While holding the flange, tighten the nut 1/16 inch beyond the alignment marks. Check that the bearing preload is slightly greater (3–5 lb-in) than that recorded in step 2. The pinion nut should be very tight.

STEP 8 Replace the driveshaft.

NOTE: The pinion seal can only be replaced one time before the crush sleeve must be replaced.

DIFFERENTIAL CARRIER SERVICE

TYPICAL STEPS INVOLVED Differential carrier service usually includes the following steps:

- An inspection of the gears and bearings before teardown
- A check for ring gear runout
- Removal and replacement of the differential and ring gear
- Removal and replacement of the pinion gear

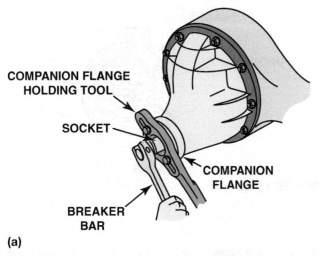

(a)

COMPANION FLANGE HOLDING TOOL

SOCKET

COMPANION FLANGE

BREAKER BAR

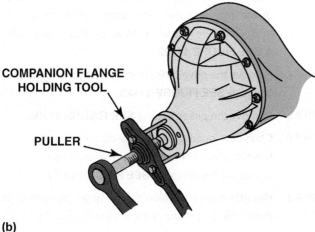

COMPANION FLANGE HOLDING TOOL

PULLER

(b)

FIGURE 11–23 (a) A companion flange holding tool is used to keep the companion flange from rotating as the pinion nut is loosened. (b) After the pinion nut has been removed, a puller is used to remove the companion flange.

CHISEL

PINION OIL SEAL

FIGURE 11–24 Use a chisel to separate the seal from the axle housing, then use a seal remover to pry the seal off.

- Inspection and repair of the differential
- Assembly adjustments for pinion depth, pinion bearing preload, backlash, and carrier bearing preload.

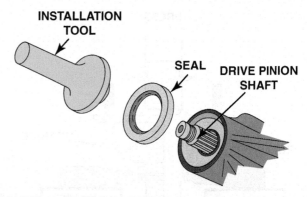

INSTALLATION TOOL

SEAL   DRIVE PINION SHAFT

FIGURE 11–25 Use a seal driver (installation tool) to seat the new seal in the axle housing.

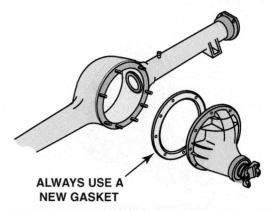

ALWAYS USE A NEW GASKET

FIGURE 11–26 The carrier (third member) is removed from the drive axle housing by removing the retaining nuts, and then the heavy assembly is carefully removed.

REMOVABLE CARRIER REMOVAL   On removable carrier axles, the carrier is removed from the axle housing to service or repair the differential, ring and pinion gears, or any of the bearings.

To remove a carrier, perform the following steps:

STEP 1   Raise and securely support the vehicle on a hoist or safety stands.

STEP 2   Remove the axles and the driveshaft.

STEP 3   Place a drain pan under the axle assembly, and remove the nuts or bolts that are securing the carrier to the housing. Also remove the copper washers used to seal the studs. ● **SEE FIGURE 11–26.**

INTEGRAL CARRIER REMOVAL   To remove an integral carrier, perform the following steps:

STEP 1   Raise and securely support the vehicle on a hoist or safety stands and remove both axles.

STEP 2   Using a punch and hammer or permanent marker, place index marks on each of the bearing caps. ● **SEE FIGURE 11–27.**

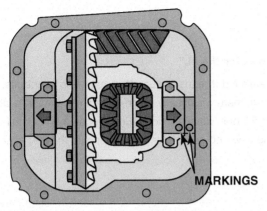

FIGURE 11–27 The bearing caps have to be stamped or marked to make sure that they are installed back in the exact same location. Not only left and right but they also need to be installed with the correct side up, the same as they were installed originally.

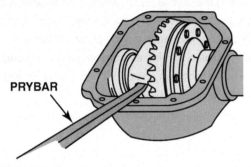

FIGURE 11–28 Use a prybar to gently pry the carrier from the housing.

STEP 3A On units with threaded adjusters, remove the adjustment locks, the carrier bearing cap mounting bolts, and the bearing caps. On threaded adjusters, remove the adjuster and lift the differential with bearing cups out of the carrier. Mark or tag the bearing cups. On shim-adjusted carriers, remove the bearing cap mounting bolts and the bearing caps.

STEP 3B On shim-adjusted carriers, remove the bearing cap mounting bolts and the bearing caps. Mark or tag the bearing cups. Some bearing caps are factory marked with an arrow only, so mark the caps right and left. The preload at the shims should be too tight to allow easy removal of the differential. Most differentials can be pried out of the carrier, but be careful not to damage the gasket surface on the carrier. ● **SEE FIGURE 11–28.**

NOTE: Some differentials can be removed by placing a box wrench on one of the ring gear bolts and turning the pinion gear so that the wrench pushes against the carrier and lifts up the differential.

 **TECH TIP**

Use the Retaining Bolts as Handles

The bores of the carrier bearing caps are normally machined after they are mounted on the carrier. This means that the cap will fit properly only in the original position. Index marks should be put on the cap before removal to ensure proper replacement. Lift the bearing cap bolts about halfway out of their holes and then use the bolts as handles to help remove the caps.

Some manufacturers recommend the use of a spreader tool to stretch the carrier. Stretching the carrier will take the pressure off the shims and bearings. When using a spreader tool, do not spread the carrier more than the manufacturer's limits, or 0.015 inch (0.4 mm).

STEP 4 As the carrier is removed from the housing, tag or mark the shims and bearing cup from each side.

STEP 5 The drive pinion gear is held in place by the companion flange, and the self-locking nut that secures it. It will require a lot of torque to loosen, often 150 to 300 lb-ft (203 to 407 N-m). Follow the steps mentioned for pinion seal replacement for removal.

INSPECTION AND CLEANING Inspection begins with a complete cleanup. After cleaning, visually inspect the ring gear and differential gears for obvious damage. The surface of the teeth should be smooth and have a polished sheen. Common ring gear wear appears as a rough, scored tooth surface or chipped or nicked teeth.

DIFFERENTIAL ASSEMBLY SERVICE

INSPECTION After cleaning, visually inspect the ring gear and differential gears for obvious damage. The surface of the teeth should be smooth and have a polished sheen. Common ring gear wear appears as a rough, scored tooth surface or chipped or nicked teeth.

RING GEAR RUNOUT **Ring gear runout** is checked if there is evidence of damage to the ring gear. Runout is usually caused by a faulty or bent differential case or an improper

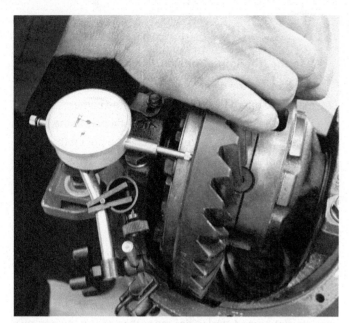

FIGURE 11–29 Ring gear runout should be less than 0.002 in. (0.05 mm) as measured by a dial indicator.

mounting of the ring gear onto the case. Because gear runout will cause backlash to change, it is sometimes referred to as **backlash variation**.

To check ring gear runout, perform the following steps:

- Mount a dial indicator with the stylus on the back of the ring gear at 90° to the gear surface The runout of a differential case can be checked using a similar procedure. ● **SEE FIGURE 11–29**.
- Rotate the ring gear and observe the indicator needle movement. This is the total indicated runout (TIR).

RING GEAR REPLACEMENT Ring gear replacement on most differentials is a matter of removing the bolts and then the gear. The bolts may be left-handed threads (marked with an "L"); check service information before removing.

NOTE: Due to the precise fit between the ring gear and the carrier, it is often difficult to remove the ring gear without binding. Take care when removing the ring gear to avoid damaging the carrier of the ring gear.

When installing the ring gear, heating the gear may be required to seat it properly onto the case. The ring gear mounting bolts must be tightened to the correct torque and in an alternating pattern, back and forth across the gear. Replacement ring gears have threaded holes and are furnished with new bolts.

NOTE: If the ring gear is to be reused, most service procedures require that NEW bolts be used for the reinstallation.

 **TECH TIP**

Look for the "L"

Left-hand threads are used on many ring gear bolts. If so, there will usually be an "L" stamped in the head of the bolt. Many manufacturers recommend installing new ring gear bolts when changing the ring gear.

 **TECH TIP**

Loosen Ring Gear Bolts First

An experienced technician will loosen the ring gear mounting bolts before removing the differential from the differential case. These bolts are normally very tight, and the differential is hard to hold when it is out of the carrier. While still in the carrier, the differential case can be held stationary by placing a block of wood between the ring and pinion gears or by placing a box wrench on one of the ring gear bolts and against the side of the carrier.

NOTE: Sometimes the ring gear is installed using rivets. These are normally removed by drilling through the rivet head, cutting the remainder of the head off with a chisel, and driving the rest of the rivet out using a punch.

PINION GEAR REMOVAL To remove a drive pinion from the housing, perform the following steps:

STEP 1 Place index marks on the end of the pinion shaft, pinion nut, and the companion flange so that the flange can be installed back on the same spline.

STEP 2 Attach a holding tool to the flange and use a socket and the longest handle available to loosen the nut.

CAUTION: Most vehicle manufactures warn to not use an impact wrench for removing or installing a pinion shaft nut. The hammering forces can easily cause the pinion shaft bearing rollers to dent the races. Use only hand tools to avoid shock loading the pinion bearings.

STEP 3 Slide the companion flange off the drive pinion shaft. If necessary, use a puller to remove the flange.

STEP 4 Use a soft hammer or brass punch to tap the pinion shaft into the carrier. Be ready to catch the pinion gear as it slides out.

PINION BEARINGS After disassembly, the parts should be cleaned in a solvent and inspected to ensure their usability.

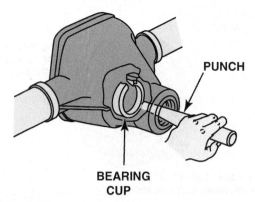

FIGURE 11–30 A damaged bearing cup can be driven out of the housing using a long punch.

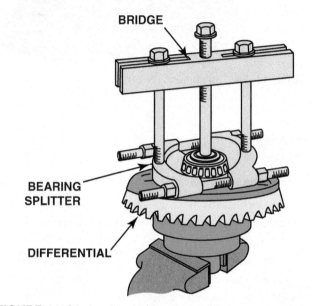

FIGURE 11–31 A puller and bearing splitter are set up to remove the differential side bearing.

If new pinion bearings are required, then the old bearing cups must also be replaced. Worn drive pinion bearing cups are normally removed from the carrier using a punch and hammer. ● **SEE FIGURE 11–30**.

New pinion bearing cups are installed by driving them into place using a bearing cup driver and hammer.

CAUTION: Never hammer directly on the new cup.

SIDE BEARINGS   Normally during disassembly, the carrier bearings are left on the differential case unless they or the shim located behind them need to be replaced. A puller is normally required to remove the side bearings. Some manufacturers recommend the use of a special puller while others use a sturdy two-jaw bearing puller and a step-plate adapter. ● **SEE FIGURE 11–31**.

The new bearing is installed using a special bearing installer. Many shops will use a section of an iron pipe of the correct diameter that fits the inner bearing race.

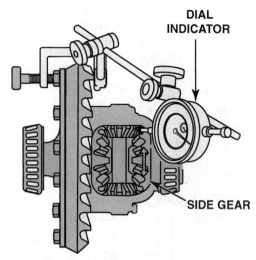

FIGURE 11–32 Differential case wear can be checked by measuring the side gear backlash using a dial indicator.

DIFFERENTIAL CASE CLEARANCE CHECKS   **Differential case clearance** is usually checked by using a dial indicator with the stylus on a side gear tooth. Hold the other side gear stationary as the first gear is moved back and forth against the lash. The amount of lash is shown by the dial indicator needle movement. One manufacturer gives a specification of 0 to 0.009 inch (0 to 23 mm). ● **SEE FIGURE 11–32**.

- Too much clearance can be reduced in some differentials by using thicker thrust washers behind the differential pinion and side gears.
- Other differentials do not use thrust washers, so the only way to reduce the clearance is to replace the worn differential parts.

NOTE: Excessive clearance in the differential gear set can cause a clunk as the lash is taken up when either the manual transmission clutch or automatic transmission is engaged. This is especially noticeable when changing direction, low to reverse, or reverse to low.

DISASSEMBLING THE DIFFERENTIAL CASE ASSEMBLY
To disassemble the differential case assembly, perform the following steps.

STEP 1   Remove the pinion shaft lock pin.

STEP 2   Slide the pinion shaft out of the case and check it for step wear.

STEP 3   Roll the pinion gears to the case window(s) and remove the pinion gears and thrust washers and the axle side gears and their thrust washers. ● **SEE FIGURE 11–33**.

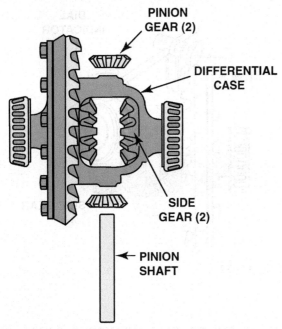

FIGURE 11–33 With the pinion shaft removed, the pinion gears can be rolled to the case windows and removed; then the side gears can be lifted out of the case.

STEP 4 Inspect the gears, thrust washers, and case surfaces for scoring and wear. Reverse this procedure to reassemble the differential.

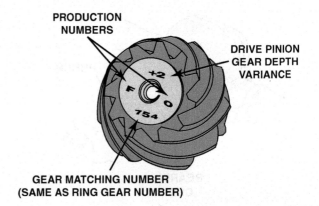

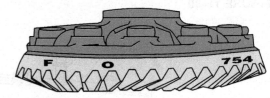

FIGURE 11–34 The ring and pinion gears are a matched set and are marked for correct pinion depth variance.

DRIVE PINION SHAFT

DRIVE PINION DEPTH The drive pinion gear and ring gear are manufactured as a matched set and must be installed as a set. Due to variances in the production of these gears, it is often necessary to vary the thickness of a shim needed to create the proper ring gear-to-drive pinion pattern:

- A plus (+) sign means the gear is too long and removing a shim(s) is required when assembling the drive pinion into the axle housing. A minus (–) sign means that the gear is too short and a shim(s) will be needed when assembling the drive pinion into the axle housing.

- Pinion depth can be checked using a gauging set and depth micrometer. This is a common method used to determine the correct shim thickness necessary to provide the proper gear pattern. ● **SEE FIGURE 11–34.**

All pinion gears use a depth shim to adjust for minor manufacturing tolerances of the gear and carrier. Pinion depth is affected by the machining of the gear and carrier, as well as by the rear bearing.

TECH TIP

Hone the Inner Race of a Pinion Bearing

Some technicians make up slip fit bearings so the shim can be easily changed. Slip fit bearings are made by honing the bearing inside diameter (ID) to enlarge it slightly. If using a slip fit bearing, be sure to check the bearing width and compensate for any width difference with the new bearing.

- The pinion depth shim is usually located between the rear bearing and the pinion gear head. If a carrier is assembled with the wrong pinion depth shim, it will need to be disassembled so that the shim can be changed.

Some adjustments require that while inserting a shim, press the bearing in place, and then check to see if the inserted shim is the correct size. If a change in the shim is needed, the pinion bearing will have to be pressed off. ● **SEE FIGURE 11–35.**

PINION DEPTH SHIM SELECTION There are four different methods used to determine the correct size for a pinion depth shim, including the following:

1. + or – markings on the pinion gear
2. Gauge block and fixtures
3. Contact patterns

At one time, many passenger vehicle drive pinion gears were marked with a + or – and a number that indicated the position of that gear relative to a perfect gear. The + or – indicated the direction, and the number (up to about 0.005 inch) indicated the distance. This number was etched or painted on the head or stem of the gear. When a ring and pinion gear set is replaced, the technician checks the markings on both the old and new pinion gears and changes the shim to compensate for any difference. ● **SEE CHART 11–2**.

Most vehicle manufacturers use a set of pinion depth gauge blocks to select the correct depth shim. These gauges are installed in the carrier, usually using the rear drive pinion bearing. Universal pinion depth measuring tools are available that can be used to determine the pinion depth. ● **SEE FIGURE 11–36**.

PINION BEARINGS The pinion shaft usually has two tapered roller bearings where the small diameter of each bearing faces each other. This arrangement allows the two bearings to absorb thrust load in both directions. When tapered roller bearings are used in a differential, it is very important that they have the proper preload. If a tapered roller bearing is too loose (too little preload), then the bearing cannot properly support and position the pinion shaft. If the preload is too great, excessive heat will quickly destroy the bearing as it expands with heat during normal operation of the rear axle assembly.

DRIVE PINION BEARING PRELOAD ADJUSTMENT After installation of the pinion depth shim, pinion seal, and rear bearing, the bearing spacer is placed on the pinion shaft and the pinion gear is installed in the carrier. The **bearing spacer** will be either a collapsible **crush sleeve** or a fixed-length solid spacer. ● **SEE FIGURE 11–37**.

This spacer keeps the two tapered roller bearings apart as the companion flange nut is tightened. The spacer allows the bearings to be squeezed against their races just tight enough to obtain the proper preload. The length of a fixed spacer is adjusted by adding or removing thin selective-size shims. A crush sleeve starts out too long and is collapsed to the

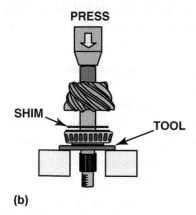

(a)

(b)

FIGURE 11–35 (a) A bearing splitter and a hydraulic press is needed to remove the pinion shaft bearing and get access to the shim. (b) The setup for pressing the bearing onto the pinion shaft with the shim in place.

OLD SHIM MARKING	NEW SHIM MARKING −4	NEW SHIM MARKING −3	NEW SHIM MARKING −2	NEW SHIM MARKING −1	NEW SHIM MARKING 0	NEW SHIM MARKING +1	NEW SHIM MARKING +2	NEW SHIM MARKING +3	NEW SHIM MARKING +4
+4	+0.008	+0.007	+0.006	+0.005	+0.004	+0.003	+0.002	+0.001	0.000
+3	+0.007	+0.006	+0.005	+0.004	+0.003	+0.002	+0.001	0.000	−0.001
+2	+0.006	+0.005	+0.004	+0.003	+0.002	+0.001	0.000	−0.001	−0.002
+1	+0.005	+0.004	+0.003	+0.002	+0.001	0.000	−0.001	−0.002	−0.003
0	+0.004	+0.003	+0.002	+0.001	0.000	−0.001	−0.002	−0.003	−0.004
−1	+0.003	+0.002	+0.001	0.000	−0.001	−0.002	−0.003	−0.004	−0.005
−2	+0.002	+0.001	0.000	−0.001	−0.002	−0.003	−0.004	−0.005	−0.006
−3	+0.001	0.000	−0.001	−0.002	−0.003	−0.004	−0.005	−0.006	−0.007
−4	0.000	−0.001	−0.002	−0.003	−0.004	−0.005	−0.006	−0.007	−0.008

CHART 11–2

A chart can be used to determine the size of the depth shim needed. These markings are no longer used by all manufacturers.

proper length as the drive pinion nut is tightened. Collapsing a crush sleeve takes a substantial amount of force.

To adjust drive pinion bearing preload using a collapsible spacer, perform the following steps:

STEP 1   Lubricate the bearings and slide the pinion gear with the rear bearing, depth shim, and new collapsible spacer into the carrier through the front bearing and seal.

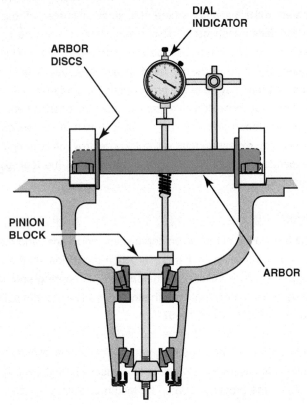

FIGURE 11–36 Special tool kit used for determining the correct pinion shaft shim thickness.

STEP 2   Lubricate the splines and seal area, and install the companion flange, being sure to align the index marks.

STEP 3   Oil the inner face of the new nut and special washer, and then install them on the pinion shaft.

STEP 4   Attach a holding tool to the flange and begin tightening the nut.

STEP 5   Continue tightening the nut with a foot-pound torque wrench as two things are checked:

   1. The minimum torque to obtain the preload and the amount of preload using an inch-pound torque wrench.

   2. Stop tightening when the preload is within specifications. ● **SEE FIGURE 11–38.**

To adjust drive pinion bearing preload using a solid spacer, perform the following steps:

STEP 1   Install the solid spacer onto the pinion shaft with a starting shim that should be thicker than needed.

STEP 2   Follow steps 1 through 4 of the procedure used with a collapsible spacer. Torque-tighten the nut to about 50 ft-lb (68 N-m) of torque.

STEP 3   If there is no free play, measure the bearing preload as described in step 5 of the collapsible spacer procedure. If the preload is within specifications, go to step 8. If the preload is too high, the starting shim will have to be replaced with a thicker one. If the preload is too low, a thinner shim is needed. If there is no preload, as expected, move on to step 4.

STEP 4   Mount a dial indicator on the carrier and position the indicator stylus on the end of and parallel to the pinion shaft. For example, if there is a starting shim size

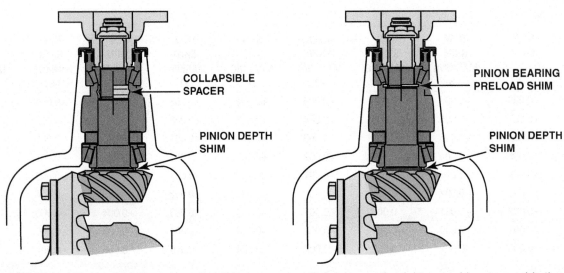

FIGURE 11–37 The pinion on the left uses a collapsible spacer, and the pinion on the right uses shims to provide the necessary preload to the pinion shaft bearings.

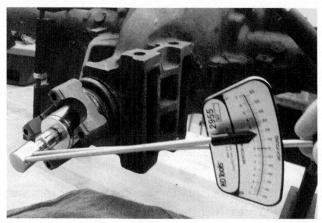

FIGURE 11–38 Using an inch-pound torque wrench to check the rotating torque of the drive pinion. This procedure is very important if the axle uses a collapsible spacer. The drive pinion nut should be gradually tightened and the rotating torque checked to prevent over tightening the nut. If the rotating torque is higher than specifications, the collapsible spacer will require replacement and the installation procedure must be repeated.

of 0.030 inch, 0.010 inch of free play, and a factor of 0.003, the procedure would be 0.030 − 0.010 − 0.003 = 0.017, for a shim size of 0.017 inch.

STEP 5 Move the pinion shaft through its free play and read the dial indicator needle movement to determine the free play.

STEP 6 Determine the shim change by subtracting a factor specified by the manufacturer and the free play from the size of the starting shim.

STEP 7 Remove the pinion gear and replace the starting shim with the size just determined. Repeat steps 1 through 3.

STEP 8 Tighten the pinion nut to the correct torque and check pinion bearing preload as described in step 3.

CARRIER ASSEMBLY AND SETUP

INSTALLING THE RING GEAR When installing the ring gear to the differential case, perform the following steps to insure that the gear is firmly seated on the differential case:

- Use an Arkansas stone or a fine file to remove any burrs on the mating surface between the ring gear and the case.
- Sometimes the ring gear will need to be heated to expand the ring gear slightly so that it fits over the case.

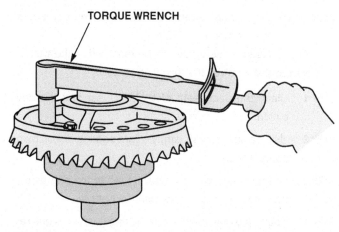

FIGURE 11–39 Torque the retaining bolts to factory specification and in the order specified in service information.

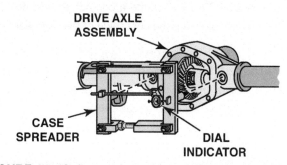

FIGURE 11–40 A spreader tool is specified to be used by some vehicle manufacturers when the differential case assembly is being installed in the housing. Always follow the vehicle manufacturer's recommended procedures.

- Use guide pins to help align the ring gear fastener holes while installing the ring gear.
- Use new retaining bolts and torque them to factory specifications. ● **SEE FIGURE 11–39.**

INSTALLING THE CASE INTO THE HOUSING Install the assembled differential case into the drive axle housing.

- Use the same shims that were removed when the case was removed from the housing as a starting point toward achieving the correct backlash and side bearing preload.
- Be sure to align the index marks on the gear teeth of non-hunting and partial non-hunting gear sets.
- Verify the bearing caps are installed in the same location as when they were removed. Some vehicle manufacturers specify the use of a spreader tool. ● **SEE FIGURE 11–40.**

GEAR MARKING COMPOUND A tooth **contact pattern** test is an excellent method for checking proper drive pinion depth as well as proper backlash between the drive pinion and the ring gear. **Gear marking compound** is available from some gear or vehicle manufacturers (GM gear marking compound, for example is part number 1052351).

Any faults in these areas will be reflected in the pattern. The pattern test involves the following steps:

STEP 1 Clean the gear teeth of the ring gear and the drive pinion.

STEP 2 Using a small brush, apply a light coating of iron oxide compound.

STEP 3 Use a small prybar to apply a load to the ring gear to achieve a more accurate contact pattern.

STEP 4 Rotate the drive pinion until the ring gear turns one revolution (about three revolutions of the drive pinion gear).

STEP 5 Repeat rotating the drive pinion in the opposite direction. This will create a contact pattern on both the drive side and the coast side of the ring gear.

NOTE: The drive side is the convex surface of the ring gear teeth. The coast side is the concave side of the ring gear. This is true except for many differentials used on the front of four-wheel-drive vehicles. In this case, the drive side in the front differential is the concave surface and the coast side is the convex surface of the ring gear teeth. Always check the service information for the vehicle being serviced for the correct interpretation of the pattern results. ● **SEE FIGURE 11–41.**

BACKLASH Backlash and carrier side bearing preload adjustments are made as the ring gear and differential are installed into the carrier. Backlash is the operating clearance between the ring and pinion gears. It is adjusted by moving the ring gear toward the pinion gear (toward the right side) to reduce backlash, or away from the pinion (toward the left side) to increase backlash. ● **SEE FIGURE 11–43.**

Incorrect backlash will cause the contact pattern on both sides of the gear tooth to be too close to the heel or too close to the toe. ● **SEE FIGURE 11–44.**

THREADED ADJUSTER PRELOAD/BACKLASH **Carrier bearing preload** places enough pressure on the carrier bearings to hold the ring gear in proper mesh with the pinion gear without putting unnecessary load and drag on the bearings. Preload is increased by moving one or both of the carrier bearing cups toward each other, and it is reduced by moving them away from each other. These adjustments are made using the threaded adjusters or by changing the shims.

To adjust backlash and carrier bearing preload using threaded adjusters, perform the following steps:

STEP 1 Clean the adjuster threads in the carrier and bearing caps. After carrier bearing preload has been adjusted,

the overall preload of the carrier should increase by a noticeable amount, about 5 to 10 inch-pounds, from the pinion bearing preload.

This is often called *case bearing preload* or *carrier bearing preload*. Be sure to align the index marks on the gear teeth of non-hunting and partial non-hunting gear sets.

STEP 2 Place the threaded adjusters in position and thread them next to the bearing cups.

STEP 3 Turn the adjusters to move the ring gear completely into mesh with the pinion gear so that there is no backlash and no clearance at the bearings.

STEP 4 Install the bearing caps, making sure to align the index marks. Align the bearing caps by threading the bolts into their holes while holding the caps upward, and then drop the caps into position.
  ▪ Rotate the differential to seat the bearings as the adjustments are made.
  ▪ When the caps drop into place, they should sit right next to the carrier.

STEP 5 Tighten the bearing cap bolts so they are snug, about 10 to 20 ft-lb (13 to 27 N-m). Rotate the differential to seat the bearings.

STEP 6 Turn the adjusters to push the differential case to the left so there is a slight backlash and then back to the right until the backlash just disappears. This is zero backlash with no load between the gears.

STEP 7 Mount a dial indicator on the carrier. Position it so that the indicator stylus is on the heel of a ring gear tooth and parallel to the ring gear in one plane while being as close as possible to tangent with the ring gear in the other plane.

STEP 8 Hold the pinion gear stationary while the ring gear is moved back and forth. There should be no backlash or indicator needle motion.

STEP 9 Keep the left-side adjuster stationary as the right-side adjuster is threaded inward. Recheck backlash, and stop adjusting when the backlash is within specifications.

STEP 10 Confirm the preload adjustment by:
  ▪ Marking the right-side adjuster position and backing the adjuster off about one-half turn.
  ▪ Slowly turning the right-side adjuster inward and watch the rollers of that bearing. When the adjuster contacts the bearing cone, the rollers should begin to rotate.
  ▪ Turning the adjuster inward at least one full adjuster lock hole but not more than two.

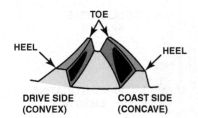

PINION DEPTH CORRECT.

BACKLASH INCORRECT—TOO MUCH
CLEARANCE BETWEEN THE PINION
AND RING GEARS.

CORRECTION

INCREASE THE THICKNESS OF THE LEFT
(RING GEAR SIDE) SHIM AND DECREASE THE
THICKNESS OF THE RIGHT SHIM AN EQUAL
AMOUNT.

SERVICE HINTS

HOW TO CHECK PATTERNS:

BRUSH GEAR MARKING COMPOUND ON THE
RING GEAR TEETH.

APPLY BRAKES SO THAT 50 LB. FT. IS NEEDED
TO ROTATE THE PINION.

ROTATE THE PINION SIX TIMES CLOCKWISE
AND SIX TIMES COUNTERCLOCKWISE.

OBSERVE THE TOOTH CONTACT PATTERN AND
MAKE ANY NECESSARY CORRECTIONS.

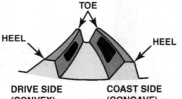

CONDITION

PINION DEPTH CORRECT.
BACKLASH CORRECT.

CORRECTION

NONE.

SERVICE HINTS

PATTERNS THAT VARY MAY BE CAUSED BY
LOOSE BEARINGS ON THE PINION OR THE
DIFFERENTIAL CASE. CHECK THESE BEARING
PRELOAD SETTINGS:

TOTAL ASSEMBLY

DIFFERENTIAL CASE

PINION

IF THESE SETTINGS ARE GOOD, LOOK FOR
DAMAGED OR INCORRECTLY ASSEMBLED
PARTS.

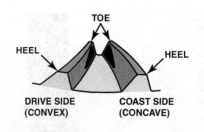

CONDITION

PINION DEPTH CORRECT.

BACKLASH INCORRECT—TOO LITTLE
CLEARANCE BETWEEN THE PINION
AND RING GEARS.

CORRECTION

INCREASE THE THICKNESS OF THE RIGHT
(RING GEAR SIDE) SHIM AND DECREASE THE
THICKNESS OF THE LEFT (RING GEAR SIDE)
SHIM.

SERVICE HINTS

SIDE BEARING GEAR LOCATIONS:

BETWEEN THE SIDE BEARING CONES AND THE
DIFFERENTIAL CASE.

BETWEEN THE SIDE BEARING CUPS AND THE
REAR AXLE HOUSING.

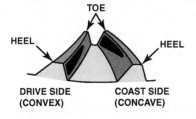

CONDITION

PINION DEPTH INCORRECT—PINION GEAR IS
TOO FAR AWAY FROM THE RING GEAR.

BACKLASH CORRECT

CORRECTION

INCREASE THE PINION SHIM THICKNESS.

SERVICE HINTS

HOW TO CHECK PATTERNS:

BRUSH GEAR MARKING COMPOUND ON THE
RING GEAR TEETH.

APPLY BRAKES SO THAT 50 LB. FT. IS NEEDED
TO ROTATE THE PINION.

ROTATE THE PINION SIX TIMES CLOCKWISE
AND SIX TIMES COUNTERCLOCKWISE.

OBSERVE THE TOOTH CONTACT PATTERN AND
MAKE ANY NECESSARY CORRECTIONS.

FIGURE 11–41 Tooth contact pattern.

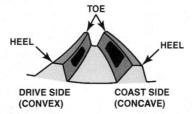

CONDITION

PINION DEPTH CORRECT.
BACKLASH CORRECT.

CORRECTION

NONE.

SERVICE HINTS

PATTERNS THAT VARY MAY BE CAUSED BY
LOOSE BEARINGS ON THE PINION OR THE
DIFFERENTIAL CASE. CHECK THESE BEARING
PRELOAD SETTINGS:

TOTAL ASSEMBLY

DIFFERENTIAL CASE

PINION

IF THESE SETTINGS ARE GOOD, LOOK FOR
DAMAGED OR INCORRECTLY ASSEMBLED
PARTS.

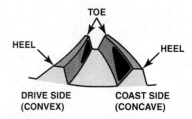

CONDITION

PINION DEPTH INCORRECT—PINION GEAR
IS TOO CLOSE TO RING GEAR.

BACKLASH CORRECT.

CORRECTION

DECREASE THE PINION SHIM THICKNESS.

SERVICE HINTS

PINION DEPTH SHIM LOCATIONS:

BETWEEN THE INNER PINION BEARING CONE
AND THE HEAD OF THE PINION GEAR.

BETWEEN THE INNER PINION BEARING CUP
AND THE REAR AXLE HOUSING.

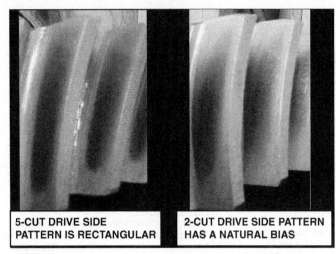

| 5-CUT DRIVE SIDE PATTERN IS RECTANGULAR | 2-CUT DRIVE SIDE PATTERN HAS A NATURAL BIAS |

FIGURE 11–42 The correct drive pattern depends on the type of ring gear. Always refer to service information. (*Courtesy of General Motors.*)

(a)

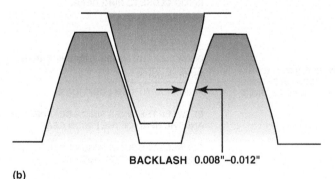

BACKLASH 0.008"–0.012"

(b)

FIGURE 11–43 (a) Backlash is determined by mounting a dial indicator to the differential housing and placing the button of the gauge against a tooth of the ring gear. Moving the ring gear back and forth will indicate on the dial indicator the amount of backlash. (b) Backlash is the clearance between the drive pinion and the ring gear teeth.

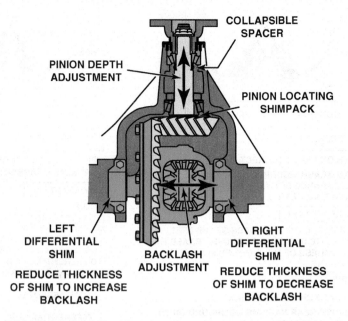

FIGURE 11–44 Backlash is adjusted by moving the position of the ring gear.

Stop at the point where the adjuster lock will line up.

OR:

- Back off the left adjuster one notch.
- Set up a dial indicator with stylus touching the side of the left bearing race.
- Turn the right bearing adjuster inward until the dial indicator shows movement of the race.
- Remove the dial indicator and turn the left adjuster back inward one notch.
- Turn the right adjuster inward one to two notches further.

OR:

- Set up a dial indicator between the carrier bearing caps to measure case spread. As the adjuster is turned inward to preload the bearings, the case will spread apart and the amount of spread can be read on the dial indicator. Some manufacturers provide a case spread specification.

STEP 11 Tighten the bearing cap bolts to the correct torque and rotate the differential to seat the bearings. ● SEE **FIGURE 11–45**.

STEP 12 Recheck backlash at four or more points around the ring gear, making sure that the backlash is within specifications and that there is not too much variation. Readjust the adjusters if backlash is incorrect. At this time, turn one adjuster out one notch and then the other one in one notch to maintain the bearing preload.

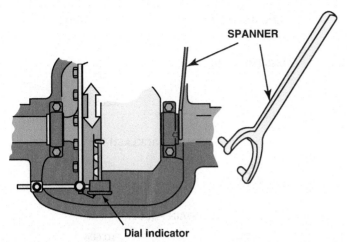

FIGURE 11–45 Using a dial indicator to adjust backlash using threaded adjusters.

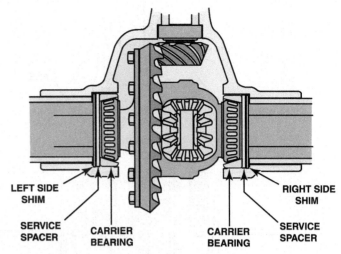

FIGURE 11–46 Cast iron production shim (OEM use), service spacer, and shim used to adjust backlash and carrier bearing preload.

? **FREQUENTLY ASKED QUESTION**

Why Should Service Shims Be Used Instead of the Factory Shims?

During manufacture of a carrier, the bearings and gears are adjusted using a single, cast iron production shim at each carrier bearing. The sizes of these two shims are carefully selected to provide the proper backlash and carrier bearing preload. The production shims are normally replaced with a fixed-size **service spacer** and a selective-size shim when the carrier is adjusted. The service shims are made from steel and they can be driven into place. The factory cast iron shims cannot be driven into place and instead should be discarded when assembling the axle. The replacement shims are available in thicknesses needed to readjust the bearings and gears. ● **SEE FIGURE 11–46**.

STEP 13 Install the adjuster locks, and then tighten the bolts to the correct torque.

PRELOAD/BACKLASH USING SHIMS To adjust backlash and carrier bearing preload using shims, perform the following steps:

STEP 1 Set the carrier with the bearing cups into the differential housing.

STEP 2 Use a group of shims, spacers, and feeler gauge pairs on each side, between the bearing cups and the carrier, so that there will be zero backlash and preload at the ring and pinion gears as well as removing any clearance at the bearings.

- Insert two feeler gauges, one at each side of the shim, below the bearing cup boss so that the shims will not cock and cause a false reading.
- The feeler gauges should have a slight but definite drag. Be sure to rotate the differential during the final readings to ensure that the bearings are seated.

STEP 3 Add the spacer, shims, and feeler gauges used on each side, and record these as shim sizes. ● **SEE FIGURE 11–47**.

STEP 4 Adjust the shim sizes to obtain the correct backlash by subtracting the specified amount from the left side and adding that amount to the right side.

STEP 5 Adjust the shim packs to obtain the correct preload by adding the specified amount to each shim pack. This will be about 0.004 to 0.006 inch (0.1 to 0.15 mm) on each side.

STEP 6 Install the selected shim. It will be necessary to use a soft hammer or a special tool to tap the second shim into place. ● **SEE FIGURE 11–48**.

STEP 7 Install the bearing caps, and tighten the bolts to the correct torque.

STEP 8 Rotate the differential several turns to make sure that there is no binding and to seat the bearings. Measure the backlash as described in step 7 of the procedure for threaded adjusters. Measure the backlash at four or more locations around the ring gear to ensure that any variation is within the limits and that the backlash is within specifications. If there is too much or too little backlash, reduce the shim pack on one side and increase the shim pack on the other side by the same amount.

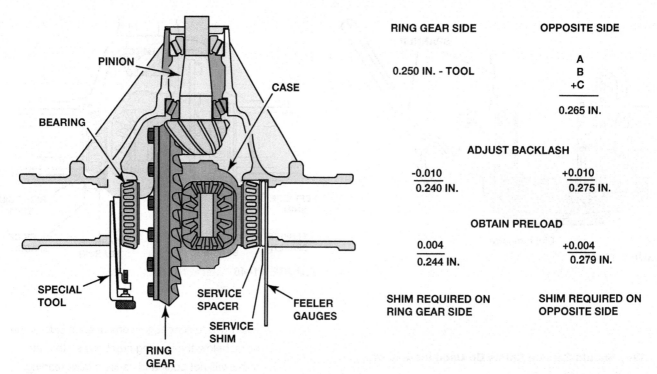

RING GEAR SIDE	OPPOSITE SIDE
0.250 IN. - TOOL	A B +C
	0.265 IN.

ADJUST BACKLASH

-0.010	+0.010
0.240 IN.	0.275 IN.

OBTAIN PRELOAD

0.004	+0.004
0.244 IN.	0.279 IN.

SHIM REQUIRED ON RING GEAR SIDE	SHIM REQUIRED ON OPPOSITE SIDE

FIGURE 11–47 Procedure used to measure and determine the correct shims. Note that in this example, a special tool (J-22779) is used to measure the gap on the left side, while a service spacer, shim, and two feeler gauges are used on the right side.

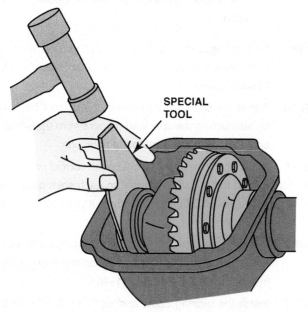

FIGURE 11–48 On many axles, it is necessary to use a special tool to install steel spacers (shims) to achieve the specified backlash and side bearing preload.

NOTE: When changing shims to correct lash, moving 0.002 inch of shim will change the lash by about 0.001 inch.

TECH TIP

Quick and Easy Shim Trick

An alternative method of adjusting backlash and carrier bearing preload is to start with too small a shim at the left side and add enough shims to obtain zero bearing clearance and preload. Now, measure the backlash and adjust the shim packs to correct backlash. Next, increase the size of both shim packs to adjust the bearing preload.

TECH TIP

A Quick Check for Ring Gear Runout

Check for a pattern variation. One steady change in pattern indicates ring gear runout. Two or more changes in pattern indicate pinion gear runout.
● **SEE FIGURE 11–49.**

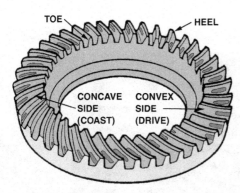

FIGURE 11–49 A pattern that changes as it goes around the ring gear is caused by ring gear runout (one pattern change) or pinion gear runout (several pattern changes).

FIGURE 11–50 Clutch packs are typical wear items in a limited-slip or locking differential. (*Courtesy of General Motors.*)

LIMITED SLIP DIFFERENTIAL SERVICE

TYPICAL CHECKS In most cases, this operation involves disassembly and reassembly of the differential with replacement of worn parts. It can also include adjusting the clearance or preload of the clutch packs and bench check for rotating torque. Cone clutch limited slip differentials use a split case, which makes disassembly easy because the plate clutch units can be serviced through the case window. ● **SEE FIGURE 11–50.**

NOTE: If the clutch plates are to be reused, they should be replaced in their original positions. Restacking the plates in different positions will result in increased wear and diminished performance.

TYPICAL ASSEMBLY PROCEDURE To disassemble a plate clutch limited slip differential, perform the following steps:

STEP 1 Carefully remove the S-shaped preload spring by tapping it through the window.

STEP 2 Roll the differential pinions around the case windows, and remove them.

STEP 3 Remove the side gear and clutch packs as a group, and tag or mark them so that they can be reassembled on the same side of the differential.

STEP 4 Clean the parts by wiping the friction surfaces with a cloth and do *not* use any solvent. The differential case and pinion gears can be washed in a solvent.

STEP 5 The clutch plates or cones should be checked for scores, grooves, or galling. Reassembly of most limited slip differentials is the reverse of the disassembly procedure. Be sure to lubricate all of the friction surfaces with the recommended gear oil. Some differentials use a shim to set the clutch pack for the correct preload or clearance, which adds a step in the reassembly procedure for determining the pack height and shim size.

The clutch pack surfaces must be thoroughly lubricated with the proper lubricant during assembly. One manufacturer recommends soaking them in the lubricant for 20 minutes.

DRIVE AXLE SERVICE

1 The rear axle fluid is drained by removing all of the inspection cover bolts except for the top one and then the cover is pried loose and the fluid drained into a suitable container.

2 The retaining pin is removed which will then allow the pinion shaft to be removed.

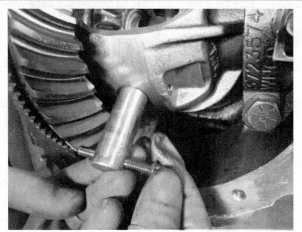

3 The pinion shaft is removed.

4 The axle is pushed inward and the C-lock removed.

5 The axle can then be removed.

6 The C-lock on the other axle is then removed and the second axle pulled out of the drive axle housing.

7 After marking the bearing caps, the retaining bolts are removed, and then the differential case is removed from the drive axle housing.

8 The axle bearing and seals are removed and will be replaced as part of the overhaul of this drive axle assembly.

9 A long holding tool to keep the pinion flange from rotating as the pinion nut is removed.

10 After the pinion shaft has been removed, the pinion bearing is then removed from the front of the housing.

11 A hydraulic press is used to press the pinion bearing off the pinion shaft.

12 The pinion depth shim is measured and recorded for future reference.

CONTINUED ▶

13 A special gauging tool is used to determine the proper pinion depth.

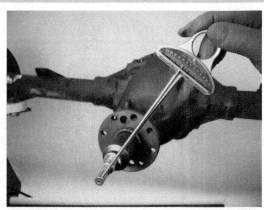

14 The pinion nut is tightened and the rotating toque checked using an inch-pound torque wrench.

15 The differential case is installed into the drive axle housing.

16 The pattern is checked and the backlash adjusted to factory specifications.

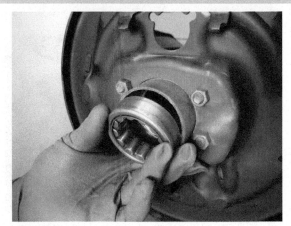

17 New bearings are installed.

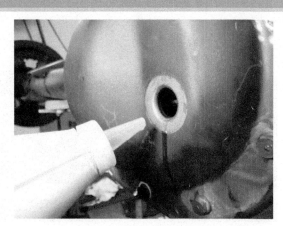

18 The drive axle cover is installed using the specified RTV to seal the cover, and then it is filled with the specified gear oil.

1. Drive axles must have clean gear oil at the proper level and of the proper type.
2. The cause of improper drive axle operation is determined using several diagnostic steps.
3. Some drive axle problems can be repaired on-vehicle.
4. Major internal drive axle problems usually require that the assembly be removed from the vehicle.
5. Drive axle disassembly and reassembly procedures vary between makes and models.
6. Presses and pullers are often required for complete disassembly.
7. Parts must be cleaned before being inspected.
8. Gears and bearings are the major wear components.
9. Four ring and pinion adjustments are required: pinion depth, pinion bearing preload, carrier bearing preload, and backlash.
10. Ring and pinion adjustment can be confirmed with a tooth contact pattern check.

REVIEW QUESTIONS

1. How can a drive axle be identified?
2. How can the gear ratio be determined?
3. How is a leak through the porous axle housing repaired?
4. What tool is needed to check pinion gear rotating torque?

CHAPTER QUIZ

1. A drive axle assembly can be identified by_____.
   a. The shape and the number of bolts for the cover
   b. RPO code
   c. Checking service information
   d. All of the above

2. Drive axles usually use gear oil labeled as _____ by the API.
   a. GL-5
   b. GL-4
   c. GL-3
   d. Any of the above

3. A worn or defective axle bearing will likely make what type of noise?
   a. Chuckle
   b. Growl
   c. Clunk
   d. Chatter

4. A low pitch rumble over 20 MPH (32 km/h) is likely caused by a worn or defective_____.
   a. Incorrect backlash or pinion depth
   b. Incorrect gear oil or worn limited slip clutches
   c. Worn carrier bearings
   d. Worn U-joints

5. To remove and replace a drive pinion seal, what should be marked before removing the pinion nut?
   a. Pinion flange
   b. Pinion nut
   c. Pinion shaft
   d. All of the above

6. The total indicated runout (TIR) of a ring gear should be_____.
   a. 0.002 inch (0.05 mm)
   b. 0.020 inch (0.5 mm)
   c. 0.200 inch (5.0 mm)
   d. 0.040 inch (1.0 mm)

7. Differential case clearance is usually checked by using a _____.
   a. Feeler gauge
   b. An inch-pound torque wrench
   c. Dial indicator
   d. Micrometer

8. Pinion depth is usually adjusted by _____.
   a. Changing the thickness of a shim under the pinion bearing
   b. Adjusting the position of the ring gear
   c. Tightening the side bearing cap bolts
   d. Adding or deleting side bearing shims

9. Backlash and carrier side bearing preload adjustments are made by_____.
   a. Adding a shim behind the pinion shaft bearing
   b. Threaded adjusters or by changing the shims
   c. Tightening or loosening the ring gear retainer bolts
   d. Using a case spreader

10. Backlash is normally_____.
    a. Less than 0.008 inch (0.2 mm)
    b. 0.008 to 0.012 inch (0.2 to 0.3 mm)
    c. 0.012 to 0.020 inch (0.3 to 0.5 mm)
    d. 0.100 to 0.120 inch (2.5 to 3.0 mm)

ELECTRICITY AND ELECTRONICS

LEARNING OBJECTIVES

After studying this chapter, the reader should be able to:

1. Explain the characteristics of electricity.
2. Differentiate between conductors, insulators, and semiconductors.
3. Explain the units of electrical measurement.
4. List the parts of a complete circuit.
5. Discuss the types of electrical circuit faults.
6. Explain how to detect and measure electrical voltage, current, and resistance.
7. Discuss the purpose of terminals, connectors, relays, and switches.
8. Explain the operation of speed sensors and throttle position (TP) sensors.
9. State the need for networks and discuss network classifications.

This chapter will help you prepare for ASE Manual Drive Train and Axles (A3) certification test content area "B" (Transmission Diagnosis and Repair).

KEY TERMS

Ammeter 217
Ampere 207
Conductors 206
Connector 218
Conventional theory 207
Crimp-and-seal connectors 220
Digital multimeter (DMM) 215
Digital volt-ohm-meter (DVOM) 215
Electricity 205
Electron theory 207
Hall Effect 223
High resistance 213
Insulators 206
Node 224
Ohmmeter 216
Ohms 208
Open circuit 210
Potentiometer 223
Relay 221
Schematic 209
Short-to-ground 210
Short-to-voltage 210
Semiconductor 207
Terminal 218
Volt 208
Voltmeter 215

GM STC OBJECTIVES

GM Service Technical College topics covered in this chapter are as follows:

1. Diagnose different electrical faults in transmission circuits using a multimeter.
2. Properly install a wiring splice.
3. Replace a terminal in a pull-to-seat and a push-to-seat connector.
4. Perform electrical testing using the appropriate test probes and leads.

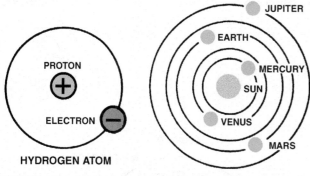

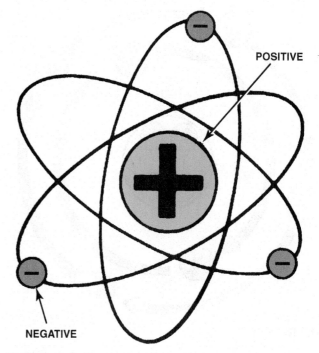

FIGURE 12–1 In an atom (left), electrons orbit protons in the nucleus just as planets orbit the sun in our solar system (right).

INTRODUCTION

The electrical system is one of the most important systems in a vehicle today. Every year more and more vehicle components and systems use electricity.

Electricity may be difficult for some people to learn for the following reasons.

- It cannot be seen.
- Only the results of electricity can be seen.
- It has to be detected and measured.

ELECTRICITY

BACKGROUND Our universe is composed of matter, which is anything that has mass and occupies space. All matter is made from slightly over 100 individual components called elements. The smallest particle that an element can be broken into and still retain the properties of that element is known as an atom. ● **SEE FIGURE 12–1.**

DEFINITION **Electricity** is the movement of electrons from one atom to another. The dense center of each atom is called the nucleus. The nucleus contains

- Protons, which have a positive charge
- Neutrons, which are electrically neutral (have no charge)

Electrons, which have a negative charge, orbit the nucleus. Each atom contains an equal number of electrons and protons.

NOTE: As an example of the relative sizes of the parts of an atom, consider that if an atom were magnified so that the nucleus were the size of the period at the end of this sentence, the whole atom would be bigger than a house.

FIGURE 12–2 The nucleus of an atom has a positive (+) charge and the surrounding electrons have a negative (–) charge.

POSITIVE AND NEGATIVE CHARGES The parts of an atom have different charges. The orbiting electrons are negatively charged, while the protons are positively charged. Positive charges are indicated by the "plus" sign (+), and negative charges by the "minus" sign (–). ● **SEE FIGURE 12–2.**

These same + and – signs are used to identify parts of an electrical circuit. Neutrons have no charge at all. They are neutral. In a normal or balanced atom, the number of negative particles equals the number of positive particles. That is, there are as many electrons as there are protons. ● **SEE FIGURE 12–3.**

MAGNETS AND ELECTRICAL CHARGE An ordinary magnet has two ends, or poles. One end is called the south pole, and the other is called the north pole. If two magnets are brought close to each other with like poles together (south to south or north to north), the magnets will push each other apart, because like poles repel each other. If the opposite poles of the magnets are brought close to each other, south to north, the magnets will snap together, because unlike poles attract each other. The positive and negative charges within an atom are like the north and south poles of a magnet. Charges that are alike will repel each other, similar to the poles of a magnet. ● **SEE FIGURE 12–4.**

That is why the negative electrons continue to orbit around the positive protons. They are attracted and held by the opposite charge of the protons. The electrons keep moving in orbit because they repel each other.

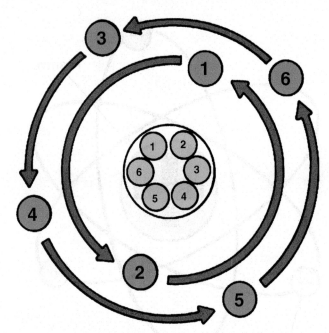

FIGURE 12–3 This figure shows a balanced atom. The number of electrons is the same as the number of protons in the nucleus.

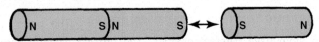

FIGURE 12–4 Unlike charges attract and like charges repel.

ELECTRON ORBITS Electrons orbit around the nucleus in rings and the outermost ring is called the "valence ring." Whether a material is a conductor or an insulator strictly depends on how many electrons are in the outer ring.

CONDUCTORS **Conductors** are materials with fewer than four electrons in their atom's outer orbit. ● **SEE FIGURE 12–5.**

Copper is an excellent conductor because it has only one electron in its outer orbit. This orbit is far enough away from the nucleus of the copper atom that the pull or force holding the outermost electron in orbit is relatively weak. ● **SEE FIGURE 12–6.**

Copper is the conductor most used in vehicles because the price of copper is reasonable compared to the relative cost of other conductors with similar properties. Examples of commonly used conductors include the following:

- Silver
- Copper
- Gold
- Aluminum
- Steel
- Cast iron

CONDUCTORS

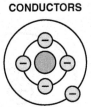

COPPER

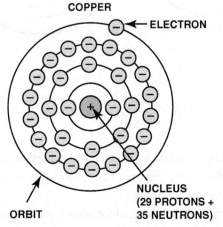

FIGURE 12–6 Copper is an excellent conductor of electricity because it has just one electron in its outer orbit, making it easy to be knocked out of its orbit and flow to other nearby atoms. This causes electron flow, which is the definition of electricity.

FIGURE 12–7 Insulators are elements with five to eight electrons in the outer orbit.

INSULATORS

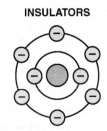

INSULATORS Some materials hold their electrons very tightly; therefore, electrons do not move through them very well. These materials are called insulators. **Insulators** are materials with more than four electrons in their atom's outer orbit. Because they have more than four electrons in their outer orbit, it becomes easier for these materials to acquire (gain) electrons than to release electrons. ● **SEE FIGURE 12–7.**

Examples of insulators include the following:

- Rubber
- Plastic
- Nylon
- Porcelain
- Ceramic
- Fiberglass

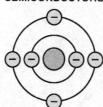
FIGURE 12-8 Semiconductor elements contain exactly four electrons in the outer orbit.

SEMICONDUCTORS

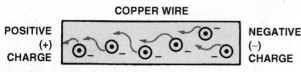
COPPER WIRE

POSITIVE (+) CHARGE

NEGATIVE (−) CHARGE

FIGURE 12-9 Electricity is the movement of electrons through a conductor.

SEMICONDUCTORS

Materials with exactly four electrons in their outer orbit are neither conductors nor insulators, but are called **semiconductors**. Semiconductors can be either an insulator or a conductor in different design applications. ● **SEE FIGURE 12-8.**

Examples of semiconductors include the following:

- Silicon
- Germanium
- Carbon

Semiconductors are used mostly in transistors, computers, and other electronic devices.

HOW ELECTRONS MOVE THROUGH A CONDUCTOR

CURRENT FLOW The following events occur if a source of power, such as a battery, is connected to the ends of a conductor—a positive charge (lack of electrons) is placed on one end of the conductor and a negative charge (excess of electrons) is placed on the opposite end of the conductor. For current to flow, there must be an imbalance of excess electrons at one end of the circuit and a deficiency of electrons at the opposite end. ● **SEE FIGURE 12-9.**

CONVENTIONAL THEORY VERSUS ELECTRON THEORY

- **Conventional theory**: It was once thought that electricity had only one charge and moved from positive to negative. This theory of the flow of electricity through a conductor is called the conventional theory of current flow. Most automotive applications use the conventional theory. ● **SEE FIGURE 12-10.**

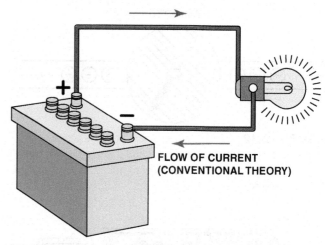
FLOW OF CURRENT (CONVENTIONAL THEORY)

FIGURE 12-10 Conventional theory states that current flows through a circuit from positive (+) to negative (−). Automotive electricity uses the conventional theory in all electrical diagrams and schematics.

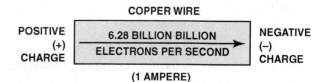
COPPER WIRE

POSITIVE (+) CHARGE

6.28 BILLION BILLION ELECTRONS PER SECOND

NEGATIVE (−) CHARGE

(1 AMPERE)

FIGURE 12-11 One ampere is the movement of 1 coulomb (6.28 billion billion electrons) past a point in 1 second.

- **Electron theory**: The discovery of the electron and its negative charge led to the electron theory, which states that there is electron flow from negative to positive.

UNITS OF ELECTRICITY

Electricity is measured using meters or other test equipment. The three fundamentals of electricity-related units include the ampere, volt, and ohm.

AMPERE The **ampere** is the unit used throughout the world to measure current flow. When 6.28 billion billion electrons (the name for this large number of electrons is a coulomb) move past a certain point in 1 second, this represents 1 ampere of current. ● **SEE FIGURE 12-11.**

The ampere is the electrical unit for the amount of electron flow, just as "gallons per minute" is the unit that can be used to measure the quantity of water flow. It is named for the French physicist Andrè Marie Ampére (1775–1836). The conventional abbreviations and measurement for amperes are as follows:

1. The ampere is the unit of measurement for the amount of current flow.

2. A and amps are acceptable abbreviations for amperes.

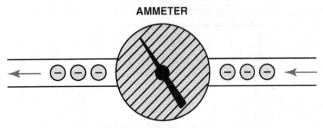

FIGURE 12–12 An ammeter is installed in the path of the electrons similar to a water meter used to measure the flow of water in gallons per minute. The ammeter displays current flow in amperes.

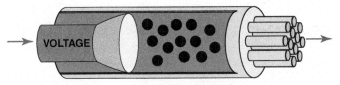

VOLTAGE IS PRESSURE

FIGURE 12–13 Voltage is the electrical pressure that causes the electrons to flow through a conductor.

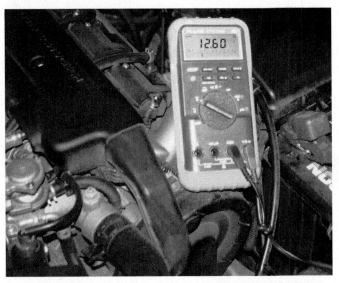

FIGURE 12–14 This digital multimeter set to read DC volts is being used to test the voltage of a vehicle battery. Most multimeters can also measure resistance (ohms) and current flow (amperes).

3. The capital letter I, for intensity, is used in mathematical calculations to represent amperes.

4. Amperes do the actual work in the circuit. It is the movement of the electrons through a light bulb or motor that actually makes the electrical device work. Without amperage through a device, it will not work at all.

5. Amperes are measured by an ammeter (not ampmeter). ● **SEE FIGURE 12–12.**

VOLTS The **volt** is the unit of measurement for electrical pressure. It is named for an Italian physicist, Alessandro Volta (1745–1827). The comparable unit using water pressure as an example would be pounds per square inch (PSI). It is possible to have very high pressures (volts) and low water flow (amperes). It is also possible to have high water flow (amperes) and low pressures (volts). Voltage is also called electrical potential, because if there is voltage present in a conductor, there is a potential (possibility) for current flow. ● **SEE FIGURE 12–13.**

The conventional abbreviations and measurement for voltage are as follows:

1. The volt is the unit of measurement for the amount of electrical pressure.

2. Electromotive force, abbreviated EMF, is another way of indicating voltage.

3. V is the generally accepted abbreviation for volts.

4. The symbol used in calculations is E, for electromotive force.

5. Volts are measured by a voltmeter. ● **SEE FIGURE 12–14.**

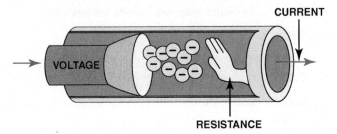

FIGURE 12–15 Resistance to the flow of electrons through a conductor is measured in ohms.

OHMS Resistance to the flow of current through a conductor is measured in units called **ohms**, named after the German physicist George Simon Ohm (1787–1854). The resistance to the flow of free electrons through a conductor results from the countless collisions the electrons cause within the atoms of the conductor. ● **SEE FIGURE 12–15.**

Resistance can be:

▪ Desirable when it is part of how a circuit works, such as the resistance of a filament in a light bulb.

▪ Undesirable, such as corrosion in a connection restricting the amount of current flow in a circuit.

The conventional abbreviations and measurement for resistance are as follows:

1. The ohm is the unit of measurement for electrical resistance.

2. The symbol for ohms is Ω (Greek capital letter omega), the last letter of the Greek alphabet.

3. The symbol used in calculations is R, for resistance.

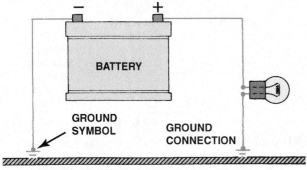

FIGURE 12–16 The return path back to the battery can be any electrical conductor, such as a copper wire or the metal frame or body of the vehicle.

4. Ohms are measured by an ohmmeter.

5. Resistance to electron flow depends on the material used.

ELECTRICAL CIRCUITS

DEFINITION A circuit is a complete path that electrons travel from a power source (such as a battery) through a load such as a light bulb and back to the power source. It is called a circuit because the current must start and finish at the same place (power source). For any electrical circuit to work at all, it must be continuous from the battery (power), through all the wires and components, and back to the battery (ground). A circuit that is continuous throughout is said to have continuity.

PARTS OF A COMPLETE CIRCUIT Every complete circuit contains the following parts

1. A power source, such as a vehicle's battery.

2. Protection from harmful overloads (excessive current flow). (Fuses, circuit breakers, and fusible links are examples of electrical circuit protection devices.)

3. The power path for the current to flow through, from the power source to the resistance. (This path from a power source to the load—a light bulb in this example—is usually an insulated copper wire.)

4. The electrical load or resistance, which converts electrical energy into heat, light, or motion.

5. A return path (ground) for the electrical current from the load back to the power source so that there is a complete circuit. (This return, or ground, path is usually the metal body, frame, ground wires, and engine block of the vehicle.) ● SEE FIGURE 12–16.

6. Switches and controls that turn the circuit on and off. ● SEE FIGURE 12–17.

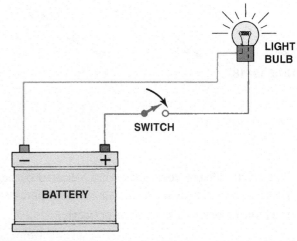

FIGURE 12–17 An electrical switch opens the circuit and no current flows. The switch could also be on the return (ground) path wire.

ELECTRICAL SCHEMATICS

TERMINOLOGY Automotive manufacturer's service information includes wiring schematics of every electrical circuit in a vehicle. A wiring **schematic**, sometimes called a *diagram*, shows electrical components and wiring using symbols and lines to represent components and wires. A typical wiring schematic may include all of the circuits combined, or they may be broken down to show individual circuits. All circuit schematics or diagrams include the following:

- Power-side wiring of the circuit
- All splices
- Connectors
- Wire size
- Wire color
- Trace color (if any)
- Circuit number
- Electrical components
- Ground return paths
- Fuses and switches

CIRCUIT INFORMATION Many wiring schematics include numbers and letters near components and wires that may confuse readers of the schematic. Most letters used near or on a wire identify the color or colors of the wire.

- The first color or color abbreviation is the color of the wire insulation.
- The second color (if mentioned) is the color of the stripe or tracer on the base color. ● SEE FIGURE 12–18.

FIGURE 12–18 The center wire is a solid color wire, meaning that the wire has no other identifying tracer or stripe color. The two end wires could be labeled "BRN/WHT," indicating a brown wire with a white tracer or stripe.

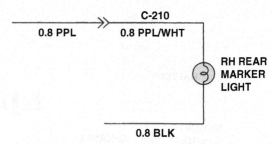

FIGURE 12–19 Typical section of a wiring diagram. Notice that the wire color changes at connection C210. The ".8" represents the metric wire size in square millimeters.

Wires with different color tracers are indicated by both colors with a slash (/) between them. For example, BRN/WHT means a brown wire with a white stripe or tracer.

WIRE SIZE

Wire size is shown on all schematics. For example, ● **FIGURE 12–19** illustrates a rear side-marker bulb circuit diagram where ".8" indicates the metric wire gauge size in square millimeters (mm^2) and "PPL" indicates a solid purple wire.

The wire diagram also shows that the color of the wire changes at the number C210. This stands for "connector #210" and is used for reference purposes. The symbol for the connection can vary depending on the manufacturer. The color change from purple (PPL) to purple with a white tracer (PPL/WHT). The ground circuit is the ".8 BLK" wire.

● **SEE FIGURE 12–20**, which shows many of the electrical and electronic symbols that are used in wiring and circuit diagrams.

TYPES OF CIRCUIT FAULTS

Circuits can experience several different types of faults or problems, which often result in improper operation. The types of faults include opens, shorts, and high resistance.

OPEN CIRCUITS

An **open circuit** is any circuit that is not complete, or that lacks continuity, such as a broken wire. ● **SEE FIGURE 12–22** on page 213.

Open circuits have the following features.

1. No current will flow through an open circuit.
2. An open circuit may be created by a break in the circuit or by a switch that opens (turns off) the circuit and prevents the flow of current.
3. In any circuit containing a power load and ground, an opening anywhere in the circuit will cause the circuit not to work.
4. A light switch in a home and the headlight switch in a vehicle are examples of devices that open a circuit to control its operation.

NOTE: A blown fuse opens the circuit to prevent damage to the components or wiring in the circuit in the event of an overload caused by a fault in the circuit.

SHORT-TO-VOLTAGE

If a wire (conductor) or component is shorted to voltage, it is commonly referred to as being shorted. A **short-to-voltage** occurs when the power side of one circuit is electrically connected to the power side of another circuit. ● **SEE FIGURE 12–23** on page 213.

A short circuit has the following features.

1. It is a complete circuit in which the current usually bypasses some or all of the resistance in the circuit.
2. It involves the power side of the circuit.
3. It involves a copper-to-copper connection (two power side wires touching together).
4. It is also called a short-to-voltage.
5. It usually affects more than one circuit. In this case, if one circuit is electrically connected to another circuit, one of the circuits may operate when it is not supposed to because it is being supplied power from another circuit.
6. It may or may not blow a fuse. ● **SEE FIGURE 12–24** on page 213.

SHORT-TO-GROUND

A **short-to-ground** is a type of short circuit that occurs when the current bypasses part of the normal circuit and flows directly to ground. A short-to-ground has the following features.

1. Because the ground return circuit is metal (vehicle frame, engine, or body), it is often identified as having current flowing from copper to steel.
2. A short-to-ground can occur at any place where a power path wire accidentally touches a return path wire or conductor. ● **SEE FIGURE 12–25** on page 213.
3. A defective component or circuit that is shorted to ground is commonly called grounded.
4. A short-to-ground almost always results in a blown fuse, damaged connectors, or melted wires.

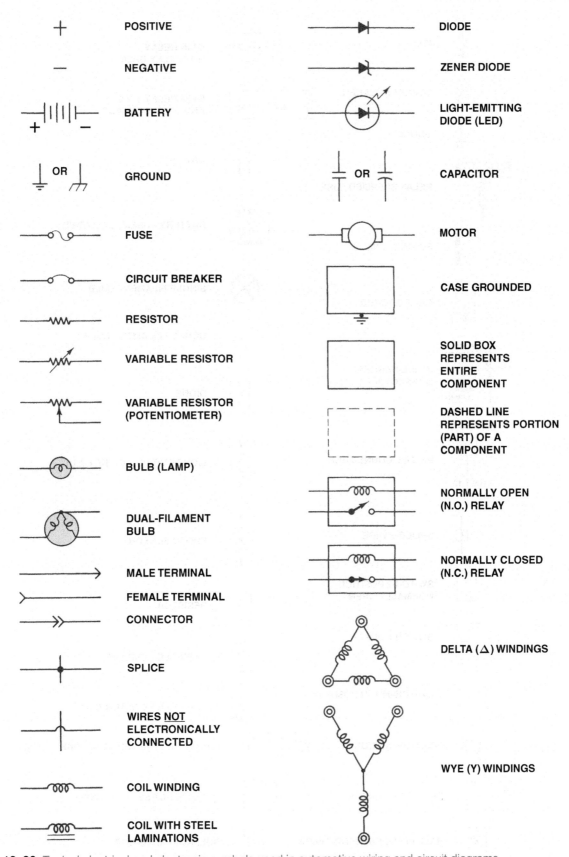

FIGURE 12–20 Typical electrical and electronic symbols used in automotive wiring and circuit diagrams.

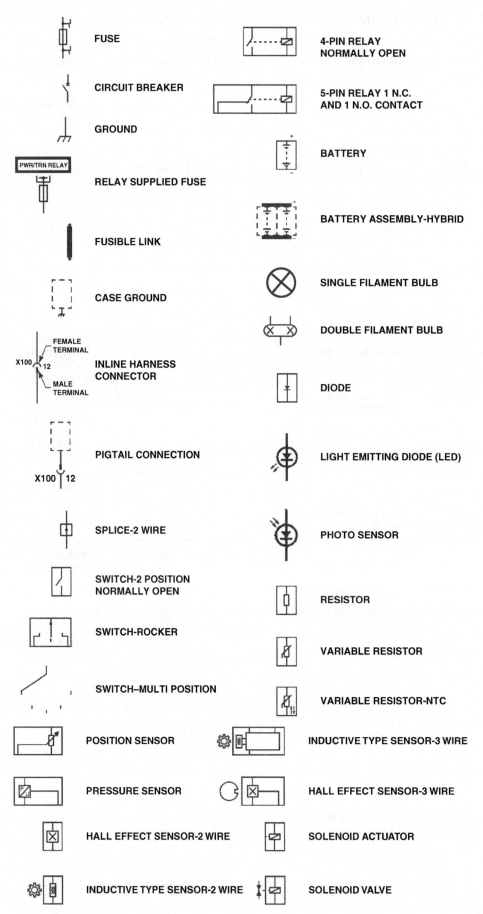

FUSE

CIRCUIT BREAKER

GROUND

PWR/TRN RELAY

RELAY SUPPLIED FUSE

FUSIBLE LINK

CASE GROUND

FEMALE TERMINAL

X100 12

INLINE HARNESS CONNECTOR

MALE TERMINAL

PIGTAIL CONNECTION

X100 12

SPLICE-2 WIRE

SWITCH-2 POSITION NORMALLY OPEN

SWITCH-ROCKER

SWITCH–MULTI POSITION

POSITION SENSOR

PRESSURE SENSOR

HALL EFFECT SENSOR-2 WIRE

INDUCTIVE TYPE SENSOR-2 WIRE

4-PIN RELAY NORMALLY OPEN

5-PIN RELAY 1 N.C. AND 1 N.O. CONTACT

BATTERY

BATTERY ASSEMBLY-HYBRID

SINGLE FILAMENT BULB

DOUBLE FILAMENT BULB

DIODE

LIGHT EMITTING DIODE (LED)

PHOTO SENSOR

RESISTOR

VARIABLE RESISTOR

VARIABLE RESISTOR-NTC

INDUCTIVE TYPE SENSOR-3 WIRE

HALL EFFECT SENSOR-3 WIRE

SOLENOID ACTUATOR

SOLENOID VALVE

FIGURE 12–21 Starting in 2008, GM began using these updated "Global" electrical symbols on electrical schematics. (Courtesy of General Motors.)

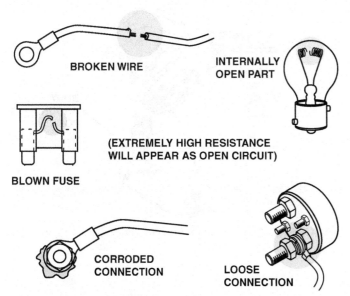

BROKEN WIRE

INTERNALLY OPEN PART

(EXTREMELY HIGH RESISTANCE WILL APPEAR AS OPEN CIRCUIT)

BLOWN FUSE

CORRODED CONNECTION

LOOSE CONNECTION

FIGURE 12–22 Examples of common causes of open circuits. Some of these causes are often difficult to find.

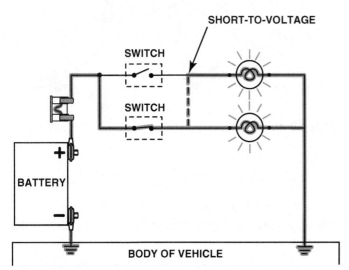

SHORT-TO-VOLTAGE

SWITCH

SWITCH

BATTERY

BODY OF VEHICLE

FIGURE 12–23 A short circuit permits electrical current to bypass some or all of the resistance in the circuit.

HIGH RESISTANCE **High resistance** is resistance higher than normal circuit resistance usually caused by any of the following:

- Corroded connections or sockets
- Loose terminals in a connector
- Loose ground connections

If there is high resistance anywhere in a circuit, it may cause the following problems.

1. Slow operation of a motor-driven unit, such as when the transfer case makes a range change
2. Dim lights
3. "Clicking" of relays or solenoids
4. No operation of a circuit or electrical component

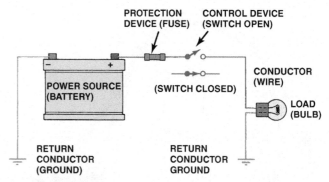

PROTECTION DEVICE (FUSE)   **CONTROL DEVICE (SWITCH OPEN)**

POWER SOURCE (BATTERY)

(SWITCH CLOSED)

CONDUCTOR (WIRE)

LOAD (BULB)

RETURN CONDUCTOR (GROUND)   **RETURN CONDUCTOR GROUND**

FIGURE 12–24 A fuse or circuit breaker opens the circuit to prevent possible overheating damage in the event of a short circuit.

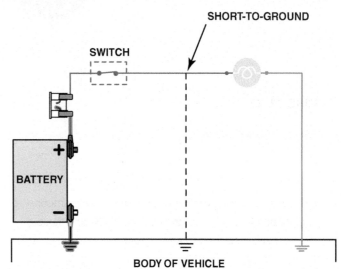

SHORT-TO-GROUND

SWITCH

BATTERY

BODY OF VEHICLE

FIGURE 12–25 A short-to-ground affects the power side of the circuit. Current flows directly to the ground return, bypassing some or all of the electrical loads in the circuit. There is no current in the circuit past the short. A short-to-ground will also cause the fuse to blow.

FUSED JUMPER WIRE

PURPOSE AND FUNCTION   A fused jumper wire is used to check a circuit by bypassing the switch or to provide a power or ground to a component. A fused jumper wire, also called a fused test lead, can be purchased or made by the service technician. ● **SEE FIGURE 12–26**.

It should include the following features:

- *Fuse:* A typical fused jumper wire has a blade-type fuse that can be easily replaced. A 10 ampere fuse (red color) is often the value used.
- *Alligator clip ends:* Alligator clips on the ends allow the fused jumper wire to be clipped to a ground or power source while the other end is attached to the power side or ground side of the unit being tested.

DRIVETRAIN ELECTRICITY AND ELECTRONICS   213

FIGURE 12–26 A technician-made fused jumper lead, which is equipped with a red 10 ampere fuse. This fused jumper wire uses terminals for testing circuits at a connector instead of alligator clips.

- *Good-quality insulated wire:* Most purchased jumper wire is about 14 gauge stranded copper wire with a flexible rubberized insulation to allow it to move easily even in cold weather.

CAUTION: Never use a fused jumper wire to bypass any resistance or load in the circuit. The increased current flow could damage the wiring and could blow the fuse on the jumper lead. Be very cautious when working on or around any computer circuit. Permanent damage to the computer or electronic module could result if power or ground goes to the wrong circuit.

TEST LIGHT

A 12-volt test light is one of the simplest testers that can be used to detect electricity. A test light is simply a light bulb with a probe and a ground wire attached. ● **SEE FIGURE 12–27**.

A test light is used to detect battery voltage potential at various test points. Battery voltage cannot be seen or felt, and can be detected only with test equipment. The ground clip is connected to a clean ground on either the negative terminal of the battery or a clean metal part of the body and the

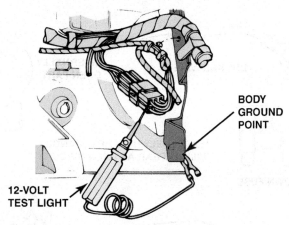

FIGURE 12–27 A 12-volt test light is attached to a good ground while probing for power.

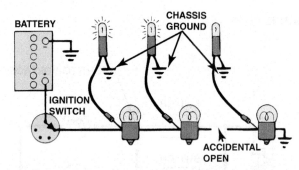

FIGURE 12–28 A test light can be used to locate an open in a circuit. Note that the test light is grounded at a different location than the circuit itself.

probe touched to terminals or components. If the test light comes on, this indicates that voltage is available. ● **SEE FIGURE 12–28**.

A purchased test light should be labeled as "12-volt test light." Do not purchase a test light designed for household current (110 or 220 volts), as it will not light with 12 to 14 volts.

USES OF A 12-VOLT TEST LIGHT A 12-volt test light can be used to check the following:

- *Electrical power:* If the test light lights, then there is power available. It will not, however, indicate the voltage level or if there is enough current available to operate an electrical load. It only indicates that there is enough voltage and current to light the test light (about 0.25 A).

- *Grounds:* A test light can be used to check for grounds by attaching the clip of the test light to the positive terminal of the battery or any positive 12-volt electrical terminal. The tip of the test light can then be used to touch the ground wire. If there is a ground connection, the test light will light.

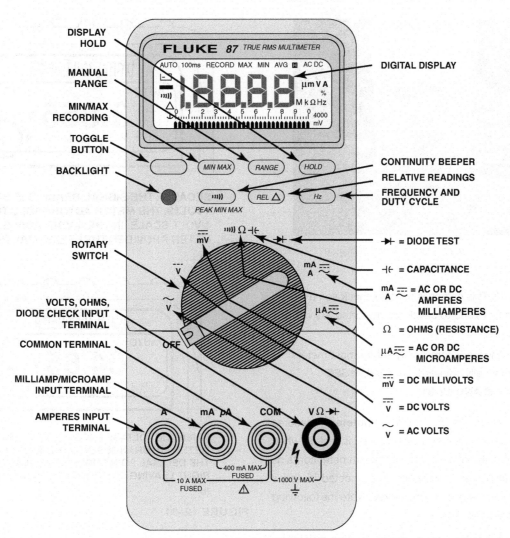

DISPLAY HOLD

MANUAL RANGE

MIN/MAX RECORDING

TOGGLE BUTTON

BACKLIGHT

ROTARY SWITCH

VOLTS, OHMS, DIODE CHECK INPUT TERMINAL

COMMON TERMINAL

MILLIAMP/MICROAMP INPUT TERMINAL

AMPERES INPUT TERMINAL

FLUKE 87 TRUE RMS MULTIMETER

AUTO 100ms RECORD MAX MIN AVG H AC DC

μm V A
% M k Ω Hz

MIN MAX   RANGE   HOLD

PEAK MIN MAX   REL △   Hz

DIGITAL DISPLAY

CONTINUITY BEEPER

RELATIVE READINGS

FREQUENCY AND DUTY CYCLE

➤+ = DIODE TEST

+⊢ = CAPACITANCE

mA �singlewavy⩵ = AC OR DC AMPERES MILLIAMPERES
A ~

Ω = OHMS (RESISTANCE)

μA ⩵ = AC OR DC MICROAMPERES

mV = DC MILLIVOLTS

V = DC VOLTS

V ~ = AC VOLTS

A   mA μA   COM   V Ω ➤+

10 A MAX FUSED   400 mA MAX FUSED   1000 V MAX

FIGURE 12–29 Typical digital multimeter. The black meter lead always is placed in the COM terminal. The red meter test lead should be in the volt-ohm terminal except when measuring current in amperes.

DIGITAL METERS

TERMINOLOGY **Digital multimeter (DMM)** and **digital volt-ohm-meter (DVOM)** are terms commonly used to describe digital meters. ● **SEE FIGURE 12–29**.

The common abbreviations for the units that many meters can measure are often confusing. ● **SEE CHART 12–1** for the most commonly used symbols and their meanings.

MEASURING VOLTAGE A **voltmeter** measures the pressure or potential of electricity in units of volts. A voltmeter is connected to a circuit in parallel. Voltage can be measured by selecting either AC or DC volts.

- *DC volts (DCV)*. This setting is the most common for automotive use. Use this setting to measure battery voltage and voltage to all lighting and accessory circuits.

SYMBOL	MEANING
AC	Alternating current or voltage
DC	Direct current or voltage
V	Volts
mV	Millivolts (1/1,000 volts)
A	Ampere (amps), current
mA	Milliampere (1/1,000 amps)
%	Percent (for duty cycle readings only)
Ω	Ohms, resistance
kΩ	Kilohm (1,000 ohms), resistance
MΩ	Megohm (1,000,000 ohms), resistance
Hz	Hertz (cycles per second), frequency
kHz	Kilohertz (1,000 cycles/sec.), frequency
Ms	Milliseconds (1/1,000 sec.) for pulse width measurements

CHART 12–1

Common symbols and abbreviations used on digital meters.

FIGURE 12–30 Typical digital multimeter (DMM) set to read DC volts.

- *AC volts (ACV).* This setting is used to check some computer sensors and to check for unwanted AC voltage from alternators.
- *Range.* The range is automatically set for most meters but can be manually adjusted if needed. ● **SEE FIGURES 12–30 AND 12–31.**

MEASURING RESISTANCE An **ohmmeter** measures the resistance in ohms of a component or circuit section when no current is flowing through the circuit. An ohmmeter contains a battery (or other power source) and is connected in series with the component or wire being measured. Note the following facts about using an ohmmeter.

- Zero ohms on the scale means that there is no resistance between the test leads, thus indicating continuity or a continuous path for the current to flow in a closed circuit.
- Infinity means no connection, as in an open circuit.
- Ohmmeters have no required polarity even though red and black test leads are used for resistance measurement.

Different meters have different ways of indicating infinity resistance, or a reading higher than the scale allows. Examples of an overlimit display include the following:

- OL, meaning over limit or overload
- Flashing or solid number 1
- Flashing or solid number 3 on the left side of the display

Check the meter instructions for the exact display used to indicate an open circuit or over-range reading. ● **SEE FIGURES 12–32 AND 12–33.**

To summarize, open and zero readings are as follows:

0.00 Ω = Zero resistance (component or circuit has continuity)

OL = An open circuit (no current flows) or the reading is higher than the scale selected.

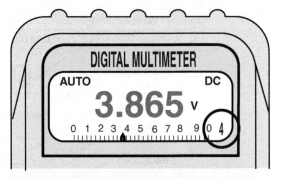

BECAUSE THE SIGNAL READING IS BELOW 4 VOLTS, THE METER AUTORANGES TO THE 4-VOLT SCALE. IN THE 4-VOLT SCALE, THIS METER PROVIDES THREE DECIMAL PLACES.

(a)

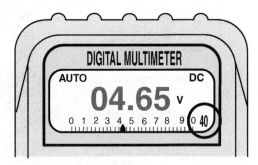

WHEN THE VOLTAGE EXCEEDED 4 VOLTS, THE METER AUTORANGES INTO THE 40-VOLT SCALE. THE DECIMAL POINT MOVES ONE PLACE TO THE RIGHT LEAVING ONLY TWO DECIMAL PLACES.

(b)

FIGURE 12–31 A typical autoranging digital multimeter automatically selects the proper scale to read the voltage being tested. The scale selected is usually displayed on the meter face. (a) Note that the display indicates "4," meaning that this range can read up to 4 volts. (b) The range is now set to the 40 volt scale, meaning that the meter can read up to 40 volts on the scale. Any reading above this level will cause the meter to reset to a higher scale. If not set on autoranging, the meter display would indicate OL if a reading exceeds the limit of the scale selected.

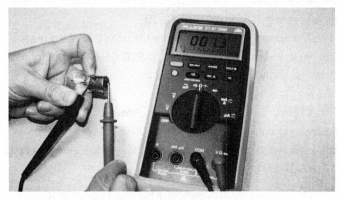

FIGURE 12–32 Using a digital multimeter set to read ohms (Ω) to test this light bulb. The meter reads the resistance of the filament.

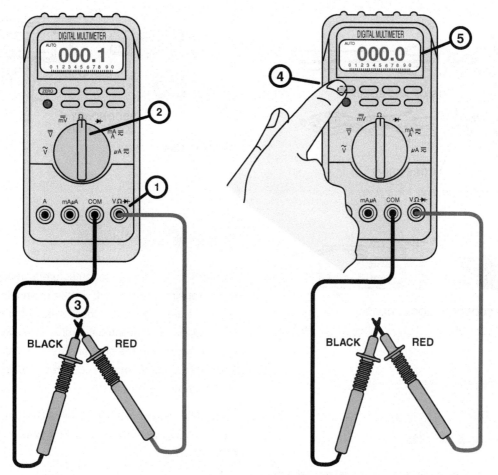

FIGURE 12–33 Many digital multimeters can have the display indicate zero to compensate for test lead resistance. (1) Connect leads in the V Ω and COM meter terminals. (2) Select the Ω scale. (3) Touch the two meter leads together. (4) Push the "zero" or "relative" button on the meter. (5) The meter display will now indicate zero ohms of resistance.

MEASURING AMPERES An **ammeter** measures the flow of current through a complete circuit in units of amperes or milliamperes (1/1,000 of an ampere). The ammeter has to be installed in the circuit (in series) so that it can measure all the current flow in that circuit, just as a water flow meter would measure the amount of water flow (cubic feet per minute, for example). ● **SEE FIGURE 12–34**.

CAUTION: An ammeter must be installed in series with the circuit to measure the current flow in the circuit. If a meter set to read amperes is connected in parallel, such as across a battery, the meter or the leads may be destroyed, or the fuse will blow, from the current available across the battery. Some DMMs beep if the unit selection does not match the test lead connection on the meter. However, in a noisy shop, this beep sound may be inaudible.

Digital meters require that the meter leads be moved to the ammeter terminals. Most digital meters have an ampere scale that can accommodate a maximum of 10 amperes.

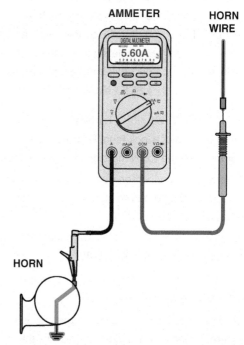

FIGURE 12–34 Measuring the current flow required by a horn requires that the ammeter be connected to the circuit in series and the horn button be depressed by an assistant.

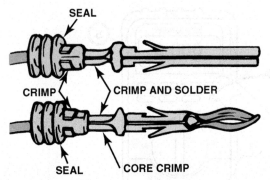

FIGURE 12–35 Some terminals have seals attached to help seal the electrical connections.

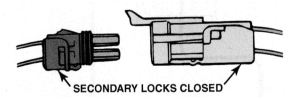

FIGURE 12–36 Separate a connector by opening the lock and pulling the two apart.

TERMINALS AND CONNECTORS

TERMINOLOGY A **terminal** is a metal fastener attached to the end of a wire, which makes the electrical connection. The term **connector** usually refers to the plastic portion that snaps or connects together, thereby making the mechanical connection. Wire terminal ends usually snap into and are held by a connector. Male and female connectors can then be snapped together, thereby completing an electrical connection. Connectors exposed to the environment are also equipped with a weather-tight seal. ● SEE FIGURE 12–35.

SERVICING TERMINALS Terminals are retained in connectors by the use of a lock tang. Removing a terminal from a connector includes the following steps.

STEP 1 Release the connector position assurance (CPA), if equipped, that keeps the latch of the connector from releasing accidentally.

STEP 2 Separate the male and female connector by opening the lock. ● SEE FIGURE 12–36.

STEP 3 Release the secondary lock, if equipped. ● SEE FIGURE 12–37.

STEP 4 Using a pick, look for the slot in the plastic connector where the lock tang is located, depress the lock tang, and gently remove the terminal from the connector. ● SEE FIGURE 12–38.

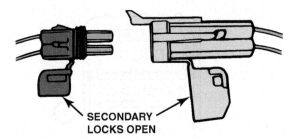

FIGURE 12–37 The secondary locks help retain the terminals in the connector.

WIRE REPAIR

SOLDERING Many manufacturers recommend that all wiring repairs be soldered. Solder is an alloy of tin and lead used to make a good electrical contact between two wires or connections in an electrical circuit. However, a flux must be used to help clean the area and to help make the solder flow. Therefore, solder is made with a resin (rosin) contained in the center, called *rosin-core solder*.

CAUTION: Never use acid-core solder to repair electrical wiring as the acid will cause corrosion. ● SEE FIGURE 12–39.

Solder is available with various percentages of tin and lead in the alloy. Ratios are used to identify these various types of solder, with the first number denoting the percentage of tin in the alloy and the second number giving the percentage of lead. The most commonly used solder is 50/50, which means that 50% of the solder is tin and the other 50% is lead. The percentages of each alloy primarily determine the melting point of the solder.

- 60/40 solder (60% tin/40% lead) melts at 361°F (183°C).
- 50/50 solder (50% tin/50% lead) melts at 421°F (216°C).
- 40/60 solder (40% tin/60% lead) melts at 460°F (238°C).

SOLDERING PROCEDURE Soldering a wiring splice includes the following steps.

STEP 1 While touching the soldering gun to the splice, apply solder to the junction of the splice and the wire.

STEP 2 The solder will start to flow. Do not move the soldering gun.

STEP 3 Just keep feeding more solder into the splice as it flows into and around the strands of the wire.

STEP 4 After the solder has flowed throughout the splice, remove the soldering gun and the solder from the splice and allow the solder to cool slowly.

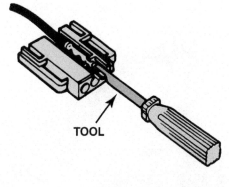

TOOL

RAISING RETAINING
FINGERS TO REMOVE
CONTACTS

LOCKING WEDGE CONNECTOR

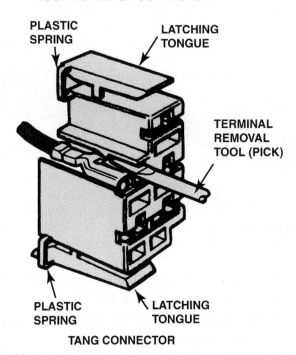

PLASTIC
SPRING

LATCHING
TONGUE

TERMINAL
REMOVAL
TOOL (PICK)

PLASTIC
SPRING

LATCHING
TONGUE

TANG CONNECTOR

FIGURE 12–38 Use a small removal tool, sometimes called a pick, to release terminals from the connector.

The solder should have a shiny appearance. Dull-looking solder may be caused by not reaching a high enough temperature, which results in a cold solder joint. Reheating the splice and allowing it to cool often restores the shiny appearance.

CRIMPING TERMINALS Terminals can be crimped to create a good electrical connection if the proper type of

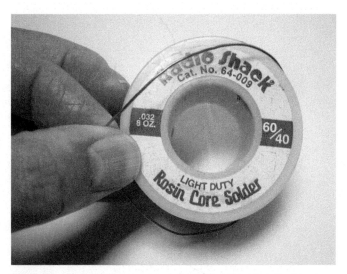

FIGURE 12–39 Always use rosin-core solder for electrical or electronic soldering. Also, use small-diameter solder for small soldering irons. Use large-diameter solder only for large-diameter (large-gauge) wire and higher-wattage soldering irons (guns).

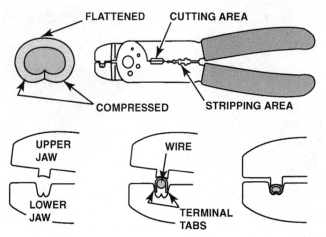

FLATTENED   CUTTING AREA

COMPRESSED   STRIPPING AREA

UPPER
JAW

WIRE

LOWER
JAW

TERMINAL
TABS

FIGURE 12–40 Notice that to create a good crimp, the open part of the terminal is placed in the jaws of the crimping tool toward the anvil or the W-shape part.

crimping tool is used. Most vehicle manufacturers recommend that a W-shaped crimp be used to force the strands of the wire into a tight space. ● **SEE FIGURE 12–40.**

Most vehicle manufacturers also specify that all hand-crimped terminals or splices be soldered. ● **SEE FIGURE 12–41.**

HEAT SHRINK TUBING Heat shrink tubing is usually made from polyvinyl chloride (PVC) or polyolefin and shrinks to about half of its original diameter when heated; this is usually called a 2:1 shrink ratio. Heat shrink by itself does not provide protection against corrosion, because the ends of the tubing are not sealed against moisture. General Motors recommends that all wire repairs that may be exposed to

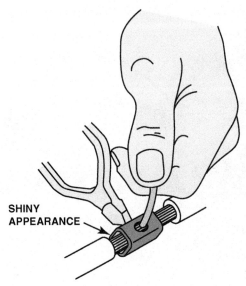

SHINY APPEARANCE

FIGURE 12–41 All hand-crimped splices or terminals should be soldered to be assured of a good electrical connection.

FIGURE 12–43 A typical crimp-and-seal connector. This type of connector is first lightly crimped to retain the ends of the wires and then it is heated. The tubing shrinks around the wire splice, and thermoplastic glue melts on the inside to provide an effective weather-resistant seal.

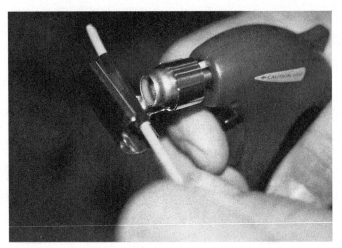

FIGURE 12–42 A butane torch especially designed for use on heat shrink applies heat without an open flame, which could cause damage.

FIGURE 12–44 Heating the crimp-and-seal connector melts the glue and forms an effective seal against moisture.

the elements be repaired and sealed using adhesive-lined heat shrink tubing. The tubing is usually made from flame-retardant flexible polyolefin with an internal layer of special thermoplastic adhesive. When heated, this tubing shrinks to one-third of its original diameter (3:1 shrink ratio) and the adhesive melts and seals the ends of the tubing. ● **SEE FIGURE 12–42**.

CRIMP-AND-SEAL CONNECTORS Several vehicle manufacturers recommend the use of crimp-and-seal connectors as the method for wire repair. **Crimp-and-seal connectors** contain a sealant and shrink tubing in one piece and are not simply butt connectors. ● **SEE FIGURE 12–43**.

The usual procedure specified for making a wire repair using a crimp-and-seal connector is as follows:

STEP 1 Strip the insulation from the ends of the wire (about 5/16 in. or 8 mm).

STEP 2 Select the proper size of crimp-and-seal connector for the gauge of wire being repaired. Insert the wires into the splice sleeve and crimp.

NOTE: Use only the specified crimping tool to help prevent the pliers from creating a hole in the cover.

STEP 3 Apply heat to the connector until the sleeve shrinks down around the wire and a small amount of sealant is observed around the ends of the sleeve, as shown in ● **FIGURE 12–44**.

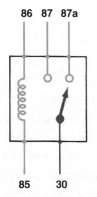

86   87   87a

85   30

(MOSTLY RELAY COILS
HAVE BETWEEN
60–100 OHMS
OF RESISTANCE)

86 - POWER SIDE OF THE COIL
85 - GROUND SIDE OF THE COIL

30 - COMMON POWER FOR RELAY CONTACTS
87 - NORMALLY OPEN OUTPUT (N.O.)
87a - NORMALLY CLOSED OUTPUT (N.C.)

FIGURE 12–45 A relay uses a movable arm to complete a circuit whenever there is a power at terminal 86 and a ground at terminal 85. A typical relay only requires about 1/10 ampere through the relay coil. The movable arm then closes the contacts (#30 to #87) and can often handle 30 amperes or more.

FIGURE 12–47 A relay often shows the schematic of the wiring in the relay.

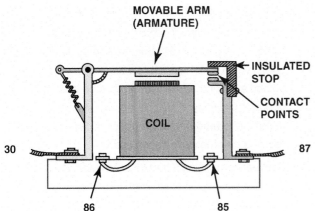

MOVABLE ARM
(ARMATURE)

INSULATED
STOP

CONTACT
POINTS

COIL

30

87

86

85

FIGURE 12–46 A cross-sectional view of a typical four-terminal relay. Current flowing through the coil (terminals 86 and 85) causes the movable arm (called the armature) to be drawn toward the coil magnet. The contact points complete the electrical circuit connected to terminals 30 and 87.

RELAYS

DEFINITION A **relay** is a magnetic switch that uses a movable armature to control a high-amperage circuit by using a low-amperage electrical switch.

TERMINAL IDENTIFICATION Most automotive relays adhere to common terminal identification. The primary source for this common identification comes from the standards established by the International Standards Organization (ISO). Knowing this terminal information will help in the correct diagnosis and troubleshooting of any circuit containing a relay. ● **SEE FIGURES 12–45 AND 12–46.**

Relays are found in many circuits because they are capable of being controlled by computers, yet are able to handle enough current to power motors and accessories. Relays include the following components and terminals.

1. Coil (terminals 85 and 86)
   - A coil provides the magnetic pull to a movable armature (arm).
   - The resistance of most relay coils is usually between 60 ohms and 100 ohms.
   - The ISO identification of the coil terminals are 86 and 85. The terminal number 86 represents the power to the relay coil and the terminal labeled 85 represents the ground side of the relay coil.
   - The relay coil can be controlled by supplying either power or ground to the relay coil winding.
   - The coil winding represents the control circuit, which uses low current to control the higher current through the other terminals of the relay. ● **SEE FIGURE 12–47.**

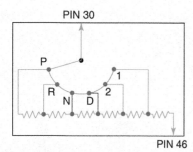

FIGURE 12–48 A typical transmission range switch is also similar to the circuit used for electronic transfer case switches. In this example, power, usually 12 volts, is applied at pin 30 and pin 46 is an input to the PCM. The change in voltage at pin 46 indicates how much resistance the circuit has, which is used to detect the gear selected.

2. Other terminals used to control the load current

- The higher amperage current flow through a relay flows through terminals 30 and 87, and often 87a.
- If there is power at terminal 85 and a ground at terminal 86 of the relay, a magnetic field is created in the coil winding, which draws the armature of the relay toward the coil. The armature, when energized electrically, connects terminals 30 and 87.

The maximum current through the relay is determined by the resistance of the circuit, and relays are designed to safely handle the designed current flow.

SWITCHES

OHMMETER CHECKS A control switch can be checked by removing it from the circuit and checking it with an ohmmeter.

- The meter leads are connected to the two terminals of the switch. If there is only one terminal, one meter lead is connected to it, and the other lead is connected to the switch body. Some switches are normally open, and the reading should be high or infinite (OL). Some switches are normally closed, and the reading should be zero ohms.
- When the switch is operated, the reading should change to the opposite value.
- A pressure switch can usually be operated using a specialized tester or by applying air pressure with a rubber-tipped air gun.

The *transmission range (TR)* switch, also called the *manual lever position (MLP)* switch, or neutral start switch, has several circuits and terminals. This switch is checked using service information to determine which terminals should have continuity as the switch is moved through its travel. ● **SEE FIGURE 12–48**.

TECH TIP

Divide the Circuit in Half

When diagnosing any circuit that has a relay, start testing at the relay and divide the circuit in half.

- **High current portion**: Remove the relay and check that there are 12 volts at the terminal 30 socket. If there is, then the power side is okay. Use an ohmmeter and check between terminal 87 socket and ground. If the load circuit has continuity, there should be some resistance. If OL, the circuit is electrically open.

- **Control circuit (low current)**: With the relay removed from the socket, check that there is 12 volts to terminal 86 with the ignition on and the control switch on. If not, check service information to see if power should be applied to terminal 86, then continue troubleshooting the switch power and related circuit.

- **Check the relay itself**: Use an ohmmeter and measure for continuity and resistance.

- Between terminals 85 and 86 (coil), there should be 60 to 100 ohms. If not, replace the relay.

- Between terminals 30 and 87 (high-amperage switch controls), there should be continuity (low ohms) when there is power applied to terminal 85 and a ground applied to terminal 86 that operates the relay. If "OL" is displayed on the meter set to read ohms, the circuit is open which requires that the relay be replaced.

- Between terminals 30 and 87a (if equipped), with the relay turned off, there should be low resistance (less than 5 ohms).

VOLTMETER CHECKS A mechanically operated switch can also be checked on the vehicle using a voltmeter.

To test a switch, perform the following steps:

STEP 1 Connect the negative meter lead to a good ground or the switch body and the positive lead to the B+ wire entering the switch. Voltage should be available to the switch.

STEP 2 Move the positive meter lead to the second switch terminal, and operate the switch. As the switch is operated, the output voltage should change from zero to the same as the input voltage or vice versa. If the voltage readings are not close to the same, there is a voltage drop, and high resistance in the switch is indicated.

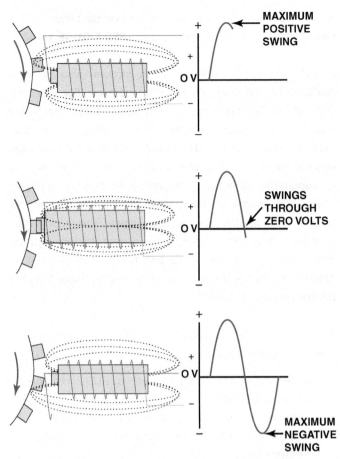

FIGURE 12–49 A magnetic sensor uses a permanent magnet surrounded by a coil of wire. The notches on the rotating shaft create a variable magnetic field strength around the coil. When a metallic section is close to the sensor, the magnetic field is stronger because metal is a better conductor of magnetic lines of force than air.

SPEED SENSORS

OPERATION Speed sensors can be either magnetic or Hall-effect-type sensors. A magnetic sensor consists of a notched wheel and a coil consisting of an iron core wrapped with fine wire. The notched wheel causes the magnetic strength changes enough to create a usable varying AC voltage signal. ● **SEE FIGURE 12–49.**

The voltage-generating speed sensor normally uses a two-wire connector and is checked using both an ohmmeter and a voltmeter.

SPEED SENSOR TESTS
To test a speed sensor, perform the following steps:

STEP 1 Disconnect the sensor, and connect the two ohmmeter leads to the two sensor terminals.

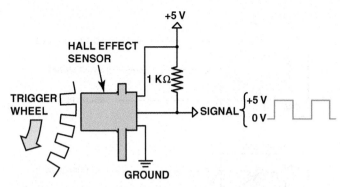

FIGURE 12–50 A Hall-Effect sensor produces an on-off voltage signal whether it is used with a blade or a notched wheel.

STEP 2 There should be a complete circuit through the unit, and the resistance reading should fall within the specified range. Excessive or infinite resistance indicates a high resistance or open circuit; too low of a reading indicates a short circuit.

STEP 3 Attach the two leads of a voltmeter to the two sensor connectors, and set the meter to AC volts.

STEP 4 Rotate the transmission shaft. As the shaft rotates, the voltmeter should show a fluctuating AC voltage reading, first + and then − of the same value.

Unlike the magnetic pulse generator, the Hall-Effect switch requires a small input voltage to generate an output or signal voltage. **Hall Effect** has the ability to generate a voltage signal in semiconductor material (gallium arsenate crystal) by passing current through it in one direction and applying a magnetic field to it at a right angle to its surface. If the input current is held steady and the magnetic field fluctuates, an output voltage is produced that changes in proportion to field strength. ● **SEE FIGURE 12–50.**

POSITION SENSORS

PURPOSE AND FUNCTION A typical 3-wire position sensor is the throttle position (TP) sensor. The powertrain control module (PCM) uses TP sensor input to determine the amount of throttle opening and the rate of change to determine shift points of an automatic transmission and for engine management.

PARTS AND OPERATION The TP sensor consists of a **potentiometer,** a type of variable resistor. A potentiometer is a variable-resistance sensor with three terminals. One end of the resistor receives reference voltage, while the other end is grounded. The third terminal is attached to a movable contact that slides across the resistor to vary its resistance. Depending

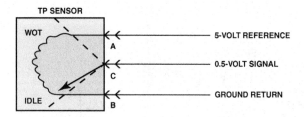

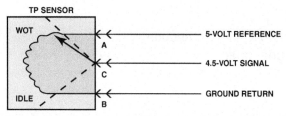

FIGURE 12–51 The signal voltage from a throttle position increases as the throttle is opened because the wiper arm is closer to the 5-volt reference. At idle, the resistance of the sensor winding effectively reduces the signal voltage output to the powertrain control module (PCM).

on whether the contact is near the supply end or the ground end of the resistor, return voltage is high or low.

A typical sensor has three wires:

- A 5-volt reference feed wire from the computer
- Signal return
- A ground wire back to the computer

● **SEE FIGURE 12–51.**

TESTING A TP SENSOR
A throttle position (TP) sensor can be checked using a voltmeter.

To test a TP sensor, perform the following steps:

STEP 1 Leave the TP sensor connector connected. Turn the ignition "ON."

STEP 2 Connect the negative lead to a good ground, and use the positive lead to probe the input voltage at the connector. It should be the specified voltage indicated in the service information.

STEP 3 Move the positive voltmeter lead to the TP output voltage lead, and measure the voltage as the throttle opens and closes. The output voltage should increase and decrease smoothly as the throttle is opened and closed.

NETWORKS

NEED FOR NETWORK
Since the 1990s, vehicles have used modules to control the operation of most electrical components. A typical vehicle will have 10 or more modules

and they communicate with each other over data lines or hard wiring, depending on the application. ● **SEE FIGURE 12–52.**

MODULES AND NODES
Each module, also called a **node**, must communicate to other modules. For example, if the driver depresses the window-down switch, the power window switch sends a window-down message to the body control module. The body control module then sends the request to the driver's side window module. This module is responsible for actually performing the task by supplying power and ground to the window lift motor in the current polarity to cause the window to go down. The module also contains a circuit that monitors the current flow through the motor and will stop and/or reverse the window motor if an obstruction causes the window motor to draw more than the normal amount of current.

TYPES OF COMMUNICATION
The types of communications include the following:

- *Differential*. In the differential form of BUS communication, a difference in voltage is applied to two wires, which are twisted to help reduce electromagnetic interference (EMI). These transfer wires are called a twisted pair.

- *Parallel.* In the parallel type of BUS communication, the send and receive signals are on different wires.

- *Serial data.* The serial data is data transmitted by a series of rapidly changing voltage signals pulsed from low to high or from high to low.

- *Multiplexing.* The process of multiplexing involves the sending of multiple signals of information at the same time over a signal wire and then separating the signals at the receiving end.

This system of intercommunication of computers or processors is referred to as a network. ● **SEE FIGURE 12–53.**

By connecting the computers together on a communications network, they can easily share information back and forth. This multiplexing has the following advantages.

- Elimination of redundant sensors and dedicated wiring for these multiple sensors
- Reduction of the number of wires, connectors, and circuits
- Addition of more features and option content to new vehicles
- Weight reduction due to fewer components, wires, and connectors, thereby increasing fuel economy
- Changeable features with software upgrades versus component replacement

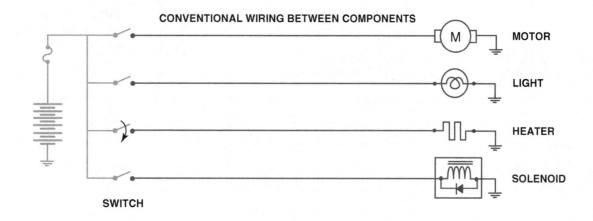

CONVENTIONAL WIRING BETWEEN COMPONENTS

MOTOR

LIGHT

HEATER

SOLENOID

SWITCH

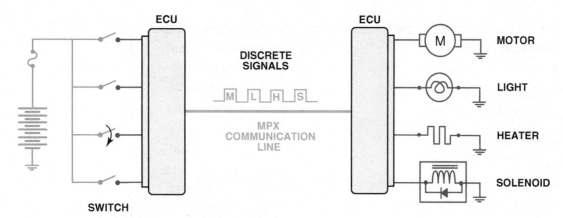

ECU

ECU

DISCRETE
SIGNALS

M L H S

MPX
COMMUNICATION
LINE

MOTOR

LIGHT

HEATER

SOLENOID

SWITCH

FIGURE 12–52 Module communications makes controlling multiple electrical devices and accessories easier by using simple low-current switches to signal another electronic control module (ECM), which does the actual switching of the current to the device.

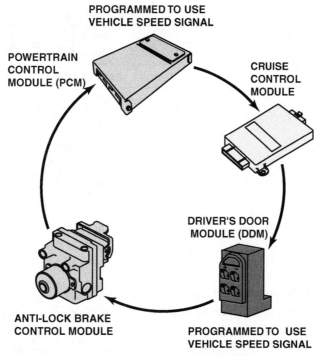

PROGRAMMED TO USE
VEHICLE SPEED SIGNAL

POWERTRAIN
CONTROL
MODULE (PCM)

CRUISE
CONTROL
MODULE

DRIVER'S DOOR
MODULE (DDM)

ANTI-LOCK BRAKE
CONTROL MODULE

PROGRAMMED TO USE
VEHICLE SPEED SIGNAL

FIGURE 12–53 A network allows all modules to communicate with other modules.

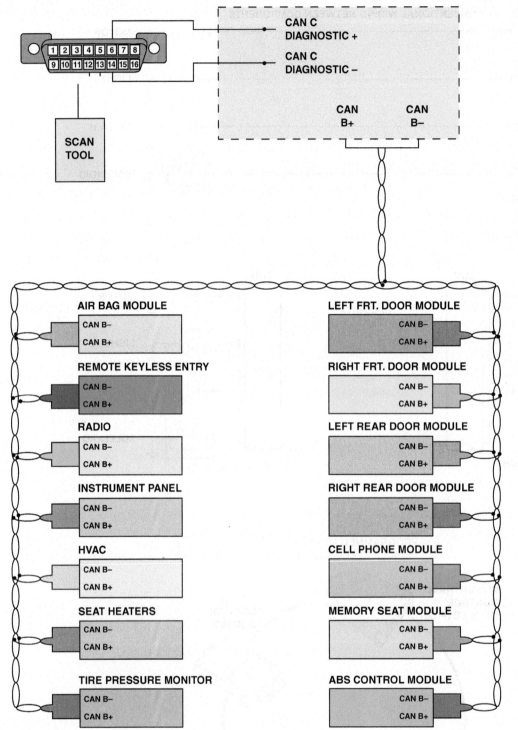

FIGURE 12–54 A typical BUS system showing module CAN communications and twisted pairs of wire.

CAN C
DIAGNOSTIC +

CAN C
DIAGNOSTIC –

CAN
B+

CAN
B–

SCAN
TOOL

AIR BAG MODULE
CAN B–
CAN B+

REMOTE KEYLESS ENTRY
CAN B–
CAN B+

RADIO
CAN B–
CAN B+

INSTRUMENT PANEL
CAN B–
CAN B+

HVAC
CAN B–
CAN B+

SEAT HEATERS
CAN B–
CAN B+

TIRE PRESSURE MONITOR
CAN B–
CAN B+

LEFT FRT. DOOR MODULE
CAN B–
CAN B+

RIGHT FRT. DOOR MODULE
CAN B–
CAN B+

LEFT REAR DOOR MODULE
CAN B–
CAN B+

RIGHT REAR DOOR MODULE
CAN B–
CAN B+

CELL PHONE MODULE
CAN B–
CAN B+

MEMORY SEAT MODULE
CAN B–
CAN B+

ABS CONTROL MODULE
CAN B–
CAN B+

NETWORK CLASSIFICATIONS

The Society of Automotive Engineers (SAE) standards include the following three categories of in-vehicle network communications.

Class A Low-speed networks, meaning less than 10,000 bits per second (bps, or 10 Kbs), are generally used for trip computers, entertainment, and other convenience features.

Class B Medium-speed networks, meaning 10,000 bps to 125,000 bps (10 Kbs to 125 Kbs), are generally used for information transfer among modules, such as instrument clusters, temperature sensor data, and other general uses.

Class C High-speed networks, meaning 125,000 bps to 1,000,000 bps, are generally used for real-time powertrain and vehicle dynamic control. High-speed BUS communication systems now use a controller area network (CAN). ● **SEE FIGURE 12–54.**

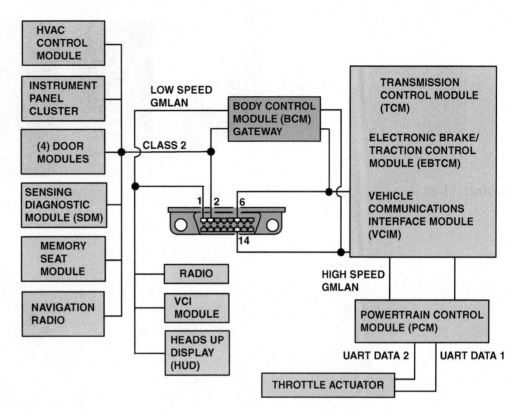

FIGURE 12–55 A schematic of a Chevrolet Equinox shows that the vehicle uses a GMLAN BUS (DLC pins 6 and 14), plus a Class 2 (pin 2). A scan tool can therefore communicate to the transmission control module (TCM) through the high-speed network. Pin 1 connects to the low-speed GMLAN network.

? FREQUENTLY ASKED QUESTION

What Are U Codes?

The "U" diagnostic trouble codes were at first "undefined" but are now network-related codes. Use the network codes to help pinpoint the circuit or module that is not working correctly. Some powertrain-related faults are due to network communications errors and therefore can be detected by looking for "U" diagnostic trouble codes (DTCs).

CONTROLLER AREA NETWORK

STANDARD Robert Bosch Corporation developed the CAN protocol, which was called CAN 1.2, in 1993. The CAN protocol was approved by the Environmental Protection Agency (EPA) for 2003 and newer vehicle diagnostics, and a legal requirement for all vehicles by 2008. The CAN diagnostic systems use pins 6 and 14 in the standard 16 pin OBD-II (J-1962) connector. Before CAN, the scan tool protocol had been manufacturer specific. ● **SEE FIGURE 12–55**.

TRANSMISSION ELECTRICAL COMPONENTS

SECOND AND THIRD GEAR BLOCKOUT SOLENOID During light acceleration and low engine load, the second and third gear blockout solenoid blocks second gear and third gear, forcing the driver of the vehicle to shift from first gear to fourth gear. This solenoid is a performance feature that allows for improved fuel economy. The components that contribute to the operation of the second and third gear blockout solenoid are the ECM, wheel speed sensor, throttle angle position sensor, second and third gear blockout indicator lamp, and barometric sensor. The second and third gear blockout lamp notifies the driver of the vehicle that the second and third gear blockout solenoid is engaged. ● **SEE FIGURE 12–56**.

The parameters the ECM monitors to determine when to activate the second and third gear blockout solenoid are based on specific operating conditions for the Camaro, Corvette, and CTS-V version of the TR6060. These conditions deal with certain vehicle speeds, barometric pressure, coolant temperature, and accelerator pedal position. Refer to Service Information for the specific criteria for the vehicle being serviced.

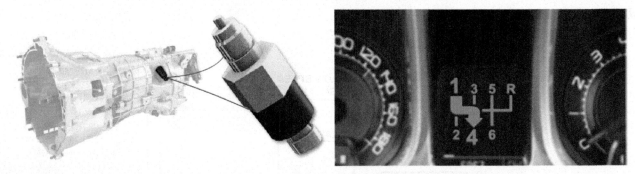

FIGURE 12–56 When the 2-3 blockout solenoid is activated the indicator illuminates. (Courtesy of General Motors.)

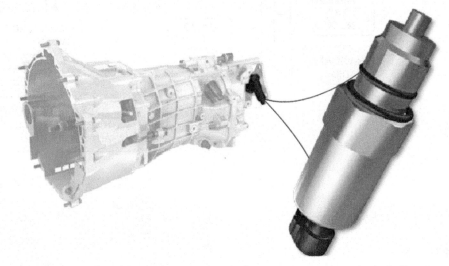

FIGURE 12–57 The reverse lockout solenoid must be turned on before reverse can be selected. (Courtesy of General Motors.)

REVERSE GEAR LOCKOUT SOLENOID The primary function of the reverse gear lockout solenoid is to prevent the driver of the vehicle from inadvertently shifting into reverse while the vehicle is moving forward at a speed faster than 4.8 km/h (3 mph). The ECM uses information regarding the vehicle's speed to determine when to activate the reverse gear lockout solenoid. The ECM opens the ground circuit of the reverse gear lockout solenoid and the solenoid is de-energized. As a result, the solenoid mechanically blocks the shift lever from going into the reverse position. ● **SEE FIGURE 12–57.**

TRANSMISSION FLUID TEMPERATURE SENSOR The transmission fluid temperature, sensor, located at the bottom of the transmission, is a safety feature. When the manual transmission is operating at temperatures higher than 163°C (325°F), the transmission fluid temperature sensor triggers a warning light on the dashboard's instrument panel. This feature helps preserve the oil viscosity in the manual transmission. If the transmission is operated at high temperatures for long periods of time, the oil breaks down and is not able to properly lubricate or cool all of the transmission's moving components.

REVERSE LIGHT CIRCUIT The reverse light switch is a push button-type switch located on the side of the transmission. When the driver of the vehicle selects the reverse position, the ECM signals to the Body Control Module (BCM) that the gear selector is in the reverse position. The BCM applies battery voltage to the backup lamps, which are permanently grounded. Once the driver of the vehicle moves the gear selector out of the reverse position, the electronic control module signals to the BCM to remove the battery voltage from the backup lamp control circuit. ● **SEE FIGURE 12–58.**

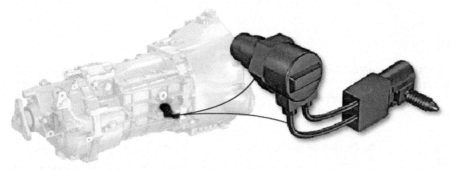

FIGURE 12–58 The reverse light switch is operated by a detent in one of the shift rails inside the transmission. (Courtesy of General Motors.)

SUMMARY

1. Electricity is the movement of electrons from one atom to another.

2. In order for current to flow in a circuit or wire, there must be an excess of electrons at one end and a deficiency of electrons at the other end.

3. Automotive electricity uses the conventional theory that electricity flows from positive to negative.

4. The ampere is the measure of the amount of current flow.

5. Voltage is the unit of electrical pressure.

6. The ohm is the unit of electrical resistance.

7. All complete electrical circuits have a power source (such as a battery), a circuit protection device (such as a fuse), a power-side wire or path, an electrical load, a ground return path, and a switch or a control device.

8. A short-to-voltage involves a copper-to-copper connection and usually affects more than one circuit.

9. A short-to-ground usually involves a power path conductor coming in contact with a return (ground) path conductor and usually causes the fuse to blow.

10. An open is a break in the circuit resulting in absolutely no current flow through the circuit.

11. Circuit testers include test lights and fused jumper leads.

12. Digital multimeter (DMM) and digital volt-ohm-meter (DVOM) are terms commonly used for electronic test meters.

13. Ammeters measure current and must be connected in series in the circuit.

14. Voltmeters measure voltage and are connected in parallel.

15. Ohmmeters measure resistance of a component and must be connected in parallel with the circuit or component disconnected from power.

16. A terminal is the metal end of a wire, whereas a connector is the plastic housing for the terminal.

17. All wire repair should use either soldering or a crimp-and-seal connector.

18. All switches and relays on a schematic are shown in their normal position either normally closed (N.C.) or normally open (N.O.).

19. A typical relay uses a small current through a coil (terminals 85 and 86) to operate the higher current part (terminals 30 and 87).

20. The use of a network for module communications reduces the number of wires and connections needed.

21. The SAE communication classifications for vehicle communications systems include Class A (low speed), Class B (medium speed), and Class C (high speed).

REVIEW QUESTIONS

1. What are ampere, volt, and ohm?

2. What is included in a complete electrical circuit?

3. Why must an ohmmeter be connected to a disconnected circuit or component?

4. List and identify the terminals of a typical ISO type relay.

5. Why is a communication network used?

CHAPTER QUIZ

1. An electrical conductor is an element with _____ electrons in its outer orbit.
   a. Less than 2
   b. Less than 4
   c. Exactly 4
   d. More than 4

2. Like charges _____.
   a. Attract each other
   b. Repel each other
   c. Neutralize each other
   d. Add

3. If an insulated wire gets rubbed through a part of the insulation and the wire conductor touches the steel body of a vehicle, the type of failure would be called a(n) _____.
   a. Short-to-voltage
   b. Short-to-ground
   c. Open
   d. Chassis ground

4. High resistance in an electrical circuit can cause _____.
   a. Dim lights
   b. Slow motor operation
   c. Clicking of relays or solenoids
   d. All of the above

5. If two power-side insulated wires were to melt together at the point where the copper conductors touched each other, the type of failure would be called a(n) _____.
   a. Short-to-voltage
   b. Short-to-ground
   c. Open
   d. Floating ground

6. When testing a relay using an ohmmeter, which two terminals should be touched to measure the coil resistance?
   a. 87 and 30
   b. 86 and 85
   c. 87a and 87
   d. 86 and 87

7. Technician A says that a good relay should measure between 60 ohms and 100 ohms across the coil terminals. Technician B says that OL should be displayed on an ohmmeter when touching terminals 30 and 87. Which technician is correct?
   a. Technician A only
   b. Technician B only
   c. Both Technicians A and B
   d. Neither Technician A nor B

8. If a wire repair, such as that made under the hood or under the vehicle, is exposed to the elements, which type of repair should be used?
   a. Wire nuts and electrical tape
   b. Solder and adhesive-lined heat shrink or crimp-and-seal connectors
   c. Butt connectors
   d. Rosin-core solder and electrical tape

9. A module is also known as a _____.
   a. BUS
   b. Node
   c. Terminator
   d. Resistor pack

10. A high-speed CAN BUS communicates with a scan tool through which terminal(s)?
    a. 6 and 14
    b. 2
    c. 7 and 15
    d. 4 and 16

chapter 13

FOUR-WHEEL AND ALL-WHEEL DRIVE

LEARNING OBJECTIVES

After studying this chapter, the reader should be able to:

1. Explain the characteristics of four-wheel-drive (4WD) vehicles.
2. Differentiate between part-time and full-time four-wheel-drive vehicles.
3. Explain the purpose and function of the central differential and transfer case in a four-wheel-drive vehicle.
4. Explain the purpose and function of electronic transfer cases and the power transfer unit of a four-wheel-drive vehicle.
5. Explain the purpose and function of couplers and torque bias devices.
6. Discuss the operation of front drive axles and drive axle/wheel disconnect systems.

This chapter will help you prepare for ASE Manual Drive Train and Axles (A3) certification test content area "F" (Four-Wheel Drive/All-Wheel Drive Diagnosis and Repair)

KEY TERMS

All-wheel drive (AWD) 235
Center differential 235
Electronic Shift on-the-Fly (ESOF) 241
Four-wheel drive (4WD) 232
Full-time 4WD 235
Locking hub 234
Manual shift on-the-fly (MSOF) 240
Mode shift 233
Open design 247

Part-time four-wheel drive 234
Power transfer unit (PTU) 244
Range shift 234
Rocker pin 240
Torque biasing device (TBD) 245
Transfer case 232
Transfer case control module (TCCM) 241
Viscous coupling 236

GM STC OBJECTIVES

GM Service Technical College topics covered in this chapter are as follows:

1. Types and characteristics of passenger car all-wheel drive system.
2. Operation of the passenger car all-wheel drive system.
3. Identify 4WD/AWD drivetrain types.
4. Identify 4WD/AWD transfer case types.
5. Recall truck 4WD/AWD transfer case mechanical operation.
6. Identify 4WD/AWD electrical modes of operation.

FIGURE 13–1 A World War II Jeep on display at the Lemay Museum in Tacoma, Washington.

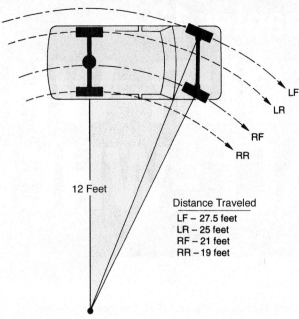

Distance Traveled
LF – 27.5 feet
LR – 25 feet
RF – 21 feet
RR – 19 feet

12 Feet

FIGURE 13–2 If a vehicle makes a right-angle turn with an inside rear-wheel radius of 12 feet, the four tires will travel the distances indicated in the same amount of time; the outside front tire will have to go about 70% faster than the inside rear tire.

FOUR-WHEEL DRIVE

PURPOSE AND FUNCTION Two-wheel-drive vehicles use engine torque to turn either the front or the rear wheels. A differential is required to allow the drive wheels to travel different distances and speeds while cornering or driving over bumps or dips in the road. A four-wheel-drive vehicle, therefore, requires two differentials—one for the front wheels and one for the rear wheels.

NOTE: The term *4 × 4* means a four-wheeled vehicle that has engine torque applied to all four wheels (four-wheel drive). A *4 × 2* means a four-wheeled vehicle that has engine torque applied to only two wheels (two-wheel drive).

The front and the rear wheels of a four-wheel-drive vehicle also travel different distances and speeds whenever cornering or running over dips or rises in the road. Therefore, a four-wheel-drive vehicle also needs a center differential to allow the front wheels to travel different distances than the rear wheels.

BACKGROUND **Four-wheel drive (4WD)** for cars, pickups, and light trucks has steadily evolved from the somewhat crude but rugged Jeep of World War II to sport cars and sport utility vehicles. ● SEE FIGURE 13–1.

PRINCIPLES A two-wheel-drive vehicle is able to power both drive wheels through the use of a drive axle and a differential. Powering all four wheels creates some issues such as:

- Not only do the wheels on the outside travel further while turning than the inside wheels, the rear wheels and tires also travel different distances than the front wheels and tires. ● SEE FIGURE 13–2.
- There is a need for a unit, usually a **transfer case**, where the engine torque can be split to either one drive axle or both to provide for four-wheel drive.

CONFIGURATIONS 4WD can be based on any drivetrain configuration including the following:

- **Front engine–RWD**—Most truck-based four-wheel systems use this arrangement.
- **Front engine–FWD**—Many passenger vehicles and sport utility vehicles (SUV) use this arrangement.
- **Mid-engine–RWD**—Some sport cars use this arrangement such as some Porsches.
- **Rear engine–RWD**—Some sport cars use this arrangement such as some Porsches.

● SEE FIGURE 13–3.

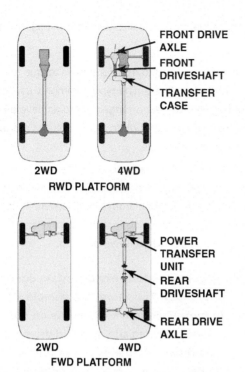

FIGURE 13–3 Four-wheel-drive vehicles can be achieved by using an existing rear-wheel-drive arrangement and adding a transfer case, or a front-wheel-drive arrangement with the addition of rear axle output shaft and center differential assembly.

TERMINOLOGY

The terms used for four-wheel-drive vehicles can be confusing. The terms and their meaning include the following:

- **Two-Wheel Drive**—In two-wheel drive, engine torque is sent to either the rear (rear-wheel-drive vehicle) or to the front (front-wheel-drive vehicle).

- **Four-Wheel Drive**—In four-wheel drive, engine torque is sent to both the front and rear axles.

- **Part-Time Four-Wheel Drive**—In a vehicle equipped with a part-time four-wheel system, both front and rear axles are mechanically connected and locked together. Driving a part-time four-wheel-drive vehicle on dry pavement can cause the drivetrain to bind unless the front wheels are disconnected usually using locking hubs. With the front hubs locked, the vehicle should only be driven on dirt, mud, or snow to avoid damage caused by driveline windup.

- **Full-Time Four-Wheel Drive**—This type of four-wheel-drive system uses a center (interaxle) differential, which allows for both the front and rear axles to rotate at different speeds. A vehicle equipped with a full-time four-wheel-drive system can be safely driven in four-wheel drive on dry pavement and under all driving conditions.

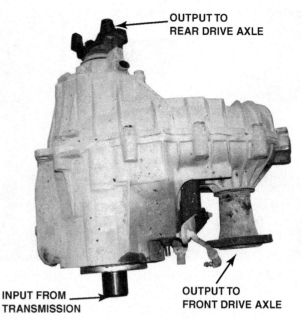

FIGURE 13–4 A typical transfer case is attached to the output of the transmission and directs engine torque to the rear or to the front and rear differentials.

- **On-Demand Four-Wheel Drive**—With an on-demand -type four-wheel-drive system, one axle is driven all the time and engine torque is only sent to the other axle when traction has been lost on the primary axle. This type of system is commonly used in front-wheel-drive-based vehicles where the front axle is driven all the time with engine torque only applied to the rear when the front wheels are starting to slip.

TRANSFER CASES

PURPOSE AND FUNCTION The purpose and function of the transfer case are to control the power flow to both the front and rear axles. Many transfer cases also provide gear reduction to increase the torque applied to the drive wheels. ● SEE FIGURE 13–4.

TYPES OF SHIFTS Most transfer cases also provide for two types of shifts:

- **Mode shift**—Either two-wheel drive or four-wheel drive may be selected. Many transfer cases also have a neutral position. The mode shift is achieved by the use of a floor-mounted lever to engage and disengage a clutch inside the transfer case. This shift is usually performed when the vehicle is stopped. However, new designs allow the mode shift to be performed under most driving conditions.

FIGURE 13–5 A typical electronic transfer case control that is used to shift between two-wheel drive and four-wheel drive (mode shift) or from four-wheel high to four-wheel low (range shift).

NOTE: The mode shift is not available on all-wheel-drive vehicles.

- **Range shift**—A low range may be selected to deliver high torque at low speeds to the drive wheels. Low range gear ratio varies with application. Commonly used ratios are 2:1, 2.5:1, 2.6:1, and 2.72:1 gear reduction. High range (usually 1:1 ratio) simply transfers engine torque at the same speed as the output shaft of the transmission.

● SEE FIGURE 13–5.

PART-TIME FOUR-WHEEL DRIVE

PURPOSE AND FUNCTION A part-time four-wheel-drive system does *not* include a center differential; therefore it is designed primarily for slow speed, off-road use. Both front and rear drive axles are driven at the same speed, and the tires must slip to compensate for speed differential on turns. Older pickups and Jeep-type vehicles use part-time 4WD that is designed to be used off-road.

PARTS AND OPERATION **Part-time four-wheel drive** has a positive, mechanical connection between the front and rear driveshafts when shifted into 4WD. 4WD is used only where there is poor traction because the front or rear tires *must* be able to slip on the road surface while cornering. Gear train bind up will occur if turns are made on pavement.

A part-time four-wheel-drive system has the following parts:

- Transfer case used to transfer engine torque to both the front and rear wheels. The type commonly used includes a sliding gear to gear arrangement to achieve a low range and then straight through to both front and rear axles for four-wheel high range.
- Locking front wheel hubs to allow the vehicle to be driven on the dry pavement in two-wheel drive mode by disconnecting the front wheel from the drivetrain. These hubs can be manual, requiring that they be switched by the driver to the four-wheel-drive position.

CAUTION: A part-time four-wheel system does NOT use a center differential. Therefore, the vehicle should only be driven in four-wheel drive when it is on dirt, mud, or snow, where the tires can slip, to avoid driveline binding caused by the different speeds of the four wheels. The vehicle will likely shake and shutter as wheel torque is applied to the four wheels on dry pavement. The tires will often slip and hop over the pavement as the driveline binds and then the wheels slip and then bind again.

LOCKING HUBS The transfer case also applies power to the front differential. Power is then applied to the front wheels through the drive axles to the **locking hubs**. In normal 4H driving on hard surfaces, the front hubs *must* be in the unlocked position. The front hubs are locked whenever driving on loose road surfaces to absorb and allow for tire slippage due to the different tire speeds front to back. This type of four-wheel-drive system is called **part-time four-wheel drive** because it can be driven in four-wheel drive only on slippery surfaces. ● SEE FIGURE 13–6.

CAUTION: Failure to unlock the front wheel hubs while driving on a hard road surface can cause serious driveline vibrations and damage to driveshafts, U-joints, and bearings, as well as to the transfer case, transmission, and even the engine.

AUTO LOCKING HUBS Another method of locking the hubs on a part-time four-wheel-drive system is with a clutch arrangement built into the hub assembly. Whenever driving on smooth, hard road surfaces, the hubs "free wheel" and allow the front wheels to rotate at different speeds from the rear wheels. When the speed difference between the wheels and the front drive axle is great, the hubs will automatically lock and allow engine torque to be applied to the front wheels. Automatic-locking hubs are unlocked by disengaging

FIGURE 13–6 Cutaway of a manually operated locking hub.

four-wheel drive at the transfer case and driving for several feet. ● **SEE FIGURE 13–7.**

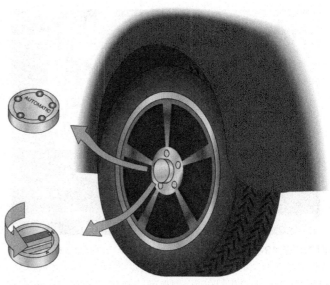

FIGURE 13–7 Manual locking hubs require that the hubs be rotated to the locked position by hand to allow torque to be applied to the front wheels. Automatic locking hubs enable the driver to shift into four-wheel drive from inside the vehicle.

FULL-TIME FOUR-WHEEL DRIVE

PURPOSE AND FUNCTION **Full-time 4WD** is also called **all-wheel drive (AWD)** or *anytime 4WD*. AWD vehicles include a transfer case that has center differential, which allows the front and rear driveshafts to be driven at different speeds to prevent drivetrain binding. AWD transfer cases that deliver power to both driveshafts all of the time are called *mechanically active*. Some AWD vehicles are passenger car based, using AWD to enhance driving on wet or icy roads, such as all Subarus.

CENTER DIFFERENTIAL A full-time four-wheel-drive system is designed for on-road use. A center differential allows front to rear speed differential for turns. Both front and rear axles drive the wheels at the same speed.

All-the-time four-wheel-drive, all-wheel-drive, and full-time four-wheel-drive systems use a **center differential**, also called *interaxle differential,* to prevent driveline harshness and vibration, commonly referred to as "driveline windup."

A center (interaxle) differential can include one of the following:

- **Standard bevel gear differential.** The bevel gear differential uses two bevel gears or spider gears attached to the output shaft of the transmission. Two to four

TECH TIP

Keep It in Four-Wheel Drive if Driving in Snow or Mud

The disadvantage with automatic locking hubs is that this design requires the vehicle to move some distance (usually a whole wheel turn, often going backwards) after engaging 4WD, in order for the hubs to engage or disengage. However, if the vehicle gets completely stuck before 4WD has been engaged, this means that vehicle cannot be placed into four-wheel drive.

differential pinion gears are attached to a carrier, which is attached to the transfer gears. In other words, it operates in the same fashion as the differential in a rear axle; power is transferred to the tire with the least traction. When there is unequal traction between the front and rear axles, the axle with the most traction is allowed to slip enough to prevent damage to driveline components. Some bevel-type center differentials use an internal clutch mechanism, much like a limited slip unit, to increase torque transfer and still lessen driveline vibration and harshness. ● **SEE FIGURE 13–8.**

- **Planetary gear differential.** A planetary gear set is often incorporated in transfer cases to act as a differential.

FIGURE 13–8 A bevel gear-type center (interaxle) differential used inside a transfer case. Bevel gear differentials normally split the torque equally between the front and rear drive axles.

FIGURE 13–10 The transfer case clutch pack is applied when four-wheel drive is needed. (Courtesy of General Motors.)

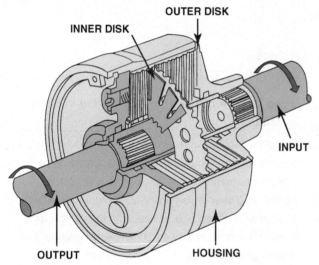

FIGURE 13–9 A viscous coupling is a sealed unit containing many steel discs. One-half of them are splined to the input shaft, with every other disc splined to the output shaft. Surrounding these discs is a thick (viscous) silicone fluid that expands when hot and effectively locks the discs together.

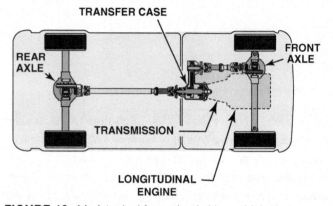

FIGURE 13–11 A typical four-wheel-drive vehicle that uses a longitudinal engine and a transfer case to send engine torque to both the front and rear wheel. Even then a 4WD vehicle can get stuck.

The torque split can be varied by using a planetary gear set as a center differential by changing the number of teeth on the various elements and how they are interconnected can result in various torque splits front to rear.

- **Viscous coupling.** A **viscous coupling** is a series of steel plates housed in a sealed steel drum. The viscous coupling is not active during equal traction conditions. It actively transfers torque during light to moderate cornering, but there is a certain amount of slippage under these conditions to prevent driveline windup. If there is a significant loss of traction, the speed differences between the front and rear axles increase, and this increase in plate speed heats the silicone fluid in the viscous coupling, causing it to thicken to the point that it transfers more torque to the axle that is losing traction. During a severe loss of traction, the viscous fluid thickens enough to lock the plates together, dividing engine torque equally 50/50 between the front and rear axles. ● **SEE FIGURE 13–9.**

- **Center clutch assembly.** Some AWD vehicles do not have a center differential; instead, they use a wet clutch assembly to engage the front drive shaft and axle. The clutch is applied according to the amount of front-wheel drive needed, controlled by a transfer case control module. ● **SEE FIGURE 13–10.**

Can a Four-Wheel-Drive Vehicle Still Get Stuck?

Yes. A four-wheel-drive vehicle can easily get stuck under some conditions depending on the type of system in the vehicle and the type of road surface.
● **SEE FIGURE 13–11**.

This can occur in the following instances:

- If the front, center, and rear differentials are open type, and if only one wheel is on a slippery surface, then the other wheels will only get the torque required by the wheel on the slippery surface and thus the vehicle may not be able to move.

- In case the rear differential is a limited slip-type and both front and center differentials are open type, then if one of the rear tires was on a slippery surface, then the vehicle could continue to move only if the other rear drive wheel was on dry pavement.

- If one front wheel and one rear wheel were on a slippery surface and the rear axle was limited slip, the vehicle may not be able to move because the center differential is an open type.

- If the vehicle is equipped with a locking center differential and a limited slip differential in the rear, then the vehicle will be equipped to go under almost every road surface condition. However, the locking center differential needs to be unlocked at a higher speed to keep the driveline from binding.

- Current technology allows the electronic brake computer to control traction by applying the wheel brake on the wheel that is spinning to increase the amount of torque that is applied to the side or end of the vehicle with the most traction. This means that many systems use open-type differentials instead of limited slip units and rely on the wheel brakes to maintain traction to all drive wheels.

TRANSFER CASES

The purpose of the transfer case is to direct engine torque to the front and rear axle assemblies. A four-wheel-drive transfer case is basically an auxiliary 2-speed transmission. It uses the transmission output as an input to a secondary gear train or planetary gear set, which provides a low and high range. The transfer of torque to the front axle output shaft can be accomplished either by a gear-to-gear transfer or a gear-and-chain transfer. A transfer case has one input shaft (connected to the output of the transmission) and two output shafts. The two output shafts are connected to the driveshafts and transfer torque to the front and rear differentials.

PLANETARY GEAR SET TRANSFER CASE Many transfer cases use a planetary gear set for gear reduction in low range. A planetary gear set includes the following three elements: ● **SEE FIGURE 13–12**.

1. **Sun gear.** This gear is in the center, like the position of the sun is in our solar system.

2. **Planet pinions.** The planet pinion gears rotate around the sun gear, like the planets around the sun, and are attached and held in place by a *planet carrier.*

3. **Ring gear.** The outer ring gear has teeth on the inside that mesh with the teeth of the planet pinion gears. The ring gear is also called the *annulus gear* or *internal gear* because the gear teeth are on the inside (rather than the outside) portion of the gear.

The gear teeth of a planetary gear set remain in constant mesh. When gear reduction is needed, the sun gear is often the drive gear and the planet carrier is often the driven gear. The gear ratio reduction depends on the number of teeth on the various gears used in a planetary gear set. To achieve direct 1:1 output from the transfer case, any two of the three elements can be locked together and the entire assembly will rotate as a unit.
● **SEE FIGURE 13–13**.

PARTS AND OPERATION Engine torque from the transmission is applied directly to the rear differential through the transfer case. ● **SEE FIGURE 13–14**.

The transfer case permits the driver to select a low-speed, high-power gear ratio inside the transfer case while in four-wheel drive. These positions and their meanings include the following:

- 4H four-wheel drive with no gear reduction in the transfer case.

- 4L four-wheel drive with gear reduction. Use of this position is usually restricted to low speeds on slippery surfaces.

- 2H two-wheel drive (rear wheels only) in high range, with no gear reduction in the transfer case.

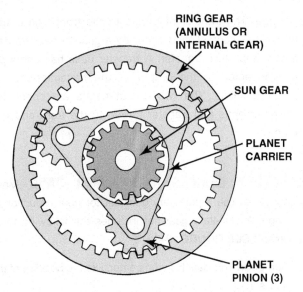

FIGURE 13–12 A typical planetary gear set used in a transfer case.

FIGURE 13–13 Cutaway of a planetary gear set transfer case.

The gear ranges can be engaged in a number of ways, such as:

- Manual lever (older vehicles) ● SEE FIGURE 13–15.
- Electrical motor (most commonly used) ● SEE FIGURE 13–16.
- Vacuum actuators (usually used to connect and disconnect the front drive axle when two-wheel drive is selected)

What Is a Gear-to-Gear Transfer Case?

Gear-to-gear transfer case is simple in design, and is an older design not currently being used. Three gear shafts are in mesh in the transfer case. One gear shaft is attached to the transmission output shaft. The second shaft acts as an idler, and the third shaft is the output to the front axle. Gear-to-gear transfer cases, in most cases, have two speeds. The first four-wheel drive low is a gear reduction that is usually around two to one (2:1). The second gear in the transfer case is a direct drive. The gears are engaged by sliding collars or synchronizers to lock the gears to the shaft. Neutral is accomplished when neither gear collar is locking a gear in place.

TWO-WHEEL-DRIVE OPERATION When the transfer case controls are in two-wheel drive, the front differential assembly is disconnected from the transfer case. This disconnection is usually accomplished by disconnecting one of the drive axles. The disconnect mechanism in the front axle and a synchronizer assembly in the transfer case combine to remove torque for the front wheels. ● SEE FIGURE 13–17.

FOUR-WHEEL-DRIVE OPERATION To achieve four-wheel drive, two things must occur.

1. A synchronizer assembly connects the torque from the engine to the front driveshaft in the transfer case.

2. The drive axles must be connected to allow the torque from the front differential.

3. The output shaft to the rear wheels are connected directly to the output shaft through the range clutch if it is in four-wheel drive high range. In Low range, the torque flows though the planetary gear set and exits through the ring gear. ● SEE FIGURES 13–18 AND 13–19.

What Is a Rocker Pin Chain?

The type of chain used in transfer cases is usually assembled from pin links and chain links and is called **"rocker pin"** type chain. The chain links are what contact the teeth of the sprocket and not the pins as with a roller-type chain. ● SEE FIGURE 13–20.

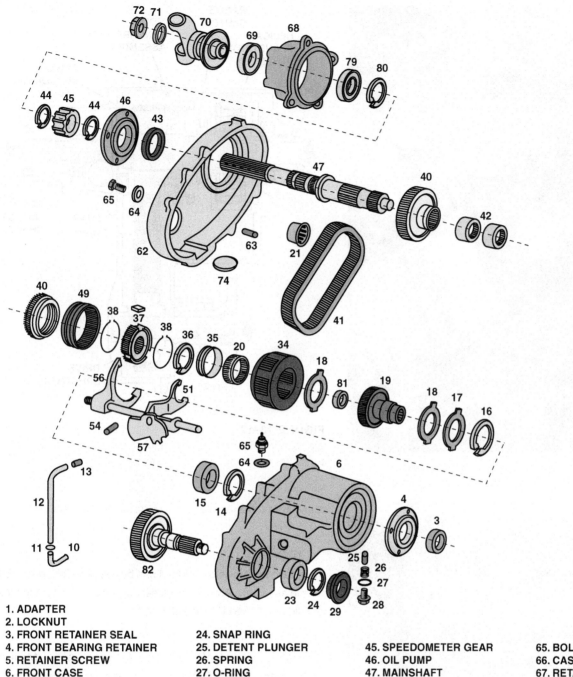

1. ADAPTER
2. LOCKNUT
3. FRONT RETAINER SEAL
4. FRONT BEARING RETAINER
5. RETAINER SCREW
6. FRONT CASE
7. CASE STUD
8. VACUUM SWITCH
9. O-RING
10. VENT
11. CLAMP
12. HOSE
13. HOSE END CAP
14. SNAP RING
15. BEARING
16. SNAP RING
17. RETAINER
18. THRUST WASHER
19. INPUT GEAR
20. PILOT BEARING
21. BEARING
22. OUTPUT SHAFT
23. BEARING

24. SNAP RING
25. DETENT PLUNGER
26. SPRING
27. O-RING
28. PLUG
29. SEAL
30. OIL SLINGER
31. YOKE
32. WASHER
33. NUT
34. LOW RANGE GEAR
35. SHIFT HUB
36. SNAP RING
37. SYNCHRONIZER
38. SPRINGS
39. STOP RING
40. SPROCKET
41. DRIVE CHAIN
42. BEARING
43. SEAL
44. SNAP RING

45. SPEEDOMETER GEAR
46. OIL PUMP
47. MAINSHAFT
48. SHIFT FORK PADS
49. RANGE FORK PADS
50. MODE FORK PADS
51. MODE FORK
52. SPRING
53. SHIFT RAIL
54. PIN
55. BUSHING
56. RANGE FORK
57. SHIFT SECTOR
58. O-RING
59. RETAINER
60. RANGE LEVER
61. NUT
62. REAR CASE
63. ALIGNMENT DOWEL
64. WASHER

65. BOLT
66. CASE BOLT
67. RETAINER SCREW
68. RETAINER
69. SEAL
70. YOKE
71. SEAL
72. YOKE NUT
73. WASHER
74. MAGNET
75. O-RING
76. OIL TUBE
77. TUBE CONNECTOR
78. SCREEN
79. BEARING
80. SNAP RING
81. PLUG
82. FRONT SHAFT
83. SNAP RING
84. GASKET

FIGURE 13–14 An exploded view of a New Venture 241 transfer case.

FIGURE 13–15 Part-time four-wheel-drive transfer cases use a manually controlled lever to perform the mode and range shifts.

FIGURE 13–16 Most transfer cases today use an electric motor to make the mode and range changes and use a dial or push button for each position.

OIL PUMP Most transfer cases also use an oil pump that is driven from the output shaft and supplies the lubricating oil throughout the assembly. The lubricating oil is usually

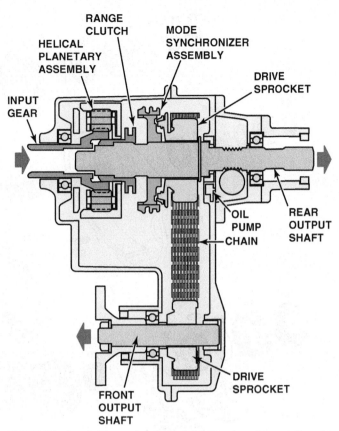

FIGURE 13–17 Two-wheel-drive/high-range torque flow in a NV231 transfer case. The sliding range clutch is shifted to the forward position by the range lever and fork, which connects the input gear to the output shaft and rear axle. The mode synchronizer sleeve is moved out of engagement from the drive sprocket to remove torque from the front axle.

automatic transmission fluid but can be a special fluid designed for the assembly. Always check service information for the type of fluid used. ● **SEE FIGURE 13–21.**

MANUAL SHIFT ON-THE-FLY SYSTEMS Manual shift On-the-fly (MSOF) transfer cases have a selector lever on floor transmission hump and may also have:

- Two sealed automatic front axle locking hubs or
- Two manual front axle hub selectors of "LOCK" and "UNLOCK" or "FREE."

To engage the four-wheel-drive system into four-wheel-drive high range, the vehicle must be moving at a low speed, usually under 50 MPH (80 km/h). To engage the four-wheel-drive low setting, the vehicle must be stopped and the transmission must be shifted to neutral, and then the four-wheel-drive low can be selected.

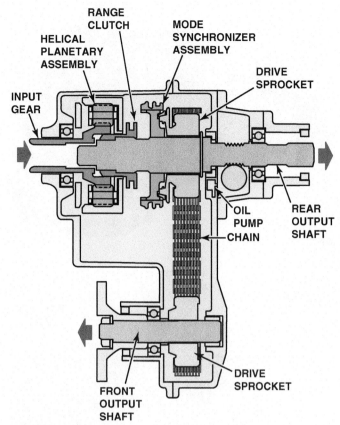

FIGURE 13–18 Four-wheel-drive/high-range torque flow in a NV231 transfer case. The range clutch position remains the same as in two-wheel drive/high-range, but the synchronizer sleeve is moved rearward and engages the drive sprocket clutch teeth. This action connects the drive sprocket to the rear output shaft, thereby applying equal torque to both front and rear output shafts.

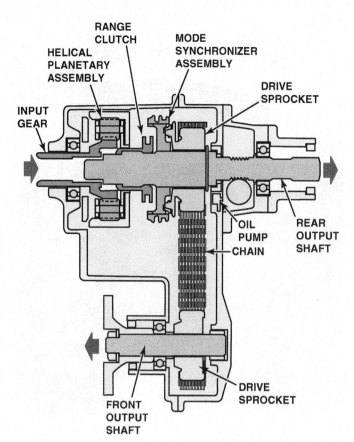

FIGURE 13–19 Four-wheel-drive/low-range torque flow in a NV231 transfer case. The mode synchronizer assembly remains engaged and the range clutch is moved to the rearward position. The annulus (ring) gear is fixed to the case and the input (sun) gear drives the pinion gears, which walk around the stationary annulus gear and drive the planetary carrier and output shaft at a speed lower than the input gear.

ELECTRONIC TRANSFER CASES

PURPOSE AND FUNCTION The transfer case motor/encoder assembly is an electric motor which is used to shift the transfer case from two-wheel high to four-wheel high and can also make a range change between four-wheel high and four-wheel low. These are used on vehicles that feature **electronic shift-on-the-fly (ESOF)** transfer cases. In an electronic transfer case the operation of the range clutch and mode synchronizer assembly is controlled by the motor/encoder assembly.

MOTOR/ENCODER ASSEMBLY Part of the motor assembly is an *encoder,* which is a position sensor that sends the actual position of the transfer case shift shaft to the **transfer case control module (TCCM)**. The TCCM uses the data from the input and output speed sensor to determine when to shift the transfer case to four-wheel drive. If the rear wheels start to slip, the TCCM commands the motor/encoder assemble to make the mode shift. The TCCM also sends a signal to the front axle motor or actuator to engage the front axle when the transfer case is engaging four-wheel high mode. ● **SEE FIGURE 13–22.**

The DC electric motor usually has an attached encoder ring or sensor that indicates the position of the transfer case motor to the TCCM. Some AWD vehicles use *smart transfer cases* that automatically lock up or drive both or either output shaft as needed for the driving conditions. The speed sensors are used to detect unequal wheel speeds and tire slippage and apply the front axle actuator so that engine power is applied to the front and rear drive axles. ● **SEE FIGURE 13–23.**

TORQUE SPLIT Planetary differentials are designed to split torque unevenly so that a percentage goes to the front axle and the remaining goes to the rear axle. The exact ratio or torque split depends on the gear ratios in the planetary gear

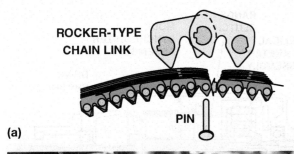

(a)

(b)

FIGURE 13-20 (a) A pin and rocker-type chain, which is also called a *rocker joint-type* chain, is used in transfer cases because of low noise and high efficiency, which improves fuel economy. (b) A rocker pin-type chain used in a transfer case. The black link faces upward and is used as an indicator to the service technician to help insure that the chain is replaced in the same side up when it is reassembled.

FIGURE 13-21 The oil pump is driven by the rear output shaft and is removed with the rear part of the case.

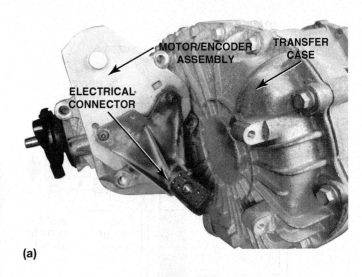

(a)

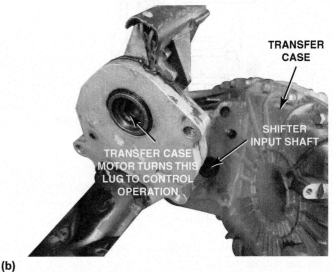

(b)

FIGURE 13-22 (a) Electronically controlled transfer cases use an electric motor to make the mode and range shifts. (b) The motor being removed from the transfer case. The assembly includes the DC motor as well as the feedback sensor so the TCCM "knows" the location of the motor.

 **TECH TIP**

Equal Tire Sizes

Full-time four-wheel drive (4WD) and AWD vehicles must have four equal-diameter tires. Unequal diameters produce different axle speeds, and this will cause excessive wear at the drive axle or center differential. A viscous coupling at the center differential will not last if it has to operate constantly.

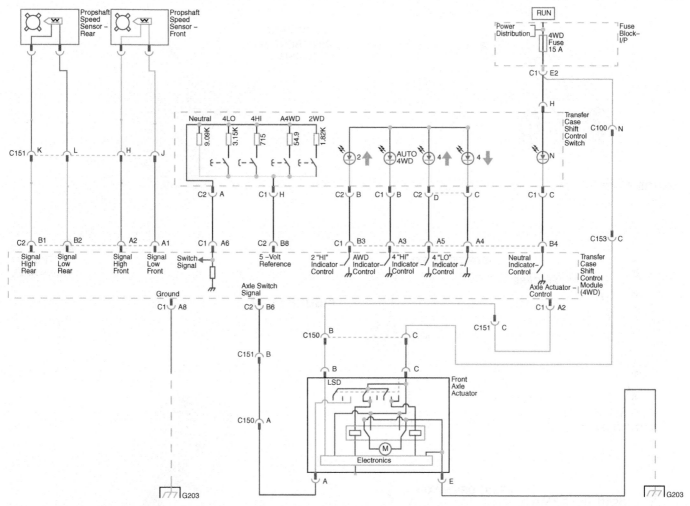

FIGURE 13–23 The driveshaft (prop shaft) speed sensor signals (upper left) are sent to the transfer case control module (TCCM), which then controls the operation of the front axle actuator.

set. This makes the vehicle drive like a rear-wheel-drive vehicle.
● **SEE FIGURE 13–24.** Some transfer cases use an internal clutch to connect the front and rear drive axles. The amount of slip of this clutch determines the torque split.

Some AWD vehicles produced by Audi, Land Rover, Lexus, Toyota, and VW use a Torsen® differential for the center differential. Torsen center differentials are designed with a torque bias ratio of 2.5:1 to 3.5:1. The two driveshafts can operate at different speeds without spin-out problems at the front or rear and smooth turning action.

Most non-planetary center differentials, however, split torque equally. It is possible, though, to lift one wheel and not get enough torque to the other three wheels to move the vehicle.
● **SEE FIGURE 13–25.**

NOTE: Some vehicles are equipped with a center differential lockout. With the lockout, at least both driveshafts and one wheel at each end will be driven.

FIGURE 13-24 A planetary center differential allows for a torque split front to rear (60/40, in this example). The split is compensated for by having different front and rear axle ratios. (Courtesy of General Motors.)

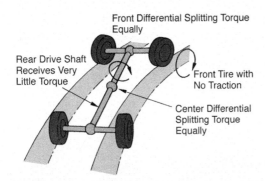

FIGURE 13–25 If the center and front differential split torque equally, an AWD vehicle can become stuck when one wheel loses traction.

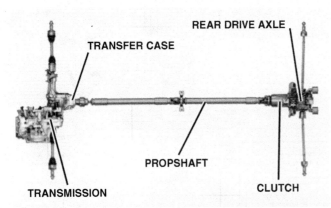

(a)

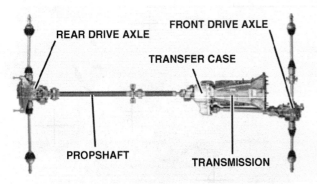

(b)

FIGURE 13–26 (a) A vehicle that is normally FWD (transverse drivetrain) has a transfer case and rear drive axle added for AWD operation. (b) An RWD vehicle (longitudinal drivetrain) includes a transfer case and front drive axle for AWD. (Courtesy of General Motors)

PASSENGER CAR ALL-WHEEL DRIVE SYSTEMS

Passenger cars with all-wheel drive systems include transverse all-wheel drive and longitudinal all-wheel drive. ● SEE FIGURE 13–26.

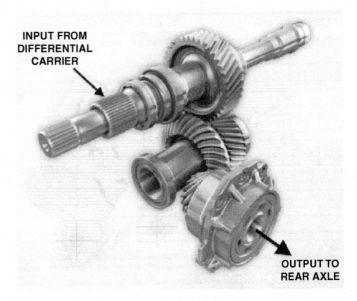

FIGURE 13–27 The final drive ring gear drives the differential carrier, which is splined to the power transfer unit input gear. (Courtesy of General Motors)

FIGURE 13–28 The clutch is electrically applied to send drive torque to the front drive axle when needed. (Courtesy of General Motors.)

TRANSVERSE ALL-WHEEL DRIVE Vehicles with transverse all-wheel drive use a transversely mounted engine and transmission located at the front of the vehicle. The transfer case, or **power transfer unit (PTU),** is attached to the transmission and sends engine power through the propshaft to the rear drive axle. A clutch between the propshaft and rear drive axle determines how much engine power is actually sent to the rear drive axle. ● SEE FIGURE 13–27.

LONGITUDINAL ALL-WHEEL DRIVE Vehicles with longitudinal all-wheel drive use a longitudinally mounted engine located at the front of the vehicle with the transmission attached to the rear of the engine. A transfer case, attached to the rear of the transmission, uses a mechanical planetary

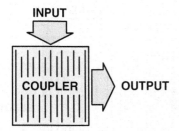

FIGURE 13–29 Coupler is used to transmit engine torque to the drive wheels in series.

FIGURE 13–30 A viscous coupling. Note that the unit is attached to the output shaft between the transfer case (or transaxle) and the rear differential. A typical viscous coupling in a sealed unit is serviced as a complete assembly.

gear set or electronic clutch to send power to the front drive axle.

There are two types of passenger car all-wheel drive systems with the longitudinal mounted transmission: full-time and on-demand. Each system has differences in components and operation. The full-time all-wheel drive system supplies power to the front and rear axles concurrently, with a split of 60% to the rear axle and 40% to the front axle. The on-demand all-wheel drive system primarily provides power to one drive axle; however, if a loss of traction is detected, the system provides torque to the second drive axle. ● **SEE FIGURE 13–28.**

COUPLERS AND TORQUE BIAS DEVICES

PURPOSE AND FUNCTION Couplers are connected in series with other drivetrain members and are used to transfer torque, much like a clutch. They can be active, meaning that they are applied only when needed, or passive and work only after a certain amount of slip has occurred. Torque bias devices use similar components but are connected to the drivetrain in parallel instead of in series.

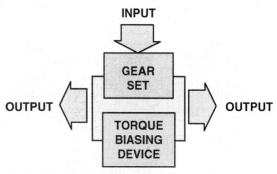

FIGURE 13–31 A TBD is used to control torque to the drive wheel in parallel.

? FREQUENTLY ASKED QUESTION

What Is the Difference Between a Coupler and a Torque Biasing Device?

Both of these devices are used in many four-wheel-drive and all-wheel-drive vehicles. The major differences include the following:

- Couplers are used to control torque between and input and output shafts and are connected in series. ● **SEE FIGURE 13–29.**

- A coupler, such as a viscous coupler, is commonly used in the rear driveshaft to transmit engine torque to the rear drive wheels on a front-wheel-drive vehicle equipped for all-wheel-drive (AWD) operation. Couplers can be located at any of the following locations depending on the exact vehicle and application.
  - Transfer case
  - Power transfer unit
  - Half shafts
  ● **SEE FIGURE 13–30.**

- A **torque biasing device (TBD)** is used to control torque between two outputs and are connected in parallel. The most commonly used TBDs are used to control the torque in a drive axle to the left and right drive wheels. Torque biasing devices can be located at any of the following locations depending on the exact vehicle and application.
  - At the axle differential between the two axle shafts. ● **SEE FIGURE 13–31.**
  - At the center differential between the front and rear driveshafts.

- Both devices may use the same or similar components but how they are connected and used in the system is what separates them from each other.

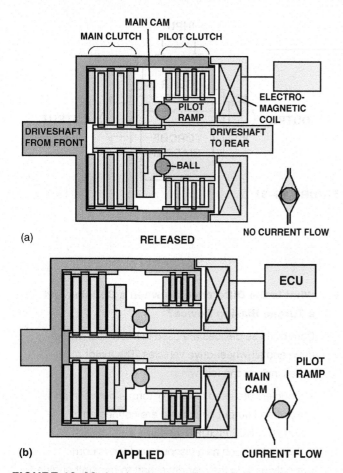

FIGURE 13–32 An electromagnetic coupler in a released (a) and applied (b) condition. When the ECU energizes the electromagnet, the pilot clutch applies to cause a speed differential between the pilot ramp and main cam, and this applies the multiplate clutch.

ELECTROMAGNETIC CLUTCH COUPLER Active couplers used in on-demand systems are dynamic and are applied as needed. These are usually multiplate clutches that are applied by the speed differential between the input and output shafts. In one design, an electromagnetic clutch applies a pilot clutch that in turn applies the main clutch that transfers power. ● SEE FIGURE 13–32.

Another design uses a solenoid to control hydraulic pressure from a gerotor hydraulic pump and the fluid pressure applies the clutch when needed. ● SEE FIGURE 13–33.

These systems are called:

- *Torque Management*
- *Interactive Torque Management System*
- *Intelligent AWD System*
- *Active Torque Dynamics*

An electromagnetic coil is used to engage a multiplate clutch to transfer torque to the rear drive axle. Electrical current to the clutch is controlled by a 4WD electronic control

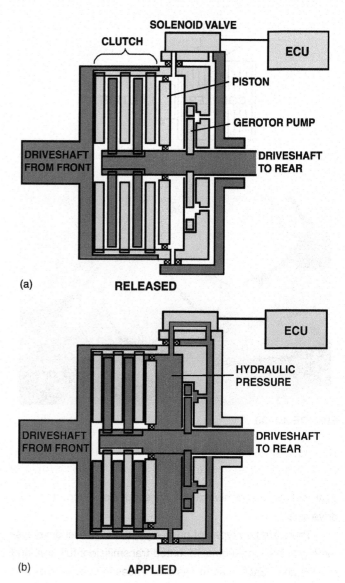

FIGURE 13–33 A hydraulic coupler in a released (a) and applied (b) condition. An input shaft–output shaft speed differential will cause the pump to develop hydraulic press, and when the ECU energizes the solenoid valve, the pressure will apply the multiplate clutch.

module (ECM) that uses the wheel speeds sensors. If the front-wheel speed is excessively greater than the rear-wheel speed, the ECM applies the clutch to drive the rear wheels. The rear wheels are driven only when necessary to improve traction.

ELECTRO-HYDRAULIC COUPLER The Haldex all-wheel-drive system is currently being used on several domestic and European vehicles. The system uses a coupling that can be installed onto the rear drive axle to connect it to the FWD system. The coupling uses a multidisc clutch that is applied hydraulically when there is an excessive speed difference between the input and output shafts.

Hydraulic pressure to apply the clutch is generated in the clutch when the input and output shafts turn at different

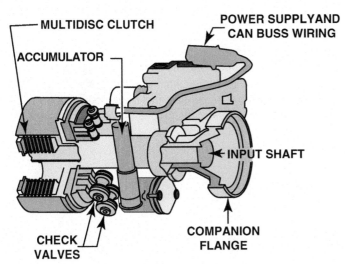

FIGURE 13–34 The Haldex system uses hydraulic pressure to apply the clutch, which can be created as soon as there is a speed differential between the input and output shafts. Hydraulic pressure and speed at which the clutch will be applied are controlled by the ECU.

speeds. When there is no speed difference, there will be no pressure. The clutch application rate is controlled electronically by software designed for the particular vehicle. ● SEE FIGURE 13–34.

FRONT DRIVE AXLES

PURPOSE AND FUNCTION The purpose and function of the front drive axle are to transfer engine torque to the front wheels. Unlike the rear drive axle, the front drive axle has to be designed to steer the front wheels as well as transmit engine torque.

PARTS AND OPERATION Except for the outer ends of the axle housing, which allow steering, most early 4WD utility vehicles have a solid front drive axle housing, which is essentially the same as the one used in the rear.

Some of the 4WD vehicles, based on a rear-wheel-drive platform, use a RWD drive axle that is simply rotated so the drive pinion points toward the rear. Axles using reverse-cut gears can be identified by a high-mounted pinion shaft.

FRONT AXLES Some older front drive axles use an **open design** with ball joints for the steering pivots and a Cardan U-joint. ● SEE FIGURE 13–35.

Most GM 4WDs mount the differential carrier to the vehicle frame or body and use a fully independent suspension. These designs usually use constant velocity-type joints. ● SEE FIGURE 13–36.

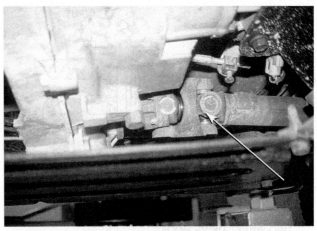

(a)

(b)

FIGURE 13–35 (a) A double Cardan U-joint used on the output driveshaft from the transfer case to the front differential assembly. (b) A Cardan-type U-joint at the front drive wheels on a Jeep Wrangler.

FIGURE 13–36 Constant velocity (CV) joints are used on the front axles of many four-wheel-drive vehicles like this Chevrolet Blazer.

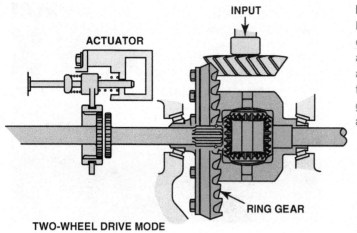

ACTUATOR

INPUT

RING GEAR

TWO-WHEEL DRIVE MODE

(a)

FIGURE 13–37 (a) When one axle shaft is disconnected, both front wheels can rotate independently, reducing excessive tire wear. (b) In four-wheel-drive mode, vacuum is applied to the front part and the opposite side is vented to atmospheric pressure retracting the shift motor stem. The shift fork and collar move into engagement with both axle shaft gears. Engine torque from the front differential can now be applied to both front axles.

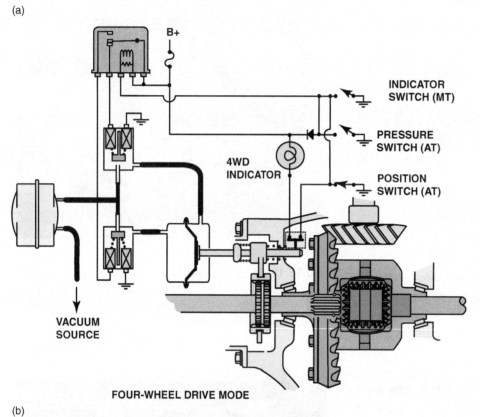

B+

INDICATOR
SWITCH (MT)

PRESSURE
SWITCH (AT)

4WD
INDICATOR

POSITION
SWITCH (AT)

VACUUM
SOURCE

FOUR-WHEEL DRIVE MODE

(b)

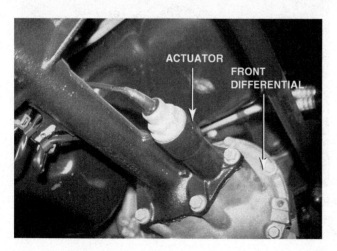

ACTUATOR

FRONT
DIFFERENTIAL

FIGURE 13–38 A General Motors sport utility vehicle front axle showing the electric axle disconnect actuator.

DRIVE AXLE/WHEEL DISCONNECT SYSTEMS

Some front drive axle assemblies include a feature that allows disconnecting one of the axle shafts. As the vehicle is driven, the wheels will drive the axles, differential, and driveshaft. A collar is shifted to connect or disconnect the two parts of the shaft. Either a vacuum or electric shift motor is used for this with the controls being activated by shifting the transfer case into or out of 4WD. ● **SEE FIGURE 13–37**.

When the transfer case is placed in two-wheel drive, the vacuum is applied to the other side of the diaphragm and the shift collar moves, unlocking the front axles.

The transfer case can disconnect the power from the driveshaft to only one of the drive axles at a time.

- The front axle of RWD-based vehicles
- The rear axle of vehicles based on FWD designs

The wheels of the disconnected axle will still drive the axle shaft and gears as well as the driveshaft, causing unnecessary wear and a decrease in fuel economy (about 0.5 mpg). ● **SEE FIGURE 13–38**.

SUMMARY

1. Early 4WD vehicles were based on front engine, RWD vehicles. Many of today's 4WD/AWD vehicles are based on front engine FWD vehicles.
2. A transfer case or power transfer unit drives the second axle.
3. AWD transfer cases/PTUs can include a differential, viscous coupler, or electromechanical clutch to control torque to the front and rear drive axles.
4. Transfer cases can use a gear set or silent chain.
5. Some transfer cases include a planetary gear set.
6. A front drive axle has outboard U-joints or CV joints to allow steering.
7. Front wheel hubs can be disconnected using a mechanical, automatic, or vacuum operation.

REVIEW QUESTIONS

1. Why must there be a center differential in a four-wheel-drive vehicle that is used on hard pavement?
2. What is the difference between a mode shift and a range shift?
3. How can a four-wheel-drive vehicle get stuck if one or more wheels are on a slippery surface?
4. How is front/rear torque split using a planetary gear–type center differential?

CHAPTER QUIZ

1. In 4 × 4, the first 4 refers to _____.
   a. Four-wheel drive
   b. Four wheels on the vehicle
   c. Four speed transfer case
   d. Four speed transmission

2. When a vehicle turns a corner, what is true about the four wheel travel?
   a. Each wheel travels a different distance.
   b. The two right side wheels turn the same distance.
   c. The two left side wheels turn the same distance.
   d. Both b and c are correct.

3. What type of four-wheel-drive system does not include a center (interaxle) differential?
   a. All-wheel drive (AWD)
   b. Full-time four-wheel drive
   c. Part-time four-wheel drive
   d. None of the above

4. Low range in a transfer case is about what ratio?
   a. 2:1 to about 3:1   c. 10:1
   b. 8:1   d. 12:1 or higher

5. What can occur if a part-time four-wheel-drive vehicle is driven on hard pavement in four-wheel drive?
   a. The vehicle will shake and shutter as engine torque is applied to the drive wheels.
   b. The vehicle will slip and hop over the pavement.
   c. The vehicle will experience driveline vibrations and damage to driveshafts, U-joints, and bearings.
   d. All of the above can occur.

6. What type of chain is commonly used in transfer case?
   a. Roller chain
   b. Double roller chain
   c. Rocker pin
   d. Any of the above depending on application

7. To engage the four-wheel-drive system into four-wheel-drive high range on manual shift on-the-fly (MSOF) transfer case, the vehicle must be moving at about what speed?
   a. Completely stopped
   b. Low speed usually under 50 MPH (80 km/h)
   c. Less than 10 MPH (16 km/h)
   d. At any speed

8. A transfer case used with a transaxle is called a _____.
   a. A coupler device
   b. A torque biasing device
   c. A power transfer unit (PTU)
   d. A torque split unit

9. What type of unit is used as a center differential inside a transfer case?
   a. Planetary gear set   c. Viscous coupling
   b. Bevel gear differential   d. Any of the above

10. Most transfer cases are lubricated using _____.
   a. An internal oil pump
   b. Splash lubrication
   c. An external pump
   d. Any of the above depending on the application

chapter 14

FOUR-WHEEL DRIVE DIAGNOSIS AND SERVICE

FOUR-WHEEL-DRIVE PROBLEM DIAGNOSIS

PROCEDURE The process of diagnosing faults or concerns in four-wheel drives and transfer cases involves the following eight steps.

STEP 1 Verify the customer concern.

STEP 2 Perform a visual inspection.

STEP 3 Check for any stored diagnostic trouble codes (DTCs) and technical service bulletins (TSBs).

STEP 4 Check scan tool data for sensor values and bidirectional control operation (if available).

STEP 5 Check electrical switches and actuators using a digital multimeter.

STEP 6 Follow service information pinpoint tests to determine the root cause.

STEP 7 Perform the needed repair.

STEP 8 Verify the repair.

VERIFY CUSTOMER CONCERN The first step is to verify the customer concern. The customer should be asked the following questions in an effort to determine as much about the problem as possible.

- What exactly seems to be the concern? (Ask the customer to be as detailed as possible.)
- When did the problem first appear?
- Is there a problem between two-wheel drive and four-wheel drive (mode change)?
- Is there a problem going between 4-High to 4-Low (range change)?
- Under what conditions do the symptoms occur? (Do they occur first thing in the morning? After the vehicle has been driven for a while?)
- Describe under what driving conditions the problem is noticed, such as when accelerating or while coasting to a stop or some other condition.
- Has the vehicle been serviced recently, such as a fluid change?

Operate the vehicle and drive it under all conditions and in both modes (two-wheel drive and four-wheel drive) and in both ranges (four-wheel high and four-wheel low).

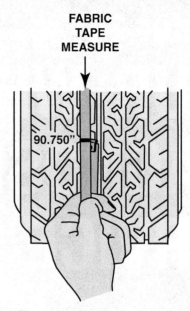

FABRIC TAPE MEASURE

90.750"

FIGURE 14–1 The measuring tape wrapped around the tire shows the circumference is 90 3/4 in. The other three tires should measure close to the same, usually within ¼ in. in circumference.

VISUAL INSPECTION

EQUAL SIZE TIRES All tires of a full-time four-wheel-drive or all-wheel-drive vehicle must be within a 1/16 in. (1.6 mm) tread depth of each other. Always check that all tires are:

- The exact same size
- The same brand (different brands even if the same size can vary in the actual diameter and width of the tire)
- The same tread depth within 2/32 in. (1/16 in.)
- The same inflation pressure within 2 PSI for best results

MEASURING TIRE CIRCUMFERENCE Tire circumference can be checked by wrapping a cloth tape measure around the tread. ● **SEE FIGURE 14–1.**

A stagger gauge can also be used to measure tire circumference. ● **SEE FIGURE 14–2.**

VISUALLY CHECK DRIVELINE Hoist vehicle safely and perform a thorough visual inspection of the driveline including the following:

- Driveshaft for damage or mud that could affect the balance of the driveshaft

FIGURE 14–2 A stagger gauge, which is commonly used by racing teams to measure the circumference of tires, is a sliding caliper-type tool calibrated to read in circumference.

FIGURE 14–3 Red rust stain is an indication that metal-to-metal contact is occurring and usually indicates that the part is worn and needs to be replaced such as in this U-joint.

 REAL WORLD FIX

The Case of the Noisy Chevrolet Pickup Truck

A GMC pickup (42,000 mi) had a noise in 4WD and would not shift out of 4WD until coasting in second gear. A test using an electronic noise-detecting device such as Chassis Ears® indicated the whining noise to be coming from the transfer case. A careful check of tire size showed 5/32 in. deeper tread on the rear tires, and a check of tire circumference showed 98 inches at the front and 99 inches at the rear. Replacement of the worn front tires fixed this problem. The mix-matched tire sizes caused the drivetrain to bind, which caused the transfer case to lock up and not be able to be shifted correctly.

- U-joints for damage or looseness (check for "rust dust").
  ● **SEE FIGURE 14–3.**
- Engine and transmission mounts for damage
- Check electrical and mechanical connections to the transfer case
- Check for leaks at the transmission or transfer case

GEAR OIL LEVEL AND CONDITION Most transfer cases and power transfer units have a gear oil-level plug in the side of the case for checking the oil level. ● **SEE FIGURE 14–4.**

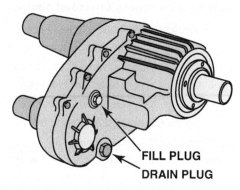

FILL PLUG
DRAIN PLUG

FIGURE 14–4 Always check the fluid level and condition as one of the first items to check when diagnosing a four-wheel-drive customer concern.

As in a manual transmission, the gear oil level should be at the bottom of the plug opening. Always use the lubricant specified by the manufacturer. The fluid used in transfer cases can include the following:

- Automatic transmission fluid (ATF)—check service information for the exact type of ATF to use.
- SAE 80W-90 gear oil—check service information for the exact viscosity and API rating required.
- Special specific transfers case fluid.

Dirty or discolored fluid gear oil should be replaced by draining the old oil and filling the transfer case with new oil of the correct type to the proper level. Many transfer cases include a drain plug so an oil change is relatively easy.

FIGURE 14–5 If the "SERVICE 4WD" warning light is on, check service information for the exact procedures to follow.

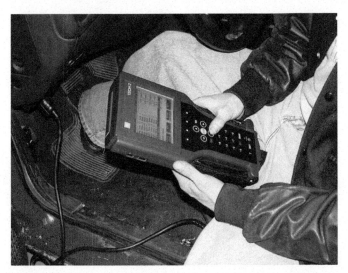

FIGURE 14–6 A TECH 2 scan tool is the factory scan tool used on General Motors vehicles and can be used to diagnose four-wheel-drive concerns.

 REAL WORLD FIX

The Case of the Skipping Chevrolet Minivan

An AWD Chevrolet SUV (38,000 mi) had an odd skip-miss feeling during acceleration. All the engine management features had been checked, and it appeared the engine was running properly. Tire circumferences were checked, and they were within 1/8" of each other. The transfer case was drained and refilled with the proper fluid, but this did not help.

A second transfer case fluid change was recommended, and this fixed the problem. This transfer case can have a stick/slip problem, similar to a limited slip differential. The second fluid change caused the clutch plates to work normally.

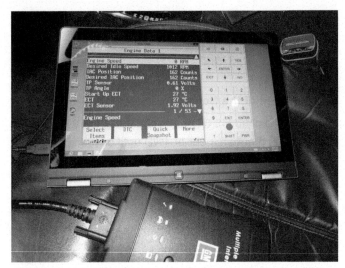

FIGURE 14–7 The Tech2Win program runs on a laptop using the MDI as an interface. (Courtesy of Jeffrey Rehkopf.)

CAUTION: Some vehicles use a transfer case made from magnesium with an aluminum oil-level plug. The plug has a small head, and it tends to seize. A wrench will easily slip and round off the small plug head. It is recommended that if the plug does not unscrew using a reasonable amount of force, then heat the case area surrounding the plug. Use a hot-air device and *DO NOT* use a torch because the magnesium case can ignite and cause a serious fire.

SCAN TOOLS Scan tools are the most important tools for any diagnostic work on all vehicles. Scan tools can be divided into the following three basic categories:

1. **Factory scan tools.** These are the scan tools required by all dealers that sell and service a specific brand of vehicle.

    On General Motors vehicles, the required scan tools are as follows:

    - Tech 2 (1996 to 2010, depends on model) ● **SEE FIGURE 14–6.**
    - Tech 2 and CAndi module (2005 to 2012, depending on model)
    - Tech 2 Win and multiple diagnostic interface (MDI) ● **SEE FIGURE 14–7.**

FOUR-WHEEL-DRIVE DIAGNOSTIC PROCEDURES

WARNING LIGHTS Often in electronically-controlled transfer cases, the controller will light a separate warning lamp to notify that the control system has detected a problem with the system. ● **SEE FIGURE 14–5.**

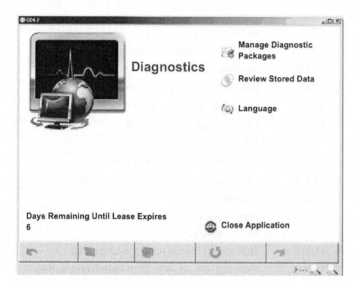

FIGURE 14–8 Global Diagnostic System 2 is required for the latest GM vehicles. (Courtesy of General Motors)

- Global Diagnostic System 2 (GDS2) and multiple diagnostic interface (MDI) (2009 and later, depending on model) ● **SEE FIGURE 14–8.**

All factory scan tools are designed to provide bidirectional capability, which allows the service technician the opportunity to operate components using the scan tool, thereby confirming that the component is able to work when commanded. Also, all factory scan tools are capable of displaying all factory parameters.

2. **Aftermarket scan tools.** These scan tools are designed to function on more than one brand of vehicle. Examples of aftermarket scan tools include the following:
   - Snap-on (various models, including the Verus, Modis, and Solus) ● **SEE FIGURE 14–9.**
   - OTC (various models, including Pegasus, Genisys, TOUCH, and Task Master)
   - AutoEnginuity and other programs that use a laptop or handheld computer for display

   While many aftermarket scan tools can display most if not all of the parameters of the factory scan tool, there can be a difference when trying to troubleshoot some faults.

3. **Global scan tools.** Global (generic) scan tools are the lowest-priced scan tools and they are designed to only be able to retrieve emission-related data as per the SAE standard J1979. The vehicle diagnostic trouble codes (DTCs) and data can be acquired by looking at the global (generic) part of the PCM and does not need to have the vehicle information entered into the scan tool. All global scan tools display only emission-related data stream information. The data displayed on this type of scan tool

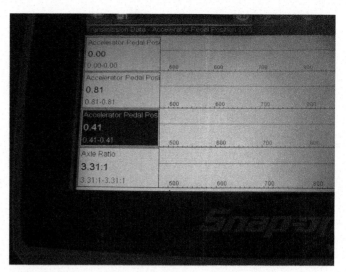

FIGURE 14–9 A Snap-on Solus scan tool is being used to troubleshoot a vehicle. This scan tool can be used on most makes and models of vehicles and is capable of diagnosing other computer systems in the vehicles such as the antilock braking system (ABS) and four-wheel-drive systems.

will be emission-related only and will NOT display faults or codes for transmission or transfer cases.

HOW TO USE A SCAN TOOL In order to get the most from a scan tool, the technician should read, understand, and follow the operating instructions. To use a scan tool perform the following steps:

STEP 1 Locate the data link connector (DLC). This 16-pin connector is usually located under the dash on the driver's side. It can be located in the center console and may be covered by a panel that can be removed without the use of tools. Check service information for the exact location of the DLC for the vehicle being serviced.

STEP 2 Connect the scan tool to the DLC. ● **SEE FIGURE 14–10.**

STEP 3 Turn the ignition key on (engine off). In most cases, the scan tool will come on automatically because the DLC has power and ground connections for the scan tool.

STEP 4 If using a factory or factory-level scan tool, select the vehicle you are scanning and enter the information requested on the screen such as:

   - Year (tenth character of the VIN)
   - Model (usually the fourth or fifth character of the VIN)
   - Engine (usually the eighth character of the VIN)
   - Any options that may be on the vehicle

STEP 5 Follow the on-screen instructions. Read and record any stored diagnostic trouble codes (DTCs). ● **SEE FIGURE 14–11.**

FIGURE 14-10 Connecting a scan tool to the data link connector (DLC) located under the dash on this vehicle.

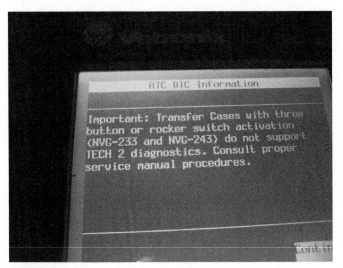

FIGURE 14-11 Not all scan tools are capable of communicating transfer case faults. Check service information for the exact procedures to follow.

DTC	DESCRIPTION
C0300	Rear propeller shaft speed sensor circuit
C0305	Front propeller shaft speed sensor circuit
C0308	Motor A/B circuit, short to ground
C0309	Motor A/B circuit, short to voltage
C0310	Motor A/B circuit, open circuit
C0315	Module ground circuit
C0323	Lock solenoid circuit, open circuit
C0324	Lock solenoid circuit, shorted to voltage
C0327	Encoder feed circuit
C0367	Front axle control circuit, shorted actuator or short to voltage
C0374	Shift control module unable to control slip
C0376	Front and rear propeller shaft speeds greater than 20% difference
C0387	Unable to complete shift as commanded
C0550	Failed shift control module test

CHART 14-1

Typical C-type DTCs associated with faults in the transfer case system.

DTC	DESCRIPTION
C0306 02	Motor A or B circuit shorted to ground
C0306 05	Motor A or B circuit shorted to voltage or open
C0321 01	Transfer case lock circuit shorted to ground
C0321 04	Transfer case lock circuit shorted to voltage or open
C0379 01	Front axle short to voltage
C0379 02	Front axle short to ground
C0379 04	Front axle open circuit

CHART 14-2

Typical DTCs with symptom codes associated with faults in the transfer case system.

RETRIEVING DIAGNOSTIC TROUBLE CODES Most four-wheel drive related trouble codes will be "B" (body) codes, "C" (Chassis) codes, or "U" (network) codes. Global-type scan tools will not be able to access these codes. Codes used for the engine that are emission-related-type codes are "P" (powertrain) codes and do not associate with the transfer case faults except if the speed sensor is faulty.

CODES Most transfer case and four-wheel-drive B and C diagnostic trouble codes are for faults with the transfer case or communication faults between the transfer case the transfer case control module (TCM). For some sample "C" DTCs, ● **SEE CHART 14-1**.

SUBCODES Sometimes the diagnostic trouble code will also have a two-digit subcode that gives additional information to help the technician find the fault. For example, B0770 DTC indicates that there is a fault in the "AWD Indicator circuit." However, with the addition of a two-digit subcode, the cause that set the code is enhanced such as:

- B0770 01—AWD indicator circuit shorted to voltage
- B0770 06—AWD indicator circuit shorted to ground or open

Note that the last two numbers added at the end of the code give additional information as to why the code was set. For some sample transfer case-related DTC codes with sub-codes, ● **SEE CHART 14-2**.

FIGURE 14–12 After checking for stored diagnostic trouble codes (DTCs), the wise technician checks service information for any technical service bulletins that may relate to the vehicle being serviced.

	GM ROTARY SWITCH (5 VOLT)	GM PUSH BUTTON (5 VOLT)	GM PUSH BUTTON (8 VOLT)	FORD ROTARY SWITCH (12 VOLT)	FORD PUSH BUTTON (12 VOLT)	DODGE (RAM) (5 VOLT)
2WD	4.1 volts	2.0 volts	3.2 volts	7.5 volts	NA	2.1 volts
AUTO 4WD	3.3 volts	4.6 volts	7.5 volts	NA	1.8 volts	2.7 volts
4WD High	2.5 volts	3.0 volts	4.8 volts	5.5 volts	6.4 volts	3.5 volts
4WD Low	1.6 volts	1.5 volts	2.4 volts	3.7 volts	9.0 volts	4.1 volts
Neutral	0.8 volts	0.9 volts	1.2 volts	NA	NA	NA

CHART 14–3

Typical voltage readings that may be measured at the four-wheel-drive control switch with the key on, engine off (KOEO). Always check service information for the exact specifications and testing procedures for the vehicle being serviced.

EXAMPLE OF A "C" CODE A C0308 diagnostic trouble code will be set when the Transfer Case Control Module (TCCM) determines a short-to-ground in motor control circuit A or B. Once the C0308 code has been activated, all of the 4WD shifter positions will be inoperative and will cause the *SERVICE 4WD* light to turn on.

CHECK TECHNICAL SERVICE BULLETINS After checking for stored diagnostic trouble codes, **technical service bulletins (TSBs)** should be checked to see if there are any faults that are addressed for the codes that have been set. ● **SEE FIGURE 14–12**.

According to studies performed by automobile manufacturers, as many as 30% problem vehicles can be repaired following the information, suggestions, or replacement parts found in a service bulletin. DTCs must be known before searching for service bulletins, because bulletins often include information on solving problems that involve a stored diagnostic trouble code.

CHECK ELECTRICAL COMPONENTS

CHECKING SWITCHES AND CONTROLS When diagnosing a four-wheel drive fault, use a scan tool or a digital multimeter and check for voltage at the switch for each position of the switch. Typical switches are multiplex switches that use a 5-volt reference and through resistors cause the mode selection signal to change voltage levels. ● **SEE FIGURE 14–13**.

TYPICAL VOLTAGE READINGS Service information should be checked for the exact voltage and resistance readings for the vehicle being serviced. Often the fault with the four-wheel-drive system can be found by checking the switch for proper operation. Then check to see that the proper voltage is being applied to the transfer case control module. For some typical readings, ● **SEE CHART 14–3**.

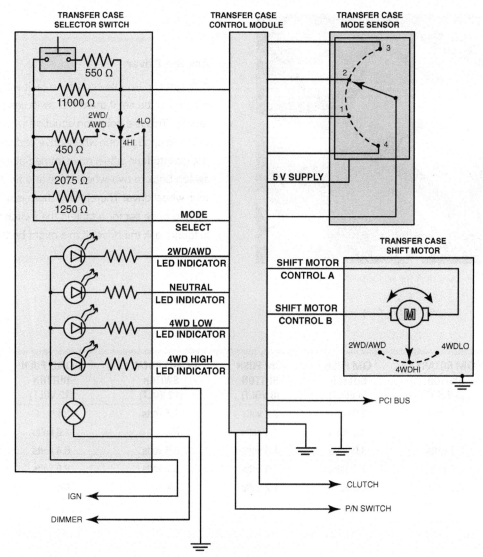

FIGURE 14–13 A typical schematic showing an electronic four-wheel-drive control switch and the wiring connections to the transfer case from the TCCM.

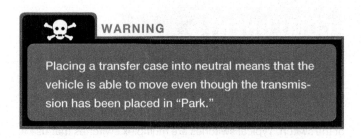

WARNING

Placing a transfer case into neutral means that the vehicle is able to move even though the transmission has been placed in "Park."

CHECKING FOR POWER AND GROUND AT MOTOR The shift control motor operates on 12 volts and ground that is routed through the TCCM. To change direction of the motor, the power and ground are reversed inside the TCCM, causing the motor to reverse directions. Most motor assemblies also include a feedback sensor that signals the TCCM the position of the motor. Check service information for the exact test procedures to follow. ● **SEE FIGURE 14–14.**

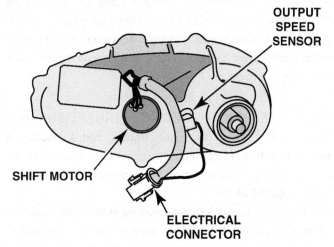

FIGURE 14–14 The voltage to the shift motor and the feedback signal voltage signals can often be tested at the electrical connector using a digital meter or by using a scan tool on some models.

TRANSFER CASE SHIFT LINKAGE ADJUSTMENT

Manually shifted transfer cases include a provision for adjusting the shift linkage to ensure that the unit can be properly engaged or disengaged in the various lever positions. The actual adjustment will vary between the makes and models; always consult the proper service manual.

To adjust a typical transfer case shift linkage, perform the following steps:

STEP 1 Remove the shift boot to access the gearshift mechanism.

STEP 2 Place the lever in the correct position. Sometimes a spacer of a certain size is specified to position the lever properly.

STEP 3 Disconnect the linkage rod swivel/trunnion from the shift lever. It should slide freely in and out of the lever. If not, adjust the trunnion position so that it is a free fit in the lever hole.

FRONT HUB REMOVAL AND REPLACEMENT

NORMAL OPERATION Some automatic hubs will not disengage under certain conditions. These hubs are designed to engage automatically when the driving action of the front axles causes the internal cam to lock the hub.

With some vehicles, these hubs need to be released by shifting the transfer case to 2WD and driving in the opposite direction for at least 10 feet (3 m). If this is not done, the front hubs can remain engaged, which will cause front wheel rotation to drive the axle, differential, and opposite axle or both axles, ring and pinion gears, and driveshaft. This can produce a noise problem and unnecessary wear.

SERVICING LOCKING HUBS Locking front hubs should be cleaned periodically, especially if the vehicle has been driven under water or in dusty conditions. Most vehicle manufacturers recommend that the hubs be cleaned and lightly coated with grease at the same time the front wheel bearings are serviced. Check the service information for the exact procedure for the vehicle being serviced. Start the inspection of the front hubs by removing the cover plate. Many problems associated with locking hubs can be corrected by cleaning and lubricating the components. If noise is heard from the hubs, carefully inspect the inner components on both sides of the vehicle. A damaged part can cause noise in the hub on the other side. Service kits are often available for the hubs. These kits contain the gaskets, seals, and retaining rings necessary for installing the hubs correctly after wheel bearing or front brake work has been completed. ● **SEE FIGURE 14–15.**

TYPICAL PROCEDURE FOR REMOVAL Some front hubs are removed by removing the bolts at the wheel hubs and sliding them off the axle and hub. Other wheel hubs have an internal snap ring that secures the splined inner sleeve to the axle. These hubs require partial disassembly in order to remove this snap ring. Some front hubs are built entirely in the wheel hub so the wheel hub encloses the wheel bearings along with the locking mechanism. To remove the hub and rotor in these units, the locking mechanism must be removed to gain access to the wheel bearing locking and adjusting nuts.

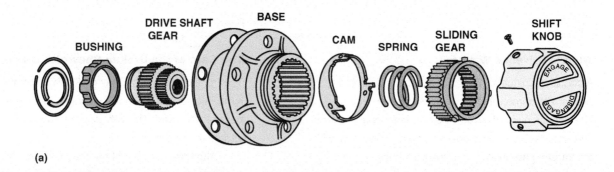

(a)

(b)

FIGURE 14–15 (a) An exploded view of a Dualmatic® manual locking hub. (b) A Warn® manual locking hub.

 TECH TIP

How to Tow a Four-Wheel-Drive Vehicle without Doing Harm

If any of the drive wheels are on the ground, the wheels are turning the axles. Depending on the exact type of four-wheel-drive vehicle being towed, this rotation of the wheels can cause severe wear; therefore, most experts suggest the following options:

- **Placing the vehicle on a flatbed or trailer.** This keeps all four wheels off the ground and is the safest method for transporting a four-wheel-drive (or all-wheel-drive) vehicle without doing any harm.

- **Hoisting the front wheels off the ground and placing the rear wheels on a dolly.** This procedure also keeps all wheels off the ground and therefore prevents any damage being done to the powertrain as a result of towing. Always check with vehicle specific information for exact towing procedures.

  If the transfer case has a neutral position, this will allow the vehicle to be towed with all four wheels on the ground. Always check the owner's manual or service information for the recommend method to use. ● **SEE FIGURE 14–16.**

Always follow the instructions found in service information. Hub replacement is the reverse of the disassembly procedure.

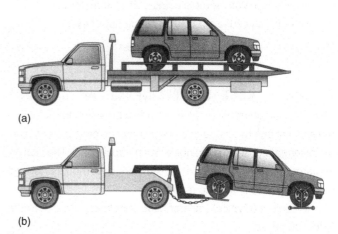

(a)

(b)

FIGURE 14–16 If a four-wheel-drive vehicle must be towed, it should be either on (a) a flatbed truck or (b) a dolly.

TRANSFER CASE/ UNIT REMOVAL AND REPLACEMENT

TYPICAL REMOVAL PROCEDURE Most transfer cases used on utility vehicles and pickups are bolted to the rear of the transmission and can be removed by following the procedure described here. Service information instructions should be followed and usually includes the following steps.

STEP 1 Raise and support the vehicle securely on a hoist or jack stands.

STEP 2 Remove any skid plates and brace rods that block access to the transfer case.

STEP 3 Disconnect the front and rear driveshafts, being sure to make index marks so that the driveshafts can be reinstalled in the same position.

STEP 4 Disconnect the speed sensors and shift connectors and linkage, including encoder motor harness or other wiring connector. Most will come out with wiring attached, for removal on the bench.

STEP 5 Support the transfer case using a transmission jack, and remove the bolts that secure the transfer case to the transmission.

STEP 6 Slide the transfer case off the rear of the transmission, and remove it from the vehicle.

REPLACEMENT OR REPAIR DECISION After the transfer case fault has been diagnosed and the fault is found to be inside the unit itself, the customer and repair shop have the following options:

1. Repair the unit and replace all needed parts.
2. Replace the unit with a used assembly from a wrecking (salvage) yard.
3. Replace the assembly with a remanufactured unit.
4. Replace with a new assembly.

Which option to use depends on the skills and talents of the shop personnel and the budget of the customer.

TRANSFER CASE INSTALLATION Installation of most transfer cases is the reverse of the removal procedure. Make sure that the gasket and seals between the transfer case and the transmission are in good condition and that the bolts are tightened to the correct torque. Some units use a **double-lip seal**, which is a seal that prevents fluid from moving to and from the transfer case to the transmission.

NOTE: If this double-lip seal where to leak, the fluid from the transfer case could be forced into the automatic transmission or the other way around. Therefore, if the fluid level is found to be low in one unit, always check the level in the other unit.

TRANSFER CASE/UNIT OVERHAUL

SERVICE PROCEDURE Because overhaul procedures and adjustments vary, service information instructions are required when repairing transfer cases. Most of the operations are the same as those used in transmissions, transaxles, and drive axles. The operations include the following:

- Disassembly
- Gear and bearing inspection
- Shift fork clearance and operation
- Chain wear check, shaft inspection
- Seal replacement
- Reassembly with adjustments for gear end float and bearing clearance or preload

NV-242 TRANSFER CASE SERVICE

1 The identification plate on the housing indicates the transfer case is a New Venture (New Process) model #242 and has a low-range gear ratio of 2.72:1.

2 Rear output shaft housing being removed.

3 Before the case can be separated, the bearing retaining snap ring must be removed using snap-ring pliers.

4 The lubricating oil pump is visible after the cover and bearing assembly have been removed.

5 The two case halves are being separated.

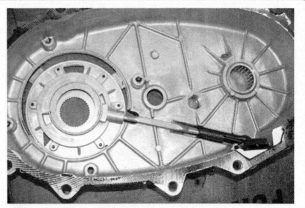

6 The oil pump assembly, pickup screen, and tube are visible on the backside of the case cover.

7 The rear output shaft and sprocket are visible on the right. The front output shaft and sprocket are visible on the left connected by the drive chain.

8 View of the shift levers and the center differential after the chain has been removed.

9 Differential being removed.

10 Center differential assembly after removal from the transfer case.

11 Mode shift fork (upper fork) is used to change two-wheel drive and four-wheel drive. The fork is attached to the range hub, which changes four-wheel-drive high to four-wheel drive low.

12 Main shaft showing the range hub (left), which changes the transfer case between four-wheel high and four-wheel low.

CONTINUED ▶

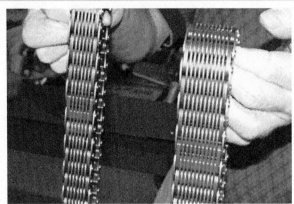

13 The chain used on the NV-242 (right) is larger than the chain used in the smaller version NV-231 (left).

14 Reinstalling the components and the drive chain.

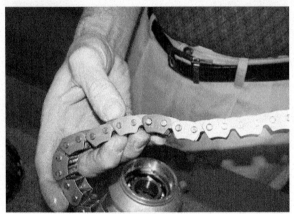

15 The drive chain should be installed with the black (dark) link(s) up.

16 Install all snap rings so that the sharpest tips face up so snap-ring pliers can grab onto the tips for easier removal.

17 Assembling the case halves.

18 The parting surface should be sealed with RTV silicone. Do not use too much or the oil pump screen can become clogged.

19 After attaching the oil pump and tube, the output shaft housing is installed.

20 The output shaft speed sensor drive gear is correctly installed in this photo. The slip yoke of the drive shaft slips onto the splines and inside the nylon gear.

SHIFT MOTOR

21 The electronically shifted version of the case is identical except that the shifting is achieved using an electric motor, shown here installed in a vehicle.

1. Transfer cases/gear sets must have clean gear oil at the proper level and of the proper type.

2. The cause of improper 4WD/AWD operation is determined using several diagnostic steps.

3. Electronic control and shift motor problems can set a diagnostic trouble code (DTC).

4. Transfer case/gear set disassembly and reassembly varies between makes and models.

5. Locking hubs need routine service including cleaning and lubricating to keep them working properly.

6. Parts must be clean before they can be fully inspected.

REVIEW QUESTIONS

1. What are the eight steps of the diagnostic procedure?

2. What type of lubricant does a transfer case require?

3. What type of scan tool should be used to diagnose transfer case problems?

4. Why is the vehicle free to move if the transfer case is placed into neutral but the automatic transmission is in the park position?

5. If a transfer case is found to be defective internally, what are the repair options?

CHAPTER QUIZ

1. The lubricant in a transfer case is being checked. What type of fluid is used in transfer cases?
   a. ATF
   b. Gear oil such as SAE 80W-90
   c. Special transfer case fluid
   d. Any of the above depending on make, model, and year of vehicle

2. The tires on a full-time four-wheel-drive or AWD vehicle should be _____.
   a. Inflated to the same inflation pressure
   b. The same size
   c. The same brand of tire
   d. All of the above

3. What type of scan tool should NOT be used to diagnose transfer case faults?
   a. Global (generic)
   b. Factory scan tool
   c. Enhanced aftermarket scan tool
   d. Either b or c

4. "Rust dust" is a sign of what type of fault?
   a. Old contaminated transfer case fluid
   b. Worn steel parts such as U-joints
   c. High resistance in electrical wiring
   d. Worn powertrain mounts

5. What type of diagnostic trouble code is usually not associated with a transfer case problem?
   a. P codes
   b. U codes
   c. B codes
   d. C codes

6. Transfer case binding or driveline windup can occur when _____.
   a. Driving an AWD vehicle on dry pavement
   b. Unequal tire sizes are used on a full-time four-wheel-drive vehicle
   c. Driving a part-time four-wheel-drive vehicle on dirt, mud, or snow
   d. Driving a four-wheel-drive vehicle in two-wheel drive

7. Most electronic transfer case controls (push button or rotary) use what type of switch?
   a. On or off
   b. Serial data
   c. Multiplex
   d. Relay

8. If a transfer case is placed into neutral, what happens if the automatic transmission is in park?
   a. The vehicle can be towed
   b. The vehicle will be able to roll
   c. The transfer case will be lockup if the transmission is in park
   d. Both a and b

9. If the transfer case fluid level is low, why should the technician check the level of the automatic transmission?
   a. Both use the same oil pan
   b. Both use ATF
   c. There may be a leaking double lip seal between the two units
   d. The fluid levels are checked using the same access plug

10. Electronic transfer cases use what type of motor?
    a. AC synchronous
    b. DC motor
    c. Stepper motor
    d. AC induction

After studying this chapter the reader will be able to:

1. Discuss how to perform a road test for vibration and noise diagnosis.
2. List the possible vehicle components that can cause a vibration or noise.
3. Describe the use of a reed tachometer or electronic vibration analyzer in determining the frequency of the vibration.
4. Discuss the procedures used in measuring and correcting driveshaft angles.

This chapter will help you prepare for ASE Manual Drive Train and Axles (A3) certification test content area "D" (Drive Shaft/Half Shaft and Universal Joint/Constant Velocity (CV) Joint Diagnosis and Repair).

Companion Flange 277	Neutral Run-up Test 270
Driveshaft Runout 277	NVH 268
EVA 267	Rolling Circumference 272
Frequency 270	Vibration Order 271
Hertz (Hz) 271	Witness Mark 268

GM Service Technical College topics covered in this chapter are as follows:

1. Verify a customer vibration concern and make quick checks.
2. Use an electronic vibration analyzer (**EVA**) diagnostic tool to isolate the source of vehicle vibrations.
3. Perform a road test to diagnose concerns related to a vibration fault.
4. Measure rear axle pinion flange runout.
5. Measure propeller shaft balance.
6. Measure propeller shaft runout.
7. Measure propeller shaft U-joint working angles.
8. Calculate tire rotation.
9. Use of EVA and Smart Strobe function.
10. Calculate orders of engine vibration.
11. Calculate engine firing frequency.

FIGURE 15-1 Many vehicles, especially those equipped with four-cylinder engines, use a dampener weight attached to the exhaust system or differential as shown to dampen out certain frequency vibrations.

WITNESS MARK

FIGURE 15-2 The exhaust was found to be rubbing on the frame rail during a visual inspection. Rubber exhaust system hangers are used to isolate noise and vibration from the exhaust system from entering the interior. These rubber supports can fail causing the exhaust system to be out of proper location. It was found by looking for evidence of **witness marks.**

CAUSES OF VIBRATION AND NOISE

Vibration and noise are two of the most frequent complaints from vehicle owners and drivers. If something is vibrating, it can move air; changes in air pressure (air movement) are what we call noise. Though anything that moves vibrates, wheels and tires account for the majority of vehicle vibration problems.

Vehicles are designed and built to prevent most vibrations and to dampen out any vibrations that cannot be eliminated. For example, engines are designed and balanced to provide smooth power at all engine speeds. Some engines, such as large four-cylinder or 90-degree V-6's, require special engine mounts to absorb or dampen any remaining oscillations or vibrations. Dampening weights are also fastened to engines or transmissions in an effort to minimize **noise, vibration,** and **harshness** (called **NVH**).

If a new vehicle has a vibration or noise problem, then the most likely cause is an assembly or parts problem. This is difficult to diagnose because the problem could be almost anything, and a careful analysis procedure should be followed as outlined later in this chapter.

If an older vehicle has a vibration or noise problem, the first step is to question the vehicle owner as to when the problem first appeared. Some problems and possible causes include the following:

Problem	Possible Causes
Vibration at idle	Engine mount could be defective or not reinstalled correctly after an engine or transmission repair.
Noise/vibration	Exhaust system replacement or repair. ● **SEE FIGURE 15–1**.

NOTE: A typical exhaust system can "grow" or lengthen up to 2 inches (5 cm) when warm, as compared with room temperature. Always inspect an exhaust system when warm, if possible, being careful to avoid being burned by the hot exhaust components.

Problem	Possible Causes
Vibration at higher vehicle speeds	Incorrect driveshaft angles could be the result of a change in the U-joints, springs, transmission mounts, or anything else that can cause a change in driveshaft angles.
Noise over rough roads	Exhaust system or parking brake cables are often causes of noise while driving over rough road surfaces. ● **SEE FIGURE 15–2**. Defective shock absorbers or shock absorber mountings are also a common cause of noise.

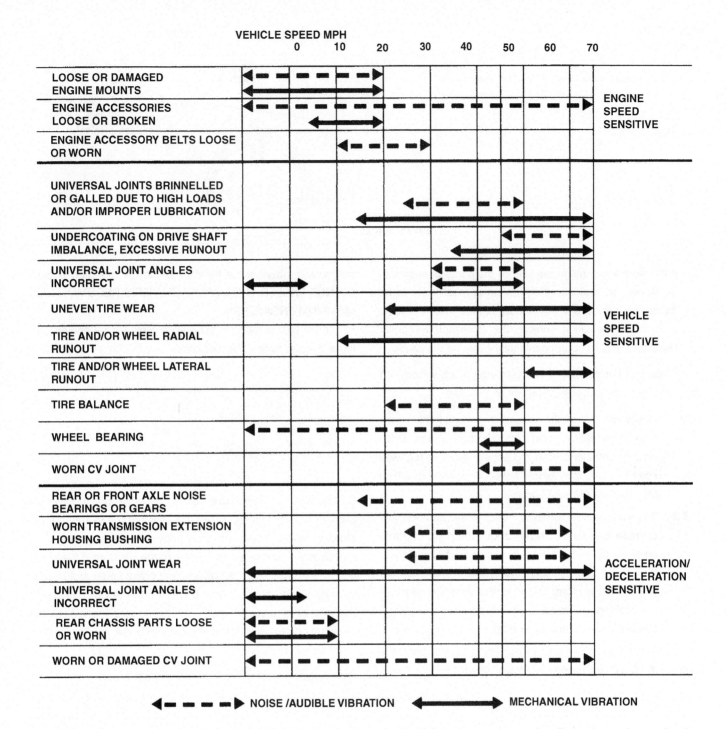

VEHICLE SPEED MPH

	0	10	20	30	40	50	60	70	

LOOSE OR DAMAGED ENGINE MOUNTS

ENGINE ACCESSORIES LOOSE OR BROKEN

ENGINE ACCESSORY BELTS LOOSE OR WORN

ENGINE SPEED SENSITIVE

UNIVERSAL JOINTS BRINNELLED OR GALLED DUE TO HIGH LOADS AND/OR IMPROPER LUBRICATION

UNDERCOATING ON DRIVE SHAFT IMBALANCE, EXCESSIVE RUNOUT

UNIVERSAL JOINT ANGLES INCORRECT

UNEVEN TIRE WEAR

TIRE AND/OR WHEEL RADIAL RUNOUT

TIRE AND/OR WHEEL LATERAL RUNOUT

TIRE BALANCE

WHEEL BEARING

WORN CV JOINT

VEHICLE SPEED SENSITIVE

REAR OR FRONT AXLE NOISE BEARINGS OR GEARS

WORN TRANSMISSION EXTENSION HOUSING BUSHING

UNIVERSAL JOINT WEAR

UNIVERSAL JOINT ANGLES INCORRECT

REAR CHASSIS PARTS LOOSE OR WORN

WORN OR DAMAGED CV JOINT

ACCELERATION/ DECELERATION SENSITIVE

◀ ─ ─ ─ ▶ NOISE /AUDIBLE VIBRATION   ◀━━━━━▶ MECHANICAL VIBRATION

FIGURE 15-3 A chart showing the typical vehicle and engine speeds at which various components will create a noise or vibration and under what conditions. (Courtesy of Dana Corporation)

TEST DRIVE

The first thing a technician should do when given a vibration or noise problem to solve is to duplicate the condition. This means the technician should drive the vehicle and observe when and where the vibration is felt or heard. See the chart in ● **FIGURE 15–3**.

Though there are many possible sources of a vibration, some simple observations may help to locate the problem quickly:

1. If the vibration is felt or seen in the steering wheel, dash, or hood of the vehicle, the problem is most likely to be caused by defective or out-of-balance *front* wheels or tires. ● **SEE FIGURE 15–4**.

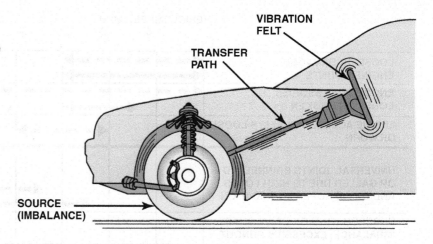

FIGURE 15-4 Vibration created at one point is easily transferred to the passenger compartment. MacPherson strut suspensions are more sensitive to tire imbalance than SLA-type suspensions.

VIBRATION FELT

TRANSFER PATH

SOURCE (IMBALANCE)

2. If the vibration is felt in the seat of the pants or seems to be all over the vehicle, the problem is most likely to be caused by defective or out-of-balance *rear* wheels or tires. In a rear-wheel-drive vehicle, the driveshaft (propeller shaft) and related components might also be the cause.

While on the test drive, try to gather as much information about the vibration or noise complaint as possible.

STEP 1 Determine the vehicle speed (mph or km/h) or engine speed (RPM) where the vibration occurs. Drive on a smooth, level road and accelerate up to highway speed, noting the vehicle speed or speeds at which the vibration or noise occurs.

STEP 2 To help pin down the exact cause of the vibration, accelerate to a speed slightly above the point of maximum vibration. Shift the vehicle into neutral and allow it to coast down through the speed of maximum vibration. If the vibration still exists, then the cause of the problem could be wheels, tires, or other rotating components, *except* the engine.

If the vibration is eliminated when shifted out of gear, the problem is related to the engine or transmission.

NOTE: If the engine or transmission has been removed from the vehicle, such as during a clutch replacement, carefully observe the location and condition of the mounts. If an engine or transmission mount is defective or out of location, engine and driveline vibrations are often induced and transmitted throughout the vehicle.

NEUTRAL RUN-UP TEST

The **neutral run-up test** is used to determine if the source of the vibration is engine related. With the transmission in Neutral or Park, slowly increase the engine RPM and with a tachometer observe the RPM at which the vibration occurs. DO NOT EXCEED THE MANUFACTURER'S RECOMMENDED MAXIMUM ENGINE RPM.

If the fault is found in the engine itself, further engine testing is needed to find the root cause.

VIBRATION DURING BRAKING

A vibration during braking usually indicates out-of-round brake drums, warped disc brake rotors, or other braking system problems. The *front* rotors are the cause of the vibration if the steering wheel is also vibrating (moving) during braking. The *rear* drums or rotors are the cause of the vibration if the vibration is felt throughout the vehicle and brake pedal, but *not* the steering wheel. Another way to check if the vibration is due to rear brakes is to use the parking brake to stop the vehicle. If a vibration occurs while using the parking brake, the rear brakes are the cause.

NOTE: Wheels should *never* be installed using an air impact wrench. Even installation torque is almost impossible to control, and overtightening almost always occurs. The use of impact wrenches causes the wheel, hub, and rotor to distort, resulting in vibrations and brake pedal pulsations. Always tighten wheel lugs in the proper sequence and with proper torque value, using a torque wrench.

VIBRATION SPEED RANGES

Vibration describes an oscillating motion around a reference position. The number of times a complete motion cycle takes place during a period of 1 second is called **frequency**

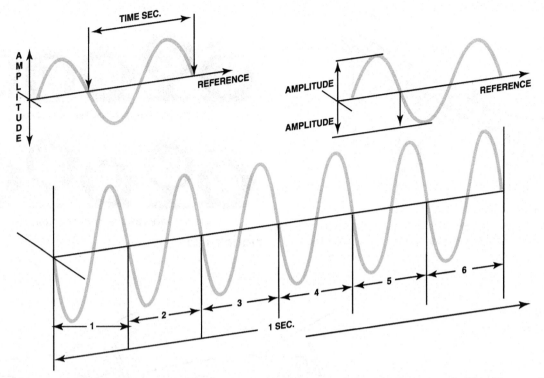

FIGURE 15-5 Hertz means *cycles* per *second*. If six cycles occur in 1 second, then the frequency is 6 Hz. The amplitude refers to the total movement of the vibrating component. (Courtesy of Hunter Engineering Company)

and is measured in **hertz (Hz)** (named for Heinrich R. Hertz, a nineteenth-century German physicist). ● **SEE FIGURES 15–5 AND 15–6.**

The unit of measure for frequency was originally cycles per second (CPS). This was changed to Hz in the 1960s.

To help understand frequency, think of the buzzing sound made by some fluorescent light fixtures. That 60-Hz hum is the same frequency as the alternating current. A 400-Hz sound is high-pitched. In fact, most people can only hear sounds between 20 and 15,000 Hz. Generally, low-frequency oscillations between 1 and 80 Hz are the most disturbing to vehicle occupants.

VIBRATION ORDER **Vibration order** is the number of vibrations created in one revolution of a component. A single high spot on a tire, for example, will cause one bump per revolution, which is a first-order vibration. If the tire rotates 10 times per second, there are 10 disturbances per second, which is also called a first-order vibration of 10Hz. If there are two bumps on a tire, a second-order vibration is created that would generate a vibration of 20 Hz if the tire were rotating 10 times per second. ● **SEE FIGURE 15–7.**

TIRE AND WHEEL VIBRATIONS Typical vehicle components that can cause vibration in specific frequency ranges at 50 mph (80 km/h) include the following:

 REAL WORLD FIX

S-10 Pickup Truck Frame Noise

The owner of a Chevrolet S-10 pickup truck complained of a loud squeaking noise, especially when turning left. Several technicians attempted to solve the problem and replaced shock absorbers, ball joints, and control arm bushings without solving the problem. The problem was finally discovered to be the starter motor hitting the frame. A measurement of new vehicles indicated that the clearance between the starter motor and the frame was about 1/8 inch (0.125 in.) (0.3 cm)! The sagging of the engine mount and the weight transfer of the engine during cornering caused the starter motor to rub up against the frame. The noise was transmitted through the frame throughout the vehicle and made the source of the noise difficult to find.

LOW FREQUENCY (5–20 HZ). This frequency range of vibration is very disturbing to many drivers because this type of vibration can be seen and felt in the steering wheel, seats, mirrors, and other components. Terms used to describe this type of vibration include *nibble*, *shake*, *oscillation*, *shimmy*, and *shudder*.

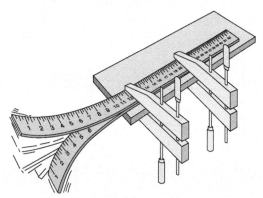

FIGURE 15-6 Every time the end of a clamped yardstick moves up and down, it is one cycle. The number of cycles divided by the time equals the frequency. If the yardstick moves up and down 10 times (10 cycles) in 2 seconds, the frequency is 5 Hertz (10 ÷ 2 = 5). (Courtesy of Hunter Engineering Company)

FIRST ORDER VIBRATION (ONCE PER REVOLUTION)

SECOND ORDER VIBRATION (TWICE PER REVOLUTION)

FIGURE 15-7 Vibration order is the number of vibrations created in one revolution of a component. (Courtesy of General Motors)

FIGURE 15-8 Determining the rolling circumference of a tire.

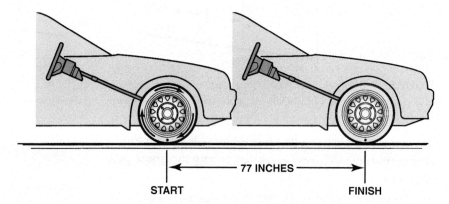

← 77 INCHES →

START   FINISH

Tires and wheels are the most common source of vibration in the low-frequency range. To determine the *exact* frequency for the vehicle being checked, the following formula and procedure can be used.

Tire rolling frequency is calculated as follows:

$$Hz = \frac{mph \times 1.47}{\text{tire circumference in ft}}$$

This formula works for all vehicles regardless of tire size. The circumference (distance around the tread) can be measured by using a tape measure around the tire. The **rolling circumference** of the tire is usually shorter due to the contact patch. To determine the rolling circumference, follow these easy steps:

STEP 1 Inflate the tire(s) to the recommended pressure. Park the vehicle with the valve stem pointing straight down and mark the location on the floor directly below the valve stem.

STEP 2 Slowly roll the vehicle forward (or rearward) until the valve stem is again straight down. Mark the floor below the valve stem.

STEP 3 Measure the distance between the marks in feet.
● **SEE FIGURE 15–8**. To change inches to feet, divide by 12 (e.g., 77 in. divided by 12 in. = 6.4 ft.). To determine the rolling frequency of this tire at 60 mph, use 6.4 feet as the tire circumference in the formula.

$$\text{Frequency} = \frac{60 \, mph \times 1.47}{6.4 \, ft} = 13.8 \, Hz$$

NOTE: **Tire circumference is critical on four-wheel-drive vehicles. The transfer case can be damaged and severe vibration can occur if the rolling circumference is different by more than 0.6 inch (15 mm) on the same axle, or more than 1.2 inch (30 mm) front to rear.**

DRIVELINE VIBRATIONS

MEDIUM FREQUENCY (20–50 HZ). This frequency range of vibrations may also be described as a shake, oscillation, or shimmy. These higher frequencies may also be called *roughness* or *buzz*. Components become blurred and impossible to focus on above a vibration of 30 Hz.

The Vibrating Van

After the engine was replaced in a rear-wheel-drive van, a vibration that felt like an engine miss was noticed by the driver. Because the vibration was not noticed before the engine was replaced, the problem was thought to be engine related. Many tests failed to find anything wrong with the engine. Even the ignition distributor was replaced, along with the electronic ignition module, on the suspicion that an ignition misfire was the cause.

After hours of troubleshooting, a collapsed transmission mount was discovered. After replacing the transmission mount, the "engine miss" and the vibration were eliminated. The collapsed mount caused the driveshaft U-joint angles to be unequal, which caused the vibration.

FIGURE 15-9 An electronic vibration analyzer.

ENGINE-RELATED VIBRATIONS

HIGH FREQUENCY (50–100 HZ). Vibrations in this range may also be *heard* as a moan or hum. The vibration is high enough that it may be felt as a numbing sensation that can put the driver's hands or feet to sleep. Engine-related vibrations vary with engine speed, regardless of road speed. Frequency of the vibration from an engine is determined from the engine speed in revolutions per minute (RPM).

$$\text{Frequency in Hz} = \frac{\text{engine RPM}}{60}$$

For example, if a vibration occurs at 3000 engine RPM, then the frequency is 50 Hz.

$$\text{Hz} = \frac{3000\,\text{RPM}}{60} = 50\,\text{Hz}$$

FREQUENCY

MEASURING FREQUENCY Knowing the frequency of the vibration greatly improves the speed of tracking down the source of the vibration. Vibration can be measured using a reed tachometer or an **electronic vibration analyzer (EVA).**
● **SEE FIGURE 15–9.**

A reed tachometer is placed on the dash, console, or other suitable location inside the vehicle. The vehicle is then

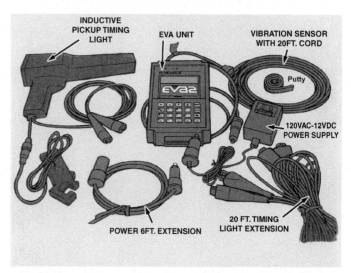

FIGURE 15-10 The EVA2 and accessories. The timing light is used with the Smart Strobe function to locate out-of-balance shafts and pulleys. (Courtesy of General Motors)

driven on a smooth, level road at the speed where the vibration is felt the most. The reeds of the reed tachometer vibrate at the frequency of the vibration.

General Motors recommends the use of the EVA2 analyzer, using a Version 3.0 software cartridge. The use of this tool, along with the Vibrate software package, is explained in GM service information (SI) under the "General Information" heading. ● **SEE FIGURE 15–10.**

NOTE: Other types of vibration diagnostic equipment may be available from vehicle or aftermarket manufacturers.

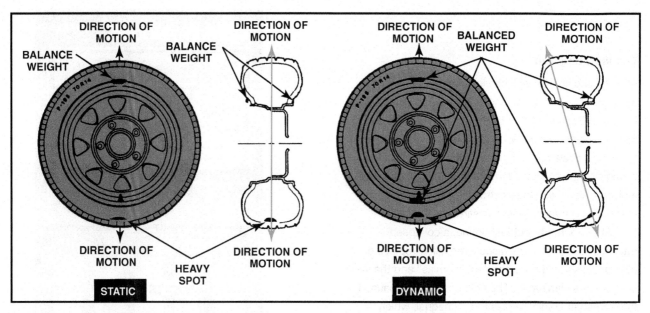

FIGURE 15-11 Properly balancing all wheels and tires solves most low-frequency vibrations.

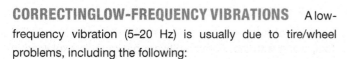

FIGURE 15-12 An out-of-balance tire showing scallops or bald spots around the tire. Even if correctly balanced, this cupped tire would create a vibration.

FIGURE 15-13 Another cause of a vibration that is often blamed on wheels or tires is a bent bearing hub. Use a dial indicator to check the flange for runout.

CORRECTINGLOW-FREQUENCY VIBRATIONS A low-frequency vibration (5–20 Hz) is usually due to tire/wheel problems, including the following:

1. Tire and/or wheel imbalance ● **SEE FIGURES 15–11 THROUGH 15–13.**

2. Tire and/or wheel radial or lateral runout

3. Radial force variation within the tire itself

4. If front-wheel drive, a bent or damaged drive axle joint or shaft

5. Warped rotors

Tires that are out of round or defective will be most noticeable at low speeds, will get better as speed increases, and then will vibrate again at highway speeds.

Tires that are out of balance will tend not to be noticeable at low speeds, and will be most noticeable at highway speeds.

NOTE: High-performance tires are manufactured with different carcass and belt package angles as well as a stiffer, harder tread rubber compound than standard tires. While these construction features produce a tire that allows sporty handling, the tire itself causes a stiff ride, often with increased tire noise. High-performance tires also generate and transmit different frequencies than regular tires. Using replacement high-performance tires on a vehicle not designed for this type of tire may create noise and vibration concerns for the driver/ owner that the technician cannot correct.

CORRECTING MEDIUM-FREQUENCY VIBRATIONS

Medium-frequency vibrations (20–50 Hz) can be caused by imbalances of the driveline as well as such things as the following:

1. Defective U-joints. Sometimes an old or a newly installed U-joint can be binding. This binding of the U-joint can cause a vibration. Often a blow to the joint with a brass hammer can free a binding U-joint. This is often called *relieving the joint*. Tapping the joint using a brass punch and a hammer also works well.

2. Driveshaft imbalance (such as undercoating on the driveshaft) or excessive runout.

3. Incorrect or unequal driveshaft angles.

Driveline vibrations are usually the result of an imbalance in the rotating driveshaft (propeller shaft) assembly.

The driveshaft of a typical rear-wheel-drive (RWD) vehicle rotates at about three times the speed of the drive wheels. The differential gears in the rear end change the direction of the power flow from the engine and driveshaft, as well as provide for a gear reduction. Front-wheel-drive (FWD) vehicles do not have medium-frequency vibration caused by the driveshaft because the differential is inside the transaxle and the drive axle shafts rotate at the same speed as the wheels and tires.

All driveshafts are balanced at the factory, and weights are attached to the driveshaft, if necessary, to achieve proper balance. A driveshaft should be considered one of the items checked if the medium-frequency vibration is felt throughout the vehicle or in the seat of the pants.

NOTE: If a vibration is felt during heavy acceleration at low speeds, a common cause is incorrect universal joint

TECH TIP

Squeaks and Rattles

Many squeaks and rattles commonly heard on any vehicle can be corrected by tightening all bolts and nuts you can see. Raise the hood and tighten all fender bolts. Tighten all radiator support and bumper brackets. Open the doors and tighten all hinge and body bolts.

An even more thorough job can be done by hoisting the vehicle and tightening all under-vehicle fasteners, including inner fender bolts, exhaust hangers, shock mounts, and heat shields. It is amazing how much this quiets the vehicle, especially on older models. It also makes the vehicle feel more solid with far less flex in the body, especially when traveling over railroad crossings or rough roads.

angles. This often happens when the rear of the vehicle is heavily loaded or sagging due to weak springs. Also, vehicle modifications that lower or raise ride height can cause incorrect U-joint angles. If the angles of the U-joints are not correct (excessive or unequal from one end of the driveshaft to the other), a vibration will also be present at higher speeds and is usually torque-sensitive.

CORRECTING HIGH-FREQUENCY VIBRATIONS   High-frequency vibrations (50–100 Hz) are commonly caused by a fault of the clutch, torque converter, or transmission main shaft that rotates at engine speed; in the engine itself, they can be caused by items such as the following:

1. A defective spark plug wire

2. A burned valve

3. Any other mechanical fault that will prevent any one or more cylinders from firing correctly

4. A defective harmonic balancer

If the engine is the cause, run in Neutral at the same engine speed. If the vibration is present, perform a complete engine condition diagnosis. Some engines only misfire under load and will not vibrate while in Neutral without a load being placed on the engine, even though the engine is being operated at the same speed (RPM).

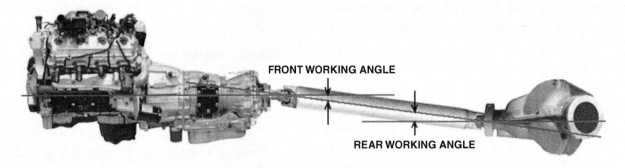

FRONT WORKING ANGLE

REAR WORKING ANGLE

FIGURE 15-14 Driveline (propshaft) working angles. (Courtesy of General Motors)

Exhaust system pulses occur at the following conditions:

4-cylinder engine	2 × engine RPM
6-cylinder engine	3 × engine RPM
8-cylinder engine	4 × engine RPM

If the exhaust system is touching the body, it will transfer these pulses as a vibration. Exhaust system vibrations vary with engine speed and usually increase as the load on the engine increases.

CHECKING DRIVESHAFT JOINT WORKING ANGLE

The working angle of a U-joint is the difference between the angles formed when two shafts intersect. In a one-piece prop-shaft system, there are two working angles present—the front and the rear. In order for proper cancellation to take place, the following are required:

- The two working angles should be equal within 1/2 of a degree.
- The working angles themselves should not exceed 4 degrees.
- Also, the working angles themselves should not be equal to zero. This is because with a zero working angle, the needle bearings within a U-joint will not rotate, causing brinelling and premature wear of the U-joint.

The rear working angle is formed by the angle of the prop-shaft and the angle of the rear axle pinion. The front working angle is formed by the angle of the prop-shaft and the angle of the transmission output shaft. ● **SEE FIGURE 15–14**.

The angles of these components are most accurately measured from the U-joint bearing caps. The bearing caps should be free of corrosion or foreign material in order to ensure accurate readings. Remove any snap rings that may interfere with

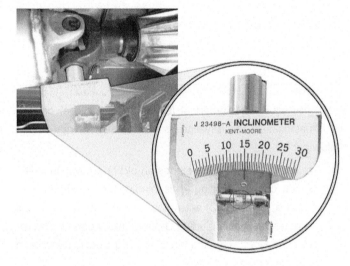

FIGURE 15-15 Use the inclinometer to measure the U-joint angles. (Courtesy of General Motors)

correct placement of the inclinometer, but be sure to reinstall them after the measurements have been taken.

In order to maintain consistent angle measurements, the measurements should all be taken from the same side of the propshaft, either the driver side or passenger side.

Service information lists specifications for driveshaft angles at the transmission and differential when these angles are critical in preventing driveline vibration. Compare results with the specifications and adjust the angles if needed.

U-JOINT WORKING ANGLE

1. Place the inclinometer on the propshaft front bearing cap.
2. Center the bubble in the sight glass and record the measurement. The bearing cap must be straight up and down to obtain an accurate reading (e.g., propshaft reads 18).
3. Rotate the propeller shaft 90 degrees and place the inclinometer on the front-drive yoke bearing cap.
4. Center the bubble in the sight glass and record the measurement (e.g., front-drive yoke reads 15 degrees). ● **SEE FIGURE 15–15**.

5. Subtract the smaller reading from the larger reading to obtain the front U-joint working angle (e.g., 18-15 = 3 degrees as the front U-joint working angle).

6. Repeat the procedure on the rear U-joint.

The two working angles in a one-piece propshaft system should be equal to within 1/2 of a degree in order for effective cancellation to take place. For example, assume that the rear working angle was equal to 3 degrees and the front working angle was also 3 degrees. Subtract the smaller figure from the larger one. In this example, both angles are the same—there is no difference to subtract. In this case, effective cancellation would take place because the difference is 1/2 degree or less and the working angles themselves are less than 4 degrees.

Incorrect driveline angles are usually caused by one or more of the following:

1. Worn, damaged, or improperly installed U-joints

2. Worn, collapsed, or defective engine or transmission mount(s)

3. Incorrect vehicle ride height (As weight is added to the rear of a rear-wheel-drive vehicle, the front of the differential rises and changes the working angle of the rear U-joint.)

4. Bent or distorted driveshaft

CHECKING DRIVESHAFT RUNOUT

Check to see that the driveshaft is not bent by performing a **driveshaft runout** test using a dial indicator. Runout should be measured at three places along the length of the driveshaft.

The maximum allowable runout is 0.030 inch (0.76 mm). If runout exceeds 0.030 inch, remove the driveshaft from the rear end and reindex the driveshaft onto the **companion flange** at 180 degrees from its original location. Remeasure the driveshaft runout. If the runout is still greater than 0.030 inch, the driveshaft is bent and needs replacement *or* the companion flange needs replacement.

MEASURING DRIVESHAFT U-JOINT PHASING

Measuring driveshaft U-joint phasing involves checking to see if the front and rear U-joints are directly in line or parallel with each other. With the vehicle on a drive-on lift, or if using

PROPSHAFT PHASING

THE U-JOINT CAPS SHOULD LINEUP WITHIN 3 DEGREES

FIGURE 15-16 Measuring U-joint phasing checks for a twisted driveshaft. (Courtesy of General Motors)

a frame-contact hoist, support the weight of the vehicle on stands placed under the rear axle. Place an inclinometer on the front U-joint bearing cup and rotate the driveshaft until horizontal; note the inclinometer reading. Move the inclinometer to the rear U-joint. The angles should match. If the angles are not equal, the driveshaft is out of phase and should be replaced. Incorrect phasing is usually due to a twisted driveshaft or an incorrectly welded end yoke. ● **SEE FIGURE 15–16**.

NOTE: Some high-performance General Motors vehicles were built with a slight difference in driveshaft phasing. This was done to counteract the twisting of the driveshaft during rapid acceleration.

COMPANION FLANGE RUNOUT

The companion flange is splined to the rear axle pinion shaft and provides the mounting for the rear U-joint of the driveshaft. Two items should be checked on the companion flange while diagnosing a vibration:

1. The companion flange should have a maximum runout of 0.006 inch (0.15 mm) while being rotated. If the flange was removed with a hammer during a previous repair, the deformed flange could cause a vibration.

2. Check the companion flange for a missing balance weight. Many flanges have a balance weight that is spot-welded onto the flange. If the weight is missing, a driveline vibration can result.

DRIVESHAFT BALANCE

If the driveshaft (propeller shaft) is within runout specification and a vibration still exists, the balance of the shaft should be checked and corrected as necessary. The end result of properly

FIGURE 15-17 Mark the driveshaft at four equal points. (Courtesy of General Motors)

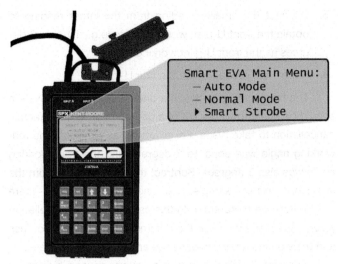

FIGURE 15-18 Connect the inductive pick-up to the EVA2 trigger loop. (Courtesy of General Motors)

fine-tuning a propeller shaft balance may be either a significant reduction or an elimination of a vibration disturbance that is related to the first-order rotation of a propeller shaft.

NOTE: The runout of the propeller shaft to be balanced and the runout of the components that the propeller shaft mates to must be within tolerances before an attempt should be made to perform this procedure.

This procedure requires the use of the Electronic Vibration Analyzer 2 (EVA2) and an inductive pick-up timing light. Refer to service information under " General Information" for more details.

1. Place the vehicle on a suitable axle contact hoist or safety stands so that the rear axle is at curb height. Remove rear wheels and brake drums. Do not apply the brakes with the drums removed.

2. Determine which end of the propshaft is generating the greatest disturbance, in order to determine where to begin installing the clamps. Mark and number the propeller shaft at four points 90 degrees apart at the end of the shaft requiring balance. ● **SEE FIGURE 15–17.**

3. Connect the EVA2 to the vehicle following the instructions. Attach the magnetic vibration sensor to the driveline component closest to the end of the driveshaft that showed the most vibration.

4. Attach the inductive pick-up of the timing light to the inductive loop of the EVA2. Set up the EVA2 to use the Smart Strobe function. ● **SEE FIGURE 15–18.**

5. Run the driveshaft at the suspected RPM and trigger the timing light. The strobe will seem to freeze one of the numbered marks on the driveshaft. This is the light spot of the driveshaft.

6. Install a band-type clamp as a weight, with the head of the clamp directly on the light spot.

7. Run the vehicle at the problem speed and note any change in the vibration.

8. Move the clamp to the other positions and run the vehicle at the complaint speed each time. Note which position gives best balance.

9. If the vibration is not affected at all or only gets worse, then one clamp is either not enough or too much. Either repeat the procedure with two clamps if the vibration was not affected, or with the equivalent of one-half of a clamp if the vibration only got worse. You can achieve the equivalent of one-half of a clamp by spreading two hose clamps. ● **SEE FIGURE 15–19.**

NOTE: Driveshaft balance is more important than front drive axle shaft balance because a driveshaft rotates much faster. A typical driveshaft rotates about three times faster than the drive wheels due to the gear reduction in the differential. Drive axle shafts rotate at the same speed as the drive wheels.

NOISE DIAGNOSIS

Noise diagnosis is difficult because a noise is easily transmitted from its source to other places in the vehicle. For example, if a rear shock absorber mount is loose, the noise may be heard

FIGURE 15-19 Typical procedure to balance a driveshaft using hose clamps.

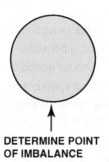

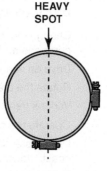

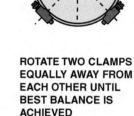

DETERMINE POINT OF IMBALANCE

HEAVY SPOT

ADD CLAMPS 180° FROM POINT OF IMBALANCE UNTIL THEY BECOME THE HEAVY SPOT

HEAVY SPOT

ROTATE TWO CLAMPS EQUALLY AWAY FROM EACH OTHER UNTIL BEST BALANCE IS ACHIEVED

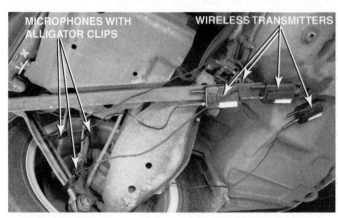

MICROPHONES WITH ALLIGATOR CLIPS

WIRELESS TRANSMITTERS

FIGURE 15-20 The Chassis Ear sensors are attached to the vehicle components and transmit to the headphone receiver.

 FREQUENTLY ASKED QUESTION

What are "Chassis Ears"?

Chassis ears is a brand name for a tool that uses microphones that can be attached to parts under the vehicle and transmit noise to a receiver. The receiver can be tuned so that a technician can listen to one microphone at a time while someone else is driving. This tool makes finding the source of a noise easier. ● **SEE FIGURE 15–20.**

 REAL WORLD FIX

Everything Is OK until I Hit a Bump

The owner of an eight-year-old vehicle asked that the vibration in the steering wheel be repaired. It seemed that the vehicle drove fine until the front wheels hit a bump in the road—then the steering wheel shimmied for a few seconds.

This problem is typical of a vehicle with excessive steering linkage freeplay. When driving straight, centrifugal (rolling) force on the tires tends to force the front wheels outward (toe-out). When one or both wheels hit a bump, the play in the linkage becomes apparent, causing the steering wheel to shimmy until the rolling force again equalizes the steering.

The service technician performed a test drive and a careful steering system inspection and discovered freeplay in both inner tie rod end sockets of the rack-and-pinion unit. The steering unit also had some power steering leakage at the tie rod bellows.

A replacement remanufactured power-rack-and-pinion steering unit was recommended to the customer. The customer approved the replacement rack and authorized the required realignment. A careful test drive confirmed that the problem was corrected.

as coming from the middle or even the front of the vehicle. As the axle moves up and down, the noise is created where metal touches metal between the shock absorber bolt and the axle shock mount. The noise is then transmitted throughout the frame of the vehicle, and therefore causes the sound to appear to come from " everywhere." To help pin down the exact location of the sound, perform a thorough test drive, including driving beside parked vehicles or walls with the vehicle windows

open. (See the following chart for driveline and bearing-type noise diagnosis.)

Some noises may be normal; a similar vehicle should be driven and compared before replacing parts that may not be defective. Noises usually become louder and easier to find as time and mileage increase. An occasional noise usually becomes a constant noise.

Noise	Diagnostic Procedure
Tire noise	Change tire pressure; if no change, then the problem is not tires but bearings, or other components.
	Drive on various road surfaces—smooth asphalt reduces tire noise.
	Rotate the tires front to rear, if possible.
	Various tread designs can cause added noise. (● **SEE FIGURE 15–21.**)
Engine/exhaust noise	Operate the engine at various speeds and loads.
	Drive faster than the speed where the noise occurs, place the transmission in Neutral, and " coast" down through the speed of maximum noise.
	Determine if the engine speed or vehicle speed is the cause of the noise.
Wheel bearing noise (● **SEE FIGURE 15–22**)	Drive the vehicle slowly on a smooth road.
	Make left and right turns with the vehicle.
	Wheel bearing noise changes as weight is transferred side-to-side.
	If noise occurs when turning to the right, then the left bearing is the cause.
	If the noise occurs when turning to the left, then the right bearing is the cause.
	Hoist the vehicle and rotate the wheel by hand to verify the roughness.
Differential side bearing noise	Drive the vehicle slowly on a smooth road.
	Differential bearing noise is a low-pitch noise that does not change when turning.
	The noise varies with vehicle speed.
Differential pinion bearing noise	A whine noise increases with the vehicle speed.
	Drive on a smooth road and accelerate, coast, and hold a steady speed (float). A defective front pinion bearing may be louder on acceleration. A defective rear pinion bearing may be louder on deceleration.
	Pinion bearing noise usually peaks in a narrow speed range.
U-joint noise	Drive slowly on a smooth road surface.
	Drive in reverse and forward.
	U-joints usually make a " chirp, chirp, chirp" noise in reverse because of lack of lubrication and brinelling from driving forward. Driving in reverse changes the force on the needle bearings in the U-joint, and noise is created.
Clutch noise	**Transmission input bearing:** Start the engine with the transmission in Neutral and the parking brake set. The clutch should be engaged (foot off the clutch pedal). If the bearing noise is heard, the transmission input bearing is the source (● **SEE FIGURE 15–23**).
	Release (throw-out) bearing: Start the engine with the transmission in Neutral and the parking brake set. Lightly depress the clutch pedal just enough to take up freeplay (usually 1 inch or less). If the noise is now heard, the source is the release (throw-out) bearing as the clutch fingers make contact with the bearing.
	Pilot bearing: Start the engine with the transmission in Neutral and the parking brake set. Push the clutch pedal fully to the floor (disengage the clutch). If the bearing noise is heard with the clutch disengaged, it is caused by the pilot bearing.

FIGURE 15-21 Tire wear caused by improper alignment or driving habits, such as high-speed cornering, can create tire noise. Notice the feather-edged outer tread blocks.

FIGURE 15-22 This bearing was found on a vehicle that had been stored over the winter. This corroded bearing produced a lot of noise and had to be replaced.

NOISE CORRECTION

The proper way to repair a noise is to repair the cause. Other methods that have been used by technicians include the following:

1. Insulating the passenger compartment to keep the noise from the passengers.

2. Turning up the radio!

FIGURE 15-23 An inner race from an input shaft bearing. This bearing caused the five-speed manual transmission to be noisy in all gears except fourth gear. In fourth gear, the torque is transferred straight through the transmission, whereas in all other gears the torque is applied to the countershaft that exerts a side load to the input bearing.

 TECH TIP

RAP It

Many technicians who service transmissions and differentials frequently replace *all* bearings in the differential when there is a noise complaint. While this at first may seem to be overkill, these technicians have learned that one defective bearing may put particles in the lubricant, often causing the destruction of all the other bearings. This practice has been called *RAP* (replace all parts), and in the case of differentials, RAP may not be such a bad idea.

 REAL WORLD FIX

Engine Noise

An experienced technician was assigned to diagnose a loud engine noise. The noise sounded like a defective connecting rod bearing or other major engine problem. The alternator belt was found to be loose. Knowing that a loose belt can "whip" and cause noise, the belt was inspected and the alternator moved on its adjustment slide to tighten the belt. After tightening the belt, the engine was started and the noise was still heard. After stopping the engine, the technician found that the alternator belt was still loose. The problem was discovered to be a missing bolt that attached the alternator mounting bracket to the engine. The forces on the alternator caused the bracket to hit the engine. This noise was transmitted throughout the entire engine. Replacing the missing bracket bolt solved the loud engine noise and pleased a very relieved owner.

While these methods are usually inexpensive, the noise is still being generated, and if a noisy bearing or other vehicle component is not corrected, more expensive damage is likely to occur. Always remember: *Almost all vehicle faults cause noise first—do not ignore the noise because it is the early warning signal of more serious and possibly dangerous problems.*

Some of the things that can be done to correct certain vibrations and noise include the following:

1. Check all power steering high-pressure lines, being certain that they do not touch any part of the body, frame, or engine except where they are mounted.

2. Carefully check, tighten, and lubricate the flexible couplings in the exhaust system. Use a drive-on lift to ensure normal suspension positioning to check the exhaust system clearances. Loosen, then tighten, all exhaust clamps and hangers to relieve any built-up stress.

3. Lubricate all rubber bushings with rubber lube and replace any engine or transmission mounts that are collapsed.

4. Replace and/or tighten all engine drive belts and check that all accessory mounting brackets are tight.

SUMMARY

1. Vibration and noise are two of the most frequently heard complaints from vehicle owners. Noise is actually a vibration (vibrations cause the air to move, creating noise).

2. A vibration felt in the steering wheel, dash, or hood is usually due to out-of-balance or defective front tires. A vibration felt in the seat of the pants or throughout the entire vehicle is usually due to out-of-balance or defective rear tires.

3. Defective engine or transmission mounts, warped rotors, and out-of-round brake drums can all cause a vibration.

4. Vibration is measured by an electronic vibration analyzer (EVA) or a reed tachometer and measured in units called Hertz.

5. Low-frequency vibrations (5–20 Hz) are usually due to tires or wheels.

6. Medium-frequency vibrations (20–50 Hz) are usually caused by driveline problems on rear-wheel-drive vehicles.

7. High-frequency vibrations (50–100 Hz) are usually caused by an engine problem.

8. Driveshafts should be inspected for proper U-joint working angles and balance.

REVIEW QUESTIONS

1. Describe how you can tell if the source of a vibration is at the front or the rear of a vehicle during a test drive.

2. Explain the terms *cycle* and *Hertz*.

3. List two types of frequency-measuring instruments.

4. Discuss why the balance of a driveshaft on a rear-wheel-drive vehicle is more important than the balance of a front-wheel-drive axle shaft.

5. Explain how to check and balance a driveshaft on a rear-wheel-drive vehicle.

CHAPTER QUIZ

1. A vibration that is felt in the steering wheel at highway speeds is usually due to _____.
   a. Defective or out-of-balance rear tires
   b. Defective or out-of-balance front tires
   c. Out-of-balance or bent driveshaft on a RWD vehicle
   d. Out-of-balance drive axle shaft or defective outer CV joints on a FWD vehicle

2. A vibration during braking is usually caused by _____.
   a. Out-of-balance tires
   b. Warped front brake rotors
   c. A bent wheel
   d. An out-of-balance or bent driveshaft

3. The rolling circumference of both tires on the same axle of a four-wheel-drive vehicle should be within _____.
   a. 0.1 inch (2.5 mm)
   b. 0.3 inch (7.6 mm)
   c. 0.6 inch (15 mm)
   d. 1.2 inch (30 mm)

4. The maximum allowable driveshaft runout is _____.
   a. 0.030 inch (0.8 mm)
   b. 0.10 inch (2.5 mm)
   c. 0.50 inch (13 mm)
   d. 0.015 inch (0.4 mm)

5. A driveshaft can be checked for proper balance by marking the circumference of the shaft in four places and running the vehicle drive wheels to spot the point of imbalance using a _____.
   a. Reed tachometer
   b. Strobe light
   c. Electronic vibration analyzer (EVA)
   d. Scan tool

6. A defective clutch release (throw-out) bearing is usually heard when the clutch is _____.
   a. Engaged in neutral
   b. Disengaged in a gear
   c. Depressed to take up any freeplay
   d. Engaged in first gear or reverse

7. Wheel-tire imbalance is the most common source of vibrations that occur in what frequency range?
   a. 5 to 20 Hz
   b. 20 to 50 Hz
   c. 50 to 100 Hz
   d. 100 to 150 Hz

8. Driveline vibrations due to a bent or out-of-balance driveshaft on a rear-wheel-drive vehicle usually produce a vibration that is _____.
   a. Felt in the steering wheel
   b. Seen as a vibrating dash or hood
   c. Felt in the seat or all over the vehicle
   d. Felt by the rear passengers only

9. Rubber is used for exhaust system hangers because the exhaust system gets longer as it gets hot and rubber helps isolate noise and vibration from the passenger compartment.
   a. True
   b. False

10. A vibration is felt in the steering wheel during braking only. A common cause of the vibration is _____.
   a. Worn idler arm
   b. Out-of-balance front tires
   c. Loose or defective wheel bearing(s)
   d. Warped or nonparallel front disc brake rotors

chapter 16

INTRODUCTION TO AUTOMATIC TRANSMISSIONS AND TRANSAXLES

LEARNING OBJECTIVES

After studying this chapter, the reader should be able to:

1. Describe the powertrain components used in automatic transmissions and transaxles.
2. Describe planetary gear set components.
3. Describe how electronic controls affect transmission/transaxle operations.
4. Describe the differences between front-wheel drive and rear-wheel drive.
5. Describe the purpose of the hydraulic system.
6. Describe the purpose of the valve body.
7. List the methods for obtaining gear reduction, overdrive, reverse, direct drive, and neutral with a planetary gear set.
8. Describe basic transmission/transaxle operation.

This chapter will help you prepare for ASE Automatic Transmission/Transaxle (A2) certification test content area "A" (General Transmission/Transaxle Diagnosis).

KEY TERMS

Rear-wheel drive (RWD) 285
Front-wheel drive (FWD) 285
Transaxle 285
Hydra-matic 285
Powertrain 285
Planetary gear sets 286
Torque converter 286
Torque converter clutch (TCC) 287
Gear train 288
Valve body 289
Governor pressure 290
Throttle pressure 290
Differential 291
Final drive 291

 ## STC OBJECTIVES

GM Service Technical College topic covered in this chapter is as follows:

1. Introduction to automatic transmission and transaxle principles used in General Motors vehicles.

FIGURE 16–1 This Aisin Warner AF 40-6 (MDK) six-speed automatic transaxle is an integral part of the powertrain. (Courtesy of General Motors)

Automatic transmissions have replaced manual transmissions in most of today's vehicles, both import and domestic. Automatic transmissions use a hydraulic system to shift gears automatically in relation to road speed and engine load conditions. Late-model automatic transmissions incorporate electronic systems to control shift timing and feel.

Automatic transmissions are used in **rear-wheel-drive (RWD)** vehicles, and automatic **transaxles** are used in **front-wheel-drive (FWD)** vehicles and some mid- and rear-engine RWD applications. Transmissions and transaxles are similar in function and operation; however, a transaxle contains the final drive and differential gears within the transaxle housing, whereas a transmission keeps them separate.

In this text, the term "transmission" is used to refer to an automatic gearbox. The term "transaxle" is generally reserved for specific transaxle references and to discuss the operations or construction characteristics that are unique to transaxle assemblies.

HISTORY AND DEVELOPMENT

Automatic transmissions are not a recent development. Some vehicles built in the first decade of the twentieth century had transmissions with gear systems similar to those used in modern automatic transmissions. In the late 1930s, General Motors and other manufacturers had automatic or semi-automatic transmissions in experimental stages or limited production. Mercedes-Benz built a limited number of vehicles with an automatic gearbox in 1914. However, General Motors introduced the first fully automatic transmission, the **Hydra-matic**, in 1940. The Hydra-matic, available on select Oldsmobile and Cadillac models, was based on a semi-automatic design used by Oldsmobile in 1938.

Most manufacturers began incorporating electronic controls into their automatic transmissions in the mid-to-late 1980s. General Motors introduced electronic controls in 1991 with the 4L30-E, 4L60-E, 4L80-E transmission, and the 4T60-E electronic transaxle.

The modern automatic transmission is no longer a stand-alone mechanical component but rather a part of the entire vehicle **powertrain**. The powertrain consists of all the components that generate, transmit, and distribute vehicle drive torque. It includes the engine, transmission, driveline, drive axles, wheels, final drive gears, and differential. Many of these individual components are integrated into the vehicle electronic control system and can affect transmission operation. To service these transmissions, a technician must understand the functional and operational relationships between these individual components and the automatic transmission or transaxle. ● **SEE FIGURE 16–1.**

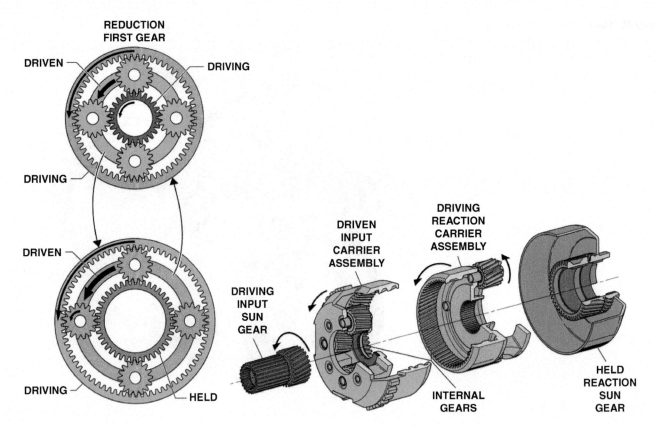

FIGURE 16–2 The automatic transmission uses a variety of planetary gear set designs. In this example, the transmission is in first gear. (Courtesy of General Motors)

AUTOMATIC TRANSMISSION OVERVIEW

The amount of torque generated by an engine is limited and inefficient at certain speeds. Therefore, it is desirable to increase the torque available to the drive wheels under certain vehicle operating conditions. By using different gear combinations, the transmission is able to provide extra torque when the need arises.

Automatic transmissions use **planetary gear sets** to provide different gear ratios. To select the appropriate gears, hydraulic clutches and/or bands hold or lock combinations of components together providing different gear ratios. ● **SEE FIGURE 16–2**.

A planetary gear set allows the gears to remain in constant mesh. The transmission selects the proper gears automatically by monitoring the demands on the vehicle through engine load and vehicle speed, then initiating hydraulic action. The automatic shifting of gears does not interrupt power flow to the wheels.

A vehicle does not require the same amount of torque under all driving conditions. For instance, it takes more effort (work) for an engine to move a vehicle from a standstill, up a steep hill, or to accelerate during a passing maneuver, than it

does to keep a vehicle moving at a constant speed on a level road. Different gear ratios also permit higher vehicle speeds. Transmission gearing must also be able to reverse direction for backing up and have a neutral position for interrupting the power flow to the wheels. ● **SEE FIGURE 16–3**.

FUNCTIONAL SECTIONS

An automatic transmission consists of several functional sections. Each section has a number of major components. To provide an overview of the basic operation of an automatic transmission, this chapter briefly examines each of these sections and their function. The main sections are as follows:

- Torque converter
- Gear train
- Hydraulic system
- Control system

TORQUE CONVERTER Automatic transmissions use a fluid clutch assembly called a **torque converter** rather than a mechanical clutch assembly. The torque converter uses

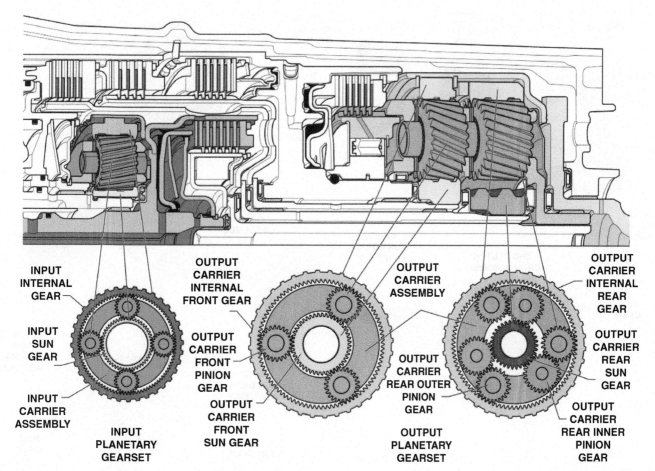

FIGURE 16–3 Planetary gear sets are used in combinations to provide forward gear ratios and a reverse ratio. (Courtesy of General Motors)

INPUT INTERNAL GEAR

OUTPUT CARRIER INTERNAL FRONT GEAR

OUTPUT CARRIER ASSEMBLY

OUTPUT CARRIER INTERNAL REAR GEAR

INPUT SUN GEAR

OUTPUT CARRIER FRONT PINION GEAR

OUTPUT CARRIER REAR OUTER PINION GEAR

OUTPUT CARRIER REAR SUN GEAR

INPUT CARRIER ASSEMBLY

INPUT PLANETARY GEARSET

OUTPUT CARRIER FRONT SUN GEAR

OUTPUT PLANETARY GEARSET

OUTPUT CARRIER REAR INNER PINION GEAR

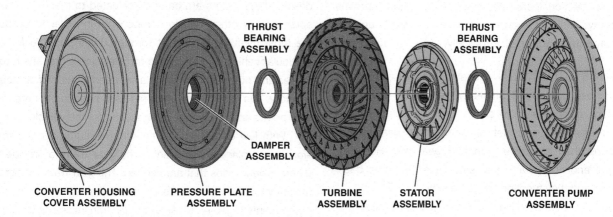

THRUST BEARING ASSEMBLY

THRUST BEARING ASSEMBLY

DAMPER ASSEMBLY

CONVERTER HOUSING COVER ASSEMBLY

PRESSURE PLATE ASSEMBLY

TURBINE ASSEMBLY

STATOR ASSEMBLY

CONVERTER PUMP ASSEMBLY

FIGURE 16–4 A torque converter and clutch assembly. (Courtesy of General Motors)

hydraulic automatic transmission fluid (ATF) to provide a fluid link between the engine and transmission. This results in a smooth, cushioned connection between the engine and transmission and it permits them to remain engaged whether the vehicle is moving or at a standstill. Also, it allows a driver to start a stopped vehicle without using a clutch pedal.

The torque converter assembly attaches to a flexplate, a flexible steel plate that serves as a flywheel. The flexplate bolts directly to the crankshaft-end flange. The torque converter receives the torque output of the engine and passes it to the transmission. The engine-to-transmission connection is made through a fluid clutch. Most late-model torque converters also contain a **torque converter clutch (TCC)** assembly. ● **SEE FIGURE 16–4**.

The TCC provides a mechanical connection between the engine and transmission under certain operating conditions,

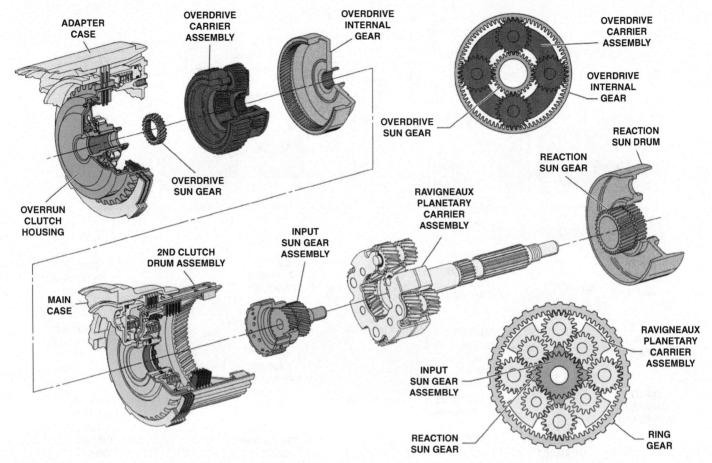

FIGURE 16–5 A gear train that includes a Ravigneaux planetary gear set. (Courtesy of General Motors)

such as cruising in high gear. This eliminates slippage from the fluid drive connection, increases drive efficiency, and improves fuel economy. The torque converter clutch is usually applied hydraulically and controlled electronically.

GEARING AND GEAR SETS Most automatic transmission gear trains use compound planetary gear sets. These are combinations of two or more simple planetary gear sets. A compound planetary gear set provides more usable gear combinations than a simple planetary gear set. However, both simple and compound gear sets have the same basic components and they function the same way.

Generally, all automotive planetary gear sets allow the transmission to produce four, five, or six forward gear ratios, a reverse gear, and a neutral gear. The transmission gearing is augmented by further gear reduction at the final-drive gear and torque multiplication within the torque converter.

Some gear ratios are more advantageous to certain vehicle needs or operations than others. The gear ratios provided by the transmission gear train allow the vehicle to be optimized for speed or torque. Lower gears allow more torque to the drive wheels but preclude high-speed operation. Higher gears allow the vehicle to operate well at high speeds but provide less torque.

Vehicle engineers select the exact gear ratios during the design stage. Gears are carefully selected to match the characteristics of other vehicle components in order to produce the most useful and efficient torque curves possible for that particular vehicle. An electronic transmission stores the torque curves and other design data in a reserved section of computer memory. The control system uses this information to determine shift points and to manage gear shifting for the vehicle.

With few exceptions (some imports), automatic transmissions use a planetary gear set in the **gear train** to provide the different gear ratios that are needed. The gear train consists of the planetary gear set, shafts, drums, and hubs that connect the components together. Most automatic transmissions use either a Simpson or Ravigneaux compound planetary gear set design or some variation of these designs. ● **SEE FIGURE 16–5.**

HYDRAULIC SYSTEM The basic operations of an automatic transmission involve the controlled use and application of pressurized hydraulic fluid. The fluid flows through passages and is controlled by valves operated by springs, pressure, or solenoids. ● **SEE FIGURE 16–6.**

An automatic transmission hydraulic system consists of all the parts and fluid circuits needed to create, regulate, and

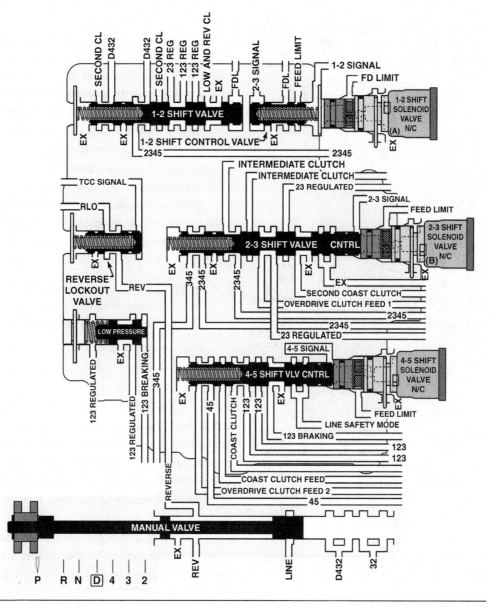

FIGURE 16–6 Example of a hydraulic circuit. (Courtesy of General Motors)

direct the hydraulic pressure and flow needed to control transmission operations. This includes the oil pump, apply devices, valves, **valve body**, and connecting passages. An electronically shifted transmission includes electronic solenoids and controls to direct fluid flow.

The transmission hydraulic system transmits motion and converts fluid pressure into the mechanical force in order to apply the clutches and bands. The hydraulic system also lubricates and cools transmission components.

OIL PUMP The oil pump is the source of fluid flow throughout the hydraulic system. Oil pumps are driven by the engine and connect to it in several ways. On most transmissions/transaxles, the torque converter drives the pump through either a drive hub or a shaft.

The oil pump provides the amount of fluid flow needed to fill the hydraulic circuits and apply the control devices. All pumps are capable of creating an excessive amount of oil pressure, volume, and flow. Therefore, all transmissions/transaxles are equipped with a pressure regulator valve or solenoid. This prevents damage to the system and provides a means of redirecting excess fluid back to the sump.

APPLY DEVICES Power flow through the gear set is controlled by applying clutches and bands. Clutches and bands are apply devices used to drive or hold various components of a planetary gear set to obtain the different gear ratios. They are applied using the hydraulic pressure that is generated by the oil pump and pressure regulation system. The transmission hydraulic system is capable of converting this fluid pressure into

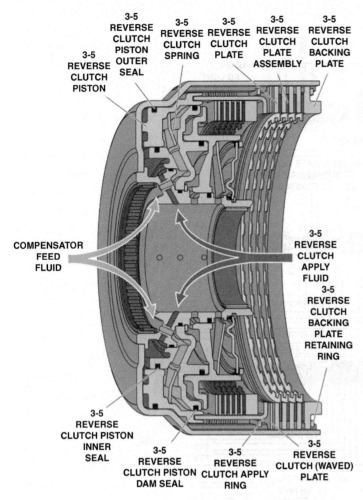

3-5 REVERSE CLUTCH PISTON OUTER SEAL

3-5 REVERSE CLUTCH PISTON

3-5 REVERSE CLUTCH SPRING

3-5 REVERSE CLUTCH PLATE

3-5 REVERSE CLUTCH PLATE ASSEMBLY

3-5 REVERSE CLUTCH BACKING PLATE

COMPENSATOR FEED FLUID

3-5 REVERSE CLUTCH APPLY FLUID

3-5 REVERSE CLUTCH BACKING PLATE RETAINING RING

3-5 REVERSE CLUTCH PISTON INNER SEAL

3-5 REVERSE CLUTCH PISTON DAM SEAL

3-5 REVERSE CLUTCH APPLY RING

3-5 REVERSE CLUTCH (WAVED) PLATE

FIGURE 16–7 A typical clutch assembly. (Courtesy of General Motors)

the mechanical force needed to apply the clutches and bands. ● SEE FIGURE 16–7.

VALVE BODY For efficient operation, the transmission must apply and release clutches and bands at the correct time. This requires an automatic transmission to be capable of monitoring vehicle needs, timing shifts, and controlling the apply devices to select the different gear ratios. The valves, valve body, and fluid distribution system handle these functions. ● SEE FIGURE 16–8.

CONTROL SYSTEM

An automatic transmission determines the proper shift points by monitoring vehicle speed and engine load. When engine load is low in relation to vehicle speed, a higher gear ratio is more efficient, so the transmission upshifts. When engine load is high in relation to vehicle speed, a lower gear ratio is more efficient, so the transmission downshifts.

NON-ELECTRONIC SHIFT CONTROL On non-electronically controlled transmissions, hydraulic shift valves in the valve body initiate gear changes. These valves balance different hydraulic pressures to direct the fluid flow. **Governor pressure** and **throttle pressure** are the two basic hydraulic pressure signals used in older automatic transmissions. Throttle pressure, an indicator of engine load, is measured through engine vacuum or throttle opening. Governor pressure, an indicator of vehicle speed, is usually influenced by the rotational speed of the output shaft.

Throttle pressure, which responds to engine load, pushes shift valves in one direction. Governor pressure, which responds to vehicle speed, pushes shift valves in the opposite direction.

- When governor pressure exceeds throttle pressure, shift valves move to allow fluid under line pressure into the proper upshift circuit. ● SEE FIGURE 16–9.
- When throttle pressure exceeds governor pressure, fluid is routed to the downshift circuit.

ELECTRONIC SHIFT CONTROL Late-model automatic transmissions use an electronic control system to manage shift timing, regulate line pressure, and control torque converter clutch operation. These systems provide very precise control of operating conditions and vehicle components. This results in better fuel economy, reduced emissions, and smoother shifts.

The use of automotive electronics has greatly increased since the mid-1980s. In the 1970s, most manufacturers switched to solid-state electronic ignition systems. In the 1980s, import and domestic manufacturers started to equip their production vehicles with electronic control systems. These systems were necessary to meet increasingly stringent emissions and fuel economy standards.

Electronic control systems have become increasingly sophisticated over the last several years. They receive input information from many vehicle functions. The latest versions integrate several systems together to manage almost all system and component operations. ● SEE FIGURE 16–10.

The electronic controls added to a typical electronic automatic transmission have not changed the essential mechanical and hydraulic operations inside the transmission. The internal components of electronic and non-electronic transmissions are almost identical. Only the *control* has changed. An electronic control system enables the engine and transmission to share vehicle operating information from many sources and uses it to react quickly to changing vehicle operating conditions.

FIGURE 16–8 Typical valve body, including the transmission control module (TCM). (Courtesy of General Motors)

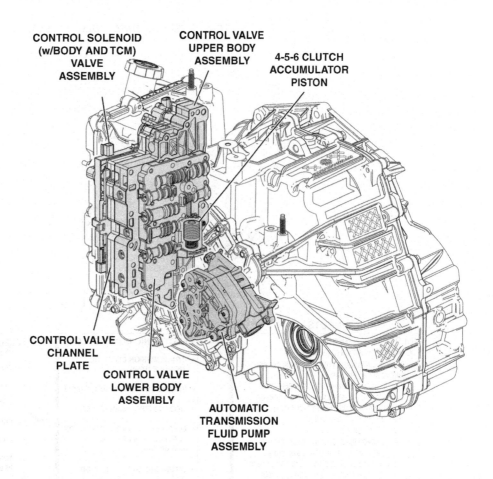

CONTROL SOLENOID (w/BODY AND TCM) VALVE ASSEMBLY

CONTROL VALVE UPPER BODY ASSEMBLY

4-5-6 CLUTCH ACCUMULATOR PISTON

CONTROL VALVE CHANNEL PLATE

CONTROL VALVE LOWER BODY ASSEMBLY

AUTOMATIC TRANSMISSION FLUID PUMP ASSEMBLY

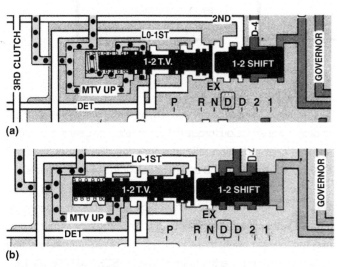

(a)

(b)

FIGURE 16–9 Hydraulic shift circuit on a non-electronically controlled transmission: (a)Before the 1 to 2 shift occurs (TV pressure exceeds governor pressure). (b) After the 1 to 2 shift has occurred (governor pressure exceeds TV pressure). (Courtesy of General Motors)

An electronic transmission is very similar in construction and operation to a non-electronic unit, and most internal components are identical. The main difference is that hydraulic pressure to the apply devices is controlled by an onboard computer system and solenoids. ● SEE FIGURE 16–11.

FINAL DRIVE GEARING

Although the gear set in the transmission provides most of the gear ratio selection for the vehicle, other drivetrain components may further modify the gear ratio or the torque available to the drive wheels. These other components may include the final drive gears, differential, and transfer case.

FINAL DRIVE AND DIFFERENTIAL **Final drive** gears provide a means of transferring the output from the transmission to the differential gears. They are the final set of reduction gears in any transmission or transaxle. These gears provide gear reduction when the vehicle requires an increase in drive torque. See

All of the torque output from the transmission passes through the same set of final drive gears, regardless of which transmission gear is selected. Final drive gears typically have a single, fixed gear ratio. Therefore, all torque output to the drive wheels is further modified by that same gear ratio.

The **differential** does not provide an actual change in gear ratio. It is used to distribute drive torque evenly to both drive wheels when the vehicle travels straight, and to compensate for the difference in wheel speed when the vehicle turns a corner.

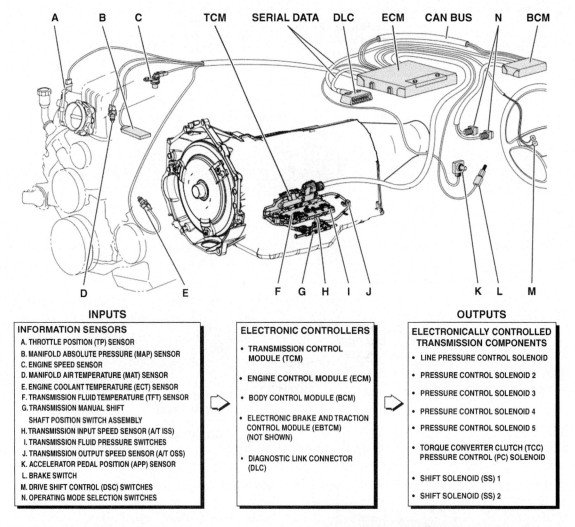

INPUTS	ELECTRONIC CONTROLLERS	OUTPUTS

INFORMATION SENSORS

A. THROTTLE POSITION (TP) SENSOR
B. MANIFOLD ABSOLUTE PRESSURE (MAP) SENSOR
C. ENGINE SPEED SENSOR
D. MANIFOLD AIR TEMPERATURE (MAT) SENSOR
E. ENGINE COOLANT TEMPERATURE (ECT) SENSOR
F. TRANSMISSION FLUID TEMPERATURE (TFT) SENSOR
G. TRANSMISSION MANUAL SHIFT
   SHAFT POSITION SWITCH ASSEMBLY
H. TRANSMISSION INPUT SPEED SENSOR (A/T ISS)
I. TRANSMISSION FLUID PRESSURE SWITCHES
J. TRANSMISSION OUTPUT SPEED SENSOR (A/T OSS)
K. ACCELERATOR PEDAL POSITION (APP) SENSOR
L. BRAKE SWITCH
M. DRIVE SHIFT CONTROL (DSC) SWITCHES
N. OPERATING MODE SELECTION SWITCHES

ELECTRONIC CONTROLLERS

• TRANSMISSION CONTROL
  MODULE (TCM)

• ENGINE CONTROL MODULE (ECM)

• BODY CONTROL MODULE (BCM)

• ELECTRONIC BRAKE AND TRACTION
  CONTROL MODULE (EBTCM)
  (NOT SHOWN)

• DIAGNOSTIC LINK CONNECTOR
  (DLC)

ELECTRONICALLY CONTROLLED TRANSMISSION COMPONENTS

• LINE PRESSURE CONTROL SOLENOID

• PRESSURE CONTROL SOLENOID 2

• PRESSURE CONTROL SOLENOID 3

• PRESSURE CONTROL SOLENOID 4

• PRESSURE CONTROL SOLENOID 5

• TORQUE CONVERTER CLUTCH (TCC)
  PRESSURE CONTROL (PC) SOLENOID

• SHIFT SOLENOID (SS) 1

• SHIFT SOLENOID (SS) 2

FIGURE 16–10 Common electronic input and output components (Courtesy of General Motors)

FINAL DRIVE TYPES AND DESIGNS The type and location of the final drive and differential gears depend on the design and configuration of the vehicle and its powertrain. Most RWD vehicles use a longitudinally mounted transmission coupled inline to an engine at the front of the chassis. These vehicles transmit torque to the drive wheels through a driveshaft to the rear axle housing. The rear axle housing usually contains the final drive and differential gears in this type of powertrain layout.

RWD vehicles typically use a hypoid ring and pinion gear set to deliver transmission torque to the wheels. The gear set provides the final gear reduction ratio, changes the direction of the drive shaft power flow 90°, and transfers power to the drive wheels.

Most FWD vehicles use a transaxle coupled to a transverse-mounted engine. In these vehicles, the final drive gears are located within the transaxle housing. Since the crankshaft is parallel to the drive axles, these vehicles do not require a redirection of power flow to drive the front wheels. ● **SEE FIGURE 16–12**.

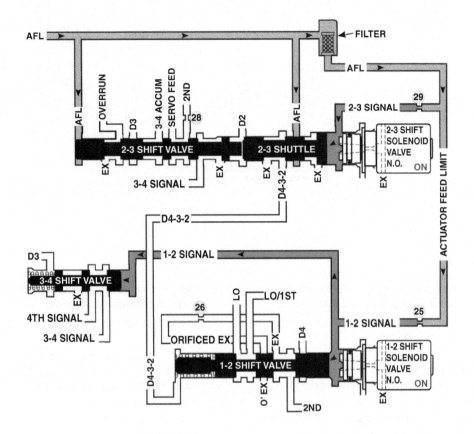

EXAMPLE A: PARK/REVERSE/NEUTRAL/FIRST GEAR

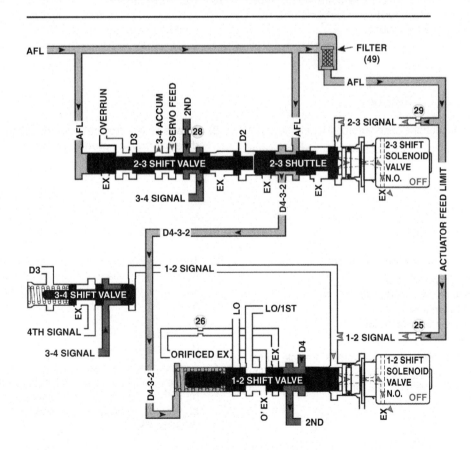

EXAMPLE B: THIRD GEAR

FIGURE 16–11 Shifting is controlled by solenoids. (Courtesy of General Motors)

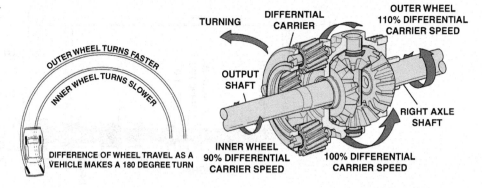

FIGURE 16–12 The differential assembly allows one axle to turn at a different rate from the other axle. (Courtesy of General Motors)

SUMMARY

1. Automatic transmissions are used in RWD vehicles and automatic transaxles are used in FWD vehicles.

2. Transaxles have the differential and final drive gears located within the transaxle housing.

3. Automatic transmission operation depends on proper engine operation and characteristics such as torque curves and axle gear ratios that relate engine performance to transmission operation.

4. A transmission provides different gear ratios to maximize engine torque and minimize engine wear.

5. Engine-operating load and vehicle speed are the two most important operating signals for both electronic and non-electronic automatic transmissions.

6. Most automatic transmissions use a planetary gear set to produce different gear ratios.

7. The torque converter provides a fluid connection between the engine and transmission.

8. Later models use a torque converter clutch (TCC) to provide a direct mechanical link between the engine and transmission under certain conditions.

9. Non-electronic automatic transmissions monitor vehicle-operating conditions mechanically and control functions hydraulically.

10. Electronic automatic transmissions monitor the same signals and manage hydraulic control directly by computer-controlled components.

REVIEW QUESTIONS

1. What are the major sections of an automatic transmission?

2. Name parts of the hydraulic system and explain what they do.

3. How is an electronically controlled automatic transmission different from a non-electronic transmission?

CHAPTER QUIZ

Choose the single most correct answer.

1. A vehicle powertrain consists of _____.
   a. Engine, transmission, and driveline
   b. Drive axles and wheels
   c. Final drive gears and differential
   d. All of the above

2. Technician A says the engine develops vehicle drive torque. Technician B says the transmission can modify engine torque and pass it to the drive wheels. Who is right?
   a. A only
   b. B only
   c. Both A and B
   d. Neither A nor B

3. Technician A says that torque and speed can be modified by using gears. Technician B says that as gear ratio increases, torque and speed increase. Who is right?
   a. A only
   b. B only
   c. Both A and B
   d. Neither A nor B

4. A transmission is used to _____.
   a. Increase drive torque for heavy engine loads
   b. Increase drive speed for light engine loads
   c. Provide a neutral power flow path
   d. All of the above

5. Technician A says that automatic transmissions use planetary gear sets to provide different gear ratios. Technician B says that automatic transmissions use a torque converter instead of a mechanical clutch. Who is right?
   a. A only
   b. B only
   c. Both A and B
   d. Neither A nor B

6. Technician A says the torque converter uses engine oil to provide a fluid link between the engine and transmission. Technician B says the torque converter is attached to the engine crankshaft and receives the engine torque output. Who is right?
   a. A only
   b. B only
   c. Both A and B
   d. Neither A nor B

7. The transmission hydraulic system _____.
   a. Transmits hydraulic force and motion
   b. Converts fluid pressure into mechanical force
   c. Lubricates and cools transmission components
   d. All of the above

8. Technician A says an automatic transmission determines shift points by monitoring vehicle speed and engine load. Technician B says that gear shifts are made by hydraulic shift valves in the oil pump. Who is right?
   a. A only
   b. B only
   c. Both A and B
   d. Neither A nor B

9. Transmission control solenoids are located _____.
   a. On the valve body
   b. Inside the clutches
   c. At the shift control lever
   d. None of these

10. Automatic transmissions use _____ to produce the different gear ratios required to propel the vehicle.
    a. Spur gears
    b. Clutch gears
    c. Planetary gears
    d. Differential gears

HYDRAULIC SYSTEM PARTS AND OPERATION

LEARNING OBJECTIVES

After studying this chapter, the reader will be able to:

1. Discuss the specifications and types of automatic transmission fluids (ATF).
2. Discuss hydraulic principles and Pascal's Law.
3. Describe the types and operation of automatic transmission/transaxle pumps.
4. Explain the different methods for controlling fluid flow and regulating pressure.
5. Identify the types of hydraulic seals.
6. Discuss ATF filters, heaters, and coolers.

This chapter will help you prepare for ASE Automatic Transmissions (A2) certification test content area "A" (General Transmission and Transaxle Diagnosis).

KEY TERMS

Automatic transmission fluid (ATF) 297
Balance valve 305
Depth filter 303
Fluid power 297
Gerotor 301
Hydraulics 297
Internal–external gear 301
Land 304
Line pressure 302
Mainline pressure 302
Micron 303
Paper filter 303
Positive displacement pump 302
Pressure regulator valve 304
Pump 300
Static seal 305
Spool valve 304
Surface filter 303
Supply pressure 302
Vane pump 301
Variable displacement pump 302

STC OBJECTIVES

GM Service Technical College topics covered in this chapter are as follows:

1. Disassemble and reassemble a gerotor and variable vane style hydraulic pump assembly.
2. Explain the purpose and composition of transmission/transaxle fluid used in GM vehicles (00510.01W-R2).

THE HYDRAULIC SYSTEM

PURPOSE AND FUNCTION   The automatic transmission's hydraulic system has several important functions. It must be able to

- Apply the clutches and bands and therefore control the transmission's power flow
- Transmit sufficient force and motion to completely apply the control units to prevent slippage
- Maintain fluid flow through the torque converter for its proper operation
- Maintain fluid flow to lubricate and cool the moving parts of the gear train

HYDRAULIC PRINCIPLES

DEFINITION   **Hydraulics**, often called **fluid power**, is a method of transmitting motion and/or force using a fluid. Hydraulics is based on the principle that liquids can flow easily through complicated paths, but they cannot be compressed. All the components in a hydraulic system are interconnected so that fluid pressure can be transmitted to all parts to work as designed.

AUTOMATIC TRANSMISSION FLUID

PURPOSE AND FUNCTION   **Automatic transmission fluid (ATF)** is highly refined oil with a viscosity similar to SAE 20W-20 oil, and is specially designed for use in automatic transmissions. Newer ATFs are lower in viscosity and are similar to SAE 0W-10 oil.

The purpose and function of ATF includes the following:

- Transfers power in torque converters
- Provides hydraulic pressure in clutches and band servos
- Lubricates bearings, bushings, and gears
- Transfers heat to cool transmission parts
- Provides the correct friction for clutch and band application
- Acts as the medium to control transmission shifting by traveling through passageways, acting on valves, and being directed by solenoids.

BACKGROUND   Early automatic transmissions used engine oil for a transmission fluid. Since internal operating conditions in engines and automatic transmissions are significantly different, a special transmission fluid was developed in the late 1940s. At first, the ATF was simply a mineral oil similar to engine oil, but dyed red.

ADDITIVES   Transmission fluid is formulated with various additives to produce favorable operating characteristics. Automatic transmission fluid contains about 10% to 15% additives. These additives are chemical compounds, and the reasons for their use are as follows:

- **Detergents-dispersants.** Keep the transmission clean and the valves free from sticking by keeping foreign items in suspension until they are removed by the filter or by draining.
- **Oxidation inhibitors.** Reduce oxidation and decomposition of the fluid, which can produce varnish and sludge.
- **Viscosity index improvers.** Change the fluid viscosity with change in temperature so that fluid thickness and shift characteristics remain stable during a range of changing temperatures.
- **Friction modifiers.** Change the fluid's coefficient of friction.
- **Foam inhibitors.** Prevent formation of air bubbles and foam in the fluid.
- **Seal swelling agents.** Produce a slight swelling of the elastomers (seals) to compensate for any wear that occurs.
- **Anti wear agents.** Reduce friction and prevent scoring and seizure of metal parts running against each other.
- **Rust inhibitors.** Prevent rust from forming on the iron and steel parts.
- **Corrosion inhibitors.** Prevent corrosion of the nonferrous parts.
- **Metal deactivators.** Form a protective film to inhibit oxidation of metal surfaces.
- **Dye.** Dye is added to make ATF red except for the fluid used in most continuously variable transmissions or dual clutch automatics which is often dyed green.

SYNTHETIC ATF   Synthetic engine oils have been available for years for military, commercial, and general public use. The term "synthetic" means that it is a manufactured product and not refined from a naturally occurring substance, as engine oil (petroleum base) is refined from crude oil. Synthetic oil is processed from several different base stocks using several different methods.

According to the American Petroleum Institute, oils are classified into the following groups.

- **Group I.** Mineral, non-synthetic base oil with few, if any, additives.
- **Group II.** Mineral oil with quality additive packages; includes most friction-modified automatic transmission fluids.
- **Group III.** Hydrogenated (hydroisomerized) synthetic compounds, commonly referred to as hydrowaxes or hydrocracked oil and is the lowest cost synthetic ATF. Most "fill-for life" ATF is made from Group III base stock.
- **Group IV.** Synthetic oils made from mineral oil and monomolecular oil called polyalpholefin (POA) and include Mobil 1 ATF.
- **Group V.** Non-mineral sources such as alcohol from corn, called diesters or polyolesters; includes Red Line and Royal Purple ATF.

Groups III, IV, and V are considered to be synthetic because the molecular structure of the finished product does not occur naturally, but is man-made through chemical processes. These are man-made oils.

- The major advantage of using synthetic ATF is its ability to remain fluid at very low temperatures, which results in consistent transmission operation regardless of operating temperature.
- The major disadvantage is cost. The cost of synthetic automatic transmission fluid can be four to five times the cost of petroleum-based fluids. A synthetic blend indicates that some synthetic fluid is mixed with petroleum base oil but the percentage of synthetic used in the blend is unknown.

TYPES The three basic types of ATF include

1. **Non-friction modified.** The first ATF did not have friction reducing additives. This type of fluid was used in early band-type automatics. Type F ATF is an example of a non-friction-modified ATF.
2. **Friction modified.** Friction-modified ATF types include Dexron.
3. **Highly friction modified.** All current original equipment manufacturers use automatic transmission fluids that are highly friction modified. These include Dexron VI, Mercon V, ATF +4, and ATF WS.

ATF EXAMPLES

GENERAL MOTORS The first transmission fluid was developed by General Motors and was labeled *Type A* transmission fluid. As transmission fluid was improved, Type A was replaced with *Type A, Suffix A; Dexron;* and then *Dexron II, Dexron II-E,* and *Dexron III.* The Dexron fluids are compatible, and Dexron III can be used in older transmissions that specify one of the older fluid types.

General Motors introduced Dexron® VI in 2005 for use in the then new six speed transmissions/transaxles. It is superior to the older versions of Dexron and is the recommended fluid for all General Motors automatic transmissions/transaxles. It has a more consistent viscosity to produce more consistent shift performance during extreme conditions and less degradation over time. This fluid has more than twice the durability and stability in tests compared to previous ATFs. ● **SEE FIGURE 17-1.**

NOTE: While most General Motors vehicles use Dexron VI, there are exceptions. For example, the Aisin TL80 transmission uses Aisin ATF-WS fluid and the Jatco MFL CVT transaxle uses ACDELCO CVT fluid. Always check the owner's manual or service information for the correct fluid; don't guess.

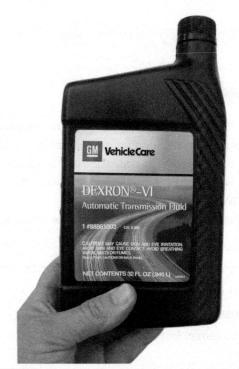

FIGURE 17-1 The use of the factory-specific fluid is the recommend fluid to insure the best possible shifting and transmission operation. (Courtesy of Jeffrey Rehkopf)

GENERAL MOTORS	DESCRIPTION
Type A	1949
Type A, Suffix A	1957 (friction modified)
Dexron	1967 (lower viscosity)
Dexron II	1978 (lower viscosity)
Dexron II-E	1990 (improved low temperature fluidity)
Dexron III	1993–2005 (improved low temperature fluidity)
Dexron VI	2005 (improved viscosity stability)

FORD/JAGUAR	DESCRIPTION
Type F	1967 (non-friction modified; designed for older band-type automatic transmissions)
Mercon	1987 (friction modified)
Mercon V	1997 (highly friction modified)
Mercon SP	Used in the Ford six speeds such as the 6R60 6HP 26 and also the 2003 and up Torque Shift
Idemitsu K-17	Jaguar X-type

CHRYSLER	DESCRIPTION
Chrysler 7176	Designed for front-wheel-drive transaxles
ATF + 2	1997 (improved cold temperature flow)
ATF + 3	1997 (designed for four-speed automatics)
ATF + 4	Used in most 2000 and newer Chrysler vehicles

HONDA/TOYOTA	DESCRIPTION
Honda Z-1	For use in all Honda automatic transaxles
Toyota Type III	Specific vehicles and years
Toyota Type IV	Specific vehicles and years
Toyota WS	Lower viscosity than Type IV; used in specific vehicles and years

MAZDA/NISSAN/SUBARU	DESCRIPTION
Mazda ATF-III	Specific vehicles and years
Mazda ATF-MV	Specific vehicles and years
Nissan Matic D	Specific vehicles and years
Nissan Matic J	Specific vehicles and years
Nissan Matic K	Specific vehicles and years
Subaru ATF	Specific vehicles and years
Subaru ATF-HP	Specific vehicles and years

AUDI/BMW/MERCEDES/ VOLVO	DESCRIPTION
Audi G-052-025-A2	Specific vehicles and years
Audi G-052-162-A1	Specific vehicles and years
BMW LA2634	Specific vehicles and years
BMW LT1141	Lifetime fill (BMW warns to not use any other type of fluid)
Mercedes 236.1	Specific vehicles and years
Mercedes 236.2	Specific vehicles and years
Mercedes 236.5	Specific vehicles and years
Mercedes 236.6	Specific vehicles and years
Mercedes 236.7	Specific vehicles and years
Mercedes 236.9	Specific vehicles and years
Mercedes 236.10	Specific vehicles and years
Volvo 97340	Specific vehicles and years
Volvo JWS 3309	Specific vehicles and years

MITSUBISHI/HYUNDAI/KIA	DESCRIPTION
Diamond SP II	Specific vehicles and years
Diamond SP III	Specific vehicles and years

CHART 17–1

Selected samples of automatic transmission fluid and some applications. Always check service information for proper specified fluid when servicing automatic transmissions/transaxles.

TOYOTA Toyota uses world standard (WS) fluid. It is formulated to provide lower viscosity at normal operating temperatures, which helps improve fuel economy. At higher temperatures, this ATF provides greater durability.

FORD Ford Motor Company has developed fluids for use in its vehicles. *Types F, CJ, Mercon,* and *Mercon V* and Mercon LV (low viscosity) are required for various Ford transmission models. Mercon can be used in place of older Ford fluids but Mercon V should be used only in transmissions that specify its use. Ford introduced Mercon SP fluid, which has the same characteristics as Dexron® VI and Toyota WS, and although these fluids are similar, they are not interchangeable.

TYPICAL ATF APPLICATIONS Automatic transmission fluid is formulated to work in specific transmissions. Using the specified fluid is the key to proper operation. ● **SEE CHART 17–1** for examples of the types and applications of selected vehicles and fluids.

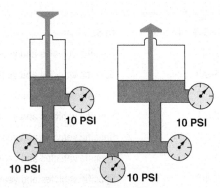

FIGURE 17–2 Fluid pressure is transmitted undiminished in all directions. Note that the pressure is equal throughout the system.

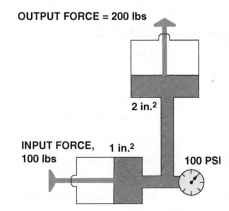

FIGURE 17–3 A 100 lb force applied on an input piston that has an area of 1 sq. in. will produce a fluid pressure of 100 PSI.

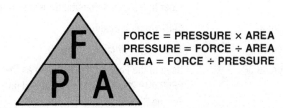

FORCE = PRESSURE × AREA
PRESSURE = FORCE ÷ AREA
AREA = FORCE ÷ PRESSURE

FIGURE 17–4 A simple memory triangle can be used to help remember the commonly used hydraulic formulas.

HYDRAULIC PRINCIPLES

PASCAL'S LAW DEFINITION Pascal's law, formulated by Blaise Pascal (1623–1662), a French mathematician, states:

- "When force is applied to a liquid confined in a container or an enclosure, the pressure is transmitted equally and undiminished in every direction."

To help understand this principle, assume that a force of 10 lb is exerted on a piston with a surface area of 1 square inch (sq. in.). Since this force, measured in lb or Newton (N), is applied to a piston with an area measured in square inches (sq. in.), the pressure is the force divided by the area, that is, "10 pounds per square inch (PSI)." It is this pressure that is transmitted, without loss, throughout the hydraulic system. ● **SEE FIGURE 17–2.**

PASCAL'S LAW FORMULA

$F = P \times A$ (force is equal to pressure multiplied by area)

$P = F \div A$ (pressure is equal to force divided by area)

$A = F \div P$ (area is equal to force divided by pressure)

where

F = force (lb) or (Newton)

P = pressure in pounds per sq. in. or (kPa)

A = area in sq. in. or (sq.cm)

When fluid pressure or force is computed, use the area of the piston and not its diameter. The area of a piston or any circle can be determined using the following formula

$$A = \pi r^2$$

where

π = 3.1416

r = one-half the diameter

The pressure in a hydraulic system becomes a force to produce work, and the amount of force can be determined by multiplying the area of the output piston by the system pressure. A force of 100 pounds pushing on a piston that has an area of two square inches produces a force of 200 lbs. (200 x1) on a piston that has an area of two square inches. ● **SEE FIGURE 17–3.**

Application force is multiplied whenever the output piston is larger than the input piston. Automatic transmissions contain valves that are moved based on which valve has the largest diameter and therefore the greater area. Force will decrease if the input piston is larger than the output piston. A simple memory triangle can be used as an aid to determine area, force, or pressure. ● **SEE FIGURE 17–4.**

PUMPS

PURPOSE AND FUNCTION Every hydraulic system requires a **pump** to maintain fluid flow and to pressurize the fluid in the system. However, the pump itself does not develop pressure but instead pressure occurs when there is a resistance to flow. Initially, fluid flows freely when a hydraulic circuit is empty or partially filled. Once the circuit is completely full, there is a resistance to further flow. At this point, pressure begins to build up in the circuit as the pump continues the fluid flow.

(a)

(b)

(c)

FIGURE 17–5 (a) Gear-type pump. (b) Gerotor-type pump. (c) Variable displacement vane-type pump.

PARTS AND OPERATION The torque converter housing is bolted to the engine flywheel, or flexplate, and rotates whenever the engine is running. The torque converter hub is keyed to the pump tangs located inside the pump housing of the transmission.

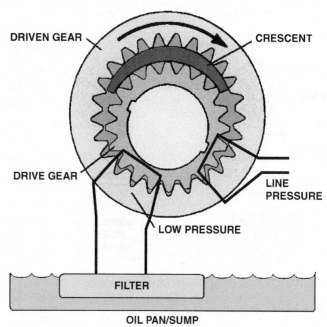

FIGURE 17–6 As a pump rotates, a low pressure (vacuum) is created as the pumping members move apart in one area, and atmospheric pressure will force fluid into this area. Pressure is created where the pumping members move together.

Three common types of rotary pumps are used to produce the fluid flow and resulting pressure in an automatic transmission. They include the following:

1. The **internal–external gear** with *crescent (or gear) pump*
2. The **Gerotor** (rotor) pump
3. The **vane pump**

   ● **SEE FIGURE 17–5**.

The pumping action in each of these pump types is essentially the same. The inner pumping member (external gear or inner rotor) is driven by the torque converter hub or a driveshaft, and the outer pumping member (the internal gear, outer rotor, or vane housing) is offset or eccentric relative to the inner gear or rotor. As the inner member rotates, a series of chambers (between the gear teeth, the rotor lobes, or vanes) increase in volume in one area and decrease in another. A low-pressure area is created in the void area where the chamber volume increases. This area is connected to a passage leading to the filter that is submerged in fluid near the bottom of the sump. Atmospheric pressure inside the transmission pushes fluid into the filter, through the intake passage, and into the pump inlet.
● **SEE FIGURE 17–6**.

As the pump rotates, fluid fills the chambers just as fast as they enlarge. On the other side of the pump the chambers get smaller and the outlet port of the pump is positioned in this area. Here the fluid is forced out of the pump and into the

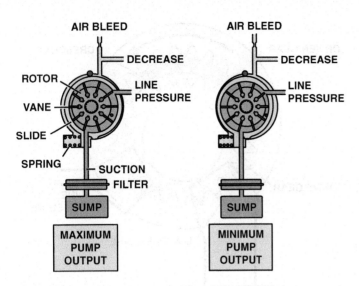

FIGURE 17–7 A variable displacement vane pump in maximum and minimum output positions. The slide is moved to the high output position by a spring. Decreased pressure comes from the pressure regulator valve.

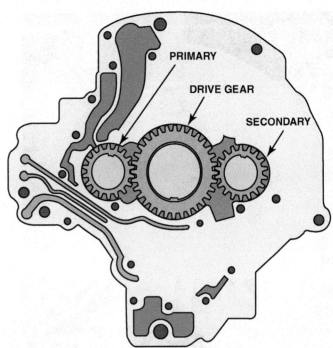

FIGURE 17–8 A dual-stage, external gear pump. Both stages are used at low engine speeds to produce enough fluid for the transmission's needs. At higher engine speeds, the output of secondary stage is vented.

passage leading to the pressure control valve and the rest of the hydraulic system. The parts in a pump must fit together with very little clearance to prevent the fluid from leaking across the pump from the high-pressure area to areas of lower pressure. The fit provides just enough clearance for the parts to move without excess drag. The pressure-regulated fluid is often called **supply pressure**, **mainline pressure,** or **line pressure**.

FIXED DISPLACEMENT PUMPS Many automatic transmissions use a fixed-size **positive displacement pump**. Every revolution of the pump will move the same volume of fluid. The faster the pump is turned, the more fluid will be pumped during a given time period. Both the gear pump and the rotor pump are positive displacement pumps.

VARIABLE DISPLACEMENT PUMPS **Variable displacement pumps** are also positive displacement in that they will pump a certain volume on each revolution, but the displacement, and therefore the fluid volume, can be changed.

This is done by moving the vane housing to reduce the size of the pumping chambers. ● **SEE FIGURE 17–7.**

Variable displacement pumps allow a large output to produce the fluid volume needed for shifts and lubrication and a reduced output when it is not needed.

DUAL-STAGE PUMPS Some transmissions use a dual-stage gear pump, which is a combination of two positive displacement pumps. Both pumps supply fluid when demands are high. The output of the second stage pump is released or vented when the primary stage can supply the needed flow and pressure. This system provides the volume of a large displacement pump at low speeds plus the economy of a small displacement pump at higher, cruising speeds. ● **SEE FIGURE 17–8.**

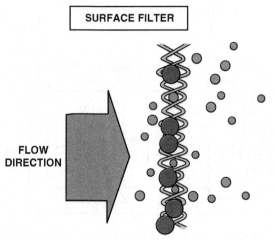

SURFACE FILTER

FLOW DIRECTION

FIGURE 17–9 A surface filter traps particles that are too big to pass through the openings in the screen.

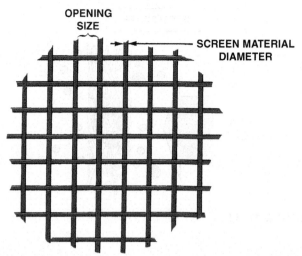

OPENING SIZE

SCREEN MATERIAL DIAMETER

FIGURE 17–10 The surface area of a surface filter is reduced somewhat by the material that makes up the screen. The size of the screen openings determines how small of a particle can be filtered.

ATF FILTERS

PURPOSE AND FUNCTION A filter is located at the pump inlet to trap dirt, metal, and other foreign particles that might cause wear in the pump, bearings, bushings, and gear train or cause sticking of the various valves.

TYPES OF FILTERS

- A **surface filter** traps the foreign particles at the outer surface. ● **SEE FIGURE 17–9**.

  This filter can be a woven screen of metal or synthetic material such as dacron or polyester. Some sources consider a **paper filter** to be a surface filter. With a metal or synthetic screen, the size of the openings varies from rather large to very fine, in the range of 50 to 100 microns (or micrometers). A **micron** is 1 millionth of a meter or 39 millionths of an inch. The symbol for micron is μm. The disadvantage of a surface filter is its limited surface area, which in turn limits its capacity. The mesh openings are the usable area. A large portion of a filter's surface is the fiber or wire that makes up the filter, with the remainder being the openings. ● **SEE FIGURE 17–10**.

- A **depth filter** traps particles as they try to pass through the filter material. Depth filters are made of felt or a synthetic material of various thickness. The thickness of the material allows room to trap particles as well as room for fluid flow. It also has the ability to trap smaller particles, has more capacity to trap particles, and can function for a longer period of time. ● **SEE FIGURE 17–11**.

? FREQUENTLY ASKED QUESTION

How Large Are Dirt Particles?

Some depth filters trap particles as small as 10 μm. The space between a bushing and the shaft is about 0.001 to 0.003 inches (0.025 to 0.076 mm), but if the shaft is loaded to one side by gear pressure, this clearance might be only the width of two or three oil molecules. A hard abrasive particle in this area will produce wear that, in turn, will produce small metal particles that cause more wear. Dirt or other particles that enter the valve body may cause a valve to stick in its bore. This can cause a no-shift problem or a partial shift with low pressure. A recent study of the fluid from eight different transmissions used for less than 3,000 miles (4,800 km) showed the following:

- 1 to 20 particles in the 50-μm size
- 800 to 8,000 particles in the 15-μm size
- More than 50,000 particles in the 5-μm size

CONTROLLING FLUID FLOW

TERMINOLOGY The fluid flow from the pressure regulator valve to the manual valve and into the control circuit is called *mainline*, *line*, or *control pressure*.

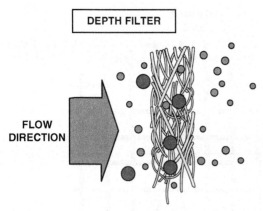

FIGURE 17-11 A depth filter is a group of woven fibers of a certain thickness. Foreign particles are trapped at different levels as they try to flow through.

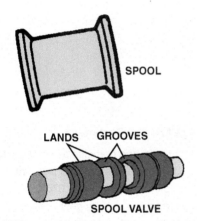

FIGURE 17-12 A spool valve resembles a spool for thread (top).

SPOOL VALVES   Flow to and from a transmission hydraulic actuator is controlled by one or more valves. Spool valves sliding in a round bore are used to control fluid flow. A **spool valve** gets its name because it looks similar to the spool that holds thread. ● **FIGURE 17-12**.

A spool valve can have two or more **lands** that fit the valve bore tightly enough so that fluid cannot escape past the valve land but also loosely enough so that the valve can slide freely in the bore. ● **SEE FIGURE 17-13**.

The annular grooves (valleys) between the lands are where the fluid flows through the valve. Typically, the valve-to-bore clearance is about 0.003 to 0.004 inches (80 to 100 μm). The close fit requires the valve to expand and contract at the same rate as the valve body. This prevents the valve from sticking or having excessive leakage. The outer edges of the lands have sharp corners to help prevent debris from wedging between the land and the valve bore. The valleys or grooves between the lands serve as fluid passages. The faces serve as pressure surfaces, called *reaction surfaces*, to produce valve movement.

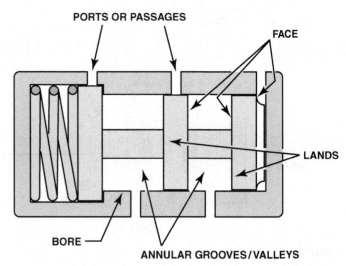

FIGURE 17-13 A spool valve and its bore. Note the names of the various parts.

Some valves are relatively long with a series of lands and grooves so fluid flow through two or more passages are controlled at the same time. The lands of a spool valve often have different diameters in order to provide different size reaction areas. A spool valve bore has fluid passages entering from the sides, which connect to the grooves (valleys) that extend clear around the valve. This is done to produce the same pressure entirely around the valve. As a spool valve is slid along the bore, the lands open up or close off the side passages and block or allow fluid flow from one place to another or to the sump to allow pressure to be exhausted.

PRESSURE REGULATION

PRESSURE REGULATOR VALVE   Transmission oil pumps are capable of creating an excessive amount of pressure quickly and therefore, every transmission uses a **pressure regulator valve**, or *pressure control valve,* to control hydraulic pressure. This is usually a spool valve and spring combination. This regulated pressure, commonly known as *mainline pressure, line,* or *control pressure,* is the working pressure for the entire hydraulic system. Most pressure regulator valves balance pump pressure on one side of the valve against a preset spring force acting on the other side of the valve. When hydraulic pressure is greater than the spring force, the valve moves in its bore far enough to uncover an exhaust port. ● **SEE FIGURE 17-14**.

The exhaust port provides a low-pressure path to the transmission oil pan (sump) where excess ATF is stored.

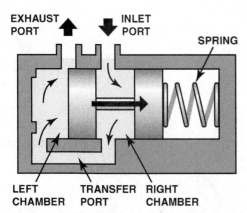

FIGURE 17-14 When pressure on the face of the pressure regulator valve overcomes spring force, the valve moves to open the exhaust port.

Excess pressurized fluid flowing through this port reduces system pressure. When hydraulic pressure drops below spring pressure, the regulator valve closes the port and pressure begins to build up again. In operation, the opening and closing of the exhaust port occurs many times per second. This sequence of events achieves a steady pressure as the valve balances both the spring pressure and the hydraulic pressure. Because of this action, this type of valve is sometimes called a **balance valve**.

ELECTRONIC PRESSURE REGULATION Electronic automatic transmissions/transaxles often regulate hydraulic system pressure using computer-controlled solenoids called by any of the following names:

- **Pressure control solenoids (PCS)**
- **Electronic pressure control (EPC)**
- **Pressure control (PC)**
- **Variable force solenoids (VFS)**
- **Force motors**

An onboard computer switches the solenoids on and off very quickly using pulse-width modulation (PWM). The solenoid pushes against an internal valve which opens and closes the hydraulic circuit it regulates. Electronic pressure control allows precise hydraulic system pressure regulation and can also be used to modify the timing and feel of transmission shifting. ● SEE FIGURE 17-15.

TYPICAL PRESSURES Line pressure is controlled by the powertrain control module (PCM) or the transmission control module (TCM) to provide the specific pressure needed by the system based on input from the sensors such as vehicle speed and engine load. In some situations line pressure can be

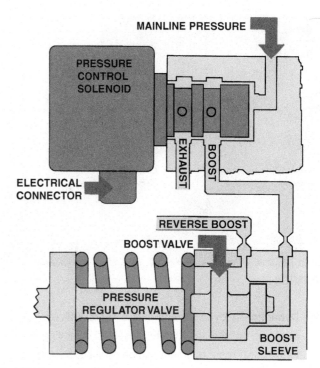

FIGURE 17-15 The pressure control solenoid controls the mainline pressure, which is in turn controlled by the powertrain control module (PCM) or the transmission control module (TCM), by applying pressure to the spring side of the pressure regulator valve.

reduced to improve fuel economy; lowering pressure reduces the load on the engine that is driving the pump.

Typical line pressures include:

- Normal line pressure—60 to 120 PSI (414 to 830 kPa)
- The accelerator pedal pressed to wide open throttle (WOT)—90 to 150 PSI (620 to 1,034 kPa)
- The gear selector in reverse or manual low (1)—150 to 300 PSI (1,034 to 2,068 kPa)

HYDRAULIC SEALS

TYPES OF SEALS Gaskets and seals are used to keep the pressure from escaping where fluid flows between parts. Seals are of two types:

1. **Static**—A **static seal** is used to seal the space between two parts that are stationary relative to each other. Static seals include gaskets and O rings that are placed between the two parts and squeezed tightly as the parts are fastened together. A static seal must provide enough compression to fill any possible voids between the two surfaces. ● SEE FIGURE 17-16.

FIGURE 17-16 A new O-ring seal being installed on a cover.

2. **Dynamic**—A dynamic seal has a more difficult job because one of the surfaces to be sealed is moving relative to the seal. The movement can be rotating, such as when the torque converter enters the front of the transmission or the fluid flows from the pump housing into a clutch assembly, or sliding. At each end of the transmission, a rotating shaft enters or leaves the transmission, and the opening through which the shaft runs must be sealed to keep the fluid in and the dirt and water out. In both cases, a metal-clad lip seal is used. A lip seal has a flexible rubber sealing lip that rubs against the revolving shaft with enough pressure so fluid cannot flow between the shaft and the seal lip. A garter spring is often used to increase this sealing pressure. ● **SEE FIGURE 17-17.**

SEALING RINGS Another type of seal are the sealing rings used to seal the fluid passages where fluid leaves a stationary member and transfers to a rotating member. ● **SEE FIGURE 17-18.**

Similar to a piston ring, this type of seal is a metal, plastic, or Teflon ring that fits tightly in its bore to make a seal while the side seals against the side of its groove. ● **SEE FIGURE 17-19.**

A seal with a small leak is sometimes desirable to lubricate a bearing area close to the sealing ring. Metal and plastic sealing rings can be a *full-circle, hook ring,* or a *butt-cut ring* with a small gap. Teflon rings can be *scarf cut* (have the ends cut at an angle so they overlap), *butt cut,* or *uncut.* ● **SEE FIGURE 17-20.**

Teflon seals can change size and require special handling. When a Teflon ring is stretched over a shaft, it must be resized to fit into the groove and bore. Special installing and resizing tools are recommended when installing Teflon sealing rings. The sliding seals for the clutch and band servo pistons are made of rubber in an O-ring, D-ring, lathe-cut seal, or lip seal

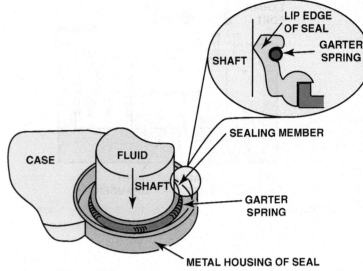

FIGURE 17-17 The sealing member of a metal-clad lip seal makes a dynamic seal with the rotating shaft while the metal case forms a static seal with the transmission case.

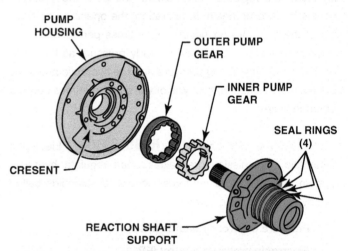

FIGURE 17-18 Sealing rings are used to seal the passages between stationary and rotating members. For example, the seal rings at the right keep the fluid flows from the pump to the front clutch from escaping.

shape. An O-ring is a rubber ring with a round cross section. A D-ring is rounded on the sealing side and square on the side where it is retained; the square portion prevents the seal from rotating. A lathe-cut seal, also called a *square-cut seal,* is a rubber ring with a square cross section. ● **SEE FIGURE 17-21.**

ATF HEATERS AND COOLERS

TEMPERATURES Transmissions are expected to perform over a wide range of temperatures. Cold fluids are much thicker than hot fluids. On a cold day, the first shifts tend to be

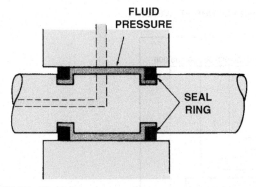

FIGURE 17-19 Fluid pressure forces a sealing ring outward in both directions to make firm contact with the side of the groove and outer diameter of the bore.

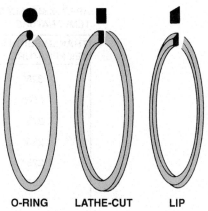

O-RING   LATHE-CUT   LIP

FIGURE 17-21 Clutch and servo piston seals are usually O-rings, lathe-cut rings, or lip seals

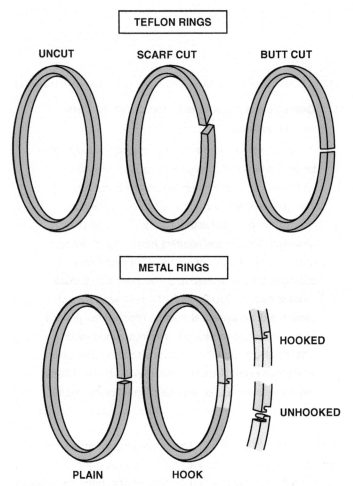

TEFLON RINGS

UNCUT   SCARF CUT   BUTT CUT

METAL RINGS

HOOKED

UNHOOKED

PLAIN   HOOK

FIGURE 17-20 Metal seal rings (bottom) have plain or hooked ends. Teflon rings (top) are either uncut, scarf cut, or butt cut.

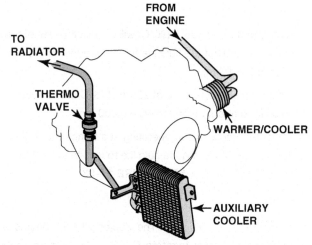

FROM ENGINE

TO RADIATOR

THERMO VALVE

WARMER/COOLER

AUXILIARY COOLER

FIGURE 17-22 Engine coolant from the engine block flows through the passages in the warmer/cooler, and then out through the thermo valve to the upper radiator tank. The thermostatic valve uses a wax element–type valve to control the flow of engine coolant through the case-mounted cooler/warmer. The thermostatic valve improves the ATF warm-up times and maintains ATF temperature within the optimum operating range between 170°F and 180°F (77°C and 82°C).

sluggish because the fluid moves slowly through the orifices and small openings. The best operating temperature for an automatic transmission is in the range of 170°F to 180°F (77°C to 82°C). This produces good fluid viscosity without excessive fluid degradation. Some transmissions use fluid heaters to improve cold operation. ● SEE FIGURE 17-22.

Probably the greatest problem for transmission fluid is heat. Excess heat significantly shortens the life of ATF. Excess temperatures cause the fluid to break down and form gum or varnish. This in turn can cause valve sticking or reduce the fluid flow in certain circuits. All transmissions use a cooler to help remove excess heat. The fluid should be changed more frequently than normal if the vehicle is driven under conditions such as towing that could result in fluid temperatures above 180°F (82°C). Adverse driving conditions that produce higher fluid temperatures are trailer towing, driving on hills, and stop-and-go driving. The torque converter is the primary source of heat in an automatic transmission. For example,

APPROXIMATELY MILEAGE TO TRANSMISSION FAILURE AT AVERAGE TEMPERATURE

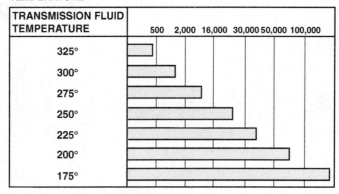

TRANSMISSION FLUID TEMPERATURE	500 2,000 16,000 30,000 50,000 100,000
325°	
300°	
275°	
250°	
225°	
200°	
175°	

FIGURE 17–23 The life of automatic transmission fluid drops drastically when the temperature increases above normal.

- A temperature of 195°F (90°C) will double the rate of fluid oxidation and cut the fluid life to half or about 50,000 miles (80,000 km).

- A transmission operating at 235°F (113°C) will reduce fluid life to about 25,000 miles (40,000 km).

- The same transmission operating at a temperature of 255°F (124°C) will reduce fluid life to less than 12,000 miles (19,000 km). ● **SEE FIGURE 17–23.**

OIL COOLER CIRCUITS The cooler oil flow begins as soon as the pump begins to rotate. Cooler oil flow then exits the pump and enters the converter. As soon as the supply circuit begins to develop pressure, the regulator valve moves slightly and opens a passage to the torque converter. This fluid flow serves several purposes including the following:

- It ensures that the torque converter is filled so it can transmit engine torque to the transmission input shaft.

- It helps control converter fluid temperature.

- It provides lubrication to the moving parts inside the transmission.

COOLER FLOW The fluid leaving the torque converter is routed out of the transmission case and through a steel line to the *transmission cooler.* The cooler is positioned in the colder (outlet) tank of the radiator. Another steel line is used to return the fluid to the transmission. A cooler is often called a *heat exchanger* because it moves heat from one location to another. Heat from the transmission fluid is transferred to the engine coolant. ● **SEE FIGURE 17–24.**

TECH TIP

Don't Tow a Vehicle with the Drive Wheels on the Ground

A vehicle with an automatic transmission should not be towed or pushed very far because there will be no lubricating fluid flow when the engine is not running. The gear sets and bushings will run dry, wear, and overheat or burn out without a constant flow of lubricating oil. Most manufacturers recommend towing only when absolutely necessary. They caution that towing should be limited to a few miles with a maximum speed of 20 to 25 mph (32 to 40 km/h). If possible, the drive wheels should be lifted off the ground or the driveshaft removed from a rear-wheel-drive (RWD) vehicle. Special cautions also should be taken when towing an all-wheel-drive (AWD) vehicle. Check the owner's manual or service information for details.

AUXILIARY FILTERS The transmission cooler tends to trap foreign particles and can become plugged, especially when the fluid is extremely dirty or contains metal particles, or when there is a torque converter clutch mechanical failure. At least one aftermarket manufacturer markets a filter that can be installed in the transmission-to-cooler line. This filter provides added protection by removing foreign particles from the fluid and preventing cooler blockage. Many filters contain a magnet to remove iron particles. If the filter gets plugged, fluid flow will be restricted or blocked completely, which then shuts off transmission lubrication. To prevent this from

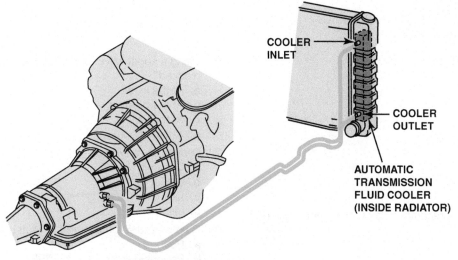

COOLER INLET

COOLER OUTLET

AUTOMATIC TRANSMISSION FLUID COOLER (INSIDE RADIATOR)

AUTOMATIC TRANSMISSION FLUID COOLER LINES

FIGURE 17–24 Automatic transmission fluid is routed from the torque converter, where most of the heat is generated, to the radiator where it is cooled. The fluid then returns to the transmission/transaxle to lubricate the bearings and bushings.

happening, many supplementary filters include a bypass valve to maintain fluid flow when the filter becomes plugged.

LUBRICATION FLOW In most transmissions, the fluid returning from the torque converter and cooler lubricates the transmission. The fluid from the cooler enters the lubrication passages at the case. It flows through holes drilled in the case to the main shaft bushings, where it passes into holes drilled in the input or output shaft. From there, it flows through the shaft to side holes that align with support bushings, thrust washers, planetary gear sets, clutch drum bushings, and clutch packs. Most transaxle final drive gears and differentials are also lubricated by this circuit.

SUMMARY

1. The hydraulic system applies the band and clutches, transmits force and motion, maintains fluid flow to the torque converter, and provides lubrication and cooling to the moving parts of the transmission.

2. Pumps produce the fluid flow in a transmission and the restriction to the flow results in the system pressure.

3. The mainline pressure is controlled by a variable pressure regulator.

4. Seals are used to confine the fluid to the appropriate passages.

5. Automatic transmission fluid is the lifeblood of an automatic transmission, and only the specified fluid should be used.

REVIEW QUESTIONS

1. What are the functions of ATF?

2. What are the three options that a technician or shop can use when selecting the ATF for a vehicle?

3. How does a variable displacement pump work?

4. How does a filter trap particles?

5. Why do some vehicles use a transmission fluid warmer and a cooler?

1. Which fluid is highly friction modified?
   a. Type A
   b. Type F
   c. ATF+4
   d. Dexron

2. What is the color of ATF?
   a. Red
   b. Yellow
   c. Blue
   d. Green

3. What type of fluid is recommended for late model General Motors vehicles?
   a. Dexron 3 or 4
   b. Dexron VI
   c. Dexron IV
   d. Any fluid called "Dexron"

4. Which is NOT a type of pump used in automatic transmissions or transaxles?
   a. Gear-type pump
   b. Gerotor-type pump
   c. Vane-type pump
   d. Cupped-wheel type pump

5. The two types of automatic transmission filters are _____ and _____.
   a. Micron and paper
   b. Surface and depth
   c. Paper and cloth
   d. Nylon and rayon

6. Using a spool valve to control fluid flow, where is the fluid blocked?
   a. At the lands
   b. At the grooves
   c. At the valleys
   d. At the spool

7. O-rings are a type of _____ seal.
   a. Dynamic
   b. Static
   c. Lip
   d. Inside

8. Fluid pressure is measured in what unit?
   a. Pounds
   b. Pounds per square inch (PSI)
   c. Newton
   d. Inches

9. Fluid pressure is controlled by _____
   a. Pressure control solenoids (PCS)
   b. Electronic pressure control (EPC)
   c. Variable force solenoids (VFS)
   d. Any of the above terms depending on application

10. Normal automatic transmission fluid temperature is _____.
    a. Between 170°F and 180°F (77°C and 82°C)
    b. 195°F (90°C)
    c. 235°F (113°C)
    d. 255°F (124°C)

CONVERTERS

TORQUE CONVERTER TERMINOLOGY

PURPOSE AND FUNCTION   The torque converter is located between the engine and the transmission/transaxle and performs the following functions.

1. Transmits and multiplies engine torque

2. Acts as a clutch between the engine and the transmission/transaxle

3. Allows slippage, which makes it possible for the transmission to be engaged even when the vehicle and wheels are stopped.

LOCATION   The torque converter is bolted to a thin metal disc called a **flexplate**. The center of the flexplate often has a pilot indentation for the nose of the converter, and the flexplate itself is bolted to the rear flange of the engine crankshaft.

The flexplate replaces the heavy flywheel used with a manual transmission. An important function of a flywheel is to smooth out engine pulsations and dampen vibrations. An automatic transmission does not require a conventional flywheel because the weight of the torque converter provides enough mass to dampen engine vibrations. An external ring gear generally attaches to the outer rim of the flexplate, while on some applications the ring gear may be welded to the outside of the torque converter cover. This ring gear engages the starter motor pinion gear to turn the engine during starting. ● **SEE FIGURE 18–1.**

ELEMENTS   The three major parts of the torque converter are given below:

- **Impeller**. The impeller is the driving member and rotates with the engine, and is located on the transmission side of the converter. When the engine is running, the flexplate and converter rotate with the crankshaft. The flexplate is flexible enough to allow the front of the converter to move forward or backward if the converter expands or contracts slightly from heat or pressure. The impeller inside the torque converter is also called the pump (not to be confused with the pump used to supply fluid under pressure to the entire transmission/transaxle). The impeller is the input to the converter. The vanes/fins inside the converter are attached to the rear of the impeller, transmission end, of the converter housing or cover. ● **SEE FIGURE 18–2.**

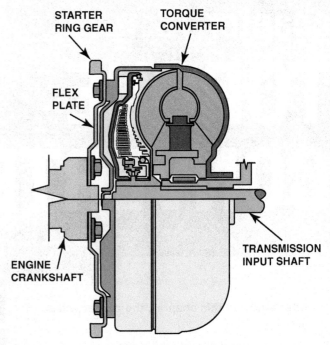

FIGURE 18–1 The torque converter bolts to the flexplate which is attached to the engine crankshaft and rotates at engine speed.

- **Turbine**. The turbine is located on the engine side of the converter. The impeller vanes pick up fluid in the converter housing and direct it toward the turbine. Fluid flow drives the turbine, and when the flow between the impeller and the turbine is adequate, the turbine rotates and turns the transmission input shaft. The turbine is the converter's output member. The center hub of the turbine is splined to the transmission input shaft. The turbine is positioned in the front, engine end, of the converter housing so the turbine vanes face the impeller vanes. ● **SEE FIGURE 18–3.**

- **Stator**. A torque converter also contains the stator, or reactor, which is mounted on a one-way clutch. The stator is the reaction member of the torque converter. The stator assembly is about one-half the diameter of the impeller or turbine. The outer edge of the stator vanes forms the inner edge of the three-piece fluid guide ring that is also part of the impeller and turbine vanes. The stator is mounted on a one-way clutch that is attached to the stationary reaction shaft splines. The reaction shaft is made as part of the transmission front pump housing and is fixed and does not rotate. The one-way clutch allows the stator to rotate clockwise but blocks counterclockwise rotation. ● **SEE FIGURE 18–4.**

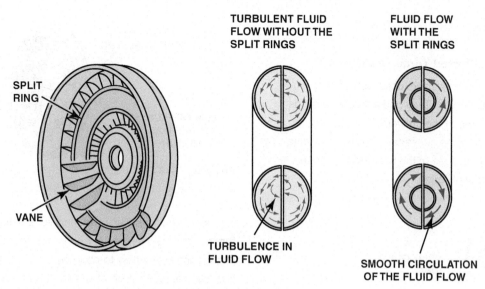

FIGURE 18-2 The split rings in the impeller and turbine help to direct the flow of fluid and improve the efficiency of the torque converter by reducing turbulence.

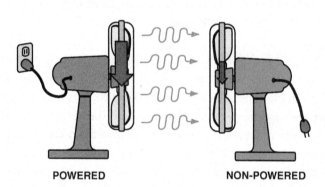

FIGURE 18-3 Two fans can be used to show how fluid, or air in the case of fans instead of automatic transmission fluid, can be used to transfer energy. If one fan is operating, which represents the impeller, the blades of a second fan (turbine) will be rotated by the flow of air past the fan that is unplugged, causing the blades to rotate.

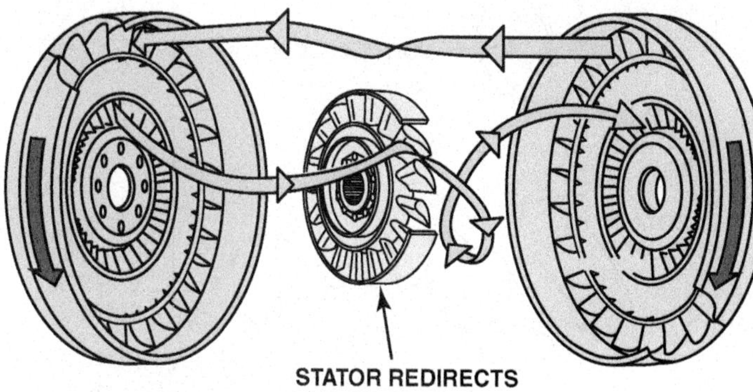

FIGURE 18-4 A torque converter is made from three parts: The impeller is located at the transmission end, attached to the housing, and is driven by the engine. The turbine is located at the engine side and is driven by the fluid flow from the impeller and drives the input shaft of the transmission. The stator redirects the flow to improve efficiency and multiply torque.

TORQUE CONVERTER OPERATION

TORQUE TRANSFER A torque converter is a *hydrodynamic* unit because it transfers power through the dynamic motion of the fluid. Most other hydraulic units transfer power through the static pressure of the fluid. When the engine is running, the converter impeller acts as a centrifugal pump. Fluid is thrown from the outer edge of the impeller vanes, and because of the curved shape of the converter cover, the fluid is thrown forward into the turbine. The impeller is turning in a clockwise direction, and the fluid also rotates in a clockwise direction as it leaves the impeller vanes. The mechanical power entering the converter is transformed in the fluid as fluid motion.

VORTEX FLOW The rotating fluid in the impeller tries to turn the turbine in a clockwise direction. If the turbine is stationary or turning at a speed substantially slower than the impeller, only part of the energy leaves the fluid to drive the turbine. Most of the fluid energy is lost as the fluid bounces off the turbine vanes. The fluid moves toward the center of the turbine, driven there by the continuous flow of fluid from the impeller.

What Is an Air-Cooled Torque Converter?

Some early torque converters used with smaller engines were air cooled. They had a shroud with fins attached to the rear of the converter cover, to force cooling airflow past the converter. Torque converters must be cooled because of the heat they generate during torque multiplication.

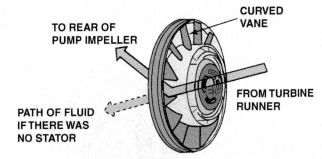

FIGURE 18–6 The fluid flow from the turbine is turned in the same direction as the impeller by the stator vanes.

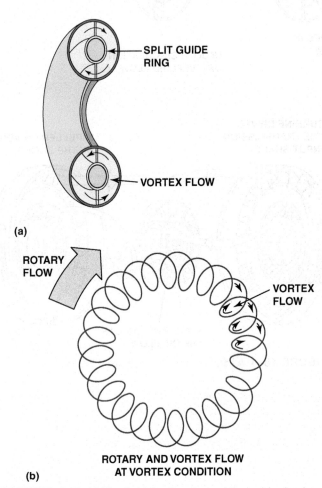

(a)

(b)

FIGURE 18–5 (a) The fluid flowing around the guide ring is called vortex flow. (b) The fluid flowing around the converter is called rotary flow.

As energy leaves the fluid, the flow slows down and returns to the center of the impeller vanes, where the impeller will pick it up and keep it circulating. This flow is called a **vortex flow**. The vortex flow is a continuous circulation of fluid outward from the impeller, around the guide ring, inward into the turbine, through the stator, and back into the impeller. The guide ring directs the vortex flow, creating a smooth, turbulence-free flow. The clockwise flow of fluid leaving the impeller, in the direction of engine rotation, is called **rotary flow**.

When the impeller is rotating substantially faster than the turbine, the fluid tends to bounce off the turbine vanes and change the rotary flow to counterclockwise direction. The fluid flow still has quite a bit of energy. It can be compared with a tennis ball thrown against a wall. The ball bounces back and travels in a different direction, but it still has most of its energy of motion. A strong counterclockwise fluid flow from the turbine would tend to work against the clockwise rotation of the impeller. ● **SEE FIGURE 18–5**.

TORQUE MULTIPLICATION The stator redirects the fluid flow in the torque converter. It returns the fluid from the turbine back to the impeller in a clockwise direction. This action helps recover any energy remaining in the fluid. The curved shape of the stator vanes and a one-way clutch make this possible. Fluid leaving the turbine in a counterclockwise direction tries to turn the stator counterclockwise. This causes the stator one-way clutch to lock up and hold the stator stationary. The smooth, curved shape of the stator vanes redirects the fluid flow in a clockwise direction. ● **SEE FIGURE 18–6**.

Torque multiplication occurs because the stator redirects the fluid flow. This occurs only when the impeller is rotating faster than the turbine. As the turbine speed increases, the direction of the flow becomes more rotary. The stator clutch overruns and the converter becomes more of a coupling, transferring power from the engine to the transmission. ● **SEE FIGURE 18–7**.

An engineering term used for torque converters is the *stall torque ratio (STR)*, which is the torque converter's ability to multiply torque. Most passenger vehicle torque converters have an STR between 1.68:1 and 2.1:1. For most converters, this means that the torque converter is able to double the torque of the engine at the stall speed of the converter.

COUPLING PHASE When the turbine speed reaches 90% to 95% of impeller speed, *coupling* occurs. The **coupling phase** occurs when the speeds of the impeller and turbine are nearly equal. Centrifugal force acting on the fluid in the spinning turbine is high enough to stop the vortex flow. At this point, there

FIGURE 18–7 A stator contains a one-way roller clutch which locks it from rotating in one direction and allows it to rotate freely in the opposite direction.

is no torque multiplication. It should be noted that this coupling speed is a relative point between the speeds of the impeller and turbine. Therefore, the coupling phase occurs at various vehicle speeds depending on throttle position and speed.

Some slippage occurs during the coupling phase. If power and load demands require, the converter can return to the torque multiplication phase. In a nonlock-up converter, the turbine almost never turns at the same speed as the engine and impeller, a condition commonly referred to as *converter slippage*. The converter's efficiency steadily improves during torque multiplication and the coupling phases to about 90% to 95%.

STALL SPEED **Stall speed** is the fastest RPM that an engine can reach while the turbine is held stationary. Stall is when the turbine is held stationary while the converter housing and impeller are spinning. This is done by shifting the transmission into gear and applying the brakes to hold the drive wheels stationary. The importance of stall speed is that an engine must be able to reach an RPM where enough torque is available to accelerate the vehicle, but not running so fast that there is poor fuel economy and excessive noise. Stall occurs to some degree each time a vehicle starts moving, either forward or backward, and each time a vehicle stops at a stop sign.

CREEP When the transmission selector is moved from park (P) or neutral (N) into a drive gear, some engine torque is transferred to the input shaft of the transmission or transaxle. The vehicle will move slightly if the brakes are released. This slight movement of the vehicle when the engine is at idle speed and the brakes are released is called **creep**. Therefore, a slight movement is normal for a vehicle equipped with an automatic transmission.

NOTE: Vehicle creep is more noticeable when the engine is cold due to the higher idle speed.

TORQUE CONVERTER CLUTCHES

PURPOSE AND FUNCTION The **torque converter clutch (TCC)** is applied to eliminate the slippage during the coupling phase, which improves fuel economy. When the TCC applies, the converter locks up, connecting the transmission input shaft directly to the engine, much like a vehicle with a manual transmission and clutch.

PARTS AND OPERATION The converter clutch is a large clutch disc called a *pressure plate* or *clutch disc*. It has friction material and a damper assembly attached to it and it is splined to the turbine. When the friction material is forced against the torque converter cover, the turbine is driven mechanically by the engine. ● **SEE FIGURE 18–8**.

The torque converter clutch is controlled by a solenoid which is controlled by the powertrain control module (PCM) or the transmission control module (TCM). The TCC is applied and released when the fluid entering the converter changes from the rear or front.

- Normal torque converter action occurs when the TCC is released, and the fluid flows from the front to the rear, past the clutch plate.
- TCC lockup occurs when the fluid enters the rear of the torque converter and forces the clutch plate against the front cover.
- TCC apply forces the fluid in front of the clutch outward, and this fluid acts like an accumulator to soften clutch application.
- When fluid is flowing into the back (turbine) side of the torque converter, pressure is applied to the back side of the clutch piston, which forces it to come in contact with the torque converter cover. This locks the turbine to the cover and all the elements of the torque converter rotate as one unit.
- In order to release the TCC, the flow of fluid in the torque converter housing is reversed. This causes the clutch piston to move away from the torque converter cover and the turbine is thus released. ● **SEE FIGURE 18–9**.

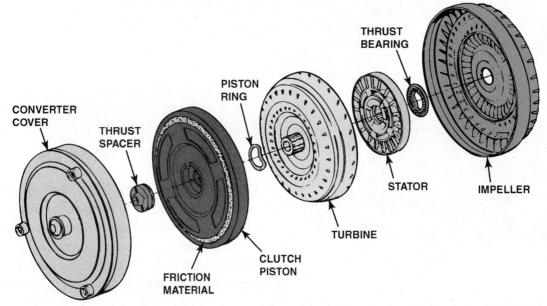

FIGURE 18–8 An expanded view of a typical torque converter assembly showing the torque converter clutch (TCC).

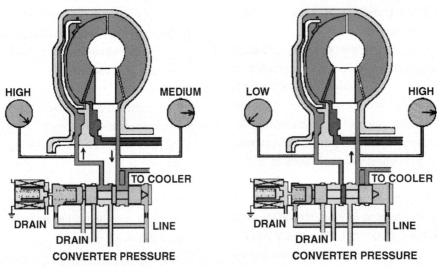

FIGURE 18–9 TCC releases fluid flows through the center of the turbine shaft to the front of the clutch disc (left). Pressure to apply the clutch enters between the converter hub and the stator support (right).

TCC fluid flow is controlled by a TCC control valve that is in turn controlled by a solenoid. TCC apply blocks the flow of fluid through the torque converter and cooler. The torque converter does not generate heat when TCC is applied, but some heat is generated by the rest of the transmission. Some fluid will be directed past the TCC control valve to provide cool fluid for transmission lubrication.

FRICTION MATERIALS USED Most TCCs use paper friction material. It can be secured to the front of the clutch disc, to the inside of the converter cover, or left free between the two.

Some vehicles use a modulated or pulsed TCC apply pressure to smooth out TCC apply. This produces a lot of slipping that can burn out paper clutch lining fairly rapidly. These converters use synthetic materials for greater endurance under more severe operating conditions. ● **SEE FIGURE 18–10.**

TCC DAMPER ASSEMBLY Clutch discs include a **damper assembly** that transfers the power through a group of coil springs. In most converters, the damper springs are grouped at the center; in others they are grouped around the outer edge. These springs are used to dampen **torsional**

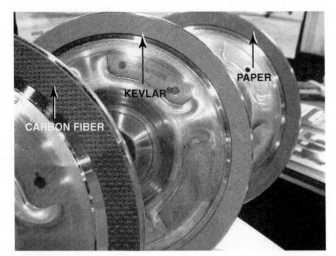

FIGURE 18-10 Torque converter clutch friction material is determined by the vehicle manufacturer to provide the needed coefficient of friction needed. For example, many older units use a paper-type friction material because they are fully applied or released, whereas most newer units use a synthetic material such as Kevlar ® or carbon fiber because the torque converter clutch is pulsed on and off, therefore requiring a more robust material for long service life.

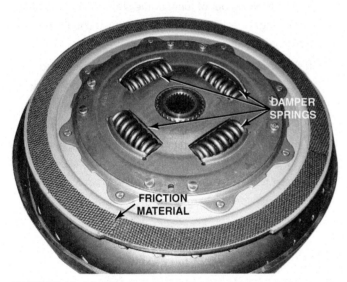

FIGURE 18-11 The damper springs used in many torque converter clutches are similar to the damper springs used in clutch discs used with a manual transmission.

? FREQUENTLY ASKED QUESTION

What Is a "Squashed Converter"?

The cross-sectional area of the impeller, turbine, and stator of most torque converters is round to give an efficient flow. The converter used with many newer transaxles has an elliptical cross-sectional shape that reduces the width of the converter. A shorter, low-profile converter, often called a *squashed converter*, makes the engine and transaxle shorter and easier to fit transversely in a vehicle. ● SEE FIGURE 18-12.

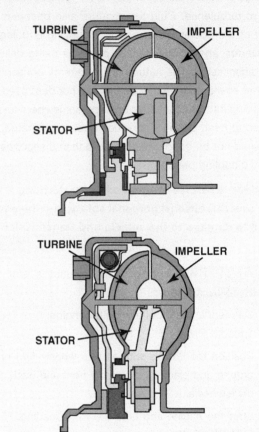

FIGURE 18-12 Most torque converters have a round cross section (top). Some new transmissions use a shorter, elliptical, squashed converter (bottom) that is about 13% shorter than a round style.

vibrations from the engine. All automotive engines produce torsional vibration at some operating speed. Torsional vibrations are small speed increases and slowdowns as the crankshaft revolves between engine cylinder firing pulses. These vibrations can produce gear noise in the transmission and drivetrain as well as a noticeable vibration and harshness in the vehicle. ● SEE FIGURE 18-11.

STALL TEST

PURPOSE OF THE TEST A stall test is used to check the stator one-way clutch inside the torque converter and the strength of the apply devices inside the transmission/transaxle.

A stall test measures stall speed of the torque converter in each of the gear positions. It is an important diagnostic test to determine transmission and torque converter condition. This test should be performed with caution because it operates the vehicle in a potentially dangerous situation: The vehicle is in gear with the throttle wide open. It is recommended that both the parking brake and the service brake be firmly applied, the wheels blocked, and the throttle be held open for a maximum of 5 seconds.

A stall test can severely damage the transmission if done incorrectly. During a stall test, the dynamic fluid pressure inside a converter becomes very high, because there is a lot of turbulence. Fluid temperature also becomes very high. All of the power the engine is producing is going into the converter, and no mechanical power is being delivered to the transmission. The natural law of energy conservation states that energy can neither be created nor destroyed. The energy going into the converter must go somewhere and it is converted to heat. Because so much heat is generated, stall tests should not be conducted for more than 5 seconds, followed by a cooling period.

CAUTION: Exercise caution when performing a stall test for several reasons: personal safety, and the chance of possible damage to the vehicle and transmission.

STALL TEST PROCEDURE To conduct a stall test, perform the following steps:

STEP 1 Connect a scan tool to monitor engine speed (RPM).

STEP 2 Position the vehicle with all four wheels firm on the ground and place blocks at the front and back of the drive wheels.

STEP 3 Start the engine and note the RPM reading. ● **SEE FIGURE 18–13.**

STEP 4 Apply the brakes firmly, move the gear selector to reverse, move the throttle to wide open, and watch the tachometer. The speed should increase to somewhere between 1500 and 3000 RPM. As soon as the speed stops increasing or goes higher than 3500 RPM, quickly note the reading and close the throttle. Record the speed.

STEP 5 Shift to neutral, and run the engine at fast idle for 30 to 60 seconds to cool the converter.

STEP 6 Repeat steps 4 and 5 with the gear selector in drive.

STEP 7 Repeat steps 4 and 5 with the gear selector in low.

CAUTION: Direct any bystanders away from the front or rear of the vehicle.

FIGURE 18–13 This 4-cylinder General Motors vehicle has a stall speed of about 2350 RPM. Notice that the gear selector is in drive and the speedometer is reading zero.

INTERPRETING STALL TEST READINGS

- **If all of the stall speeds were within the specification range.** The apply devices for the three gear ranges are all sound and in good shape. The apply devices for some gear(s) cannot be applied with the vehicle at rest so they cannot be stall tested.

- **If all of the stall speeds were equal but low.** The engine is weak, out of tune, or the stator one-way clutch is slipping. Checking engine performance should indicate which is at fault.

- **If the stall speeds are normal, but the vehicle has normal acceleration and has reduced performance at higher speeds.** The stator one-way clutch could be seized in a locked-up condition.

- **If the stall speed is high in one or two of the gear ranges.** One or more of the apply devices is slipping. Consult a clutch and band application chart to determine which apply devices are at fault.

TORQUE CONVERTER SERVICE

REPLACEMENT A torque converter is considered to be part of the transmission and should be serviced or replaced when a transmission is overhauled. A torque converter is always replaced with a new or rebuilt unit if it has an internal failure. Most shops do not rebuild torque converters. There are companies that specialize in torque converter overhaul.

Torque converters tend to collect the metal, dirt, and other debris that enter with the fluid. It is impossible to thoroughly check a torque converter without cutting it open. The

What Is a High Stall Speed Converter?

A high stall speed converter is called a *loose converter*. A low stall speed converter is called a *tight converter*. When a vehicle is standing still, the turbine is not rotating. As the vehicle accelerates, the engine RPM increases quickly to the torque capacity of the converter (stall speed) and then it stabilizes. As the turbine speed increases, the engine speed also increases. A loose converter allows a higher engine RPM relative to the turbine RPM.

The actual stall speed of a torque converter is determined by the following factors.

- Amount of engine torque
- Diameter of the converter
- Angle of the impeller vanes
- Angle of the stator vanes

A high-torque engine has the ability to turn the impeller faster against a stalled turbine than a small or weak engine. A low-torque engine is normally equipped with a looser converter.

- If the converter is too tight, the engine RPM cannot increase to the point of usable power and the vehicle would lose acceleration and overall performance.
- A converter that is too loose will cause the engine to operate at excessive speed. The result will be poor fuel economy, excessive noise, and reduced performance because of the excessive slippage.

In production, the torque converter capacity/ stall speed is matched to the engine size and vehicle weight to produce the best vehicle performance and fuel economy. Depending on the engine, different converters are used with a transmission model. One manufacturer uses eight different converters with one transmission model. The technician must ensure that the correct replacement converter is used.

internal shape and the centrifugal force inside a torque converter can pack dirt and debris around the outer diameter. Foreign material can also lodge in the clutch lining of a lock-up torque converter. Some shops flush and check the torque converter during every transmission overhaul. Other shops install a rebuilt torque converter as standard practice. High-mileage transmissions, the ones that show a lot of metal wear,

FIGURE 18–14 Visually check the pump drive notches or tangs for damage and the hub sealing surface for wear.

and units with lock-up torque converters are candidates for replacement.

TORQUE CONVERTER CHECKS The torque converter should be checked to make sure it is in usable condition when the transmission is removed. These checks include the following:

1. **Visual inspection.** It includes the following steps:
   - Check the outer side (especially at the welds) for wetness, which might indicate a leak.
   - Check the mounting drive studs or threaded holes and lugs for physical damage.
   - Check the pilot area for damage.
   - Check the hub for signs of seal or bushing area wear.
   - Check the pump drive tangs or lugs for wear or damage. ● **SEE FIGURE 18–14**.
   - Check the starter ring gear, if used, for wear or damage.

2. **Stator one-way clutch operation.** It includes the following steps:
   - Place the converter flat on a bench.
   - Reach into the hub so one finger contacts the splines. ● **SEE FIGURE 18–15**.
   - Rotate the splines in a clockwise direction. If they rotate, the clutch is probably locked.
   - Try to rotate the splines counterclockwise. If they rotate, the clutch is slipping.

NOTE: A commercial stator-holding tool may be used to check a one-way clutch. This tool can be inserted into a groove in the thrust washer on some stators to keep it and the stator from rotating. Next, a special one-way clutch-tool is inserted into the stator splines, and a torque

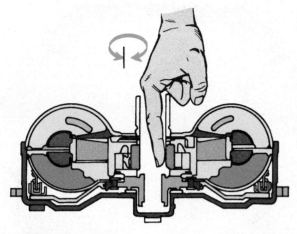

FIGURE 18–15 A stator clutch can be checked by reaching into the hub so a finger contacts the splines. The splines should rotate in one direction but not in the other.

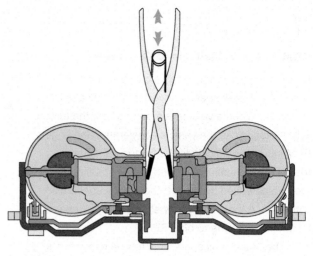

FIGURE 18–16 A quick end-play check can be made by gripping the turbine or stator splines and trying to move the turbine or stator in and out.

wrench is used to apply torque to the tool and one-way clutch inner race. The one-way clutch should turn freely in a clockwise direction, and it should lock and hold at least 10 foot pound (14 N-m) of torque in a counterclockwise direction. Do not apply any more torque than this because the special tool can break. A torque converter with a faulty one-way clutch must be replaced.

3. **Turbine end play.** End play is normally measured using a dial indicator. Two styles of dial indicator fixtures are commonly used to measure end play.

   ▫ One fixture uses an expandable stem that fits into the turbine splines and is expanded to lock into the splines. The dial indicator is positioned and adjusted so the measuring stylus is against the fixture and the dial reads zero. The fixture and turbine are lifted as far as they will go. The travel (end play) is read on the dial indicator.

   ▫ Another fixture for checking end play is designed so the torque converter sits on top of it. The measuring stem is moved upward to contact the turbine splines, and the dial indicator is adjusted to zero. Then the turbine is lifted as far as possible. The end play is read on the dial indicator.

   The end play can be felt as the turbine or stator is lifted and then lowered. Some manufacturers publish torque converter end-play specifications. If no specifications are available, use the rule of thumb that 0.030 inch (0.8 mm) is normal and 0.050 inch (1.3 mm) is the maximum allowable end play. A torque converter with excess end play (more than 0.050 inch) should be rebuilt or replaced. ● **SEE FIGURE 18–16**.

4. **Internal interference.** Torque converter interference should be checked twice, first with the turbine and stator toward the front and a second time with these toward the rear. To check a converter for internal interference, perform the following steps:

   ▪ Set the torque converter on a bench with the hub up. Gravity will move the turbine and stator toward the front of the torque converter.

   ▪ Insert the transmission pump stator support into the torque converter so the support splines engage the stator clutch splines.

   ▪ Insert the transmission input shaft into the torque converter so its splines enter the turbine splines.

   ▪ Rotate the pump and input shaft in both clockwise and counterclockwise directions, one at a time and together. If there is any sign of contact or rubbing, either a rubbing or grating sound or rough feel, the torque converter needs to be replaced.

   ▪ Turn the whole assembly over so the turbine and stator move toward the rear of the torque converter.

   ▪ Repeat Step 4. Again, any sign of internal contact indicates a torque converter that should be rebuilt or replaced.

5. **Lock-up clutch operation.** Two styles of testers are available for checking torque converter clutches.

   ▪ One type uses adapters that replace the turbine shaft and allow a vacuum to be exerted on the front side of the clutch plate assembly. If this chamber can hold a vacuum, the center seal and the clutch lining (which forms the outer seal) are good.

   ▪ The second tester style uses adapters that attach to the turbine, which uses air pressure to apply the

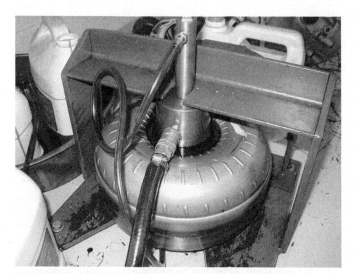

FIGURE 18–17 A leak-test fixture has been placed on the torque converter. It will be filled with ATF and then inspected for leaks.

TECH TIP

Converter Drain-Back Test

If the fluid leaves the torque converter when the engine is off, the vehicle will not move when the engine is restarted until the torque converter is refilled by the pump, which causes a delay. If torque converter drain back is suspected, operate the vehicle until it is at normal operating temperature, and drive the vehicle through several full-shift cycles. Check and adjust the fluid level if it is low, and shut off the engine. Allow the vehicle to sit for 30 to 60 minutes, then recheck the fluid level and mark it on the dipstick. Allow the vehicle to sit for 24 hours and then recheck the fluid level. If the level has risen by 1 inch (25 mm) or more, converter drain back has occurred. This means that the sealing rings around the torque converter are not able to seal properly and this means that the transmission or transaxle has to be removed to correct this condition.

clutch. With the clutch applied, torque is exerted to try to turn the turbine. A good torque converter clutch locks the turbine and prevents it from turning.

6. **External leakage.** The torque converter must be pressurized to test for a leak. A special tool with an expandable plug that fits into the hub and a device to keep the plug in place is used. The plug is equipped with an air chuck to allow pressure to be added. ● **SEE FIGURE 18–17**.

A torque converter that passes inspection is reusable. One that fails one or more of the checks should be replaced with a new or rebuilt unit. A torque converter that has turned blue from overheating has failed internally and should be replaced.

NOTE: All torque converters are balanced but a service technician is not able to verify that it is balanced. To avoid possible balance issues, purchase torque converters from a known company that checks the balance of all converters before they are packaged and sent out for sale.

SUMMARY

1. The torque converter is located between the engine and the transmission/transaxle and performs the following functions:
   a. Transmits and multiplies engine torque
   b. Acts as a clutch between the engine and the transmission/transaxle
   c. Allows slippage, which makes it possible for the transmission to be engaged in gear even when the vehicle and wheels are stopped.

2. The three major parts of the torque converter are the turbine, impeller, and stator.

3. A torque converter is a hydrodynamic unit because it transfers power through the dynamic motion of the fluid.

4. The flow of fluid inside a torque converter is both rotary and vortex flow.

5. When the turbine speed reaches 90% to 95% of impeller speed, coupling occurs.

6. Stall speed is the fastest RPM that an engine can reach while the turbine is held stationary.

7. The torque converter clutch is applied to eliminate slippage, thereby improving fuel economy.

8. A stall test is used to check the stator one-way clutch and the strength of the apply devices inside the transmission/transaxle.

9. A torque converter is considered to be part of the transmission and should be serviced or replaced when a transmission is overhauled.

1. What are the three elements inside a torque converter?
2. What is the difference between rotary flow and vortex flow?
3. What is the purpose and function of a torque converter?
4. How much torque is a torque converter able to multiply?
5. What precautions are needed to be adhered to when performing a stall test?

1. The parts of a torque converter include _____.
   a. Flexplate, housing, and turbine
   b. Turbine, impeller, and stator
   c. Impeller, flexplate, and housing
   d. Stator, turbine, and housing

2. When the impeller and turbine are rotating at about the same speed, this is called _____.
   a. Coupling
   b. Stall speed
   c. Torque multiplication
   d. Vortex flow

3. Creep is _____.
   a. Normal operation
   b. Caused by slippage inside the torque converter
   c. Causes the vehicle to move slightly when the engine is at idle speed and the transmission is in drive gear.
   d. All of the above

4. A stall test is used to check the _____.
   a. Stator
   b. Impeller
   c. Turbine
   d. Torque converter clutch

5. What happens when the torque converter clutch is locked?
   a. Converter slippage is no more than 96%
   b. The impeller and turbine rotate at the same speed
   c. The turbine rotates slightly slower than the impeller
   d. The transmission will overheat

6. The torque converter clutch circuit is controlled by the _____.
   a. Driver
   b. Fluid temperature
   c. Command from the PCM/TCM
   d. Fluid pressure

7. A torque converter can be checked by a technician for all of the following except _____.
   a. Leaks
   b. Proper balance
   c. Stator one-way clutch operation
   d. Turbine end play

8. If the stall speed is lower than specified, what could be the cause?
   a. Incorrect ATF was used in the automatic transmission/transaxle
   b. A slipping stator clutch
   c. Defective turbine
   d. Slipping torque converter clutch

9. A torque converter can multiply engine torque at the stall speed by about _____.
   a. Double
   b. Three times
   c. 10 times
   d. 100 times

10. A vehicle creeps faster than normal when the engine is cold. What is the most likely cause?
    a. Normal operation
    b. A TCC stuck in the applied position
    c. A defective stator one-way clutch
    d. Incorrect ATF

TRANSMISSION GEAR SETS

LEARNING OBJECTIVES

After studying this chapter, the reader will be able to:

1. Explain how power can be transferred through planetary gear sets to produce the various ratios.
2. Discuss the Simpson gear set and identify the different types of Simpson gear trains.
3. Discuss the Ravigneaux gear set.
4. Explain the operation of the LePelletier gear train.

This chapter will help you prepare for ASE Automatic Transmission/Transaxle (A2) certification test content area "A" (General Transmission/Transaxle Diagnosis).

KEY TERMS

High-reverse clutch 332
LePelletier gear set 325
Nonsynchronous 330
Planet carrier 324
Ravigneaux gear set 325
Ring gear 324
Simpson gear set 325
Sun gear 324
Synchronous 330

GM STC OBJECTIVES

GM Service Technical College topic covered in this chapter is as follows:

1. Diagnose mechanical component operation to determine proper/improper operation.

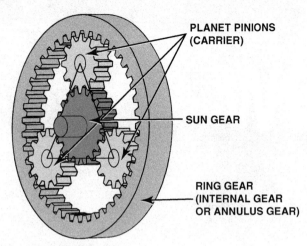

FIGURE 19–1 A typical planetary gear set showing the terms that are used to describe each member.

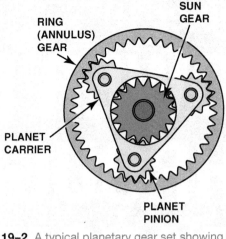

FIGURE 19–2 A typical planetary gear set showing the planet carrier which supports all of the pinion gears (also called planet pinion gears).

PLANETARY GEAR SETS

RATIOS Planetary gear sets are able to provide the following conditions:

- neutral
- one or more gear reductions
- direct-drive ratio (1:1)
- reverse
- overdrive

The exact ratio for reduction and overdrive is achieved by varying the number of teeth on the sun and ring gears.

SIMPLE PLANETARY GEAR SET
A simple planetary gear set consists of three primary components.

- Sun gear
- Planet carrier (including planet pinion gears)
- Ring (annulus) gear

The **sun gear** gets its name from its position at the center of the gear set. The **planet carrier** holds the pinion gears, also known as planet gears, which revolve around the sun gear. The planet carrier assembly is commonly referred to simply as "the carrier." The outermost member of the gear set is the **ring gear**, an internal gear with teeth on the inside. The ring gear is sometimes called an annulus or internal gear. The pinion gears are in constant mesh with both the sun gear and the ring gear. ● **SEE FIGURE 19–1.**

The pinion gears are free to rotate on pins that are part of the carrier, and the entire assembly rotates to direct torque flow. Most transmission gear sets use three, four, or even five planet pinions. The pinions are fully meshed with both the sun gear and internal ring gear *at all times*.

The planetary gears never disengage to change gear ratios but torque is redirected. Both input and output torque flow through a planetary gear set occurs along a single axis.

PLANETARY GEAR SET TORQUE FLOW In a planetary gear set, the following operations are executed in order to achieve the various gear ratios and reverse.

- One of the members is being driven (input).
- One of the members is being held (reaction member).
- One of the members is the output.

Therefore, driving one element will cause all of the other gears to rotate as well. This allows the gear set to provide different gear ratios, depending upon how torque is transmitted through the assembly. ● **SEE FIGURE 19–2.**

Each member of a planetary gear set can play any one of these three roles (drive, held, or driven) to transmit torque. The various combinations of drive, held, and driven members result in the number of gear ratios available and change the direction of rotation as well for reverse.

NOTE: The held member can also be allowed to move in one direction or another as it is being held and does not necessarily need to be held to zero RPM to create a variable gear ratio. This is done in hybrid electric vehicle transmissions.

NEUTRAL, FORWARD, OR REVERSE	REDUCTION, OVERDRIVE, OR DIRECT DRIVE	PLANETARY GEAR ACTION
Neutral		When there is no driving member or reaction member, neutral results.
Forward	Direct drive, 1:1	When there are two driving members, direct drive occurs.
Forward	Reduction	When the carrier is the output, a forward reduction occurs.
Forward	Overdrive	When the carrier is the input, an overdrive occurs.
Reverse	Reduction or OD	When the carrier is the reaction member, a reverse occurs.
F or R	OD	When the sun gear is the output, an overdrive occurs.
F or R	Reduction	When the sun gear is the input, a reduction occurs.
Reverse	Reduction or OD	When one external gear drives another, reverse rotation occurs.
Forward	Any	When an external gear drives an internal gear or vice versa, same-direction rotation occurs.

CHART 19–1

Planetary gear set fundamentals.

Torque flows through a planetary gear set in several steps to get from the drive action of the first member to the driven action of the last member.

- The terms *drive* and *driven* describe how any two gears work together.

- When three or more gears are involved, the second gear is a *driven* gear in relation to the first, but it becomes a *drive* gear in relation to the third gear. ● **SEE CHART 19–1**.

FREQUENTLY ASKED QUESTION

Which Companies Build Automatic Transmissions?

Many larger automobile manufacturers make their own automatic transmissions, including General Motors, Ford, Chrysler, and Honda. However, several companies manufacture automatic transmissions and transaxles that are used in a variety of vehicles. These include the following:

- **ZF Friedrichshafen AG.** This German company manufactures manual and automatic transmissions and transaxles for many vehicle manufacturers, including Mercedes, BMW, Volvo, VW, Audi, Jaguar, Chrysler, Bentley, and Maserati.
- **Aisin AW.** This Japanese company makes automatic transmissions for many vehicle manufacturers, including General Motors, Ford, Toyota, Nissan, Mazda, Mitsubishi, Subaru, Kia, and VW.
- **JATCO (Japan Automatic Transmission Company).** This is a Japanese manufacturer of automatic transmissions and transaxles for many vehicle manufacturers, including General Motors, Nissan, Mazda, Infiniti, VW, Mitsubishi, and Suzuki.

COMPOUND GEAR SETS   There are several different designs of planetary gear sets. The most popular compound planetary design is the **Simpson gear set**. This gear set was named for its inventor, Howard Woodworth Simpson (1892–1963), who was an American automotive engineer. ● **SEE FIGURE 19–3**.

- **Simpson gear set.** Combines one sun gear with two carriers with planet gears and two ring gears. A simple planetary gear set and a Simpson gear set can be combined to provide four- and five-speed transmissions.

- **Ravigneaux gear set.** Combines one carrier that has two sets of planet gears with two sun gears, and one ring gear. ● **SEE FIGURE 19–4**.

- **LePelletier gear set.** A Ravigneaux gear set and a simple planetary gear set can be combined to get six, seven, and eight speeds and is known as the **LePelletier gear set** (pronounced "la-plet-e-ay").

CALCULATING GEAR RATIOS   A simple planetary gear set can produce seven different gear ratios, plus neutral. The gear ratio is changed by changing the input (driving) and the

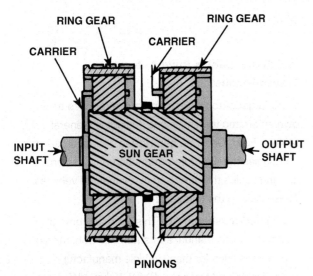

FIGURE 19–3 A Simpson planet gear set is composed of two ring gears and two planet carrier assemblies that share one sun gear.

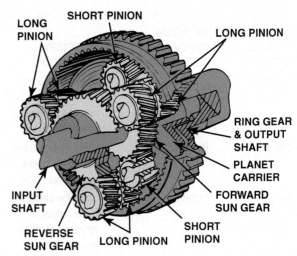

FIGURE 19–4 A Ravigneaux gear set is composed of two sun gears, one planet carrier that supports two sets of pinion gears, and a single ring gear.

reaction (held) members. The various conditions that can be achieved are as follows:

A. If the ring gear is held and the sun gear is driven, the planet gears are forced to rotate as they move around inside the ring gear. The result is an increase in torque and a decrease in speed. The formula for calculating the gear ratio is (sun + ring) ÷ sun.

B. If the ring gear is held and the carrier is driven, the planet gears are forced to rotate as they move around inside the ring gear. This is the reciprocal, or inverse (opposite), of A. The opposite of a reduction ratio is an overdrive ratio. The formula for calculating the gear ratio is sun ÷ (sun + ring).

C. If the sun gear is held in reaction and the ring gear is driven, the planet gears are forced to rotate as they move around the sun gear. The result is an increase in torque and decrease in speed. The formula for calculating the gear ratio is (sun + ring) ÷ ring.

D. If the sun gear is held and the carrier is driven, the planet gears are forced to rotate as they move around the sun

gear. The result is an increase in speed and a decrease in torque. The formula for calculating the gear ratio is ring ÷ (sun + ring). This ratio is the reciprocal of C.

E. If the carrier is held and the sun gear is driven, the planet gears will rotate and act as idlers and the planet gears drive the ring gear in a direction opposite to the sun gear. The result is a reverse with an increase in torque and a decrease in speed. The formula for calculating the gear ratio is ring ÷ sun.

F. If the carrier is held and the ring gear is driven, the planet gears will rotate and act as idlers, driving the sun gear in a direction opposite to the ring. The result is a reverse with an increase in speed and a decrease in torque. The formula for calculating the gear ratio is sun ÷ ring. This ratio is the reciprocal of "E" above.

NOTE: A technician rarely needs to calculate planetary gear set ratios. The gear ratio formulas are shown here for those who are interested or for reference. ● SEE FIGURE 19–5. ● SEE CHART 19–2.

SUN GEAR	PLANET CARRIER	RING GEAR	SPEED	TORQUE	DIRECTION
Input (Drive)	Output (Driven)	Held	Maximum reduction	Increase	Same as input
Held	Output (Driven)	Input (Drive)	Minimum reduction	Increase	Same as input
Output (Driven)	Input (Drive)	Held	Maximum Increase	Reduction	Same as input
Held	Input (Drive)	Output (Driven)	Minimum Increase	Reduction	Same as input
Input (Drive)	Held	Output (Driven)	Reduction	Increase	Reverse of input
Output (Driven)	Held	Input (Drive)	Increase	Reduction	Reverse of input

CHART 19–2

If any two members are locked together, then the resulting output is 1:1 ratio in the same direction as the input. If no member is held (locked), then there is no output (neutral).

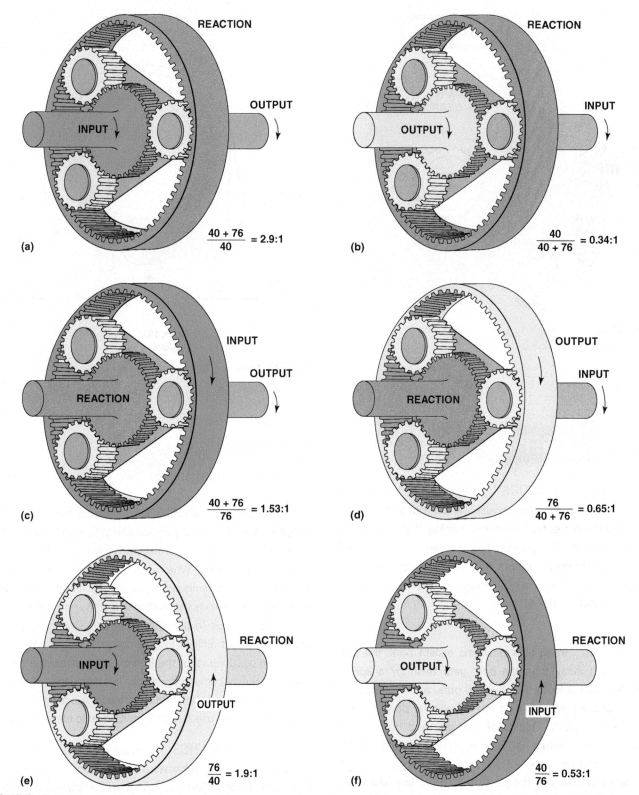

FIGURE 19–5 The gear ratio through a planetary gear set depends on which part is driven, which part is held, and which part is the output. The formula used to calculate the ratio is included with each illustration. Each gear set uses a 40-tooth sun gear and a 77-tooth ring gear.

Manufacturers usually provide clutch and band application charts for their transmissions, and these charts show which apply devices are used for each gear range. Each apply device drives a particular gear set member or holds it in reaction. Clutch and band charts are very helpful in understanding the power flow through a transmission. They are also very helpful when diagnosing transmission failures.

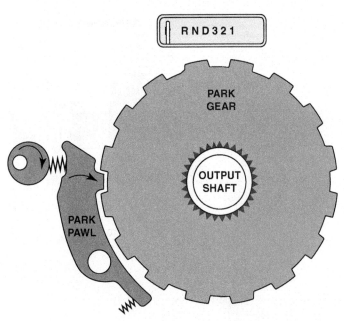

FIGURE 19–6 The parking pawl engages and locks the output shaft to the transmission case.

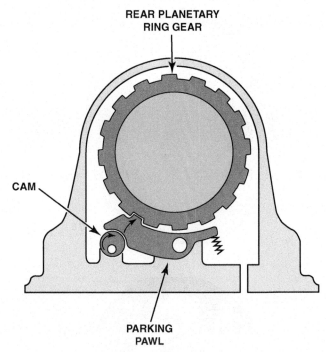

FIGURE 19–7 When the control rod is moved, the locking cam pushes the pawl into engagement with the parking gear.

PARK POSITION

PURPOSE AND FUNCTION Every automatic transmission and transaxle includes a park position. A shift into park prevents the transmission's output shaft from turning, thus holding the vehicle stationary. The parking gear has large gear-like teeth and is mounted on the output shaft of the transmission. The **park pawl** (sometimes called a lever) moves on a pivot pin in the case. ● **SEE FIGURE 19–6**.

OPERATION In all gear positions except park, the park pawl is held away from the park gear teeth by a spring. When the gear selector is moved to park, a circular cam on the end of the park actuating rod pushes the pawl to mesh with the gear teeth. This holds the gear and output shaft stationary. The actuating cam is spring loaded. If the gear teeth and pawl are not aligned, the gear selector lever can still be shifted into the park position but the vehicle will not be held until the output shaft rotates slightly, then the spring moves the cam, which in turn moves the pawl into engagement.

The shift into park is a mechanical connection that should be made with the driveshaft stopped. ● **SEE FIGURE 19–7**.

TRANSMISSION SCHEMATICS

DESCRIPTION Transmission parts and their operations are often illustrated using pictures and cutaway drawings. They show the bare essentials of the transmission gear train in the simplest way possible. When viewing a typical cutaway view of a gear train, the transmission is usually split lengthwise through the middle. This shows the relationship of the parts, but in many cases, it is difficult to tell where one part stops and another begins, making it difficult to trace the path of the power flow. Many exploded views of the internal parts show the front or back of a clutch, carrier, or gear, but it is difficult to tell what the backside connects to unless a separate view is given. Exploded views are typically used by parts personnel to identify parts.

READING SCHEMATICS An easier way to view transmission operation is by using schematics. Transmission schematics resemble stick drawings. Schematics use symbols for the parts and a line shows the link between the parts. Similar to electrical schematics, the major objective is to simplify the transmission as much as possible. A schematic is most useful when tracing the power flow. At present, there is no industry-wide standard for automatic transmission symbols and manufactures can use different formats for their transmission schematics. ● **SEE FIGURE 19–8**.

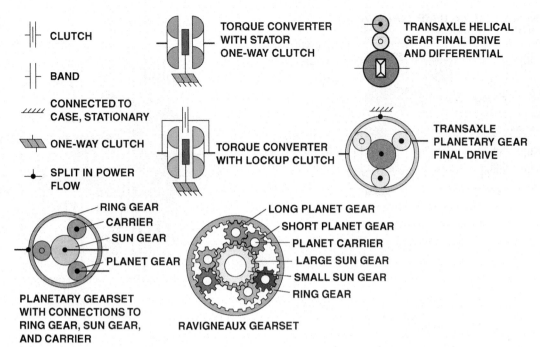

FIGURE 19–8 Common symbols used in the transmission schematics to illustrate the various parts.

SIMPSON GEAR TRAIN TYPES

BACKGROUND The Simpson gear set consists of a double sun gear that is meshed with the planet gears of the two carriers and is a compound gear set commonly used in many three-speed transmissions/transaxles. Most of the automatic transmissions used in domestic vehicles during the 1960s and 1970s used this gear train. The better-known Simpson gear train transmissions are as follows:

Aisin-Warner: Three-speed models

Chrysler Corporation: 36 and 37 RH (Torqueflite A-727 and A-904) transmissions and the 31TH (A-404, A-413, A-415, and A470) transaxles

Ford Motor Company: Cruisomatic C3, C4, C5, and C6 and JATCO transmissions

General Motors: The 3L80 (THM 400), THM 200, 250, 350, 375, and 425 transmissions and 3T40 (THM 125) and THM 325 transaxles

JATCO: Three-speed models

Toyota: A40, A41, A130, A131, and A132

Although transmissions using a Simpson gear train are similar, they are not identical. The power flow through the gear set is essentially the same. They all have two input or driving clutches and a one-way reaction clutch, but the reaction members vary.

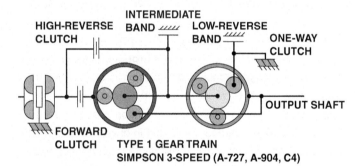

FIGURE 19–9 Type 1 gear set is a three-speed Simpson gear train that uses bands to hold the sun gear and reaction carrier. Note that the reaction carrier can also be held by a one-way clutch.

GEAR SET TYPES 1, 2, 3, AND 4 The major difference between these transmissions is the type of reaction member. A multiple-disc clutch can handle more torque than a band. It has a much larger friction area and multiple case connections. A clutch is more complex than a band and requires more space. To help understand these different arrangements, they will be grouped into similar types, as follows:

- **Type 1**—transmissions use a band for both reaction members. ● **SEE FIGURE 19–9.**
- **Type 2**—transmissions use a multiple-disc clutch for the reaction carrier and a band to hold the sun gear.
- **Type 3**—transmissions use a multiple-disc clutch, a one-way clutch, and an overrun band for the sun gear reaction member and a multiple-disc clutch to hold the reaction carrier. (When a one-way clutch is used for a

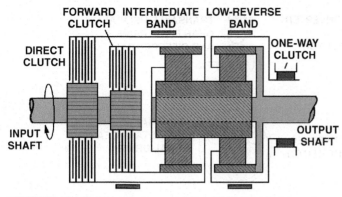

FIGURE 19–10 The one-way clutch of this type 1 gear set serves as the reaction member in first gear with the gear selector in Drive (D1). The low-reverse band is applied in manual first (M1) to allow engine compression braking.

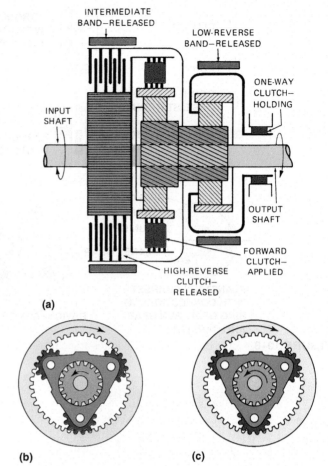

(a)

(b)   **(c)**

FIGURE 19–11 (a) In drive low (D1), the front ring gear is driven while the rear carrier is held by the one-way clutch. A reverse reduction occurs in both (b) the front unit and (c) the rear unit.

reaction member, an overrun band or clutch is applied to hold the reaction member during deceleration.)

- **Type 4**—transmissions use a multiple-disc clutch, a one-way clutch, and an overrun band for the sun gear reaction member and a band to hold the reaction carrier.

NONSYNCHRONOUS AND SYNCHRONOUS DESIGNS

Type 3 and 4 units are **nonsynchronous** (asynchronous) designs. A nonsynchronous transmission is a unit that uses a one-way clutch to allow an upshift that requires only the application of the next driving or reaction member. All four types use a nonsynchronous 1–2 shift in drive. The 2–3 upshift timing is less critical because the disc clutch is used with a one-way clutch and the clutch stays applied while the one-way clutch simply overruns as the upshift occurs. A **synchronous** design transmission means that during an upshift, the new driving or reaction member must be timed or synchronized with the release of a driving or reaction member. The band used in synchronous designs must be released at an exact time for the upshift, and it must reapply at the exact time during a downshift. ● SEE FIGURE 19–10.

The nonsynchronous arrangement is great for upshifts, but is ineffective during deceleration. Similar to the one-way clutch in first gear, the one-way clutch overruns during deceleration.

NEUTRAL Neutral is achieved by not applying the input clutches. Power enters the transmission from the torque converter but travels only as far as the released clutches. When shifted into neutral, some transmissions apply one of the clutches needed for first or reverse to prevent a harsh engagement when the vehicle is shifted into gear.

FIRST GEAR The Simpson gear set has two slightly different first gears—drive-1 and manual-1—the difference being in how the reaction carrier is held. In both gear ranges, power flows through the gear set when the front ring gear is driven and the reaction carrier is held. All Simpson gear sets use a clutch to drive the front (input) ring gear. Transmission types 1 and 4 use a one-way clutch and a band and types 2 and 3 use a one-way clutch and a holding clutch to hold the reaction carrier. In drive-1, the one-way clutch is used and it provides self-application and release. In manual-1, a band or holding clutch is applied to provide engine compression braking during deceleration. ● SEE FIGURE 19–11.

When manual-1 (low) is selected, the one-way clutch is assisted by either a band (types 1 and 4) or a multiple-disc clutch (types 2 and 3). The band is called the *low and reverse* or **low-reverse band**. The multiple-disc clutch is called a **low-reverse clutch**. The power flow is exactly the same as in drive-1 except that power can be transmitted from the drive shaft to the engine during deceleration. This provides engine (compression) braking as the vehicle slows. Engine braking is easily noticed by comparing the deceleration of a vehicle in drive-1 and manual-1.

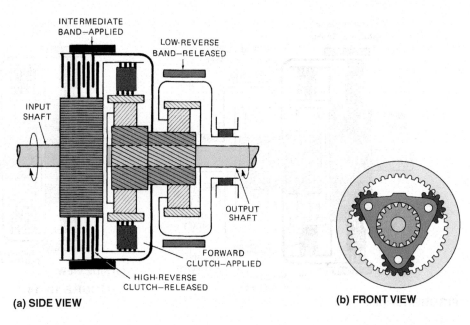

FIGURE 19–12 In second gear, the ring gear is driven while the sun gear is held, and the planet gears walk around the sun gear and force the carrier to revolve at a reduced speed.

(a) SIDE VIEW

(b) FRONT VIEW

For simplicity, this holding member will be called either a low-reverse band or a low-reverse clutch in this text.

In drive-1 (low), the following occur.

- The **forward clutch** is applied to drive the input ring gear in a clockwise direction.
- The output/front carrier will not rotate because it is connected to the driveshaft.
- The front planet gears are driven clockwise.
- The sun gear is driven in the reverse direction (counterclockwise) at a reduced speed.
- The reaction carrier is held from turning counterclockwise by the one-way clutch (or the low-reverse band or clutch in manual-1).
- The rear planet gears are driven clockwise.
- The rear ring gear is driven clockwise at a reduced speed.
- The output shaft and driveshaft are driven clockwise at a reduced speed.

The gear set is producing two reverse reduction ratios, and the result is a forward (clockwise) rotation of the driveshaft. The overall ratio will be about 2.45:1 to 2.74:1 depending on the size of the gears used in a specific transmission.

SECOND GEAR The sun gear must be held stationary in second gear. This is done by a band in type 1 and 2 transmissions or a multiple-disc clutch plus a one-way clutch in type 3 and 4 transmissions. Type 3 and 4 transmissions use an **intermediate clutch** and an *intermediate one-way clutch*. When the intermediate clutch is applied, it holds the outer race of the intermediate roller clutch stationary. The one-way clutch locks, holding the sun gear from rotating counterclockwise. Because the one-way clutch will only hold in one direction, these units have two slightly different power flows in second gear: **drive-2** and **manual-2**. Manual-2 applies an intermediate overrun band to provide engine compression braking during deceleration. For simplicity, we will call this reaction member either an intermediate band or intermediate clutch in this text.

In drive-2 (intermediate), the following occur.

- The forward clutch stays applied to drive the input ring gear clockwise. ● **SEE FIGURE 19–12**.
- The intermediate band or clutch applies to hold the sun gear stationary (reaction member).
- The front planet gears are driven clockwise and walk around the sun gear.
- The front carrier is driven clockwise.
- The front carrier drives the output shaft clockwise at about a 1.5:1 ratio.

THIRD GEAR Third gear in this gear set is direct drive with a 1:1 ratio. It is produced by applying both driving clutches (forward and high-reverse) and either releasing the intermediate band in synchronous transmissions (types 1 and 2) or allowing the intermediate roller clutch to overrun in nonsynchronous transmissions (types 3 and 4). The gear set locks up because the ring gear is trying to turn the planet pinions clockwise while the sun gear is trying to turn them counterclockwise.

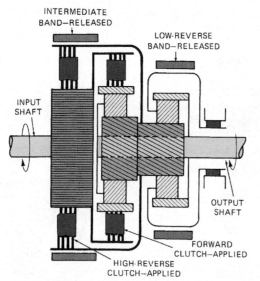

FIGURE 19–13 In third gear, both driving clutches are applied so two members (the ring and sun gears) of the same gear set are driven. This locks the gears and produces a 1:1 gear ratio.

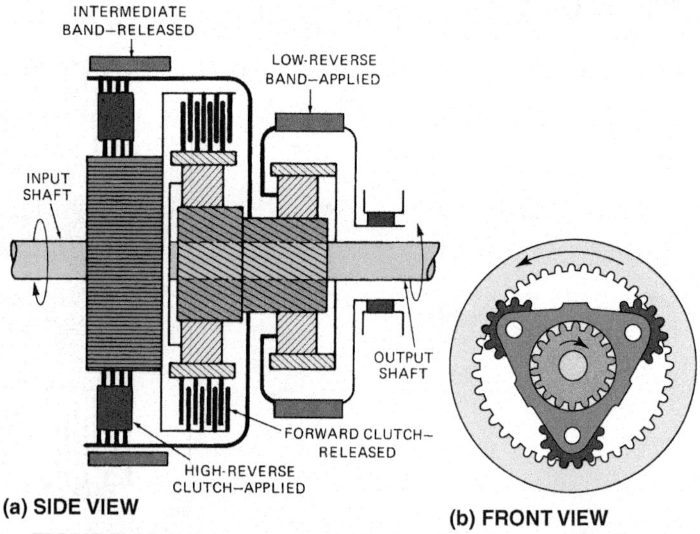

(a) SIDE VIEW   **(b) FRONT VIEW**

FIGURE 19–14 In reverse, the sun gear is driven while the carrier is held. The planet gears act as idlers and cause the ring gear to revolve in a reverse direction at a reduced speed.

In drive-3 (high), the following occur.

- The forward clutch stays applied to drive the input ring gear clockwise.
- The **high-reverse clutch** applies to drive the sun gear clockwise.
- The front planet gears become locked in the carrier.
- The front carrier is driven clockwise at the same speed as the ring and sun gears.
- The front carrier drives the output shaft clockwise at a 1:1 ratio. ● **SEE FIGURE 19–13.**

REVERSE   Reverse in a Simpson gear train occurs when the high-reverse clutch and the low-reverse band or clutch are applied. The high-reverse clutch drives the sun gear (input member) while the carrier (reaction member) in the rear gear set is held stationary by the low-reverse band or clutch. The planet gears act as idlers, reversing the power flow as they transfer power from the smaller sun gear to the larger ring gear. A reverse reduction is produced at the output ring gear of about 2.07:1 to 2.22:1. ● **SEE FIGURE 19–14.**

SHIFT TIMING EXAMPLE   As a vehicle accelerates from a stop to cruising speed, the driving and reaction members have to apply and release in an exact operating sequence. When they apply, they must come on at a precise rate. To illustrate this, we will follow an upshift sequence during a hard acceleration with shift points occurring at 4800 RPM.

In first gear, the ratio will be 2.5:1, so the vehicle driveshaft will be revolving at 1920 RPM (4800 ÷ 2.5) when the 1–2 upshift occurs. Second gear has a ratio of 1.5:1, so the engine speed will drop from 4800 to 2800 RPM (1920 × 1.5) during the shift. ● **SEE FIGURE 19–15.**

FOURTH GEAR MADE POSSIBLE   The Simpson gear train with an additional simple planetary gear set is used to produce a four-speed overdrive transmission or transaxle. The overdrive planetary gear set provides two speeds: direct 1:1 and overdrive. When the overdrive planetary gear set is in direct drive it turns the Simpson planetary gear set input at engine speed. When the overdrive gear train is in direct drive 1:1, the Simpson gear train will shift from first to second and then to third. If the overdrive planetary gear set is in overdrive, it will turn the Simpson planetary gear set input faster than engine speed. The three-speed Simpson gear train will operate as described earlier. To get overdrive, the overdrive planetary gear set will be in overdrive and the Simpson gear set will be in direct 1:1. To get reverse, the overdrive gear set will be in direct and the Simpson will be in reverse. The more common transmissions using this gear set are as follows:

- Chrysler 42RH (A-500), 46RH (A-518)
- Ford 4R44E (A4LD), 5R55E, and E4OD
- GM 4T80-E, THM-200-4R, and 325–4L
- Jeep AW-4
- Nissan E4N7IB
- Toyota A40 and A340 series

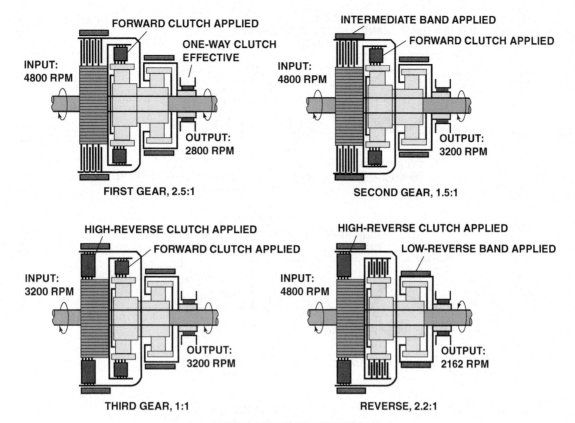

FORWARD CLUTCH APPLIED
ONE-WAY CLUTCH EFFECTIVE
INPUT: 4800 RPM
OUTPUT: 2800 RPM
FIRST GEAR, 2.5:1

INTERMEDIATE BAND APPLIED
FORWARD CLUTCH APPLIED
INPUT: 4800 RPM
OUTPUT: 3200 RPM
SECOND GEAR, 1.5:1

HIGH-REVERSE CLUTCH APPLIED
FORWARD CLUTCH APPLIED
INPUT: 3200 RPM
OUTPUT: 3200 RPM
THIRD GEAR, 1:1

HIGH-REVERSE CLUTCH APPLIED
LOW-REVERSE BAND APPLIED
INPUT: 4800 RPM
OUTPUT: 2162 RPM
REVERSE, 2.2:1

TRIPLE 1 SHIFT SEQUENCE

FIGURE 19–15 The full-throttle shift sequence for a type 1 transmission showing the apply devices and the output shaft speed at the 1–2 and 2–3 upshifts. Reverse is also shown.

OVERDRIVE In most of these transmissions, the overdrive gear set is built into the area at the front of the case between the torque converter and the main gear set. The input shaft from the torque converter is connected to the carrier of the overdrive gear set, and the ring gear of the overdrive gear set is arranged so it becomes the input of the main gear set. The Chrysler 42RH and 46RH have the overdrive gear set built into the transmission extension housing to cause a speed increase between the main gear set and the output shaft.

GEAR SET TYPES 5, 6, 7, AND 8 For examples of types 5, 6, 7, and 8 that use the Simpson gear train, ● **SEE FIGURE 19–16.**

The Chrysler 42RH and 46RH are a little unusual in that one hydraulic piston and return spring is used for both the direct clutch and the overdrive clutch (type 5 gear train). The very strong return spring is used to release the overdrive clutch and apply the direct clutch. Hydraulic pressure at the piston releases the direct clutch and then almost immediately applies the overdrive clutch. With this arrangement, the gear set is locked in either direct drive or overdrive with the over-running clutch transferring power while the upshift or downshift is made.

In the 4R44E/5R55E (type 6), the power is transferred directly from the carrier to the ring gear. In the GM 200-4R (type 7), the gear set is locked because the one-way clutch does not allow the sun gear to overrun the carrier. The type 8 gear train describes the power flow through a Jeep AW-4 transmission.

Like other power flows using a one-way clutch, these gear sets overrun during deceleration and do not produce engine (compression) braking. To prevent this in manual-1, M2, or M3, the overdrive clutch in the Ford 4R44E/5R55E, overrun clutch in the 200-4R, or the O/D direct clutch in the AW-4 are applied. This locks the overdrive gear assembly so it operates in direct drive in both acceleration and deceleration. ● **SEE FIGURE 19–17.**

RAVIGNEAUX GEAR SETS

DESCRIPTION The Ravigneaux gear set uses

- a single carrier that has two sets of intermeshed planet gears,
- two sun gears, and
- a single ring gear.

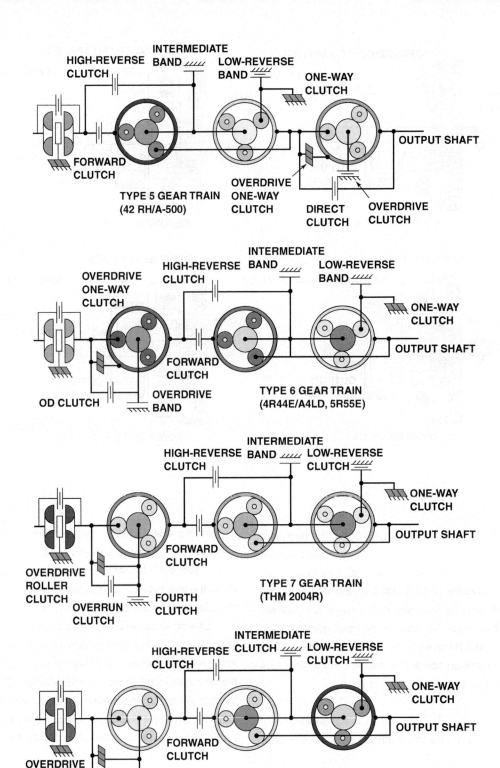

FIGURE 19–16 Types 5, 6, 7, and 8 gear sets illustrate the different four-speed gear train arrangements that combine a Simpson three-speed gear set with an overdrive unit.

The planet gears are different lengths. The two sun gears have different diameters and are independent of each other. On one side of the Ravigneaux gear set, the sun gear meshes with the short pinion gears, which in turn mesh with the longer pinion gears which are meshed with one of the ring gears. On the other side of the gear set, the long pinion gears mesh with the other ring gear and sun gear. In some transmissions, the ring gear is in mesh with the short pinions.

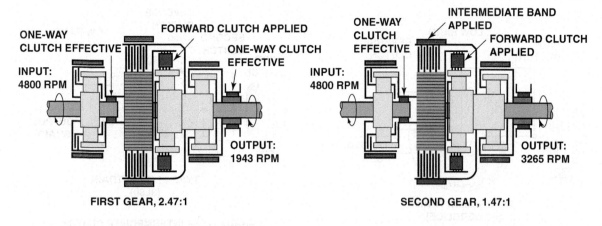

FIRST GEAR, 2.47:1

SECOND GEAR, 1.47:1

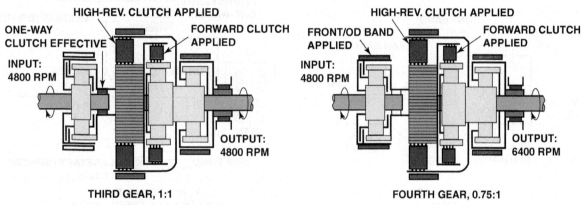

THIRD GEAR, 1:1

FOURTH GEAR, 0.75:1

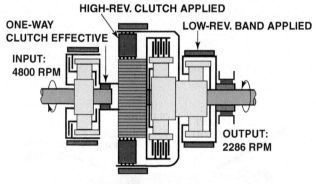

REVERSE, 2.1:1

FIGURE 19–17 The full-throttle shift sequence for a type 6 transmission showing the apply devices and the output shaft speed at the 1–2, 2–3, and 3–4 upshifts, plus reverse.

EXAMPLES The Ravigneaux gear set is used in the following.

- **Two-speed transmissions**—Chrysler Powerflite, the Ford two-speed, and the General Motors Powerglide, and THM 300
- **Three-speed transmissions**—Ford FMX and General Motors 3L30 (THM 180)
- **Three-speed transaxles**—Ford ATX, KM 171 to 175 versions
- **Four-speed transmission**—Ford 4R70W (AOD)
- **Four-speed transaxles**—Ford 4EAT, KM 175 to 177, and ZF-4

The exact arrangement of the gear set varies depending on the usage. ● SEE FIGURE 19–18.

FOUR-SPEED RAVIGNEAUX ARRANGEMENT AND OPERATION The Ford 4R70W (AOD) (type 12 gear set) uses a four-speed version of the Ravigneaux gear train. The first version of this transmission, the AOD, has an additional input shaft (the direct driveshaft) and an additional clutch (the direct clutch). These are arranged so the carrier can be an input member in third and fourth gears as well as a reaction member in first and reverse. The direct driveshaft is driven by a damper assembly at the front of the torque converter so it is a

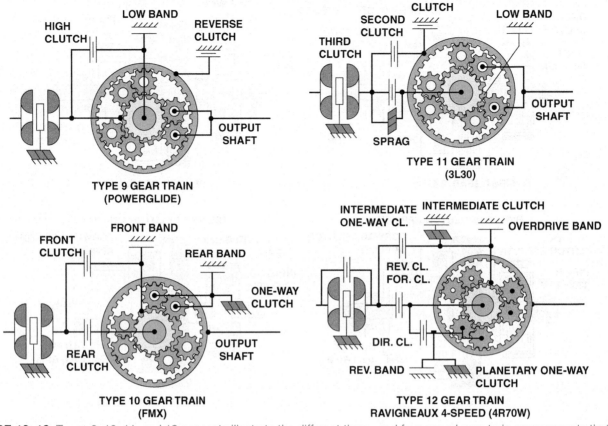

FIGURE 19–18 Types 9, 10, 11, and 12 gear sets illustrate the different three- and four-speed gear train arrangements that use a single Ravigneaux gear set.

How Was the Powerglide Different?

Two-speed transmissions were used in the 1950s and 1960s and are still a popular transmission used in racing. They are no longer in production, but so many were produced that they are still encountered. The most common was the Chevrolet Powerglide (type 9 gear set).

In two-speed Ravigneaux transmissions, the small **primary sun gear** is attached to the input shaft so it is always an input. The large sun gear, called the **secondary sun gear,** is either a reaction member or an input member. The carrier is the output member, and the ring gear can be a reaction member. A driving clutch is placed on the input shaft so the secondary sun gear can be driven, and a band is placed around the clutch drum so the secondary sun gear can be held in reaction. The clutch is often called the *high clutch*, and the band is called a *low band*. The ring gear is held by either a band (first version) or a multiple-disc clutch (second version), called either a *reverse clutch* or a *reverse band*. ● **SEE FIGURE 19–19.**

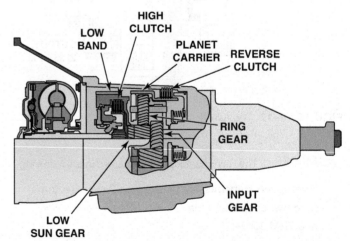

FIGURE 19–19 When a Powerglide is in low gear, the low band is applied to hold the low sun gear stationary. At this time, the long pinions will be driven by the input sun gear and walk around the low sun gear to drive the carrier.

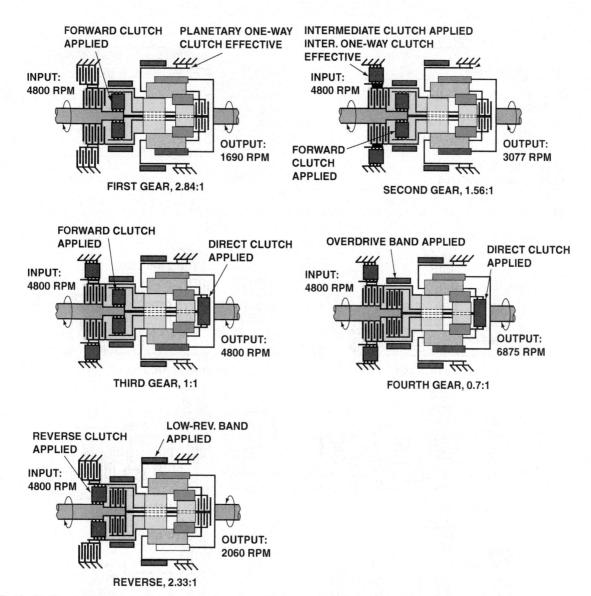

FORWARD CLUTCH APPLIED   PLANETARY ONE-WAY CLUTCH EFFECTIVE

INPUT: 4800 RPM

OUTPUT: 1690 RPM

FIRST GEAR, 2.84:1

INTERMEDIATE CLUTCH APPLIED INTER. ONE-WAY CLUTCH EFFECTIVE

INPUT: 4800 RPM

FORWARD CLUTCH APPLIED

OUTPUT: 3077 RPM

SECOND GEAR, 1.56:1

FORWARD CLUTCH APPLIED

DIRECT CLUTCH APPLIED

INPUT: 4800 RPM

OUTPUT: 4800 RPM

THIRD GEAR, 1:1

OVERDRIVE BAND APPLIED

DIRECT CLUTCH APPLIED

INPUT: 4800 RPM

OUTPUT: 6875 RPM

FOURTH GEAR, 0.7:1

REVERSE CLUTCH APPLIED

LOW-REV. BAND APPLIED

INPUT: 4800 RPM

OUTPUT: 2060 RPM

REVERSE, 2.33:1

FIGURE 19–20 The full-throttle shift sequence for a type 12 transmission showing the apply devices and the output shaft speed at the 1–2, 2–3, and 3–4 upshifts and reverse.

purely mechanical input into the gear set. Newer versions use a more conventional torque converter with a converter clutch and connect the direct clutch to the forward clutch by a short stub shaft.

The first-, second-, and reverse-gear power flows in the 4R70W are the same as those in the old FMX unit used by Ford, with the exception that the intermediate clutch is used to hold the carrier for a reaction member in second gear. In third gear, the direct-drive clutch is applied to drive the carrier while the forward clutch remains applied to drive the small forward sun gear. This locks the planet gears and drives the ring gear in direct drive. The intermediate clutch remains applied, but it becomes ineffective because the intermediate one-way clutch overruns. ●**SEE FIGURE 19–20.**

LEPELLETIER GEAR TRAIN

OPERATION The LePelletier gear train combines a simple planetary gear set with a Ravigneaux gear set providing six forward speeds. The combination is fairly simple, using only five multiplate clutches and, in some transmissions, a one-way clutch. Three of the clutches are driving members and the other two are used in reaction. This gear set is used in the Ford 6R60 and 6R80 and General Motors 6L80E transmissions, and transmissions produced by Aisin and ZF. ●**SEE FIGURE 19–21.**

Because the ring gear is always an input and the sun gear is always a reaction member (it is splined to the back of the pump), the simple gear set is always in reduction. The C1 and C3

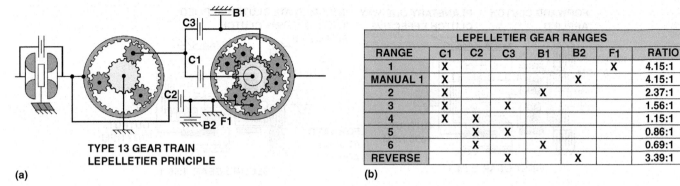

FIGURE 19–21 (a) A schematic view of a type 13, LePelletier six-speed gear set (b) and a clutch application chart.

(a)
TYPE 13 GEAR TRAIN
LEPELLETIER PRINCIPLE

(b)

	LEPELLETIER GEAR RANGES						
RANGE	C1	C2	C3	B1	B2	F1	RATIO
1	X					X	4.15:1
MANUAL 1	X				X		4.15:1
2	X			X			2.37:1
3	X		X				1.56:1
4	X	X					1.15:1
5		X	X				0.86:1
6		X			X		0.69:1
REVERSE			X		X		3.39:1

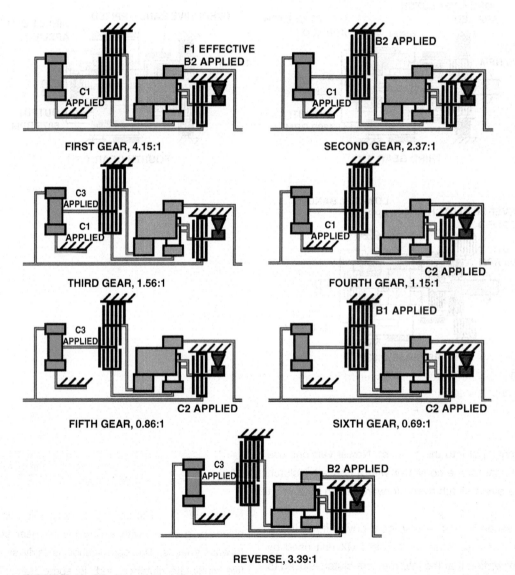

FIGURE 19–22 A type 13 shift sequence.

clutches can provide a reduced speed input to the Ravigneaux gear set. The Ravigneaux gear set is arranged like a type 12 gear set, with three possible inputs and two reaction members.

This gear set has four reduction ratios and two overdrive ratios, with a gear ratio spread of over 6:1. Compared to current five-speed transmissions, these six-speed transmissions have fewer control devices and weigh about 13% less. Because of the close gear ratios and lighter weight, they also promise fuel mileage increases of 5% to 7%, and provide faster acceleration. ● **SEE FIGURE 19–22.**

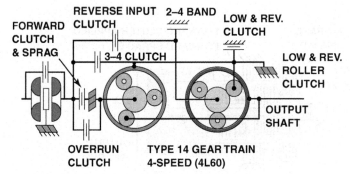

FIGURE 19–23 A schematic view of a type 14, GM 4L60-E four-speed gear set.

GM 4L60-E AND OTHERS

A four-speed gear set was developed by General Motors and introduced in the 4L60-E (THM 700-R4) rear-wheel-drive transmission. It has two simple planetary gear sets that have the ring gears interconnected with the carriers of the other set. A second version of this gear set is used in the following units:

- Chrysler 41TE (A-604) (front-wheel-drive unit) and 42LE (rear-wheel-drive unit)
- Ford AX4N, AX4S (AXOD), and CD4E units.
- General Motors uses this type of gear set in the 4T60-E, 4T65-E, and 4T80-E transaxles.

The 4L60-E (THM 7004R) rear-wheel-drive unit is a type 14 gear train and uses four multiple-disc clutches plus a one-way clutch as driving members and one multiple-disc clutch, a one-way clutch, and a band for holding members. ● **SEE FIGURE 19–23.**

The driving clutches are arranged so they can drive the sun gear and ring gear in the front gear set, called the **input gear set**, and the sun gear and carrier in the rear gear set, called the **reaction gear set**. The input housing contains three of the driving clutches and the hub for the fourth. There are two ways that the front sun gear can be driven. One way is through the *forward clutch* and forward one-way clutch, called a **forward sprag**, and the other way is through the *overrun clutch*. The overrun clutch is used in manual first (M1), M2, and M3 to provide engine braking during deceleration.

The rear carrier (and front ring gear) can be held by the one-way clutch, *low-roller clutch*, or the multiple-disc *low and reverse clutch*. The rear sun gear can be held by the *2–4 band* to serve as a reaction member as well as a driving member.

In neutral, all clutches are released so the power flows no farther than the input housing. ● **FIGURE 19–24.**

41TE/42LE The 41TE (A-604) and 42LE (Type 15) use a similar gear set to the 4L60 (THM 700R4), with different input and output members and a reversal of the gear set so the front ring gear and the rear carrier are the output members. This produces slightly different power flows.

NOTE: The 41TE transmission is also unique in that no bands or one-way clutches are used. This type of transmission/transaxle is called a *clutch-to-clutch* transmission.

Three of the multiple-disc clutches used in the 41TE are driving members and the other two clutches are holding members. The driving clutches are arranged so they can drive the front sun gear (closest to the engine), the front carrier, or the rear sun gear. Driving the carrier in the front gear set also drives the ring gear in the rear gear set. The holding clutches are arranged so one clutch can hold the sun gear in the front gear set. The other clutch can hold the ring gear in the rear gear set as well as the carrier in the front set.

Clutch application is controlled by the manual valve and four solenoid valves. The solenoid valves are controlled by the transaxle electronic control module, and they are opened and closed to produce the automatic upshifts and downshifts. They are also operated at the exact rate to produce the proper clutch application and release for good shift quality. In neutral, the three driving clutches are released. The low-reverse clutch is applied to hold the reaction member as soon as the transmission is shifted into first or reverse gear. ● **SEE FIGURE 19–25.**

A clutch and band chart is shown in ● **CHART 19–3.**

4T60/AX4N

The General Motors 4T60-E (THM 440), 4T65-E, and 4T80-E and the Ford AX4N (AXOD), AX4S, and CD4E transaxles use gear sets that are very similar to the arrangement in the 41TE. These transaxles have the front carrier and the rear ring gears combined and are the output members. The rear carrier and the front ring gear can be a driving member, a reaction, or neither. The rear sun gear can only be a reaction member. The 4T60 is illustrated as a type 16 gear train. ● **SEE FIGURE 19–26.**

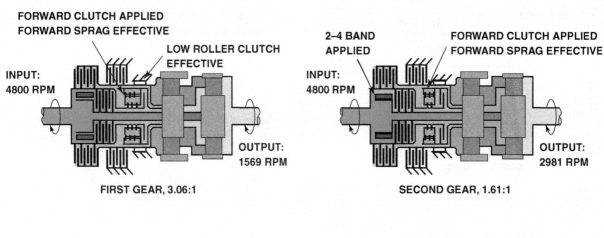

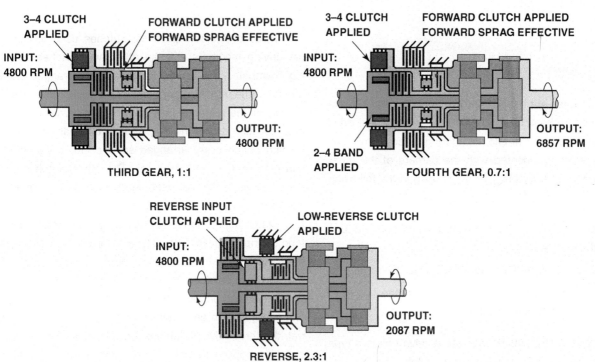

FIRST GEAR, 3.06:1

SECOND GEAR, 1.61:1

THIRD GEAR, 1:1

FOURTH GEAR, 0.7:1

REVERSE, 2.3:1

FIGURE 19–24 The full-throttle shift sequence for a type 14, 4L60 transmission showing the apply devices and the output shaft speed at the 1–2, 2–3, and 3–4 upshifts and reverse.

FORD CD4E

The Ford CD4E is another version of the four-speed gear set and is a type 17 gear train. It is a compact transaxle with a chain drive between the transmission gear set and the planetary reduction gears and differential of the final drive. The power flows through this gear set are quite similar. ● **SEE FIGURE 19–27.**

GM 6T70/FORD 6F50

OPERATION   The type 18 gear set was developed jointly by Ford (6F50) and General Motors (6T70 and 6T75). It uses three simple planetary gear sets and has each carrier connected to the ring gear of another set. The sun gear of the center gear set is connected to the input shaft, so it is always driven. It uses two driving clutches, three reaction clutches (brakes), and one

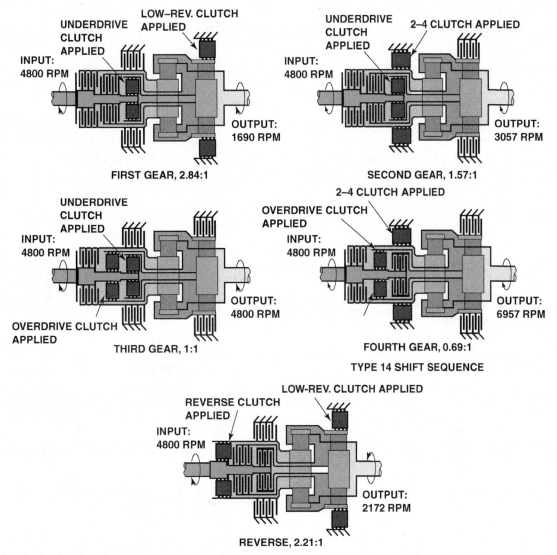

FIGURE 19-25 The full-throttle shift sequence for a type 15, 41TE transmission showing the apply devices and the output shaft speed at the 1–2, 2–3, and 3–4 upshifts and reverse.

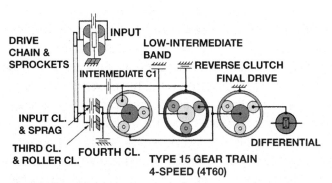

FIGURE 19-26 A schematic view of a type 16, GM 4T60 four-speed gear set. The Ford AX4N gear set is similar.

mechanical diode (one-way clutch). The front carrier and rear ring gear are the output. Except for first gear with the one-way clutch, it uses clutch-to-clutch shifts. It has a low 4.48:1 first gear, and an overdrive 0.74:1:1 sixth gear. ● **SEE FIGURE 19–28.**

NON-PLANETARY GEAR SETS

Several automatic transmission designs do not use planetary gear sets. These designs are attempts to produce a smaller, simpler, lighter, and less expensive transmission that will produce better fuel mileage with lower exhaust emissions.

GEAR	UNDERDRIVE CLUTCH	LOW-REV. CLUTCH	2–4 CLUTCH	OVERDRIVE CLUTCH	REVERSE CLUTCH
D1	Applied	Applied			
D2	Applied		Applied		
D3	Applied			Applied	
D4			Applied	Applied	
R		Applied			Applied
Planetary	Drives Rear	Holds Front	Holds	Drives Front	Drives
Member	Sun	Carrier & Rear Ring	Front Sun	Carrier & Rear Ring	Front Sun

CHART 19–3

Four-speed gear train band and clutch application, type 15.

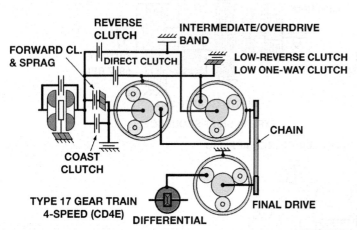

FIGURE 19–27 A schematic view of a type 17, Ford CD4E four-speed gear set.

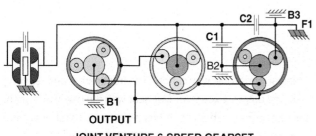

(a)

JOINT VENTURE 6-SPEED GEARSET

JOINT VENTURE GEARSET						
RANGE	C1	C2	B1	B2	B3	F1	RATIO
1			X			X	4.48:1
MANUAL 1			X		X		4.48:1
2			X	X			2.87:1
3	X		X				1.84:1
4		X	X				1.41:1
5	X	X					1:1
6		X			X		0.74:1
REVERSE	X				X		2.88:1

(b)

FIGURE 19–28 (a) A schematic view of (a) a type 18, joint venture six-speed gear set and (b) a clutch application chart.

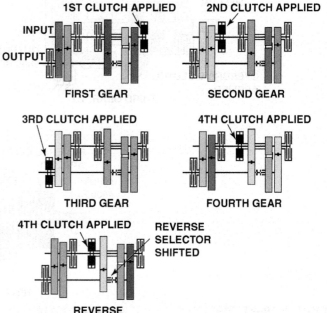

FIGURE 19–29 The shift sequence for a non-planetary four-speed transmission showing the apply devices.

An example is the Saturn transaxle automatic transmission (TAAT) that uses constant-mesh helical gears, much like those in a manual transmission. The major difference is that manual transmissions use a mechanical clutch and synchronizer assemblies that are shifted through manual linkage, and the automatic transmissions use a torque converter and hydraulically applied clutch packs. The power flow for each gear range goes through a pair of gears and each gear range uses a different gear set.

A garage shift into first or reverse is made by applying that particular clutch pack. Upshift and downshift timing and ratio changes are made by applying the next clutch pack while releasing the previous one. All shifts, with one exception, occur with the application of a single clutch pack. The exception is reverse, which requires the movement of the reverse selector and the engagement of the fourth clutch. ● **SEE FIGURE 19–29.**

SUMMARY

1. The gear set in an automatic transmission must provide a
   - neutral
   - one or more gear reductions
   - direct-drive ratio (1:1)
   - reverse
   - overdrive

2. In a planetary gear set, the following is done to achieve the various gear ratios and reverse.
   - One of the members is being driven (input).
   - One of the members is being held (reaction member).
   - One of the members is the output.

3. A synchronous design transmission means that during an upshift, the new driving or reaction member must be timed or synchronized with the release of a driving or reaction member.

4. A nonsynchronous transmission is a unit that uses a one-way clutch to allow an upshift that requires only the application of the next driving or reaction member

5. There are three basic types of planetary gear sets used: Simpson, Ravigneaux, and LePelletier.

6. Combinations of Simpson or Ravigneaux gear sets with a simple planetary gear set will produce four, five, six, eight, or more gear ratios.

REVIEW QUESTIONS

1. In a planetary gear set, what needs to be done to achieve the various gear ratios and reverse?

2. How is a 1:1 ratio achieved using a planetary gear set?

3. What needs to be done with a planetary gear set to achieve neutral?

4. What is the difference between a nonsynchronous and a synchronous design?

5. What type of gears do the Hondamatic and the Saturn transaxle automatic transmission (TAAT) use?

CHAPTER QUIZ

1. How many planet pinions are used in a planetary gear set?
   a. Two
   b. Three
   c. Four
   d. Three, four, or five

2. When are the planet gears fully meshed with the sun gear and ring gear?
   a. All the time
   b. During torque multiplication
   c. During gear reduction
   d. When overdrive is occurring

3. A Simpson gear train consists of _____.
   a. Two sun gears, one planet carrier, and one ring gear
   b. One sun gear, two planet carriers, and one ring gear
   c. One sun gear with two carriers with planet gears and two ring gears
   d. Two sun gears with two planet carriers and one ring gear

4. A Ravigneaux gear set _____.
   a. Uses two carriers that have three sets of planet gears with one sun gear and one ring gear
   b. Combines one carrier that has two sets of planet gears with two sun gears, and one ring gear
   c. Combines one carrier that has one set of planet gears with two sun gears, and two ring gears
   d. Uses two carriers that have two sets of planet gears with two sun gears, and two ring gears

5. LePelletier gear train uses _____.
   a. A Ravigneaux gear set and a simple planetary gear set
   b. Two Simpson gear sets tied together
   c. A Simpson gear set and a simple planetary gear set combined
   d. Two Ravigneaux gear sets combined

6. A nonsynchronous design _____.
   a. Requires that a clutch or band be released before another clutch is applied
   b. Allows an upshift that requires only the application of the next driving or reaction member
   c. Uses a Simpson gear set only
   d. Uses a Ravigneaux gear set only

7. A synchronous design _____.
   a. Requires that a clutch or band be released before another clutch is applied
   b. Allows an upshift that requires only the application of the next driving or reaction member
   c. Uses a Simpson gear set only
   d. Uses a Ravigneaux gear set only

8. How many forward ratios does a 6T70 transaxle have?
   a. Seven
   c. Five
   b. Four
   d. Six

9. Which transmission is a rear-wheel-drive unit?
   a. 4L60E
   c. 6F60
   b. 41TE
   d. 4T80E

10. What type of gears do the Hondamatic and the Saturn transaxle automatic transmission (TAAT) use?
    a. Simpson gear sets
    b. Ravigneaux gear set
    c. Helical cut constant mesh
    d. LePelletier gear set

chapter 20
CLUTCHES AND BANDS

LEARNING OBJECTIVES

After studying this chapter, the reader will be able to:

1. Identify the components of a multiple-disc driving clutch and describe its operation.
2. Identify the components of a one-way driving clutch and describe its operation.
3. Discuss holding clutches and bands.
4. Explain shift quality.

This chapter will help you prepare for ASE Automatic Transmission/Transaxle (A2) certification test content area "A" (General Transmission/Transaxle Diagnosis).

KEY TERMS

Accumulator 356
Belleville plate 356
Clutch-to-clutch 346
Cushion plate 356
Direct clutch 346
Double-wrap band 354
Driving devices 346
Drum 346
Dynamic friction 350
Flex band 353
Freewheel shift 356
Friction plates 357
Front clutch 346

Garage shifts 351
High-reverse clutch 346
Mechanical diode 353
Reaction devices 346
Rigid band 353
Separator plate 347
Shift feel 355
Single-sided plate 350
Static friction 350
Steels 347
Synchronous 124
Wave plate 346

 ## STC OBJECTIVES

GM Service Technical College topics covered in this chapter are as follows:

1. Diagnose mechanical component operation to determine proper/improper operation.
2. Perform a series of proper garage shifts.

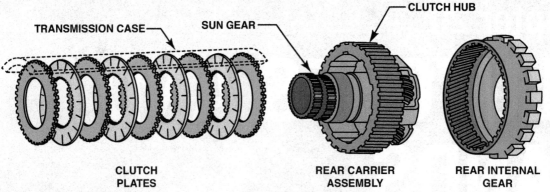

FIGURE 20–1 A multiple-disc clutch can hold or drive a member of a gear set.

INTRODUCTION

There are several paths for power to flow through an automatic transmission, and each path provides a different gear ratio. These power paths are controlled by clutches and bands, also called driving and reaction members. The **driving devices** connect the turbine shaft from the torque converter to the elements of the planetary gear train. The **reaction devices** connect (lock) a member of the gear train to the transmission case. ● **SEE FIGURE 20–1.**

DRIVING DEVICES

PURPOSE AND FUNCTION The driving devices provide the input to the planetary gear set. The turbine shaft (which transfers power into the transmission) is normally built as part of or splined to one or more of the driving devices.

TERMINOLOGY Driving devices are usually multiple-plate disc clutches. In most cases, they will be at the front of the transmission, just behind the pump. Although the parts perform the same job, the driving clutches are often given different names by different manufacturers. An example of this involves the two clutches in front of a Simpson gear train transmission.

- Chrysler Corporation calls the first clutch the **front clutch**.
- Ford Motor Company calls it a **high-reverse clutch**.
- General Motors Corporation and Toyota call it a **direct clutch**.
- Toyota commonly calls it C2.

SYNCHRONIZING SHIFTS Automatic shifts must be timed to happen quickly without the possibility of being in two gears at the same time. A gear set will lock up if it has two ratios at the same time. In order to prevent this from happening, transmission manufacturers adopt the following two strategies:

1. The first strategy is **synchronous**, *overlap*, or **clutch-to-clutch** shifting. This requires that one apply device be timed or synchronized with the application of the apply device for the next gear range.

2. The second strategy is called *nonsynchronous, asynchronous*, or *freewheel shifts*. Nonsynchronous shifts use one or more one-way clutches as driving or reaction devices. A one-way clutch will self-release during a shift as soon as the next clutch applies, eliminating the need to synchronize the shifts.

MULTIPLE-DISC DRIVING CLUTCHES

PARTS INVOLVED The parts of a clutch assembly include the following:

- drum
- hub
- lined plates (discs)
- unlined discs (steels)
- pressure plate
- apply piston
- piston return springs.

The **drum**, also called the *housing*, has internal splines that mate with external splines on the steel plates for the externally lugged discs, usually the unlined discs. The inner diameter

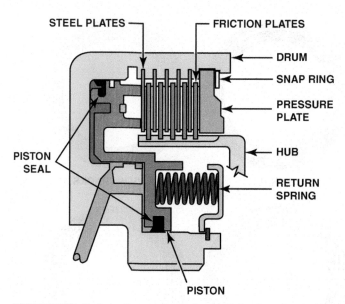

FIGURE 20–2 A sectioned view of a multiple-disc clutch. Note the piston to apply the clutch and the spring(s) to release it.

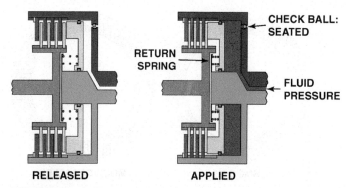

FIGURE 20–3 The apply piston is released (left) by the coil springs. Fluid pressure moves the piston to apply the clutch (right).

of the drum is machined for the apply piston and its inner and outer seals. The drum of the forward clutch is usually built as part of or splined to the input or turbine shaft.

The friction plates are alternated in between the steel plates. The friction plates are splined to a hub in the center of the clutch pack. When pressure applies the clutch the drum and hub are locked together. A clutch can be built as a single unit or combined with another drum or hub of a second clutch assembly. ● SEE FIGURES 20–2 AND 20–3.

CLUTCH PLATES

- The unlined plates are called **steels**, or **separator plates**. They are flat pieces of steel stamped into the desired shape. A steel plate is usually about 0.070 to 0.100 inches (1.78 to 2.54 mm) thick. After being stamped, the plate is carefully flattened. An unlined steel plate usually has lugs on its outer diameter to engage with the clutch drum/housing or transmission case. The steel plates used in current automatic transmissions are very smooth and often have a polished appearance with a surface roughness of 12 to 15 micro-inches. Steel plates have a secondary purpose of serving as heat sinks to help remove heat from the lined friction plates.

- Plates lined with friction material are called **friction plates**, *friction disc,* or simply *frictions*. These plates are also made from stamped steel with lining material bonded to each side. The engagement lugs are usually on the inner diameter. A friction plate is about 0.063 to 0.086 inch (1.6 to 2.2 mm) thick, and the friction material is about 0.015 to 0.030 inch (0.4 to 0.8 mm) thick.

LINING SURFACE The lining material can have a plain, smooth, flat, or a grooved friction surface. A grooved plate can have one of several grooving patterns cut or stamped into the friction material. The grooves help fluid leave or enter between the unlined and lined plates during a shift. The different grooving patterns help control the speed with which the fluid leaves the friction area to produce different shift-quality characteristics. The faster the oil leaves, the faster the clutch can apply. However, the longer the oil stays between the plates, the more heat can be absorbed by the oil. Different clutch packs for the same transmission will often use lined plates with different grooving patterns. Clutches that apply with the vehicle at rest can be smooth because apply rate is not important. Clutches that are used for upshifts will often have a groove pattern. ● SEE FIGURE 20–4.

NOTE: Some new clutch designs use friction plates with directional grooving. These are a slanted groove that must face the proper direction. Some have an inner spline shape that allows the plate to be installed only in the proper direction.

FRICTION LINING MATERIALS Clutch lining material is a mix of natural and man-made fibers, fillers, and binders. The exact mixture is selected to provide the desired clutch apply duration and heat resistance characteristics. Clutch friction material includes the following:

- **Paper**—Paper-based friction material is the most commonly used material and offers smooth and chatter-free performance. ● SEE FIGURE 20–5.

- **Aramid (Kevlar)**—This synthetic material is used in clutches that are under heavy stress, such as in heavy-duty vehicle transmissions.

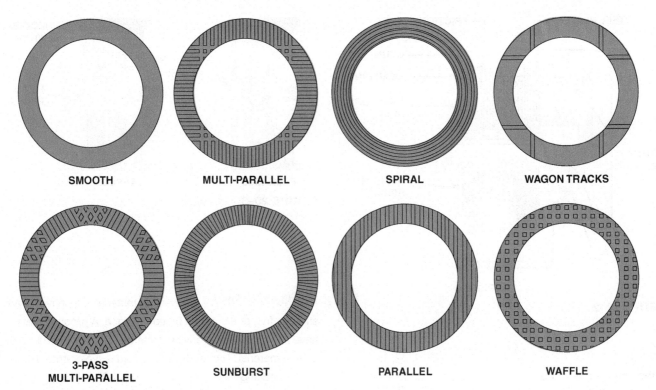

SMOOTH MULTI-PARALLEL SPIRAL WAGON TRACKS

3-PASS
MULTI-PARALLEL SUNBURST PARALLEL WAFFLE

FIGURE 20–4 Friction plates often have a groove pattern to help wipe fluid away, dissipate heat, eliminate clutch noise, and change friction qualities during apply and release. A smooth plate is the coolest and slowest to apply and the waffle plate will apply the fastest.

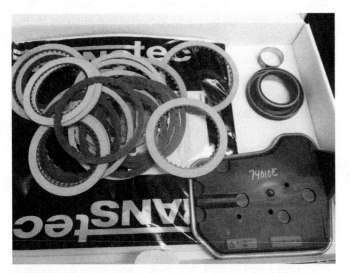

FIGURE 20–5 Most clutches included in overhaul kits use paper as the basis for the lining material.

Fillers help determine the density, porosity, and flexibility. Some commonly used filler materials include the following:

- diatomaceous earth
- graphite/carbon
- friction particles

Binders hold the mix together and the most common binder is thermosetting phenolic resin.

CLUTCH OPERATION

CLUTCH PACK APPLY An automatic transmission shifts when hydraulic pressure applies or releases a clutch. Hydraulic pressure causes the clutch or servo piston to move, taking up the clearance, and then squeezes the parts together. The force that a clutch piston exerts on the clutch plates is a product of piston area multiplied by hydraulic pressure. A rotating, driving clutch has a piston with an outside diameter (OD) of about 6 inches (152 mm) and an inner diameter (ID) that can vary from 2 to 5 inches (102 to 127 mm). ● **SEE FIGURES 20–6 AND 20–7**.

The clutch is applied when pressurized transmission fluid is applied to the back of the piston, clamping the frictions to the steels. ● **SEE FIGURE 20–8**.

CLUTCH PACK RELEASE The clutches are flooded with transmission fluid while released, and during application this fluid prevents any heat generated by friction from overheating the lining. Theoretically, there will always be a film of fluid between the friction and steel plates.

Manufacturers often provide some means of adjusting the released clearance in a clutch pack. There must be sufficient

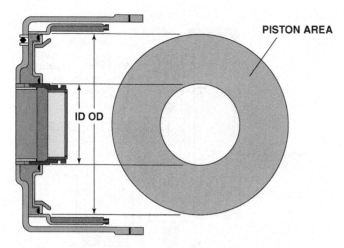

PISTON AREA: 6" OD = 28.27 in.²
              3" ID = –7 in.²
           AREA = 21.27 in.²

(3 × 3 × 3.1416)
(1.5 × 1.5 × 3.1416)

FIGURE 20–6 A typical clutch piston area is determined by subtracting the area of the inner diameter from the area of the outer-circle diameter.

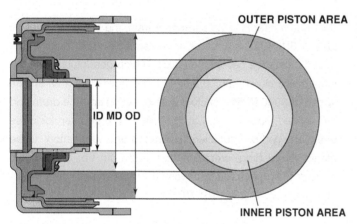

OUTER PISTON AREA:	INNER PISTON AREA:
6" OD = 28.27 in.²	4" MD = 12.56 in.²
4" MD = –12.56 in.²	3" ID = –7 in.²
AREA = 15.71 in.²	AREA = 5.56 in.²

FIGURE 20–7 Some clutch pistons use a middle seal so the piston will have two working areas.

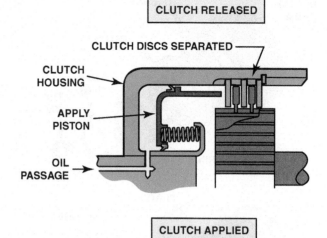

FIGURE 20–8 Pressurized oil is sent to the apply side of the piston to force the clutch discs together.

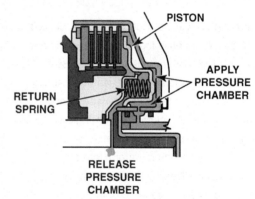

FIGURE 20–9 The baffle that supports the return springs also forms a chamber for release pressure. The clutch is released when fluid pressure enters this chamber as pressure is released from the apply side of the piston.

clearance between the plates to ensure that there is no drag when released. This clearance should be about 0.010 to 0.015 inches (0.25 to 0.38 mm) between each friction surface-lined and unlined plate. Clutch pack clearance is also called *piston travel*. Common methods of adjusting clutch pack clearance are selective size retaining rings, pressure plates, and steel plates. A selective part is available in several thicknesses, and when a clutch is assembled, the correct width or thickness is selected. ● **SEE FIGURE 20–10**.

PRESSURE BALANCED RELEASE Traditionally, clutches are released by the spring(s), but this might be too slow in newer clutch-to-clutch transmissions. The clutch is applied when fluid pressure is sent to the apply side of the piston. Releasing pressure from the apply side and sending fluid pressure, also called *compensator* or cancel pressure, to the release side produces a precisely controlled clutch release. ● **SEE FIGURE 20–9**.

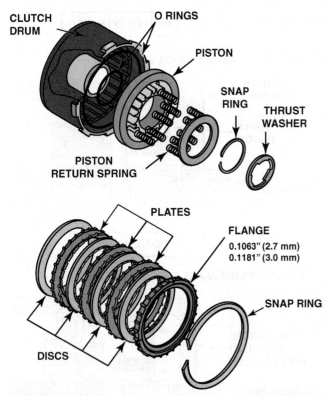

FIGURE 20–10 Clutch stack clearance is adjusted using either the large or the small flange (backing plate). Other clutches may use a selective snap ring.

DOUBLE- AND SINGLE-SIDED FRICTION PLATES

Single-sided plates have friction material on one side only, and half of the plates have lugs on the inner diameter while the other half have them on the outer diameter. Single-sided plates run cooler than two-sided plates, a feature that allows for more power transfer. The plates can be made thinner so that more plates can be put into a clutch pack. Single-sided plates have encountered problems of uneven heating because one side gets hotter, and the plate tends to deform into a conical shape. This problem has been solved by mechanically distorting the plates slightly or by specially designed grooves cut in the end plates.

FORCES INVOLVED

When a clutch is applied, the plates are squeezed together and torque is transferred from the friction plates to the steel plates. The amount of torque that can be transferred is determined by the following factors: diameter and width of the friction surfaces, number of friction surfaces (two per lined plate), and the amount of force being applied (hydraulic pressure times the piston area). The greater the plate area, number of plates, piston size, or hydraulic pressure, the greater the torque capacity.

When a clutch is released, there must be clearance between the plates. There is often a considerable speed differential between the friction and steel plates. For example,

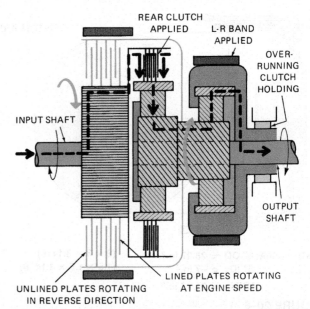

FIGURE 20–11 When this transmission is in first gear, the sun gear and unlined plates of the front clutch rotate counterclockwise while the hub and lined plates of this clutch rotate clockwise. Any drag will produce heat that can cause clutch burnout.

during first gear in a Simpson gear train, the sun gear revolves at a 2.5:1 ratio in reverse (counterclockwise). Imagine the speed difference between a released high-gear clutch with the input shaft, clutch hub, and lined plates revolving at an engine speed of 3000 RPM in a clockwise direction and the drum and the unlined plates turning at 7500 RPM in a counterclockwise direction. Without sufficient clearance and lubrication, these plates would drag, create friction, and burn up. The oil flow through the grooves and between the plates helps cool the friction surfaces. ● **SEE FIGURE 20–11.**

STATIC AND DYNAMIC FRICTION A transmission engineer is concerned with three different friction conditions in a clutch:

1. While the clutch is released, there should be no friction or drag.

2. While applied, there should be sufficient **static friction** to transfer torque without slippage.

3. While applying, there should be the proper **dynamic friction** to get a good, smooth shift.

The amount of friction between two objects or surfaces is commonly expressed as a value called the *coefficient of friction* and is represented by the Greek letter μ (mu). The coefficient of friction, also referred to as the friction coefficient, is determined by dividing tensile force by weight force. The tensile force is the pulling force required to slide one of the surfaces across the other. The weight force is the force pushing down on the object being pulled. ● **SEE FIGURE 20–12.**

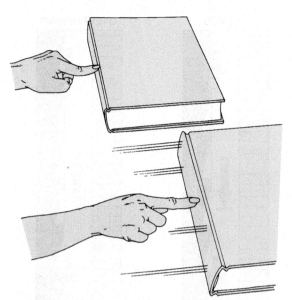

FIGURE 20–12 When pushing against a stationary book, the static friction resists motion. Pushing against the same book while it is sliding is easier because the dynamic friction is less.

The friction characteristics of a clutch are designed to work with the friction characteristics of the transmission fluid.

GARAGE SHIFTS Some clutches in an automatic transmission are applied while the vehicle is at rest. The neutral-to-drive and neutral-to-reverse shifts are called **garage shifts**.

- The clutches for first or reverse gear need a high amount of static friction because of the amount of torque required to get the vehicle moving. The garage shifts can occur slowly so they are usually less severe than the 1–2, 2–3, or 3–4 shifts; they may take 3 or 4 seconds to apply.

- Clutches that are applied while the vehicle is in motion are called *power shift* elements. They are applied under power and have to transfer substantial torque as they are applied. These clutches must have a high dynamic coefficient of friction.

ONE-WAY DRIVING CLUTCHES

PURPOSE AND FUNCTION In most transmissions, a one-way clutch allows rotation in a clockwise direction but blocks counterclockwise rotation.

- Applying and holding in a one-way clutch is often referred to as holding or being *effective.*

- Releasing it is called ineffective or *noneffective.*

ROLLER CLUTCH A roller clutch is made up of a smooth inner race, a ramped outer race, a series of rollers and energizing springs, and a cage or guide to contain the springs. Some roller clutches are made with a ramped inner race and a smooth outer race. Each roller fits in the ramp or cam section of the race. An energizing spring pushes the roller so there is a light contact between the roller, the ramp, and the smooth race. Counterclockwise rotation of the hub will wedge the rollers so they become locked between the inner and outer races. When locked, they will block any further rotation in that direction. Clockwise rotation will unwedge the rollers, and each roller will simply rotate, much like a roller bearing. The inner hub will rotate freely or overrun in a clockwise direction. ●**SEE FIGURE 20–13.**

SPRAG CLUTCHES A sprag clutch uses smooth, hardened inner and outer races and a series of sprags that are mounted in a special cage. A sprag is an odd-shaped part that somewhat resembles an hourglass or fat letter *S* when viewed from the end. A sprag has two effective diameters. The major diameter is greater than the space between the inner and outer races, and the minor diameter is smaller than this space. The sprags are mounted in a cage that spring loads each sprag in a direction to "stand up" or wedge the major diameter between the two races. A clockwise rotation of the inner race causes the sprags to rotate in the stand-up direction. This causes them to wedge firmly between the two races and lock the races together. A counterclockwise rotation of the inner race rotates

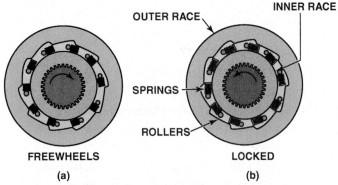

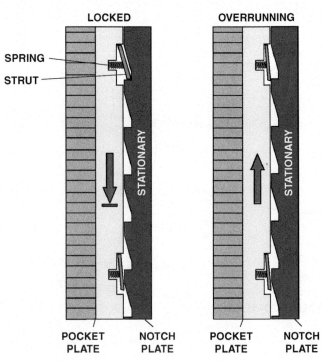

FIGURE 20–13 (a) Roller one-way clutch in released (free) position. When the inner roller clutch race rotates faster than the outer support, the rollers move out of the wedge and are free to rotate, thereby unlocking the one-way clutch. (b) Roller one-way clutch in the locked (held) position. Note how the rollers are wedged into the ramp that is machined into the outer support.

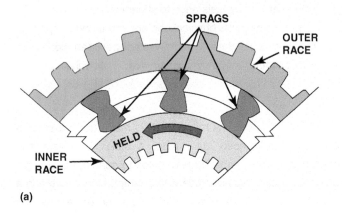

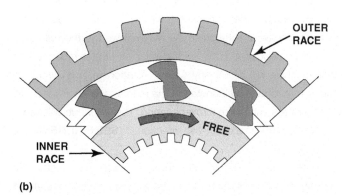

FIGURE 20–14 (a) The sprag in the holding (locked) position. Note how the long portion of the sprag is wedged between the inner and outer race. (b) The sprag in the released position. The inner race is free to rotate faster than the outer race.

the sprags in the opposite (laydown) direction. Each sprag tends to lie down so its minor diameter is between the races, and the inner race rotates freely. ● SEE FIGURE 20–14.

MECHANICAL DIODE A **mechanical diode** is a type of one-way clutch. It uses spring-loaded, rectangular struts in the face of one clutch ring, the pocket plate that can engage

FIGURE 20–15 A mechanical diode. The struts can move out of the pocket plate to engage the notch plate, and this will lock the pocket plate. The pocket plate can overrun in the opposite direction.

notches in the face of another ring, the notch plate. The struts are pushed into their pockets when the clutch is overrunning, and they can move outward, about 15 degrees, to engage the notch plate to lock up. Because the compressive forces through the strut are in the load direction, only one or two of the struts need to engage. A mechanical diode is much stronger than a roller or sprag clutch. ● SEE FIGURE 20–15.

ONE-WAY CLUTCH OPERATION A one-way clutch can be placed as an input to a gear set. In some transmissions a one-way clutch is always driving the forward planetary gear set at input shaft speed. In other transmissions, such as the General Motors 4T65-E, one-way clutches are driven through multiple-disc clutches to become effective in first and third gears. One-way clutches will overrun as the transmission shifts into the next higher gear.

HOLDING/REACTION DEVICES

PURPOSE AND FUNCTION A holding member acts as a brake to hold a planetary gear set member in reaction. Three types of holding devices are used: multiple-disc clutches, bands, and one-way clutches. Multiple-disc clutches and

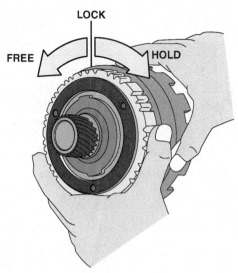

FIGURE 20–16 This clutch hub and sprag clutch should rotate freely in a counterclockwise direction but should lock up in the opposite direction.

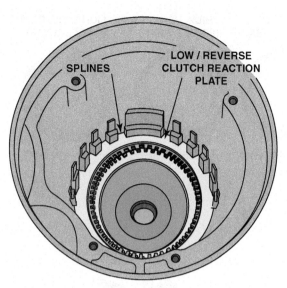

FIGURE 20–17 This transmission low/reverse clutch is a holding clutch. Note the splines in the case for the clutch plates.

 FREQUENTLY ASKED QUESTION

What Is a Clutch-to-Clutch Type Transmission?

A clutch-to-clutch transmission or transaxle is a unit that does not use one-way clutches and instead just uses multiple-plate clutches for all clamping functions. The primary reason for not using one-way clutches is that the metal particles that are detached from these assemblies are attracted to the magnetic solenoids. These particles can clog the screens and reduce the flow of fluid through the solenoid valves. This leads to many types of transmission or transaxle failures that are prevented by not using steel-on-steel units such as roller clutches or mechanical diodes.

bands are applied by hydraulic pressure and are controlled by the valve body. A one-way clutch is mechanically controlled; it allows rotation in one direction only. ● **SEE FIGURE 20–16**.

HOLDING CLUTCHES

PURPOSE AND FUNCTION A multiple-disc holding clutch is quite similar to a driving clutch. The difference is that the transmission case is the clutch drum, and the clutch plates splined to it do not rotate. Some manufacturers call these clutches a *brake*.

PARTS AND OPERATION The lugs on the outside of the unlined plates fit into slots built into the case. ● **SEE FIGURE 20–17**.

Like a driving clutch, the lugs on the inner diameter of the lined plates fit over the hub, which is often a part of the planetary gear train or the outer race of a one-way clutch.

The hydraulic piston can be built into the case, at the back of the front pump assembly, or in a center support. The stationary position of the piston and cylinder makes it relatively easy to provide fluid to it. Like a driving clutch, the piston is normally returned to a released position by springs.

ONE-WAY HOLDING CLUTCHES One-way clutches are commonly used as reaction devices. The outer race is often secured directly to the transmission case so it cannot rotate.

BANDS

PURPOSE AND FUNCTION The purpose of a band is to prevent rotation of the drum it is wrapped around. The drum can be a member of the planetary gear train.

TYPES A band is a circular strip of metal that has lining bonded to the inner surface. It wraps around the smooth surface of a drum. There are three types of bands:

1. A single thick, heavy band, also called a **rigid band**.
2. A single thin, light band, also called a *flexible* or **flex band**.
3. A split, **double-wrap**, heavy band. ● **SEE FIGURE 20–18**.

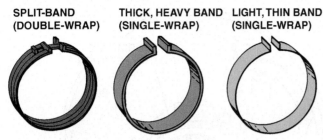

FIGURE 20–18 Transmission bands come in several designs and thicknesses.

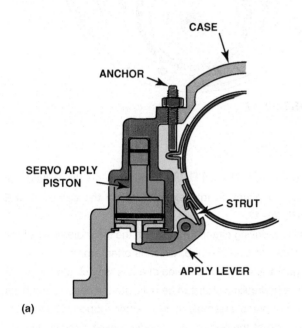

(a)

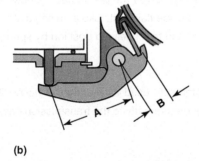

(b)

FIGURE 20–19 (a) This band uses an adjustable anchor that allows the clearance to be easily adjusted. (b) Note that the apply lever will increase apply force.

A rigid band is strong and provides a good heat sink to absorb some of the friction heat during application. The disadvantage with a rigid band is that it is relatively expensive and does not always conform to the shape of the drum. A flex band is less expensive and, because of its flexibility, can easily conform to the shape of the drum. Double-wrap bands give more holding power and are often used for reverse or manual first gears. Each band type has end lugs so it can be attached to

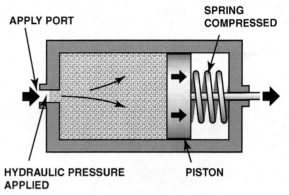

FIGURE 20–20 A servo uses hydraulic pressure to move a piston, which applies a band.

the anchor and the servo. A small link, commonly called a *strut*, is often used to connect the lugs of the band to the anchor or the servo piston rod. ● SEE FIGURE 20–19.

FRICTION MATERIALS ON BANDS The friction material used on a band is similar to that used on clutch plates. Paper- and cloth-based materials are normally used. The drum must be a smooth cylinder with straight sides in order to have complete contact with the band lining. The lining surface of the band is often grooved to help control fluid flow during apply and release operations. Similar to a clutch, band friction material and grooving are designed to operate with a specified fluid to ensure good shift quality and long life.

SERVOS   The servo is the hydraulic assembly that applies the band. Its main components include a

- cylinder
- piston
- piston rod/pin
- return spring

  ● SEE FIGURE 20–20.

The piston rod pushes directly on the end of the band on most servos. Some servo pistons are connected to the band through a lever or linkage attached to the band strut.

A band lever provides a force increase because of the lever ratio. The ratio will require more piston travel to apply the band but increases the application force acting on the end of the band. Some manufacturers incorporate a band adjustment screw in the apply lever. Other manufacturers use selective-size servo piston rods for band adjustment. ● SEE FIGURE 20–21.

ADJUSTMENT   The anchor for the band can be a fixed or adjustable point in the transmission case. Some bands have

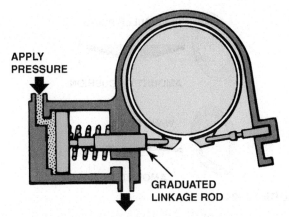

APPLY PRESSURE

GRADUATED LINKAGE ROD

FIGURE 20–21 One end of a band is held stationary and the other end is attached to the servo.

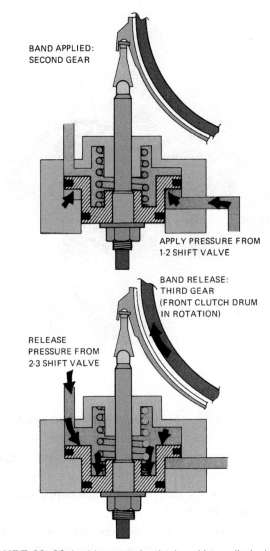

BAND APPLIED: SECOND GEAR

APPLY PRESSURE FROM 1-2 SHIFT VALVE

BAND RELEASE: THIRD GEAR (FRONT CLUTCH DRUM IN ROTATION)

RELEASE PRESSURE FROM 2-3 SHIFT VALVE

FIGURE 20–22 In this example, the band is applied when 1–2 shift valve pressure pushes upward on the servo piston (top). It will release when 2–3 shift valve pressure pushes the piston downward (bottom). Note the larger area above the piston.

an adjustable anchor, which provides a method of adjusting the clearance between the band and the drum. The bands that are adjustable are usually the rigid bands that have thick lining. Most bands use thin linings and are not adjustable. There must be enough clearance to ensure there is no band-to-drum contact with the band released, but too much clearance might cause slippage if the band does not apply completely. A band that is too loose or too tight has an adverse effect on shift timing.

BAND OPERATION When fluid pressure enters the servo, the servo piston moves, tightening the band around the drum. The amount of torque that a band can absorb before slipping is determined by the band-to-drum contact area, type of band, drum diameter, fluid type, and the force squeezing the band onto the drum.

When a band releases, the servo piston backs off, and the springy, elastic nature of the band causes it to move away from the drum. A servo piston can be released by either spring pressure and/or hydraulic pressure.

- When the shift has to be made to neutral, the release speed is not important. Normally, servos use only a release spring.

- During an upshift, the band release must be fast and carefully timed. The release of many bands is done by using fluid pressure from the clutch being applied. For example, in a Simpson gear train transmission during a 2–3 shift, the fluid pressure to apply the third-gear clutch is also used to release the second-gear band.

- During a downshift, band apply must be quick and firm. ● **SEE FIGURE 20–22.**

SHIFT QUALITY

TERMINOLOGY As a power shift occurs, there must be a smooth transition from one apply device to the next. The smoothness of the shift is referred to as shift quality or **shift feel**.

A shift should be smooth without any unusual noises. In order for this to occur, the clutches and bands must apply smoothly and quietly. The timing of the band releasing from second gear and the clutch applying for third gear must be precise. Any improper noises such as squeaks, squawks, or shrieks or operations such as engine RPM flare, jerks, bumps, or harsh application are considered faults that need to be corrected.

FIGURE 20-23 A band accumulator piston and spring being removed from a GM 4T65-E.

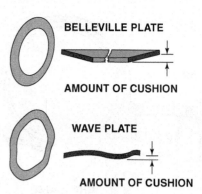

FIGURE 20-24 Two cushion plates: The Belleville plate has a coned shape; the wave plate has a wavy shape. Both of them will flatten slightly as the clutch is applied.

ACCUMULATORS An **accumulator** is tied hydraulically to the clutch or band servo, and absorbs fluid during the pressure buildup stage when a clutch or band applies. This has the effect of slowing the pressure increase and lengthening the time it takes for the friction device to lock up. ● **SEE FIGURE 20-23.**

As clutch or band apply pressure is entering the apply side of the accumulator, fluid must leave the opposite, exhaust side of the accumulator piston. The pressure on the apply side and rate of stroke depends on how easily the fluid leaves the exhaust side. An accumulator valve or shift control valve is often placed in the accumulator exhaust passage. The shift must be completed before the accumulator completes its stroke. If the accumulator piston reaches the bottom before the shift is complete, there will be a sudden pressure increase that will cause a *slide-bump shift*. This is a shift with poor quality that starts smooth, but ends harsh.

WAVE PLATE Clutch shift quality is controlled by the type of lining material and grooving, the use of wave or Belleville plates, the type of fluid used, and the speed at which fluid moves the piston.

A **wave plate** is an unlined plate that is wavy, not flat. A **Belleville plate**, like a Belleville spring, is also not flat. These are often called **cushion plates**. ● **SEE FIGURE 20-24.**

If either plate is used in a clutch pack, it will be placed between the piston and the first unlined plate or between the last unlined plate and the pressure plate. Both plates are designed to compress slightly under pressure during clutch application. The result is to slightly prolong the clutch apply time.

Many transmissions do not use Belleville or wave plates. Hydraulic controls (accumulators and orifices) are used to control piston movement and produce the desired shift quality. Electronically controlled transmissions have even greater ability to alter shift quality. The shift solenoids and hydraulic pressure control solenoids can be turned off and on, or cycled to produce the desired shifts.

SHIFTS INVOLVING ONE-WAY CLUTCHES A one-way clutch is an ideal driving or reaction member for automatic shifts. It applies or holds when it is needed and self-releases or overruns when it is not needed. Its operation is controlled by the load direction on the inner or outer race so shift timing is automatic. When the transmission upshifts, the reaction or driving member for the next gear is applied, and the one-way clutch simply overruns. This is called a nonsynchronous or asynchronous shift and the shift elements do not need to be synchronized. It is also called a **freewheel shift**.

DECELERATION WITH ONE-WAY CLUTCHES When the throttle is released while in a gear that uses a one-way clutch, the transmission will go into neutral as the one-way clutch overruns. This action is good if the vehicle is coasting to a stop, but can cause concern if going down a steep hill.

1. The power flow through a gear set is controlled by driving and reaction devices.

2. The driving and reaction devices are multiple-disc clutches, one-way clutches, and bands.

3. Multiple-disc clutches are the primary driving devices and are also used to hold planetary members in reaction.

4. One-way clutches are primarily used to hold planetary members in reaction, but can be used with a multiple-disc clutch as a driving device.

5. Bands are used to hold a planetary member in reaction.

6. The timing of the apply devices has a direct effect on shift quality.

REVIEW QUESTIONS

1. What is the difference between a driving device and a reaction device?

2. What is the difference between synchronous and nonsynchronous shifts?

3. What parts are included in a typical clutch pack assembly?

4. Why do some clutch discs use friction material on only one side?

5. What is the purpose and function of an accumulator?

CHAPTER QUIZ

1. The _____ connects the turbine shaft from the torque converter to the elements of the planetary gear train.
   a. Reaction devices   c. Driving devices
   b. Accumulator   d. Servo

2. The _____ connect (lock) a member of the gear train to the transmission case.
   a. Reaction devices   c. Driving devices
   b. Accumulator   d. Servo

3. The apply device that is most commonly used as a driving member is a _____.
   a. Cone clutch   c. One-way clutch
   b. Multiple-disc clutch   d. Band

4. Plates lined with friction material are called _____.
   a. Friction disc   c. Friction plates
   b. Simply frictions   d. Any of the above

5. Some clutches in an automatic transmission are applied while the vehicle is at rest. This application of the clutch(es) is often called a _____ shift.
   a. Static   c. Synchronous
   b. Garage   d. Nonsynchronous

6. The lining material most often used is made from _____.
   a. Paper
   b. Asbestos
   c. Inorganic fibers
   d. Any of the above depending on application

7. Typical clearance should be about _____ between each friction surface-lined and unlined plate.
   a. 0.001 to 0.005 inches (0.025 to 0.012 mm)
   b. 0.010 to 0.015 inches (0.25 to 0.38 mm)
   c. 0.020 to 0.035 inches (0.050 to 0.090 mm)
   d. 0.050 to 0.075 inches (1.3 to 1.9 mm)

8. What is an example of a one-way clutch?
   a. Multi clutch pack
   b. Band
   c. Roller clutch
   d. Accumulator

9. The torque-carrying capacity of a clutch is determined by the _____.
   a. Number of plates
   b. Amount of lining area on the plates
   c. Amount of pressure squeezing the plates together
   d. All of the above

10. How does an accumulator work?
    a. Slows the application of the clutch or band
    b. Includes a solenoid to apply a clutch
    c. Supplies high-pressure ATF to a band so it applies quickly
    d. Accumulates extra ATF for use when it is low in the case of a leak

ELECTRONIC TRANSMISSION CONTROLS

358

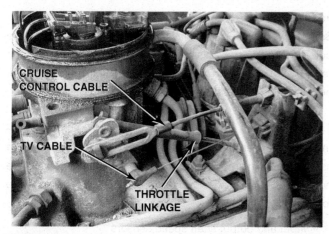

FIGURE 21–1 The throttle valve (TV) cable on a 4T60 transaxle.

HYDRAULICALLY CONTROLLED TRANSMISSIONS

BACKGROUND From the 1940s until the early 1990s, most automatic transmissions were hydraulically controlled. Hydraulically controlled automatic transmissions/transaxles use valves to control when to shift instead of sensors that are used in electronically controlled transmissions/transaxles. These valves use mainline pressure to develop other hydraulic circuit pressures within the transmission. Pressure valves are normally spool valves that link to external components.

In order for hydraulically controlled transmission/transaxles to operate correctly, they must be able to monitor engine load and vehicle speed.

ENGINE LOAD Engine load can be detected using either a throttle valve (TV) or a vacuum moderator valve.

- **Throttle Valve**—The hydraulically controlled transmission throttle valve senses engine load and uses that information to delay the upshift on hydraulically controlled automatic transmissions. Throttle valves have linkages or cables that connect them mechanically to the throttle plates, and they respond directly to engine load. ● SEE FIGURE 21–1.

  A low engine load develops low throttle pressure while a higher load develops higher throttle pressure. The throttle position (TP) sensor has replaced the need for throttle valves in electronically controlled automatic transmissions/transaxles.

- **Vacuum Modulator Valve**—A vacuum modulator is used to convert engine manifold vacuum into a signal pressure

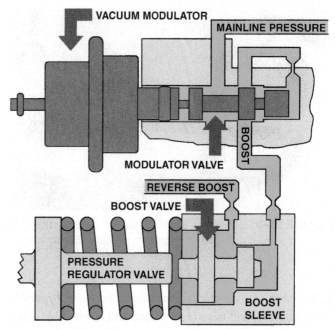

FIGURE 21–2 A vacuum modulator moves the modulator valve depending on the vacuum of the engine. A heavy load on the engine causes the vacuum to be lower than when the engine is operating under a light load. The spool valve applies mainline pressure to the boost sleeve of the pressure regulator valve, which causes the mainline pressure to increase.

that increases as engine vacuum decreases. The modulator is connected to the intake manifold vacuum with a rubber hose or steel line. A vacuum modulator can be used on hydraulically controlled transmissions/transaxles to help determine the shift point based on engine load. The purpose of the vacuum modulator is to delay the upshifting of the transmission based on the engine load. ● SEE FIGURE 21–2.

Engine load examples:

- **Light engine load.** Manifold vacuum is high; shifts occur at lower speeds.

- **Heavy engine load.** Manifold vacuum is low; shifts occur at higher speeds.

The manifold absolute pressure (MAP) sensor or mass airflow (MAF) sensor and throttle position (TP) sensor serve in place of the vacuum modulator valve in measuring engine load on electronically controlled automatic transmissions/transaxles.

VEHICLE SPEED The governor valve monitors vehicle road speed and uses that operating signal to develop governor pressure. The governor valve normally follows transmission output shaft rotation speed, which increases with vehicle speed. Mechanical governors contain "flyweights" that move in relation to centrifugal forces caused by the speed of the

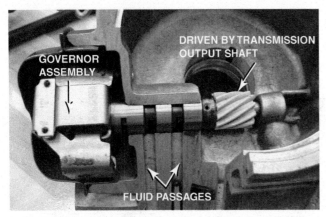

FIGURE 21–3 A governor assembly is used on older hydraulically controlled automatic transmissions/transaxles to control shift points based on vehicle speed.

output shaft. As the output shaft speed increases flyweights move outward, and this in turn moves an internal valve which controls the output pressure. As the speed increases, governor pressure also increases. Governor pressure opposes throttle pressure at the shift valves to control upshifts and downshifts in relation to vehicle speed. ● **SEE FIGURE 21–3.**

TECH TIP

Who's in Charge Here?

On these older transmissions the governor pressure and throttle pressure are fighting to determine when to upshift. The governor pressure "wants to shift" and the throttle pressure "allows it to shift." It is this mechanical discussion that causes higher upshift RPMs when there is more throttle opening.

TRANSMISSION CONTROL MODULE

TCM All recent automatic transmissions are controlled by electronic components and circuits. Typical transmission control systems contain many components. An automatic transmission can be controlled by its own computer, called a **transmission control module (TCM)**, or a *transmission control unit (TCU)*. The transmission can also be controlled through either the body control module (BCM) or the powertrain control module (PCM). Each manufacturer has its own design criteria and terminology. The TCM is normally located outside the

transmission in a protected, relatively cool and clean location. Some newer transmissions have the TCM mounted on the valve body inside the transmission. The primary advantage is the reduction of wiring and the elimination of electrical connectors, both sources of potential problems.

TERMINOLOGY When the TCM is located inside the transmission, this design is often called a *control solenoid valve assembly*, *mechatronic*, and *solenoid body* and reduces the number of wires entering the transmission because of the following:

- Input and output shaft speed sensors
- Transmission range sensor
- Fluid pressure sensors
- Fluid temperature sensor
- Shift and pressure control solenoids are connected directly to the TCM

The wire connections to the rest of the vehicle include:

- Hi and Lo CAN transmits data to and from the ECM, BCM, and PCM
- Ignition on
- Diagnostic connection
- Ground

The TCM in some transmissions is about the same size as a common credit card. A concern with an internal TCM is the possibility of overheating the electronic components. One design has a thermocouple temperature sensor(s) mounted in the TCM circuit board, and if the temperature rises above 288°F (142°C), it will go into failure mode/default. The TCM normally keeps relatively cool by contact with the transmission case, and a spring bracket is used to ensure tight contact. ● **SEE FIGURE 21–4.**

PURPOSE AND FUNCTION Many features of an electronic transmission, such as shift timing and quality, torque converter clutch apply timing, and quality, are software driven. A vehicle manufacturer can use the same transmission and adjust the operating characteristics with software for variations of particular vehicles. Some transmission control modules allow calibration values to be reprogrammed by technicians in the field.

The TCM receives data from the sensors and other control modules, and when these signals match the program stored in the TCM's memory, the TCM sends a signal to one or more electrical actuators to control the shifting operation of the transmission.

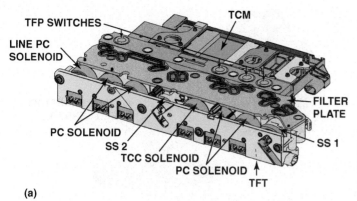

(a)

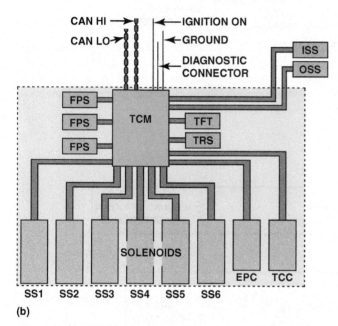

(b)

FIGURE 21–4 (a) This control solenoid assembly contains four transmission fluid pressure (TFP) switches, a line pressure control (PC) solenoid, four pressure control (PC) solenoids, two shift solenoids (SS), a torque converter clutch (TCC) solenoid, a transmission fluid temperature (TFT) sensor, and the transmission control module (TCM). It also has a vehicle harness connector and connectors to the shift position switch and the input and output speed sensors. (b) A simplified view is also shown.

OPERATION

The TCM can be programmed to incorporate several different operating strategies that are stored in the memory. The types of memory include the following:

- *Random access memory (RAM).* This is temporary memory that is cleared every time the vehicle is turned off.

- *Read-only memory (ROM).* The TCM/processor can read from ROM but cannot save any information to ROM.

- *Programmable read-only memory (PROM).* This is similar to a ROM but is programmed for a specific vehicle.

- *Electronically erasable programmable read-only memory (EEPROM).* This is similar to PROM but can be erased and reprogrammed. This is often called *reflashing.*

- *Keep alive memory (KAM).* ROM that is always connected to power so it retains memory. This can store information such as transmission adaptive strategies and the data will be lost if a battery becomes discharged or is disconnected.

SENSORS

PURPOSE AND FUNCTION Sensors are the TCM inputs. They monitor the things that can affect transmission operation: vehicle speed, input shaft speed, transmission fluid temperature, the selected gear range, and engine coolant temperature, RPM, and load. A typical transmission sensor can be a switch that is made to open or close at certain pressures or temperatures, a transducer that senses pressure, a thermistor that senses temperature, or a speed sensor that measures vehicle speed or shaft RPM. The various sensor types (organized by the type of electrical signal) include the following:

- Frequency generators (creates an AC signal with a frequency relative to speed and the TCM monitors the signal frequency)

- Voltage generator (creates a voltage signal that is relative to speed and the TCM monitors the voltage)

- Potentiometer or variable resistor (alters resistance)

- Switches (an on–off signal)

- Thermistor (changes resistance relative to temperature)

- Transducer (changes resistance relative to pressure)

- Serial data (an on–off signal coming from another control module)

TRANSMISSION RANGE SWITCH The **transmission range (TR) switch**, also called the *manual lever position (MLP)* sensor, is used as an input to the PCM/TCM, which indicates the drive range requested by the driver. The transmission range switch is usually located on the outside of the case on the transmission/transaxle housing and attached to the shifter. As the gear range selector is moved, the TR switch can make a variety of switch connections for each gear range. These inputs allow the TCM to determine which gear range has been selected. The TR switch is used by the TCM to

- Keep the engine from starting in any gear position except park or neutral

- Allow a progressive 1–2–3–4 shift sequence in drive

FIGURE 21–5 The transmission range switch is usually located on the case where the shifter cable attaches to the manual valve lever. The switch also includes the switch for the backup lights and the park/neutral switch which is used to prevent the start being engaged unless the shifter is in park or neutral.

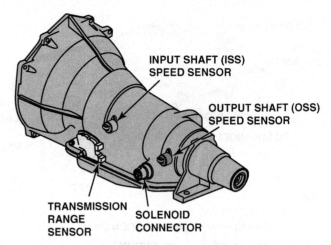

FIGURE 21–7 Speed sensors are used by the powertrain control module (PCM) or the transmission control module (TCM) to control shifts and detect faults such as slippage when the two speeds do not match the predetermined ratio for each gear commanded.

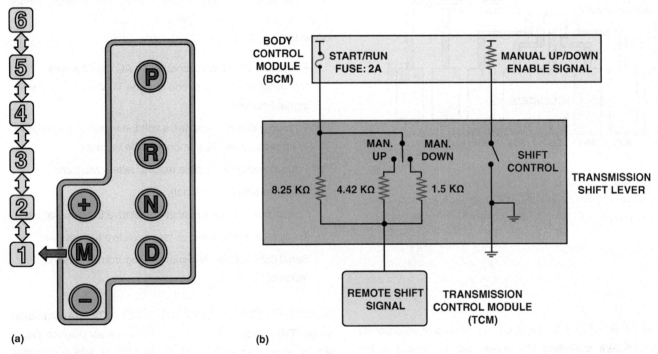

FIGURE 21–6 Moving the shift lever to the M (manual) position (a) activates the up/down, +/− switches that will cause an upshift or downshift (b).

- Limit upshifts in manual ranges
- Operate the backup lights in reverse. ● **SEE FIGURE 21–5**.

Some vehicles are equipped with a manual position where the driver can request one gear position by moving the shift lever to the manual position. ● **SEE FIGURE 21–6**.

SPEED SENSORS Speed sensors measure the speeds of the input and output shafts or sometimes of other shaft speeds in the automatic transmission or transaxle. The output shaft speed sensor is often used to provide vehicle speed information to the PCM and for adaptive learning. ● **SEE FIGURE 21–7**.

Speed sensor design includes:

- **Magnetic**—Most speed sensors use a coil of wire that is wrapped around a magnetic core. This sensor is mounted next to a toothed ring or wheel. As the toothed ring revolves, an alternating voltage is produced in the sensor. ● **SEE FIGURE 21–8**.

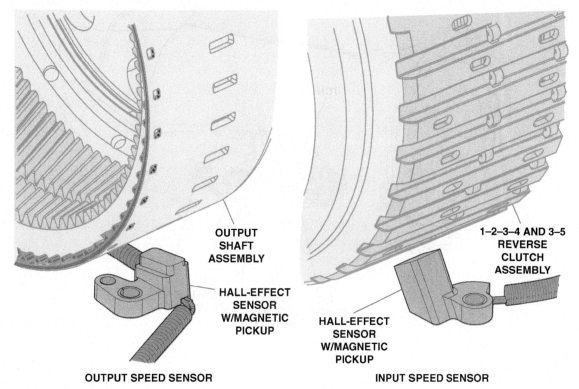

OUTPUT SPEED SENSOR

INPUT SPEED SENSOR

FIGURE 21–8 The ISS and OSS are triggered by slots or notches on the transmission drum assemblies. (Courtesy of General Motors)

- **Hall-Effect**—Some speed sensors are Hall-Effect and create an on–off square wave signal that is used directly by the PCM/TCM for speed detection.

SPEED SENSOR LOCATIONS

- The **Input speed sensor (ISS)** measures the speed of the transmission input shaft, which is driven by the converter turbine. This is also called **turbine speed sensor (TSS)** because it is used to determine the speed of the turbine shaft.
- The **output speed sensor (OSS)** is also called the **vehicle speed (VS) sensor** and is used by the PCM for speedometer and cruise control operation as well as for transmission/transaxle operation and shift-related fault detection.

The sensors on older transmissions are mounted through the transmission case with external connector. Newer vehicles have the speed sensors (and most other electrical components) mounted inside the transmission, attached directly to the valve body. **SEE FIGURE 21–9.**

PRESSURE SENSORS/SWITCHES
Most pressure sensors use a transducer, which is a variable resistance that produces a signal that is relative to pressure. The *line pressure sensor (LPS)* is a transducer that converts line pressure to a variable resistance.

Many transmissions include *pressure switches* at the valve body. The signal from the pressure sensor tells the TCM

that the circuit has pressure. The TCM uses these signals along with other information to determine TCC lockup and shift timing. **SEE FIGURE 21–10.**

TEMPERATURE SENSORS The **transmission fluid temperature (TFT)** sensor can also be called a *transmission*

? FREQUENTLY ASKED QUESTION

What Is Pressure Logic?

Pressure switches are used to monitor which clutch has pressure but the PCM/TCM can use the information from the switches to verify which gear the transmission/transaxle is operating. Some pressure switches are normally open (N.O.) and others are normally closed (N.C.) and the gear that the unit is operating in can be determined by the switch positions. An open circuit is represented by a binary code "1" and measures 12 volts while a grounded circuit binary code is "0" and measures 0 volts. Depending on the position of the manual valve, fluid is routed to the pressure switch manifold (PSM). The PCM/TCM uses information from the on/off positioning of the switches to adjust line pressure, torque converter clutch (TCM) apply, and to control shift solenoid operation. **SEE FIGURE 21–11.**

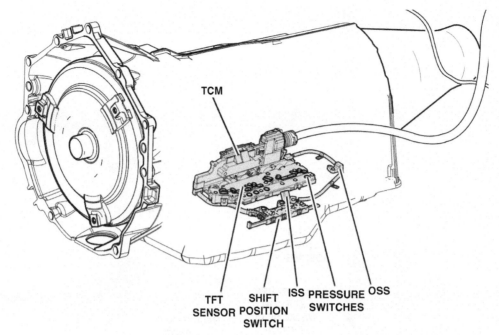

FIGURE 21–9 The transmission control module and sensors are assembled inside the transmission on most newer vehicles. (Courtesy of General Motors)

FIGURE 21–10 The pressure switch manifold (PSM) used in a GM 4L60E consists of diaphragm switches with seals around each one that are bolted to the valve body over holes for each clutch circuit.

oil temperature (TOT) sensor. Most temperature sensors are thermistors, a type of variable resistor that changes electrical resistance relative to temperature. These are called negative temperature coefficient (NTC) thermistors. The signal from a thermistor is the inverse of the temperature because it has high resistance at low temperatures and a low resistance at high temperatures. For example, a particular transmission fluid temperature sensor has a resistance of 37 to 100 ohms (Ω) at 32°F to 58°F (0°C to 20°C) and 1,500 to 2,700 ohms (Ω) at 195°F to 230°F (91°C to 110°C). ● SEE FIGURE 21–12.

This sensor is used by the PCM or TCM to detect the temperature of the automatic transmission fluid. This signal is used to determine the best shift points and to regulate line pressure. It will cause the PCM or the TCM to engage the torque converter clutch (TCC) sooner and disable overdrive, to help reduce the fluid temperature if it reaches higher than normal.

BRAKE SWITCH A brake switch mounted at the brake pedal provides a signal when the brake is depressed. It signals the TCM that the brake is applied, and the TCC should be released. The brake switch is also called a **brake on/off (BOO)** switch. ● SEE FIGURE 21–13.

INPUTS SHARED WITH THE PCM Many factors are used by the TCM to determine when to shift. Many sensors are used by the PCM for engine operation and are also used to help the engine and transmission/transaxle work together to provide smooth efficient operation and produce the best performance with the lowest possible exhaust emission and the best possible fuel economy. The sensors that are used for both the engine and the transmission include the following:

- *Throttle position (TP) sensor.* This variable resistor (potentiometer) provides a voltage signal that is relative to throttle opening. It provides a throttle position signal to the TCM.

- *Engine coolant temperature (ECT).* This variable resistor (thermistor) monitors engine temperature. It signals the TCM that the engine is at operating temperature or approaching an overheat temperature.

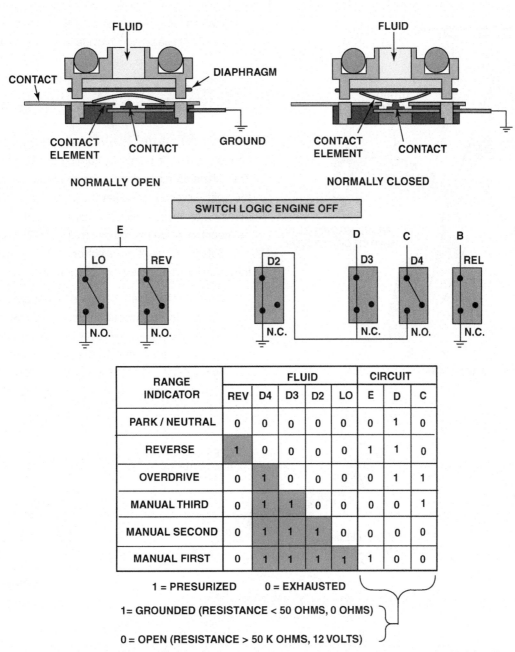

NORMALLY OPEN   **NORMALLY CLOSED**

SWITCH LOGIC ENGINE OFF

RANGE INDICATOR	FLUID					CIRCUIT		
	REV	D4	D3	D2	LO	E	D	C
PARK / NEUTRAL	0	0	0	0	0	0	1	0
REVERSE	1	0	0	0	0	1	1	0
OVERDRIVE	0	1	0	0	0	0	1	1
MANUAL THIRD	0	1	1	0	0	0	0	1
MANUAL SECOND	0	1	1	1	0	0	0	0
MANUAL FIRST	0	1	1	1	1	1	0	0

1 = PRESURIZED   0 = EXHAUSTED

1= GROUNDED (RESISTANCE < 50 OHMS, 0 OHMS)

0 = OPEN (RESISTANCE > 50 K OHMS, 12 VOLTS)

FIGURE 21–11 Some switches are electrically normally open (N.O.) and others are normally closed (N.C.) and are used to provide gear selection information to the PCM/TCM.

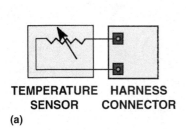

TEMPERATURE SENSOR   **HARNESS CONNECTOR**

(a)

TEMPERATURE		RESISTANCE (OHMS)
°C	°F	
140	284	0.6 k
120	248	1.1 k
100	212	2.1 k
80	176	3.8 k
50	122	10 k
30	86	27 k
10	50	69 k
−10	14	193 k
−30	−22	600 k

(b)

FIGURE 21–12 (a) A transmission fluid temperature sensor can be checked by connecting an ohmmeter to the harness connector terminals. (b) The resistance should change as the temperature changes.

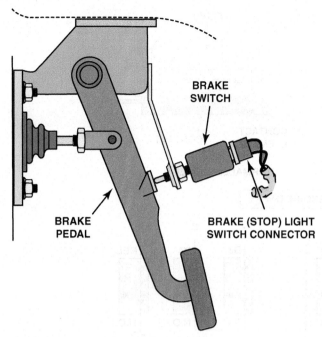

FIGURE 21–13 The brake (stop light) switch is mounted at the brake pedal. It provides a brake-apply signal to the TCM.

- Manifold absolute pressure (MAP) and mass airflow sensor (MAF). These sensors provide engine load signal to the PCM.

TRANSMISSION SOLENOIDS

TYPES OF SOLENOIDS An electronic transmission controls the shift points by turning a solenoid(s) on and off. The solenoids in turn control the hydraulic pressure that moves the shift valves or operates the torque converter clutch. It is common for these solenoids, along with other components, to be mounted inside the transmission. ● SEE FIGURE 21–14.

Solenoids used in electronically controlled automatic transmissions/transaxles are as follows:

- **On–off solenoids.** These can be normally open to fluid flow or normally closed to block fluid flow. Shift solenoids control the pressure force, which in turn controls the position of the shift valve. They are commanded on or off by the PCM or TCM. The resistance of most on–off shift solenoids is 10 to 15 ohms. ● SEE FIGURE 21–15.

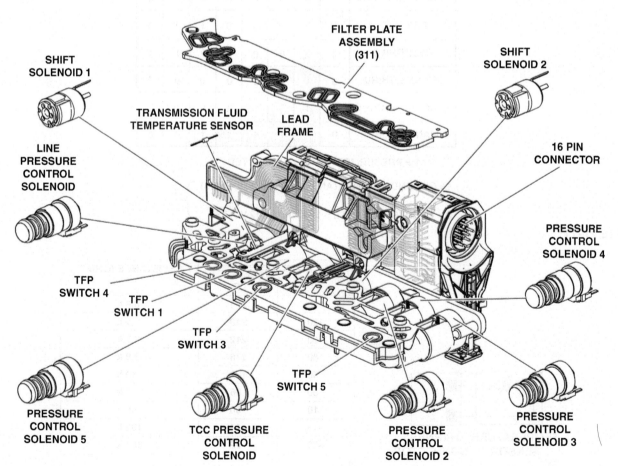

FIGURE 21–14 Electrical and electronic components are mounted inside the transmission, attached to the valve body. (Courtesy of General Motors)

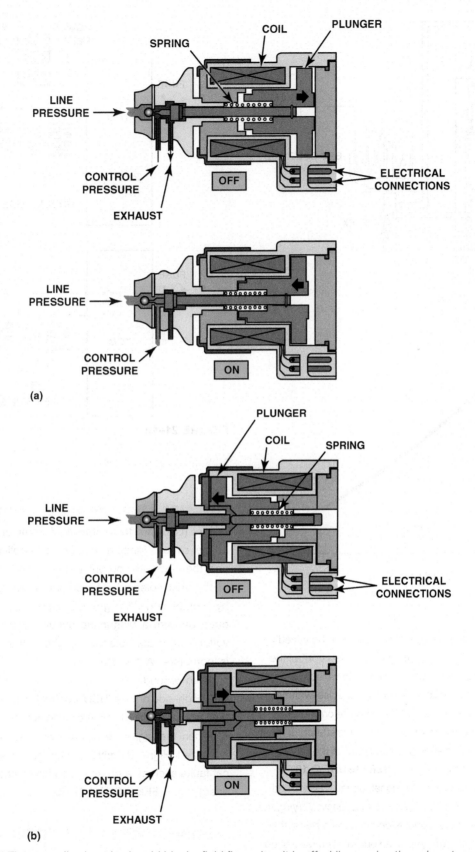

FIGURE 21–15 (a) The normally closed solenoid blocks fluid flow when it is off while opening the exhaust; and when it is on, it opens the valve. (b) The normally open solenoid allows fluid flow when it is off; and when it is on, it closes the valve while opening the exhaust.

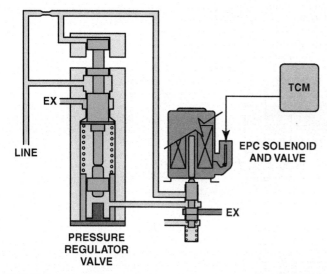

FIGURE 21–16 The signal from the TCM can cause the EPC solenoid to change the pressure regulator valve to adjust line pressure.

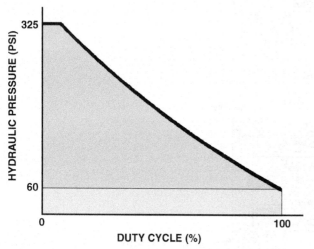

FIGURE 21–17 Line pressure increases as the duty cycle of the EPC solenoid decreases.

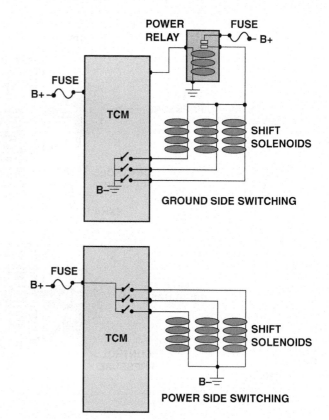

FIGURE 21–18 Solenoid control occurs when the PCM/TCM completes the circuit to ground (top) or switches on B+ (bottom). The ground connection is also B−.

- **Linear solenoids.** This type of solenoid can be varied by changing the amount of on time to precisely control the fluid flow through the solenoid valve. The variable power or ground applied to the linear solenoids is pulse-width modulated (PWM) and allows the PCM precise control over the shifting and the fluid pressure. The resistance of most linear (PWM) shift solenoids is about half of the on–off type and range from 4 to 6 ohms. ● **SEE FIGURE 2–16**.

A PWM signal is a digital signal, usually 0 volts and 12 volts, which is cycling at a fixed frequency. Varying the length of time that the signal is on provides a signal that can vary the on and off time of an output. The ratio of on time relative to the period of the cycle is referred to as duty cycle. The torque converter clutch (TCC), pressure control solenoids (PCS), and some shift solenoids are pulse-width modulated-type solenoids. ● **SEE FIGURE 21–17**.

LOW-SIDE AND HIGH-SIDE DRIVERS Low-side drivers (LSD) are transistors that complete the ground path in the circuit. Ignition voltage is supplied to the solenoid and the computer output is connected to the ground side of the shift solenoid. The computer energizes the solenoid by completing the ground path. Low-side drivers can often perform a diagnostic circuit check by monitoring the voltage from the solenoid to check that the control circuit is complete. A low-side driver, however, cannot detect a short-to-ground.

High-side drivers (HSD) control the power side of the solenoid from the PCM/TCM. A ground is provided to the solenoid, so when the high-side driver switches, the solenoid will be energized. High-side drivers inside modules can detect electrical faults such as a break in continuity when the circuit is not energized. ● **SEE FIGURE 21–18**.

ELECTRONIC PRESSURE CONTROL

- The transmission's hydraulic pump pressure regulator valve is controlled by the pressure regulator valve that is controlled by a pulse-width-modulated solenoid called
- **Electronic pressure control (EPC) or**

EPC AMPERES	PRESSURE PSI (kPa)
0.0	169–195 PSI (1,165–1,345 kPa)
0.1	167–194 PSI (1,151–1,338 kPa)
0.2	161–190 PSI (1,110–1,310 kPa)
0.3	155–186 PSI (1,069–1,282 kPa)
0.4	144–177 PSI (993–1,220 kPa)
0.5	133–167 PSI (917–1,151 kPa)
0.6	120–153 PSI (827–1,055 kPa)
0.7	102–138 PSI (703–952 kPa)
0.8	83–119 PSI (572–821 kPa)
0.9	62–97 PSI (427–669 kPa)
1.0	53–69 PSI (365–476 kPa)

CHART 21–1

Typical electronic pressure control (EPC) current and line pressure comparison.

- **Pressure control solenoid (PCS) or**
- *Variable force solenoid (VFS) or*
- *Force motor*

The EPC is normally closed, which results in high regulated pressure.

- Current (a maximum of about 1 ampere) allows the solenoid to open, which reduces the regulated pressure. The EPC PWM by the PCM/TCM operates at a fixed frequency, usually at 300 to 600 Hz depending on the unit.

- The higher the duty cycle, the more current and the lower the pressure.

- The lower the duty cycle, the less the current and the higher the pressure. ● **CHART 21–1.**

HOW IT ALL WORKS

ELECTRONIC The transmission control module (TCM) uses information from the various engine and transmission/transaxle sensors and then commands the shift solenoids to operate, which controls the timing of the shifts. ● **SEE FIGURE 21–20.**

HYDRAULIC A solenoid can be cycled (pulsed on and off) or line pressure can be increased or decreased by adjusting the electrical signal to the electronic pressure control (EPC) or shift solenoid. The solenoids in turn control the hydraulic pressure that moves the shift valves or operates the torque converter clutch. ● **SEE FIGURE 21–21.**

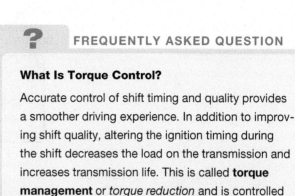

? FREQUENTLY ASKED QUESTION

What Is Torque Control?

Accurate control of shift timing and quality provides a smoother driving experience. In addition to improving shift quality, altering the ignition timing during the shift decreases the load on the transmission and increases transmission life. This is called **torque management** or *torque reduction* and is controlled by the PCM/TCM. ● **SEE FIGURE 21–19.**

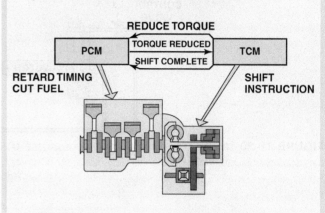

FIGURE 21–19 When the transmission control module (TCM) is ready to begin an upshift, it signals the powertrain control module (PCM) to reduce engine torque. This produces a smoother shift with less wear in the transmission.

ADAPTIVE STRATEGIES

DEFINITION Most late model electronically controlled automatic transmissions/transaxles use the PCM or TCM to monitor the time it takes to complete a shift. The PCM can determine this from the comparison between the engine speed and the output speed sensor data. When a shift is commanded, there should be a change in the speed of the output shaft. If the change in speed is more than normal, which could indicate normal wear in the clutch pack, the PCM can learn from this and start the shift sooner to allow time for the clutch to be fully engaged. The adjustment is called **adaptive control**, or **adaptive learning**, which keeps shift duration within a certain time period as determined by the driver's habits.

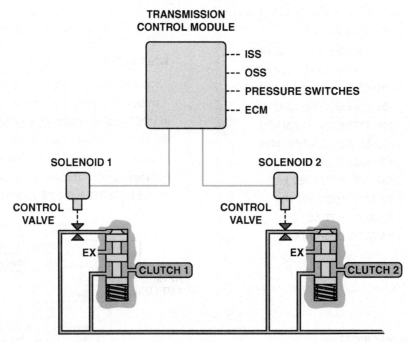

FIGURE 21–20 Using data from the various sensors, the TCM can apply or release the clutches. During an upshift, solenoid 1 can control how fast clutch 1 releases as solenoid 2 controls how fast clutch 2 applies to keep the shift time at the proper speed.

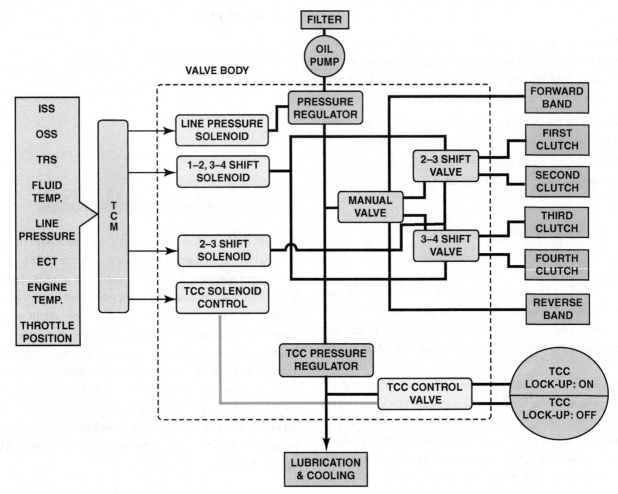

FIGURE 21–21 A diagram showing the relationship between the electronic and hydraulic controls.

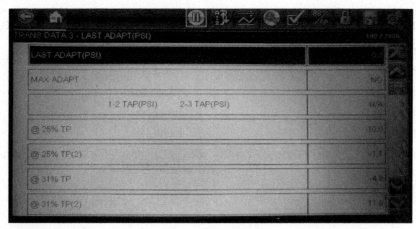

FIGURE 21–22 A scan tool display showing the adaptive (TAP) pressure changes at various throttle positions.

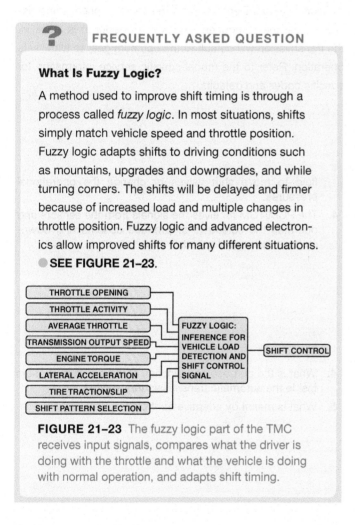

? FREQUENTLY ASKED QUESTION

What Is Fuzzy Logic?

A method used to improve shift timing is through a process called *fuzzy logic*. In most situations, shifts simply match vehicle speed and throttle position. Fuzzy logic adapts shifts to driving conditions such as mountains, upgrades and downgrades, and while turning corners. The shifts will be delayed and firmer because of increased load and multiple changes in throttle position. Fuzzy logic and advanced electronics allow improved shifts for many different situations. ● **SEE FIGURE 21–23**.

THROTTLE OPENING
THROTTLE ACTIVITY
AVERAGE THROTTLE
TRANSMISSION OUTPUT SPEED
ENGINE TORQUE
LATERAL ACCELERATION
TIRE TRACTION/SLIP
SHIFT PATTERN SELECTION

FUZZY LOGIC: INFERENCE FOR VEHICLE LOAD DETECTION AND SHIFT CONTROL SIGNAL

SHIFT CONTROL

FIGURE 21–23 The fuzzy logic part of the TMC receives input signals, compares what the driver is doing with the throttle and what the vehicle is doing with normal operation, and adapts shift timing.

TYPICAL ADAPTIVE CONTROLS Transmissions use input and output speed sensors, allowing the TCM to determine the gear ratio and how long it takes to make the shift.

- Chrysler refers to the adaptive control as the **clutch volume index (CVI)**, which is the length of time it takes to fill the clutches with fluid.

- General Motors call their adaptive control **Transmission Adapt Pressure (TAP)** system, which manages oil pressure to control clutch fill rates. The TAP values are sorted by cell, with each cell being a different throttle opening. The PCM/TCM can add pressure to compensate for clutch pack wear up to 30 PSI, which is displayed on a **scan tool**. ● **SEE FIGURE 21–22**.

- Honda calls it *clutch fill volume index* which is shown on a scan tool as a number. The higher the number, the more fluid volume is required to fill a clutch and can be used to see if there are worn friction plates in a certain clutch pack.

Check service information for details for the proper clutch volumes on the unit being serviced.

Some vehicles have additional shift control modes, and these provide earlier or later and smoother or faster shifts.

- The driver can choose economy mode, which causes the transmission to shift early with a smooth shift feel.

- When switched to power mode, the transmission shifts later and more firmly.

DEFAULT (LIMP-IN) AND PROTECTION MODE A default (or limp-in) gear is the forward speed that is used if there is a failure in the electronic or computer system. On older transmissions, if neither of two shift solenoids were engaged, then a default gear is selected by the manual valve. ● **SEE CHARTS 21–2 AND 21–3**.

Depending on the exact make and model of the transmission or transaxle, the default gear can be second, third, or fourth gear.

On newer transmissions a transmission **protection mode** will be selected, depending on what gear the transmission was in at the time of the fault. Electrical failure of any shift solenoid

GENERAL MOTORS 4T60-E (FRONT-WHEEL-DRIVE TRANSAXLE)		
Gear Range	Solenoid A	Solenoid B
First gear	ON	ON
Second gear	OFF	ON
Third gear	OFF	OFF
Fourth gear	ON	OFF

CHART 21-2

In this example, the vehicle would start out and remain in third gear if there was a fault with the computer or wiring.

GENERAL MOTORS 4L80-E (REAR-WHEEL-DRIVE TRANSMISSION)		
Gear Range	Solenoid A	Solenoid B
First gear	ON	OFF
Second gear	OFF	OFF
Third gear	OFF	ON
Fourth gear	ON	ON

CHART 21-3

In this example, the vehicle would start out and remain in second gear if there was a fault with the computer or wiring.

or pressure control solenoid will result in a default to the protection mode.

As an example, if the transmission is in first, second, or third gear during an electrical failure, the transmission will default to third gear. If the transmission is in fourth, fifth, or sixth gear when an electrical failure occurs, the transmission will default to fifth gear.

Mechanical failure within a shift solenoid or pressure control solenoid will again result with the transmission going into a protection mode. Depending on the vehicle speed, transmission range, the component and which position it is stuck in, the transmission will default to the optimum gear to allow safe operation. Refer to the model-specific service information for specific codes and defaults.

SUMMARY

1. Electronic controls are used for accurate automatic operation of the transmission/transaxle.
2. Electronic controls use sensors to monitor various operational inputs that will be used to control the operation of the transmission.
3. The hydraulic operation of the transmission is controlled by solenoids that are switched to redirect pressurized fluid to move shift valves or change the operational pressures.
4. The PCM/TCM receives the signals from the sensors and operates the solenoids to produce upshifts and downshifts at the proper speed.

REVIEW QUESTIONS

1. What are the four sensors that are used by the automatic transmission/transaxle controller to determine when to shift?
2. What are the types of computer memory used in the PCM/TCM?
3. What is the purpose and function of the input and output speed sensors?
4. What is the purpose and function of the pressure sensors inside the automatic transmission/transaxle?
5. What is meant by adaptive controls?

CHAPTER QUIZ

1. What electronic control module is used to control the shifting of an electronically controlled automatic transmission/transaxle?
   a. PCM
   b. TCM
   c. TCU
   d. Any of the above depending on application

2. What type of sensor measures temperature?
   a. Potentiometer
   b. Thermistor
   c. Transducer
   d. Frequency generator

3. What type of sensor measures speed?
   a. Potentiometer
   b. Thermistor
   c. Transducer
   d. Frequency generator

4. The transmission range (TR) switch is used to _____.
   a. Keep the engine from starting in any gear position except park or neutral
   b. Limit upshifts in manual ranges
   c. Operate the backup lights in reverse
   d. All of the above

5. The input speed sensor is also called a _____.
   a. Output speed sensor (OSS)
   b. Vehicle speed (VS) sensor
   c. Turbine speed sensor (TSS)
   d. Any of the above depending on make and model

6. The output speed sensor is also called a_____.
   a. Input speed sensor (ISS)
   b. Vehicle speed sensor
   c. Turbine speed sensor
   d. Any of the above depending on make and model

7. What type of sensor is the transmission fluid temperature (TFT) sensor?
   a. Negative temperature coefficient (NTC) thermistor
   b. Potentiometer
   c. Rheostat
   d. Transducer

8. Linear solenoids are used for _____.
   a. TCC
   b. Pressure control
   c. Transducer
   d. All of the above depending on application

9. What does electronic pressure control (EPC) solenoid use to control mainline pressure?
   a. Resistance   c. Current
   b. Torque   d. Voltage

10. Adaptive control means _____.
   a. The time it takes to make a shift
   b. The delay between the command and when the shift occurs
   c. The change in the pressure or timing to keep the shift occurring at the same time to make up for wear
   d. The default position which may be second, third, or fourth gear depending on application

chapter 22

HYBRID ELECTRIC VEHICLE TRANSMISSIONS AND TRANSAXLES

LEARNING OBJECTIVES

After studying this chapter, the reader will be able to:

1. Identify the types of hybrid vehicles.
2. Identify the levels of hybrids.
3. Explain how an automatic transmission can be converted for use in hybrid electric vehicles.
4. Identify the components of a two-mode hybrid transmission system and explain its operation.
5. Discuss the operation of different hybrid vehicle transmissions.

This chapter will help you prepare for ASE Automatic Transmission/Transaxle (A2) certification test content area "A" (General Transmission/Transaxle Diagnosis).

KEY TERMS

Electronically variable transmission (EVT) 379

Internal combustion engine (ICE) 375

GM STC OBJECTIVE

GM Service Technical College topic covered in this chapter is as follows:

1. Basic introduction to characteristics of transmissions/transaxles as used in General Motors advanced technology vehicles.

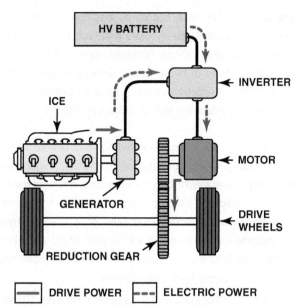

FIGURE 22–1 The power flow in a typical series-hybrid vehicle.

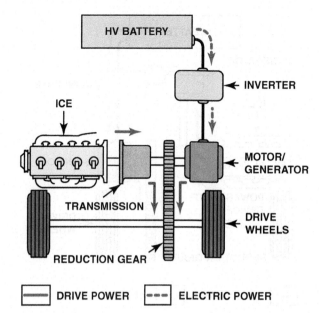

FIGURE 22–2 The power flow in a typical parallel-hybrid vehicle.

TYPES OF HYBRID VEHICLES

SERIES HYBRID The types of hybrid electric vehicles include series, parallel, and series–parallel designs. In a series hybrid design, sole propulsion is by a battery-powered electric motor, but the electric energy for the batteries comes from another onboard energy source, such as an **internal combustion engine (ICE)**. In this design, the engine turns a generator and the generator can either charge the batteries or power an electric motor that drives the transmission. The internal combustion engine never powers the vehicle directly.
● **SEE FIGURE 22–1.**

The engine is only operated to keep the batteries charged. Therefore, the vehicle could be moving with or without the internal combustion engine running. Series-hybrid vehicles also use regeneration braking to help keep the batteries charged. The engine is designed to just keep the batteries charged, and therefore, is designed to operate at its most efficient speed and load. The Chevrolet VOLT is an example of a series-hybrid design.

ADVANTAGES An advantage of a series-hybrid design is that no clutch or torque converter is needed. A series hybrid does not give the owner "range anxiety" that often affects owners of electric vehicles who are concerned that they may not have enough electric power to make it home or to a charging station.

DISADVANTAGES A disadvantage of a series-hybrid design is the added weight of the internal combustion engine as compared to an electric vehicle. The engine is actually a heavy onboard battery charger. Also, the electric motor and battery capacity have to be large enough to power the vehicle under all operating conditions, including climbing hills. All power needed for heating and cooling must also come from the batteries, so using the air conditioning in hot weather and the heater in cold weather reduces the range that the vehicle can travel on battery power alone.

PARALLEL HYBRID In a parallel-hybrid design, multiple propulsion sources can be combined, or one of the energy sources alone can drive the vehicle. In this design, the battery and engine are both connected to the transmission. The vehicle using a parallel-hybrid design can be powered by the internal combustion engine alone, by the electric motor alone (full hybrids only), or by a combination of engine and electric motor propulsion. In most cases, the electric motor is used to assist the internal combustion engine.

ADVANTAGES One of the advantages of using a parallel-hybrid design is that by using an electric motor or motors to assist the internal combustion engine, the engine itself can be smaller than would normally be needed. ● **SEE FIGURE 22–2.**

NOTE: A parallel-hybrid design could include additional batteries to allow for plug-in capability, which could extend the distance the vehicle can travel using battery power alone.

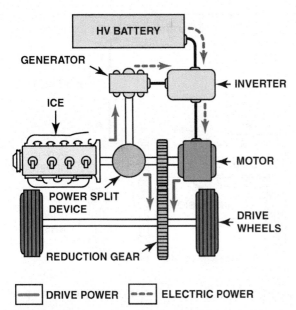

HV BATTERY

GENERATOR

ICE

INVERTER

MOTOR

POWER SPLIT
DEVICE

DRIVE
WHEELS

REDUCTION GEAR

—— DRIVE POWER   ---- ELECTRIC POWER

FIGURE 22–3 A series–parallel hybrid design allows the vehicle to operate in electric motor mode only or in combination with the internal combustion engine.

DISADVANTAGES One disadvantage of a parallel-hybrid design is that complex software is needed to seamlessly blend electric and ICE power. Another concern about the parallel-hybrid design is that it has to be engineered to provide proper heating and air-conditioning system operation when the ICE stops at idle.

SERIES–PARALLEL HYBRID Toyota, Ford, and GM Two Mode hybrids are classified as series–parallel hybrids because they can operate using electric motor power alone or with the assistance of the ICE. Series–parallel hybrids combine the functions of both a series and a parallel design. The internal combustion engine may be operating even though the vehicle is stopped if the electronic controller has detected that the batteries need to be charged. ● **SEE FIGURE 22–3.**

NOTE: The internal combustion engine may or may not start when the driver starts the vehicle depending on the temperature of the engine and other conditions. This can be confusing to some who are driving a hybrid electric vehicle for the first time and sense that the engine did not start when they tried to start the engine.

LEVELS OF HYBRIDS

MILD HYBRID A mild hybrid will incorporate idle stop and regenerative braking but is not capable of using the electric motor to propel the vehicle on its own without help from the internal combustion engine. A mild hybrid system has the

advantage of costing less, but saves less fuel compared to a full hybrid vehicle and usually uses a 42-volt electrical motor and battery package (36-volt batteries, 42-volt charging). An example of this type of hybrid is the General Motors parallel-hybrid truck (PHT) (starter/generator flywheel system) and the Saturn VUE (belt alternator starter [BAS] system).

MEDIUM HYBRID A medium hybrid uses 144- to 158-volt batteries that provide for engine stop/start, regenerative braking, and power assist. Like a mild hybrid, a typical medium hybrid is not capable of propelling the vehicle from a stop using battery power alone. Examples of a medium-hybrid vehicle include the 2012 and later Chevrolet Malibu and Buick LaCrosse. The BAS system was updated in 2011 (now called eAssist) to include the following changes:

1. Uses a 15 kW electric motor-generator, up from 10 kW.

2. Uses a 115-volt lithium ion battery pack instead of a 36-volt NiMH battery.

FULL HYBRID A full hybrid, also called a strong hybrid, uses a 201 to 300 volt battery, and provides for idle stop, regenerative braking, and is able to propel the vehicle using the electric motor(s) alone. Each vehicle manufacturer has made its decision on which hybrid type to implement based on its assessment of the market niche for a particular model. Examples of a full or strong hybrid include the General Motors Two-Mode trucks, Ford Escape SUV, Toyota Highlander, Lexus RX400h, Lexus GS450h, Toyota Prius, and Toyota Camry. The fuel savings are about 30% to 50% for full-hybrid systems.

ONE-MOTOR/TWO-MOTOR/THREE-MOTOR SYSTEMS

ONE-MOTOR HYBRIDS Hybrid electric vehicles that use one electric motor include VW, Nissan, Honda, and General Motors. In these units, an electric motor is attached to the engine crankshaft and is used to perform two functions:

1. Start the gasoline engine (ICE)

2. Act as a generator to charge the high-voltage batteries.

General Motors also uses a belt alternator starter system, which uses a belt-driven motor/generator attached to the front of the engine. Hybrids that use one motor are often mild hybrids and usually are not able to power the vehicle using electric power alone.

FIGURE 22–4 The rear electric motor on a Lexus RX 400h SUV.

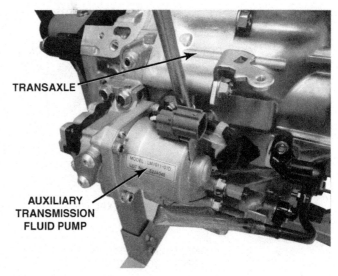

FIGURE 22–5 The auxiliary transmission fluid pump maintains pressure during idle-stop mode.

TWO-MOTOR HYBRIDS Hybrid electric vehicles that use two motors are the most commonly used hybrids and are used by Toyota, Ford, and General Motors in their full-size two-mode trucks. Each electric motor serves two purposes:

- The motor/generator attached to the engine, usually labeled M/G1, is used to start the gasoline engine and to charge the high-voltage batteries.
- The motor/generator that is connected to the drive wheels, usually labeled M/G2, is used to propel the vehicle and to recharge the high-voltage battery during deceleration (regenerative braking).

Two-motor hybrid electric vehicles are full (strong) hybrids and are capable of propelling the vehicle using electric motor power alone for short distances.

THREE-MOTOR HYBRIDS Three-motor hybrid electric vehicles are usually two-motor hybrids that use an additional electric motor to propel the rear wheels for all-wheel-drive capability. Hybrid electric vehicles that use three electric motors include the Toyota Highlander and Lexus Rx400/450h SUVs. ● **SEE FIGURE 22–4.**

HYBRID ELECTRIC VEHICLE (HEV) TRANSMISSIONS

AUTOMATIC TRANSMISSIONS CONVERTED FOR USE IN HYBRID VEHICLES In order to adapt a conventional automatic transmission to a hybrid power train, an electric auxiliary pump is used to maintain fluid pressure in the transmission during internal combustion engine (ICE) idle stop. This pump is powered by a DC brushless (AC synchronous) motor, which requires a special controller to provide the correct operating frequency and pulse width. When the auxiliary pump is operating, it sends hydraulic pressure to the transmission regulator valve, and then on to the manual valve where it is directed to the appropriate clutches. This prevents the transmission from shifting into "neutral" when the ICE is in idle stop. Once the ICE restarts, the auxiliary pump is turned off and hydraulic pressure is again supplied by the mechanically driven transmission fluid pump. ● **SEE FIGURE 22–5.**

eASSIST AUXILIARY TRANSMISSION FLUID PUMP The transmissions on vehicles equipped with the eAssist system are modified to include an electric auxiliary transmission fluid pump. This externally mounted pump maintains the transmission fluid pressure while the engine is in the auto stop mode. The pump outputs pressurized fluid through a tube into the main fluid pressure passages of the transmission. A check valve within the fluid passages of the transmission prevents the fluid from losing pressure and circulating through the mechanical pump. The electric pump ensures that the transmission clutches remain applied for a smooth acceleration once the engine starts.[1]

---

[1] General Motors Center of Learning Course # 18070.45W.

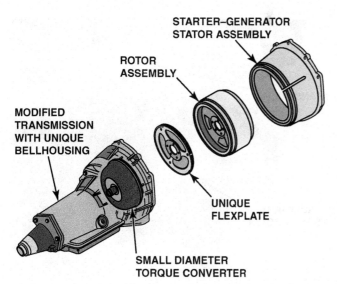

FIGURE 22–6 Integrated starter–generator (ISG) assembly adapted to a production 4L60E transmission. Note that the torque converter diameter is smaller to fit inside the rotor assembly.

GM PARALLEL HYBRID TRUCK

DESCRIPTION AND OPERATION The transmission in the 2004–2008 Chevrolet Silverado/GMC Sierra parallel-hybrid pickup is based on the 4L60E electronically controlled automatic transmission design with minor modifications to adjust for its role in a hybrid power train. The specific model used in the hybrid pickup is known as the M33. The transmission is controlled by the PCM, which receives signals from other vehicle sensors to determine load and speed and command appropriate transmission operation.

CONSTRUCTION Changes were made to accommodate the addition of the *integrated starter–generator* (ISG) inside the bell housing assembly. The transmission was modified where it was absolutely necessary, but otherwise used as much of the original design as possible. The primary change was a decrease in the diameter of the torque converter in order for it to fit inside the rotor assembly of the ISG. ● SEE FIGURE 22–6.

The rotor assembly is bolted directly to the engine crankshaft and wraps around the torque converter. A separate flex plate inside the rotor is used to drive the torque converter. The bell housing is a separate part of the most recent 4L60E transmission case design, and this was replaced with a special unit that was large enough to enclose the ISG stator assembly.

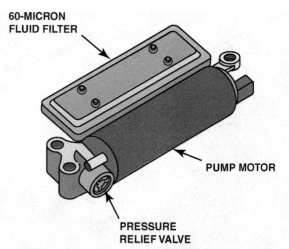

FIGURE 22–7 Electric secondary fluid pump from a 4L60E transmission in a GM hybrid pickup.

To limit heat buildup in the smaller torque converter, a different TCC control strategy was used so that lockup would be commanded earlier. This also required the use of a torque converter with a multiplate clutch (TCC) in order to handle the torque generated by the V-8 engine.

OPERATION In start/stop (idle stop) mode the engine stops, which will in turn stop the transmission oil pump and cause the transmission to go into "neutral." To prevent this, an electric secondary fluid pump is installed on the valve body inside the transmission oil pan. Whenever the engine goes into idle stop, the electric fluid pump is turned on to maintain oil pressure on the transmission forward clutch and keep the drivetrain connected to the engine. This results in a smoother transition between idle stop and engine restarting as the vehicle resumes operation. ● SEE FIGURE 22–7.

To enable regenerative braking, the hybrid version of the 4L60E transmission is made to apply the overrun clutch during coasting or braking in the D4 range and either third or second gear. This allows power to be transmitted back through the torque converter, which can then be used to generate electric current for recharging the 42-volt battery pack.

SERVICE Service and diagnostic procedures include the following:

- This transmission requires Dexron VI fluid. The filter on the electric secondary fluid pump is replaceable but is not a regular maintenance item.

- Transmission pressure testing can be performed using the line pressure tap located on the transmission case. These tests are most often done by attaching a pressure gauge to the fitting on the side of the transmission and operating the transmission under various load conditions and road speeds.

- A scan tool can be used to access DTCs (diagnostic trouble codes) and also to perform bidirectional testing of the transmission solenoids.

TWO-MODE HYBRID TRANSMISSION

POWER FLOW The transmission used in the GM two-mode hybrid (2008–2014) is designed specifically for use in hybrid vehicles. The two-mode hybrid transmission used in General Motors hybrid trucks is labeled 2ML70 and is also used by Dodge and Chrysler. This unit features two 60-kW motors inside the transmission, a 300-volt battery pack, and a V-8 engine.

A two-mode hybrid electric vehicle is capable of increasing fuel economy by about 25%, depending on the type of driving conditions. Like all hybrids, the two-mode combines the power of a gasoline engine with that of electric motors and includes the following:

- Regenerative braking that captures kinetic energy that would otherwise be lost
- Idle stop (start/stop)

COMPONENTS This two-mode unit is called an **electronically variable transmission (EVT)**. It includes three simple planetary gear sets with four multiplate clutches. It has four fixed gear ratios with two EV ratios for smooth, more efficient operation. The components of the two-mode transmission include the following:

- Two 60-kW electric motor/generators assemblies called motor/generator A and B, usually abbreviated MG A and MG B.
- Three planetary gear sets (one is located in front of motor/generator A, another is located between the two motor/generators, and the last planetary gear set is located behind motor/generator B).
- Four wet plate clutches (two friction [rotating] and two [reaction/stationary] clutch assemblies). ● **SEE FIGURE 22–8.**

FIGURE 22–8 The two-mode transmission has orange high-voltage cable entering the unit to carry electric energy from the high-voltage battery pack to propel the vehicle and also to charge the battery during deceleration.

The vehicle starts moving in EV 1 with a variable ratio from infinite low to 1.7:1. If the vehicle is launched with the engine off, M/G A will spin the engine crankshaft so it can start running.

EV 2 has a ratio between 1.7:1 and 0.5:1.

FIRST MODE OF OPERATION The first mode is for accelerating from standstill to second gear. At low speed and light load, the vehicle can be propelled by:

- Either electric motor alone
- The internal combustion engine (ICE) alone
- Or a combination of the two (electric motor and/or ICE)

In this mode, the engine (if running) can be shut off under certain conditions and everything will continue to operate on electric power alone. The hybrid system can restart the ICE at any time as needed. One of the motor/generators operates as a generator to charge the high-voltage battery, and the other works as a motor to assist in propelling the vehicle.

SECOND MODE OF OPERATION The second mode takes the vehicle from second gear through to overdrive. At higher loads and speeds, the ICE always runs. In the second mode, the motor/generators and planetary gear sets are used to keep torque and horsepower at a maximum. As the vehicle speed increases, various combinations of the four fixed ratio planetary gears engage and/or disengage to multiply engine torque, and allows one or the other of the motor/generators to perform as a generator to charge the high-voltage battery. ● **SEE FIGURE 22–9.**

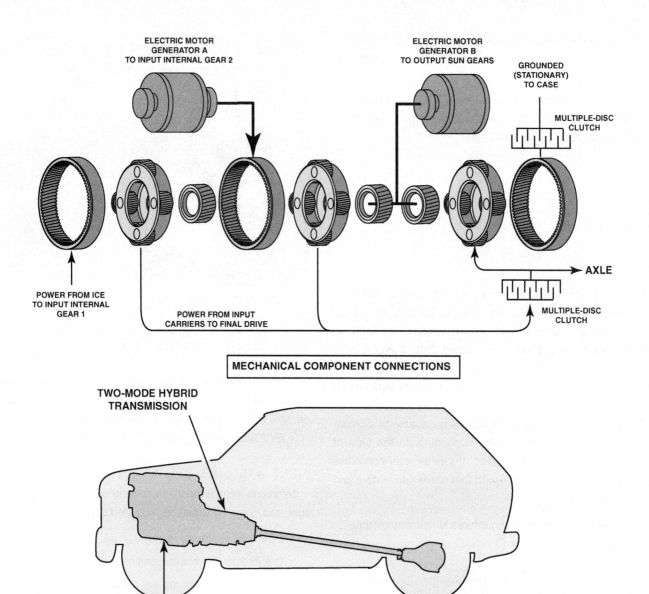

FIGURE 22–9 Using two planetary gear sets, the ICE can be maintained in the most efficient speed of about 2000 RPM under most operating conditions.

TWO-MODE SERVICE Routine service is all that is needed or required of the two-mode transmission. Fluid level check and visual inspection should be all that is required until the first scheduled fluid change. Always use Dexron VI. Faults in the system will often set a diagnostic trouble code (DTC). Unit repair requires an engine hoist or the lift arm of a vehicle lift to remove the motor assembly. ● **SEE FIGURE 22–10.**

CHEVROLET VOLT TRANSMISSION

The Volt 4ET50 is a fully automatic, front-wheel-drive transaxle, variable-speed, electronically controlled transmission. It consists primarily of a torque dampener assembly, an integral main and auxiliary fluid pump and housing, one planetary gear set,

(a)

(b)

FIGURE 22–10 (a) Disassembly of the 2ML70 transmission requires the use of a lift or engine hoist to remove the motor assembly. (b) The motor assembly after being removed for the transmission.

FIGURE 22–11 The 4ET50 transaxle, showing drive motor/generator B and final drive. (Courtesy of General Motors)

two friction (rotating) and one mechanical (stationary) clutch assemblies, a hydraulic pressurization and control system, and two internal electric motors. Drive motor/generator A has a power rating of 55 kW and drive motor/generator B is rated at 111 kW. ● **SEE FIGURE 22–11.**

TORQUE DAMPENER AND CLUTCH The torque dampener contains internal torsional springs, fluid, input shaft, and a clutch. The torque dampener acts as a spring coupling to smoothly transmit power from the engine flexplate to the transmission. The dampener provides a mechanical direct drive coupling of the engine to the transmission. The clutch is applied during engine starting and stopping events.

PLANETARY GEAR SET AND CONTROL The planetary gear set provides the electrically variable forward mode ratios and reverse. Changing ratios is fully automatic and is accomplished through the use of a transmission control module (TCM) located inside the transmission and the drive motor generator power inverter module (PIM) located under hood. Both the TCM and the PIM receive and monitor various electronic sensor inputs and use this information to vary the torque output at the optimum time based on throttle position.

The TCM commands shift solenoids and variable bleed pressure control solenoids to control torque timing and feel. All the solenoids, including the TCM, are packaged into a self-contained control solenoid valve assembly.

HYDRAULIC SYSTEM The main hydraulic system primarily consists of a gerotor-type pump, control valve body assemblies, dampener housing, and case. The pump maintains the working pressures needed to stroke the clutch pistons that apply or release the friction components. These friction components, when applied or released, support the automatic ratio qualities of the transmission.

The hydraulic system also uses a secondary system and consists of an auxiliary pump located inside of the transmission. This is a gerotor-type pump, electric three-phase high voltage (HV) motor, electric harness, and control module. The control module is located inside of the PIM under the hood. This pump maintains working pressures when the engine is off.

FRICTION COMPONENTS

The friction components used in this transmission consist of three multiple disc clutches. The multiple disc clutches combine with a planetary gear set and electric motor to deliver the different ratios, forward and reverse. The gear set then transfers torque through the final drive assembly.

GEAR RANGES

The transmission may be operated in any of the following gear ranges:

- P (PARK) This position locks the wheels and prevents the vehicle from rolling either forward or backward. PARK is the best position to use when starting the vehicle.

- R (REVERSE) This position allows the vehicle to be operated in a rearward direction. This is done by the drive motor with generator B and is an electric-only mode.

- N (NEUTRAL) In this position, the propulsion system does not connect with the wheels.

- D (DRIVE) Drive range should be used for all normal driving conditions for maximum efficiency and fuel economy. Drive range allows the transmission to operate in electrically variable modes, providing various ratios and output torque.

- L (Low) This position is used for the "feel" of engine braking and can be used for the slowing of the vehicle once the throttle is lifted. While in the position, the vehicle will slow quicker and use the drive motor generator B to more aggressively collect energy during a regenerative braking event.

ELECTRONIC COMPONENTS

The 4ET50 transmission contains the electronic components listed below:

- A/Trans Manual Shift Shaft Position Switch Assembly
- A/Trans Output Speed Sensor Assembly
- Control solenoid valve assembly
- Drive motor/generator assembly—unit A
- Drive motor/generator assembly—unit B
- Electric auxiliary fluid pump motor assembly

This transmission operates in four electronically variable transmission modes. High-voltage three-phase cables connect the two motor/generators and the electric auxiliary fluid pump drive motor assembly to the drive motor control modules. The high-voltage electric auxiliary fluid pump drive provides transmission fluid pressure during engine-off operation. ● **SEE FIGURE 22–12.**

CAUTION: Always perform the high-voltage-disabling procedure prior to servicing any high-voltage component or connection. Personal protection equipment (PPE) and proper procedures must be followed. The high-voltage disabling procedure will perform the following tasks:

- Identify how to disable high voltage.
- Identify how to test for the presence of high voltage.
- Identify the condition under which high voltage is always present and personal protection equipment and proper procedures must be followed.

Failure to follow the procedures exactly as written may result in serious injury or death.[2]

CHEVROLET SPARK TRANSMISSION

The electric drive motor and generator assembly within the transmission propel the vehicle. The final drive assembly consists of a planetary gear set and differential assembly. The planetary set includes a sun gear, ring gear, and output carrier assembly.

To achieve a final drive reduction, the ring gear is held by the transmission case and the input is the sun gear. The sun gear is driven by the main shaft, which is directly splined to the drive motor and generator rotor assembly. The main shaft also contains a wheel with teeth that the park pawl engages when the transmission is placed in park. The left- and right-hand output axle shafts are splined to engage a differential side gear in the final drive. ● **SEE FIGURE 22–13.**

MOTOR/GENERATOR The 85-kilowatt drive motor/generator assembly is used for vehicle propulsion and regenerative braking. This motor/generator assembly is comprised of a stator and a rotor. The stator is a wire coil comprised of three-phase circuits, identified as phases U, V, and W. The three-phase circuits are connected in a "Y" configuration, with each of the three high voltage cables connecting to one three-phase circuit of the stator. The drive motor/generator rotor is supported by bearings at each end. The electromagnetic field, created by the energized stator, forces the rotor to rotate in either a forward or a reverse direction.

[2]General Motors Service Information document ID # 2424317 and 2423980.

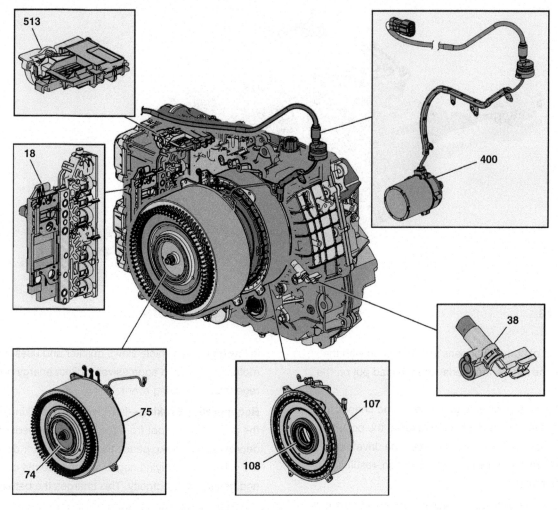

(18) **CONTROL SOLENOID VALVE ASSEMBLY**

(38) **A/TRANS OUTPUT SPEED SENSOR ASSEMBLY, INTERNAL TO TRANSMISSION**

(74) **DRIVE MOTOR/GENERATOR ROTOR ASSEMBLY – UNIT B**

(75) **DRIVE MOTOR/GENERATOR STATOR ASSEMBLY – UNIT B**

(107) **GENERATOR/DRIVE MOTOR STATOR ASSEMBLY – UNIT A**

(108) **GENERATOR/DRIVE MOTOR ROTOR ASSEMBLY – UNIT A**

(400) **ELECTRIC AUXILIARY FLUID PUMP MOTOR ASSEMBLY**

(513) **A/TRANS MANUAL SHIFT SHAFT POSITION SWITCH ASSEMBLY**

FIGURE 22–12 Electrical and electronic components of the 4ET50 transaxle. (Courtesy of General Motors)

LUBRICATION   A gerotor-type mechanical pump lubricates and cools the components. The pump is an electric three-phase 360-volt AC high-voltage motor mounted internally to the transmission under the transmission fluid pan. The pump operates under low pressure and only runs when vehicle speed is detected.

This electronic drive unit requires the use of DEXRON® HP transmission fluid, where HP stands for high performance. DEXRON® HP transmission fluid is a fully synthetic version of DEXRON® VI.

OPERATING MODES

Drive and Reverse—When the vehicle is shifted into drive, current is sent to the drive motor/generator to propel the vehicle forward. As the accelerator pedal is pressed, the amplitude and frequency of the three-phase current is modified to provide enough torque to move the vehicle. As the vehicle gains speed, the amplitude and frequency of the three-phase current begins lowering the torque output and increases the speed of the drive motor/generator. The

FIGURE 22–13 Chevrolet Spark electric drive transmission (1ET35). (Courtesy of General Motors)

modification of current happens in conjunction with the position of the accelerator pedal and the load put on the vehicle.

When selecting reverse gear, there is no change in physical or mechanical gearing. In reverse, the polarity of the current is switched, which forces the drive motor/generator to rotate in the opposite direction, resulting in reverse operation.

Low Gear—Low gear is also available to provide the feel of increased engine braking and may be used for slowing the vehicle more aggressively than the drive gear. When in low gear, the vehicle slows quicker and uses the drive motor/generator to aggressively collect energy during a regenerative braking event.[3]

Regenerative Braking—In regenerative braking, when the driver lifts his foot from the accelerator pedal and depresses the brake pedal, the electric motor decelerates the vehicle by applying negative torque to the output shaft and generating electricity. This charges the battery.[3]

---

[3] General Motors Center of Learning Course # 17440.14D.

SUMMARY

1. Automatic transmissions used in HEVs incorporate an electric auxiliary pump to provide transmission fluid pressure at engine idle stop.

2. The two-mode transmission uses two electric motors and planetary gear sets to produce an electronically variable transmission (EVT).

3. The Chevrolet Spark transmission uses an electric motor and a planetary final drive unit.

REVIEW QUESTIONS

1. What are the differences in the operation of an automatic transmission that has been modified for use in a hybrid electric vehicle?

2. What is the difference between a mild and full hybrid?

3. How does a two-mode hybrid work?

1. In a GM two-mode hybrid electric vehicle, when can the vehicle be powered by electric power alone?
   a. During the first mode
   b. During the second mode
   c. During either the first or second mode
   d. During heavy load conditions regardless of mode

2. Modifications to automatic transmissions used in hybrid vehicles include _____.
   a. Electric auxiliary transmission fluid pump
   b. Larger torque converter
   c. Increased number of plates in multiple-disc clutches
   d. Both a and b are correct

3. What is the purpose of the auxiliary transmission fluid pump on a hybrid vehicle?
   a. Helps cool the inverter
   b. Keeps the clutches from releasing during idle-stop
   c. Maintains fluid level in the transmission reservoir
   d. None of these

4. A GM two-mode transmission includes all of these components EXCEPT _____.
   a. Fluid pump
   b. Four planetary gear sets
   c. Four clutch packs
   d. Electric drive motors

5. How many clutch packs does the Chevrolet Spark transmission contain?
   a. One
   b. Two
   c. Three
   d. None of these

6. The GM eAssist vehicle uses a specially designed CVT transmission.
   a. True
   b. False

7. A Toyota hybrid is what type of hybrid?
   a. Series
   b. Series/parallel
   c. Parallel
   d. None of the above

8. Which type of hybrid vehicle cannot propel a vehicle from a stop using electric motor power alone?
   a. Mild hybrid
   b. Medium hybrid
   c. Strong hybrid
   d. Both a and b

9. What is meant by "range anxiety"?
   a. When the driver notices that the ICE has stopped during a stop
   b. When a driver is driving an electric-only vehicle
   c. A passenger who notices that the engine starts and then stops when riding in a hybrid electric vehicle
   d. Any of the above

10. When is the clutch applied on a Chevy Volt?
   a. During engine starting
   b. In fourth gear
   c. In all forward gears
   d. In reverse only

chapter 23

CONTINUOUSLY VARIABLE TRANSMISSIONS

After studying this chapter, the reader will be able to:

1. Describe the construction of a continuously variable transmission and discuss its advantages and disadvantages.
2. Discuss the electronic controls and operation of a CVT.
3. Explain the diagnosis of a CVT, including pressure testing and CVT fluid and noise issues.

This chapter will help you prepare for ASE Automatic Transmission/Transaxle (A2) certification test content area "A" (General Transmission/Transaxle Diagnosis).

KEY TERMS

Continuously variable transmission (CVT) 387

Input speed sensor (ISS) 390

Line pressure solenoid (LPS) 391

Output speed sensor (OSS) 390

Primary oil pressure (POP) 390

Primary pressure sensor (PPS) 390

Pull chain 389

Push belt 389

Ratio control motor 391

Rubber band effect 388

Secondary oil pressure (SOP) 390

Secondary pressure sensor (SPS) 390

Transmission range sensor (TRS) 390

Transmission temperature sensor (TTS) 390

Variators 388

GM STC OBJECTIVES

GM Service Technical College topic covered in this chapter is as follows:

1. Operational characteristics of CVT transaxles that may be encountered at GM service facilities.

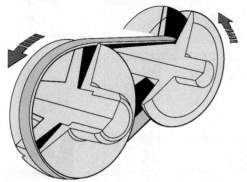

DRIVE PULLEY: WIDE/SMALL DIAMETER

DRIVEN PULLEY: NARROW/LARGE DIAMETER
LOW RATIO, ABOUT 2.5:1

(a)

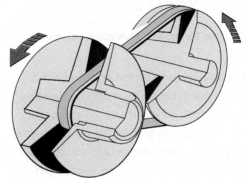

DRIVE PULLEY: NARROW/LARGE DIAMETER

DRIVEN PULLEY: WIDE/SMALL DIAMETER
HIGH RATIO, ABOUT 0.5:1

(b)

FIGURE 23–1 A belt and pulley CVT uses variable-width pulleys to provide an infinite number of speed ratios.

CONTINUOUSLY VARIABLE TRANSMISSION (CVT)

PURPOSE AND FUNCTION A **continuously variable transmission (CVT)** is usually found on some front-wheel-drive vehicles that use a transaxle. A CVT varies the gear ratio in a continuous manner instead of in a series of steps or fixed gear ratios. The power flow is through a steel belt between two pulleys that change their width and effective diameter. When the vehicle accelerates from a standing start, the driving pulley is small and the driven pulley is large. This gives a gear reduction identical to a small gear driving a large gear, which provides an increase in torque and a decrease in speed. CVTs are more efficient than either manual or automatic transmissions while still providing the driving ease of an automatic transmission.

ADVANTAGES A CVT offers the following advantages over a planetary-gear automatic transmission.

- Compact, very short
- Lighter weight
- Constant, stepless acceleration with engine staying at the RPM for maximum power
- Efficient fuel use and emissions, cruise with engine staying at the RPM for maximum efficiency
- Lower internal power loss

One method used to compare transmissions is the engine revolutions for a specific driving cycle. A test vehicle using a 3.0-L engine and a CVT showed 3% fewer revolutions than the same vehicle with a five-speed transmission and 11% less than with a four-speed transmission. This should equal a gain of about 12% in fuel economy.

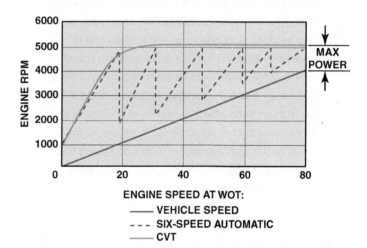

FIGURE 23–2 Engine speed and vehicle speed of a CVT transaxle compared to a typical six-speed conventional automatic transaxle.

These transmissions are used by Audi, Chevrolet (Spark), Dodge, Ford, Honda, Subaru, Toyota, Nissan, and some Saturns.

CONTINUOUSLY VARIABLE GEAR RATIOS As the speed increases, the diameter of the driving pulley increases as the sides of the pulley move together. While this happens, the driven pulley is made wider and therefore smaller in diameter. At cruising speeds, the driving pulley is larger than the driven pulley, which produces an overdrive ratio.

The pulleys change size smoothly and evenly, which produces a somewhat odd sensation when the vehicle accelerates from a stop. When the throttle is depressed, the engine speed increases to the point of good torque output, and the gear ratio selected by the CVT causes the engine to stay at this RPM while the vehicle accelerates. The pulleys move to higher ratios as vehicle speed increases. This is a different sensation than the familiar engine speed increase in each gear and the engine speed decrease after an upshift. ● **SEE FIGURES 23–1 AND 23–2.**

What Is It Like to Drive a Vehicle Equipped with CVT?

For most people, driving a vehicle equipped with a continuously variable transmission (CVT) is the same as driving the vehicle equipped with a conventional automatic transmission/transaxle. The vehicle creeps slightly when the brake is released and accelerates normally when the throttle is opened. Because no shifts occur, the first thing the driver and passenger notice is that it is very smooth. If the vehicle is equipped with a tachometer, the driver may notice that the engine speed increases when first accelerating and often remains higher until the vehicle speed increases. During periods of rapid acceleration, the engine speed may be close to its maximum and thereby create noise and vibration often not experienced in a similar vehicle. Because the vehicle speed slowly catches up to the engine speed, this effect is often referred to as the "**rubber band effect**" and is most noticeable only during periods of rapid acceleration. However, the fuel economy improvement of a CVT compared to a conventional automatic transmission makes the slight difference a reasonable trade-off.

CONSTRUCTION

TERMINOLOGY Instead of using three or more gears, a continuously variable transmission uses two variable-width pulleys, sometimes called **variators**, to change the gear ratio.

OPERATION The pulleys used in CVT design can vary their width by varying the hydraulic pressure applied to them. Each pulley has a movable face and a fixed face.

- The movable face for each pulley is attached to a piston that has hydraulic control pressure applied to it.
- Higher application pressure on the movable face causes the pulley to become narrow and this makes the steel belt ride closer to the outside diameter of the pulley. A lower application pressure will allow the pulley to become wider and the belt will ride closer to the pulley axis.

If a low hydraulic pressure is applied to the drive pulley and a high hydraulic pressure is applied to the driven pulley, a low speed ratio is achieved.

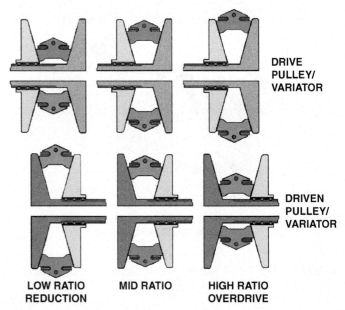

DRIVE PULLEY/ VARIATOR

DRIVEN PULLEY/ VARIATOR

LOW RATIO REDUCTION   MID RATIO   HIGH RATIO OVERDRIVE

FIGURE 23–3 The drive pulley is wide while the driven pulley is narrow for a low ratio vehicle start (left). The ratio changes by making the drive pulley narrow and the driven pulley wider.

A CVT (continuously variable transmission) has an infinite number of gear ratios between its lowest ratio (about 3.7:1) and highest ratio, which is a 0.27:1 overdrive.

A CVT improves efficiency by changing ratios from underdrive/reduction to overdrive in a gradual, continuous manner. The primary/drive pulley is attached to the input shaft. The secondary/driven pulley is on the output shaft and drives the final drive gears. Each pulley, also called a *sheave*, has two sides:

1. One is fixed so it cannot move
2. The other can float sideways to change pulley width.

When the vehicle is at rest, the primary pulley is wide so the belt sits low on the pulley, and the secondary pulley is narrow so the belt sits high. This produces the lowest underdrive ratio. ● **SEE FIGURE 23–3**.

The secondary pulley is spring loaded to force it to a narrow position. The primary pulley is adjusted to control the gear ratio, and the secondary pulley is adjusted to maintain tension on the belt. The belt must never be loose between the pulleys.

- At start, the pulley halves/discs on the input (primary) shaft are spread apart, and the pair of pulley halves on the output (secondary) shaft are pushed together. This produces a small pulley driving a large pulley, which produces the lowest drive ratio.
- As the vehicle moves, the floating side of the primary pulley moves inward, making the pulley narrower and forcing the belt to move out to a wider diameter. This produces a higher gear ratio.

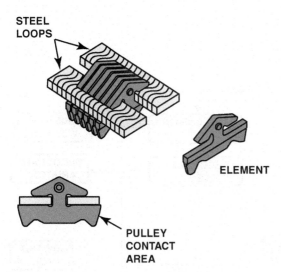

FIGURE 23–4 A typical push-type CVT belt construction.

VEHICLES THAT USE A PUSH-TYPE CVT (BELT-TYPE)	VEHICLES THAT USE A PULL-TYPE CVT (CHAIN-TYPE)
Honda (Accord, Civic, Civic hybrid, Insight hybrid)	Audi (A4, S4, RS4)
Dodge Caliber	Ford (500, Freestar, Freestyle)
Jeep (Compass, Patriot)	Mercury (Montego, Monterey)
Mini Cooper	Subaru Lineartronic (Legacy, Forester, Impreza, Outback)
Mitsubishi (Lancer, Outlander)	
Nissan (Altima, Cube, Maxima, Murano, Rogue, Sentra, Versa)	
Saturn (Aura, Ion, Vue)	
Subaru Justy	
Suzuki SX4	
Toyota Corolla	
Chevrolet (Spark)	

CHART 23–1

Vehicles that use a CVT transaxle, separated by type: either push-type (belt) or pull-type (chain). Check service information for the exact years and types of transmissions used for each model.

- Both pulleys must maintain enough pressure on the drive belt to transfer the required torque. Fluid pressure is used to force the drive piston/pulley to a narrower position and the driven pulley to a wider position. The secondary pulley is spring loaded to force it to a narrow position. The primary pulley is adjusted to control the gear ratio,

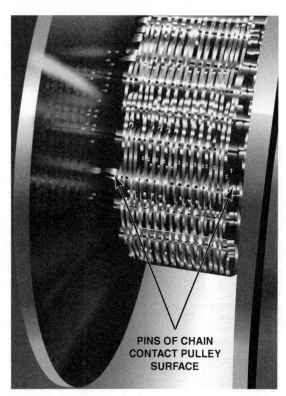

FIGURE 23–5 The pull chain looks similar to a silent chain.

and the secondary pulley is adjusted to maintain tension on the belt. The belt must never be loose between the pulleys.

A reverse gear set, controlled by a multiplate clutch pack, is used to produce reverse.

DRIVE BELT Two different styles of fixed-length steel belts are used.

1. **Push belt** It is made up of about 400 wedge-shaped segments that are held together by two steel bands. Each band is made of multiple layers to allow flexibility. The segment sides contact the pulley sides. A push belt is often called the *Van Doorne design*. This style of belt is directional and is usually marked with an arrow to show belt direction. ● SEE FIGURE 23–4.

2. **Pull chain** It is made up of links and link pins, much like a silent chain. The ends of the link pins contact the pulley sides. This style is also called a *Luk chain drive*. ● SEE FIGURE 23–5.

● SEE CHART 23–1 for list of vehicles that use each type of continuously variable automatic transaxles.

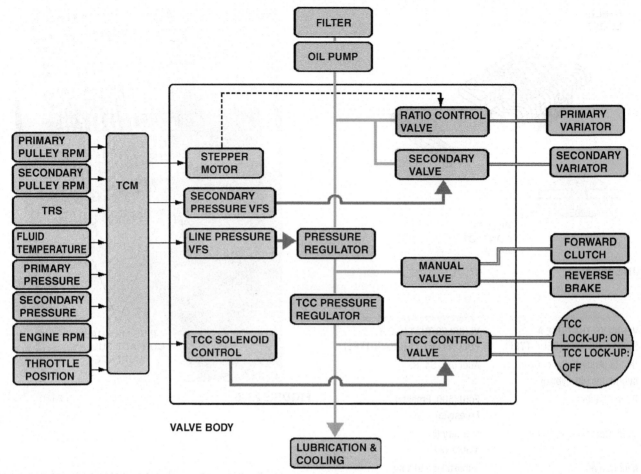

FIGURE 23–6 Block diagram showing the relationship between the TCM, electrical actuators, valve body, and hydraulic actuators for a CVT transmission.

CVT ELECTRONIC CONTROLS

The transmission control module (TCM) of a CVT uses direct and indirect inputs to monitor transmission and engine operation. ● **SEE FIGURE 23–6.**

INPUTS   Direct inputs are as follows:

- **Transmission range sensor (TRS).** A multi contact switch operated by the manual shift lever
- **Input speed sensor (ISS).** Can be a magnetic or a Hall-effect sensor
- **Output speed sensor (OSS).** Can be a magnetic or a Hall-effect sensor
- **Primary pressure sensor (PPS).** A pressure transducer to monitor primary pulley pressure. The pressure measured is called the **primary oil pressure (POP)**

- **Secondary pressure sensor (SPS).** A pressure transducer to monitor secondary pulley pressure. The pressure measured is called the **secondary oil pressure (SOP)**
- **Transmission temperature sensor (TTS).** A negative temperature coefficient (NTC) thermistor used to measure temperature of the transaxle

INPUTS FROM CAN BUS   Indirect inputs from CAN bus include the following:

- PCM requests
- Engine output torque
- Brake switch
- ABS status signals
- Charging system voltage
- Engine RPM
- Engine coolant temperature

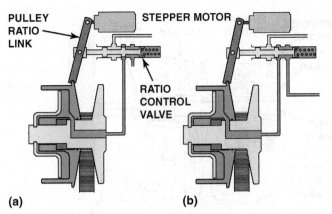

FIGURE 23–7 (a) The stepper motor and pulley ratio link with the CVT in low ratio. (b) The stepper motor has extended, moving the ratio link and ratio control valve; this should cause the primary pulley to become narrower to produce a higher ratio.

- Accelerator pedal position
- Vehicle speed
- A/C system requests

OUTPUTS The TCM controls the drive ratio to match vehicle needs. It can adjust the ratio during vehicle cruise to produce the maximum fuel economy, best emissions, or maximum pulling power. It continuously monitors ISS and OSS signals to ensure that the speeds match the desired ratio.

- The stepper motor, also called a **ratio control motor,** is a linear position motor that changes the position of the upper end of the pulley ratio link. The stepper motor controls the hydraulic ratio valve through the link, which in turn controls fluid flow to the piston. The lower end of this link moves with the floating side of the primary/drive pulley and the *ratio control valve* is connected to the center of this link. Movement of the stepper motor or the floating sheave will move the ratio control valve to produce a ratio change. ● **SEE FIGURE 23–7.**
TCM outputs include the following:

- Stepper motor that operates the ratio control valve which controls the ratio changes commanded by the TCM.
- **Line pressure solenoid (LPS),** which controls the line pressure to the transmission hydraulic system.
- *Secondary pressure solenoid (SPS),* which controls the pressure to the secondary pulley system.
- TCC lockup solenoid, which controls the torque converter clutch operation.

The TCM controls the drive ratio to match vehicle needs. It can adjust the ratio during vehicle cruise to produce the

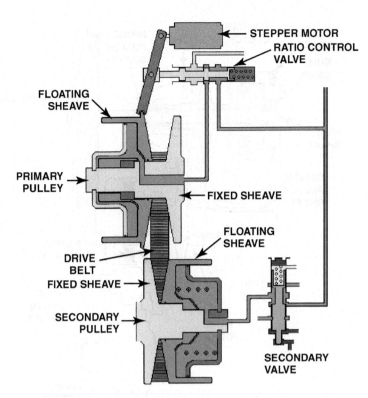

FIGURE 23–8 Movement of either the stepper motor or primary floating sheave will move the ratio control valve to add or remove fluid from the primary pulley. The secondary valve maintains the necessary pulley pressure on the drive belt.

maximum fuel economy, lowest emissions, or maximum pulling power. ● **SEE FIGURE 23–8.**

The TCM also controls fluid pressure to the secondary/driven pulley and torque converter as well as TCC lockup. Some vehicles use predetermined stepper motor position to mimic upshifts and downshifts.

CVT OPERATION

STARTING With no fluid pressure, the secondary pulley spring forces the floating side to a narrow, high-belt position, which in turn moves the primary pulley to a wide, low-belt position. This produces an underdrive that is always used as the vehicle starts moving. Continued fluid flow to the primary piston will change the ratio from an underdrive/reduction through 1:1 to an overdrive.

REVERSE A planetary gear set is needed for reverse-direction operation, and this is a simple planetary with a carrier that can be held by the reverse clutch. The input shaft drives the ring/internal gear, and the sun gear drives the shaft to the primary pulley.

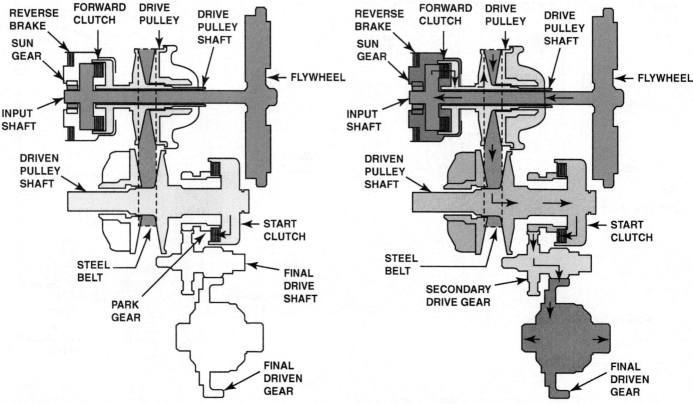

FIGURE 23–9 Honda CVT power flow in park (P) and neutral (N).

FIGURE 23–10 Honda CVT operation in drive (D) or low (L).

FORWARD OPERATION A forward clutch is mounted on the input shaft from the torque converter; it is mounted inside a clutch drum that also contains the planetary ring gear. When it applies, the forward clutch drives the planetary sun gear so both the sun and ring gears are driven. This locks the gear set to produce a 1:1 ratio.

CVT TORQUE CONVERTER

Most CVT transmissions use a low-profile elliptical torque converter with a lockup clutch. Since CVTs are infinitely variable, the torque converter is not needed once the vehicle is moving. Therefore, the converter is used to multiply the torque to get the vehicle moving from a stop, and then becomes a mechanical connection between the engine and the CVT. The torque converter clutch apply will occur at about 12 MPH (20 km/h) and stay locked until the vehicle comes to a stop. Some small vehicles with CVTs do not use a torque converter. The forward and reverse clutches are released for stops and one will be applied to start the vehicle moving.

HONDA CVT

OPERATION The Honda CVT is also used as part of the hybrid system on some Honda vehicles. There are three multiple-disc clutches used in the internal gear train, one for each of the following:

- Forward clutch
- Reverse brake
- Start clutch

In the Honda Civic CVT, a start clutch, which slips when the vehicle is stopped with the engine running, is used instead of a torque converter. ● **SEE FIGURE 23–9.**

In park (P) or neutral (N), none of the clutches have hydraulic pressure applied to them, which prevents engine torque from being applied to the drive pulley shaft. The forward clutch and the start clutch are in operation whenever the transmission is placed in a forward gear position (D or L). ● **SEE FIGURE 23–10.**

For the reverse function, a planetary gear set is used in conjunction with the reverse brake. When the reverse brake is applied, the planet carrier is held and the sun gear (splined to

FIGURE 23–11 Location of the Honda CVT start clutch.

the input shaft) causes the ring gear to turn backward. The ring gear is attached to the drive pulley through the forward clutch drum, so the drive pulley also turns backward. This torque is sent through the start clutch and the vehicle moves in reverse.

START CLUTCH The start clutch has multiple responsibilities, including the following:

1. The start clutch is engaged whenever the vehicle is moving, in either forward or reverse.

2. It helps the vehicle accelerate from a standstill by slipping and then fully engaging once the vehicle is moving, similar to a manually operated clutch. ● **SEE FIGURE 23–11.**

The Honda CVT, like any other automatic transmission, uses hydraulic pressure to perform its various functions. The belt drive, the multiple-disc clutches, and the control system will all stop functioning without hydraulic pressure. This pressure is supplied by a chain-driven pump that is driven by the transmission input shaft.

NOTE: Some vehicles equipped with a continuously variable transmission (CVT) have shifter paddles on the steering wheel or a manual shift mode on the gear selector. When using these paddles to upshift or downshift, the transmission control module selects preprogrammed ratios, which give the driver a sense that it is actively shifting gears.

CHEVROLET SPARK CVT

The JATCO CVT transmission is a continuous variable transmission with a pair of variable pulleys, a steel belt, and a shifting ratio (two-speed) planetary gear set. The key to CVT

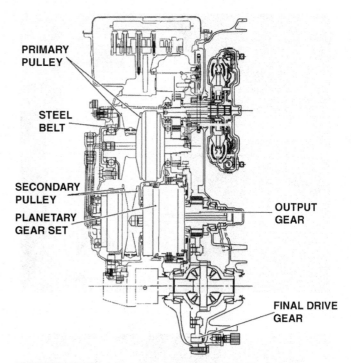

FIGURE 23–12 A drawing of the JATCO CVT transaxle, showing the two-speed planetary gear set (auxiliary gear box) on the output drive gear. (Courtesy of General Motors)

operation is the steel belt running in two pulleys, each with a variable diameter. Each pulley consists of one fixed sheave and one moving sheave. ● **SEE FIGURE 23–12.**

Oil pressure applied to the primary and secondary pulleys determines how far apart or how close together the sheaves are. This causes the groove width of the pulley to become wider or narrower. When the sheaves are further apart, the belt rides deep within the sheaves, and when the sheaves are closer together, the belt rides higher. The sheaves in the two pulleys move opposite to each other. As one set moves closer, the other moves further apart. Because the length of the belt never changes, the belt moves inward on one pulley and outward on the other. This determines both ratio and torque capacity.

The groove width changes continuously from low status to overdrive status according to the operating conditions. Input signals of engine load, engine RPM, and vehicle speed change the operation pressures of the primary pulley and the secondary pulley, which controls the pulley groove width. Along with the change of the pulley groove width, the belt contact radius is changed. This allows continuous and stepless gear shifting from low to overdrive.

The gear ratio of the Spark CVT is expanded with the use of an auxiliary gearbox, which is a planetary gear set attached to the output pulley. The two forward gear ratios are 1.821:1 and 1.000:1 and the reverse gear ratio is 1.714:1. ● **SEE FIGURE 23–13.**

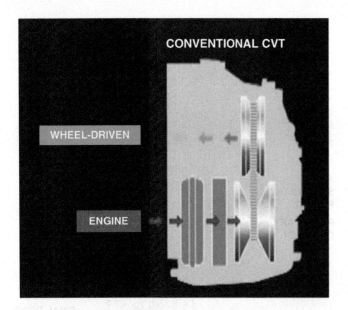

CONVENTIONAL CVT

WHEEL-DRIVEN

ENGINE

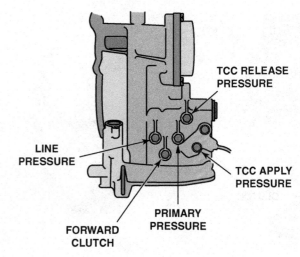

TCC RELEASE
PRESSURE

LINE
PRESSURE

TCC APPLY
PRESSURE

PRIMARY
PRESSURE

FORWARD
CLUTCH

FIGURE 23–14 The pressure tap locations that may be found on a CVT transaxle.

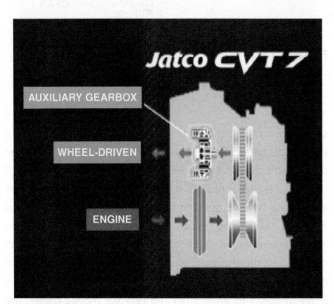

Jatco CVT 7

AUXILIARY GEARBOX

WHEEL-DRIVEN

ENGINE

FIGURE 23–13 The auxiliary gearbox allows for smaller pulleys and a wider range of gear ratios. (Courtesy of General Motors)

The CVT is controlled by a dedicated transmission controller. Some of the inputs to the controller are carried on the CAN bus (engine RPM, torque, pedal, ABS, etc.). Sensors on the transmission include primary, secondary, and output speeds, line pressure, transmission oil temperature, and inhibitor switch. Outputs include pressure control and engine torque request via CAN.

PRESSURE TESTING A CVT

TYPICAL PRESSURES Measuring the CVT oil pressures is similar to performing pressure testing on conventional automatic transmissions/transaxles. Always check service

FIGURE 23–15 Using the exact fluid recommended by the vehicle manufacturer is the preferred choice when servicing a CVT transaxles. (Courtesy of General Motors)

information for the exact procedures to follow and the location of the pressure tap. ● **SEE FIGURE 23–14.**

Typical pressures include the following:

- Mainline pressure 70 to 900 PSI (485 to 6,200 kPa))
- Primary pressure 15 to 900 PSI (100 to 6,200 kPa))
- Secondary pressure 15 to 900 PSI (100 to 6,200 kPa)

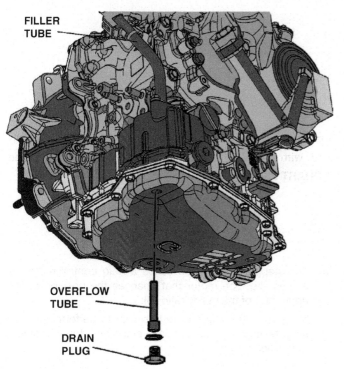

FILLER TUBE

OVERFLOW TUBE

DRAIN PLUG

FIGURE 23–16 This transmission uses an overflow tube to indicate proper fluid level. There is no dipstick. (Courtesy of General Motors)

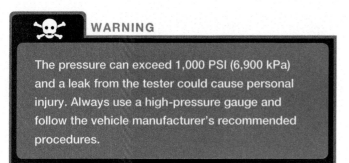

WARNING

The pressure can exceed 1,000 PSI (6,900 kPa) and a leak from the tester could cause personal injury. Always use a high-pressure gauge and follow the vehicle manufacturer's recommended procedures.

CVT FLUID

CHECKING CVT FLUID LEVEL A dipstick is used to check the level in some units, and fluid may be poured into the dipstick pipe to bring the level up if it is low. CVT fluid is usually green to help distinguish it from conventional ATF.

CAUTION: Wipe off the dipstick before removing it to prevent any dirt from falling into the fill tube when checking the level of the fluid. Any dirt in the fluid can cause severe damage to the CVT transaxles.

REPLACING CVT FLUID When replacing the CVT fluid, make sure that the specified CVT fluid is used. There is often a drain plug on the transmission pan, and a filler hole located on

DIAGNOSTIC TROUBLE CODE (DTC)	DESCRIPTION
P0219	Engine speed excessive—check for speed sensor or transmission slip codes
P0571	Brake switch fault detected
P0707; P0708	TCM detects improper signal from transmission range switch (P0707—signal low; P0708—signal high)
P0711; P0712; P0713	Transmission temperature sensor (TSS) fault detected (P0711—circuit performance; P0711—signal low; P0713—signal high)
P0716; P0717	Transmission input speed sensor (ISS) fault detected (P0716—circuit performance; P0717—no signal).
P0721; P0722	Transmission output speed sensor (OSS) fault detected (P0721—circuit performance; P0722—no signal).
P0730	Incorrect gear ratio detected (transmission slip)
P0746	Line pressure sensor performance issue detected
P0776; P0777	Secondary pressure sensor (SPS) fault detected (P0776—performance fault; P0777—stuck on).
P0842; P0843	Primary oil pressure (POP) sensor fault detected (P0842—sensor circuit low; P0843—sensor circuit high).
P0847; P0848	Secondary oil pressure (SOP) sensor fault detected (P0847—sensor circuit low; P0848—sensor circuit high).

CHART 23–2

Typical continuously variable transmission (CVT) diagnostic trouble codes (DTCs) and code description. Transmission-related DTCs are usually P07XX or P08XX, where XX represents the specific fault code.

the transmission case. When refilling the CVT, be sure to check the level regularly to make sure it is not being overfilled. Both the drain and filler plugs should have their gaskets replaced before installing them in their respective holes. Be certain to observe torque specifications when tightening these plugs to prevent damage to the threads in the transmission case and oil pan.

OVERFLOW TUBE Some CVT transmissions use an overflow tube as a level-check device. On these transmissions, a short tube is threaded into the pan from the bottom and the drain plug covers the lower-end of the tube. ● **SEE FIGURE 23–16**. If a few drops of fluid comes out when the drain plug is removed, it indicates the fluid level is correct, right at the level of the top of the overflow tube.

- **To check the fluid level.** Bring the transmission to the proper temperature and remove ONLY the drain plug. If no fluid comes out it is underfilled. If fluid drains out it is overfilled.

- **To drain the fluid.** Remove the drain plug and then remove the overflow tube. This will drain the fluid.

CVT-RELATED DIAGNOSTIC TROUBLE CODES

For some of the diagnostic trouble codes (DTCs) associated with a CVT transmission and the description, see ● **CHART 23–2.**

SUMMARY

1. A continuously variable transmission (CVT) varies the gear ratio in a continuous manner instead of in a series of steps or fixed gear ratios.
2. A pair of hydraulically controlled variable-size pulleys is used with a steel-link drive belt or chain.
3. Two different styles of fixed-length steel belts are used. A push belt or a pull chain is used.
4. The transmission control module (TCM) of a CVT uses direct and indirect inputs to monitor transmission and engine operation.
5. The stepper motor, also called a ratio control motor, is a linear position motor that changes the position of the upper end of the pulley ratio link.
6. Measuring the oil pressure is similar to performing pressure testing on conventional automatic transmissions/transaxles.

REVIEW QUESTIONS

1. What is the advantage of a CVT compared to a regular six-speed transmission?
2. What are the types of belts used in a CVT?
3. What controls the movement of the variator?
4. What is the purpose and function of the ratio control motor?

CHAPTER QUIZ

1. How is a variable ratio achieved in a CVT?
   a. By using multiple gears
   b. By using a steel belt with two variable-width pulleys
   c. By using a start clutch assembly
   d. By using a variable-torque converter
2. What is meant by "rubber band effect"?
   a. A CVT uses a large rubber band
   b. A rubber band is used to apply the clutches inside a CVT
   c. The vehicle speed slowly catches up to the engine speed
   d. Just a slang term for the variator pulleys
3. What is the difference between a push belt and a pull chain?
   a. A push belt is made up of about 400 wedge-shaped segments
   b. A pull chain is made up of links and link pins
   c. A pull chain looks similar to a silent chain
   d. All of the above

4. Which is NOT an advantage of a CVT?
   a. Larger in size
   b. Lighter weight
   c. Lower internal power loss
   d. Efficient fuel use
5. Which statement is *false*?
   a. The primary/drive pulley is attached to the input shaft
   b. Both sheaves are fixed so they cannot move
   c. The movable face for each pulley is attached to a piston that has hydraulic control pressure applied to it
   d. The primary pulley is adjusted to control the gear ratio, and the secondary pulley is adjusted to maintain tension on the belt
6. Which of these is a *direct input* to the TCM?
   a. Accelerator pedal position
   b. Primary pressure sensor (PPS)
   c. Vehicle speed
   d. Brake switch

7. TCM outputs include_____.
   a. Stepper motor that operates the ratio control valve
   b. Line pressure solenoid (LPS)
   c. Secondary pressure solenoid (SPS)
   d. All of the above

8. Mainline pressure on a CVT can exceed_____.
   a. 500 PSI (3,450 kPa)
   b. 750 PSI (5,200 kPa)
   c. 900 PSI (6,200 kPa)
   d. 2,000 PSI (13,800 kPa)

9. The recommended fluid to use in a CVT is usually _____.
   a. Dexron VI ATF
   b. Specific CVT fluid
   c. Mercon V or Dexron VI
   d. Any of the above depending on the specific unit

10. Which diagnostic trouble code is associated with secondary pressure sensor (SPS)?
    a. P0776   c. P0440
    b. P0300   d. P0172

DUAL CLUTCH AUTOMATIC TRANSMISSIONS/ TRANSAXLES

LEARNING OBJECTIVES

After studying this chapter, the reader will be able to:

1. Discuss the parts and operation of a dual clutch transmission/transaxle.
2. Explain the construction of a GETRAG DCT 450 transaxle.
3. Describe the diagnostic and service procedures for a dual clutch transmission/transaxle system.

This chapter will help you prepare for ASE Automatic Transmission/Transaxle (A2) certification test content area "A" (General Transmission/Transaxle Diagnosis).

KEY TERMS

- Automated manual transmission (AMT) 399
- Clutch cooling flow solenoid (CCFS) 403
- Clutch pressure cut (CPCUT) 403
- Clutch shift pressure solenoid 403
- Concentric clutch 400
- Direct shift gearbox (DSG) 399
- Line pressure solenoid (LPS) 403
- Parallel clutch 400
- Porsche Doppelkupplung (PDK) 399
- Shift cooling multiplex solenoid (SHCMS) 403
- Twin clutch transmission 399

 ## STC OBJECTIVES

GM Service Technical College topic covered in this chapter is as follows:

1. Operational characteristics of dual clutch transmissions/transaxles that may be encountered at GM service facilities.

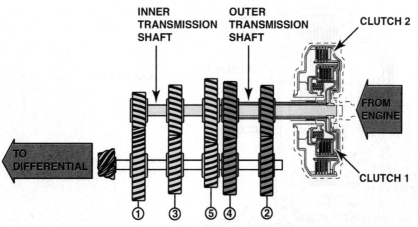

FIGURE 24-1 A dual clutch automatic uses the best features of an automatic transmission without the power loss of a torque converter.

PURPOSE AND FUNCTION

A dual clutch automatic transmission or transaxle uses a manual-type transmission and two clutches that engage either the inner or outer transmission input shaft. This type of transmission is designed to achieve the following goals, compared to a conventional automatic transmission or transaxle equipped with a torque converter and planetary gear sets.

1. Improve fuel economy.
2. Reduce the cost of assembly by using manual transmission components.
3. Improve the speed of gear changes.
4. Provide smoother operation.

TERMINOLOGY A dual clutch automatic transmission/transaxle can also be referred to as the following:

- **Direct shift gearbox (DSG).** Most commonly used by the VW/Audi Group (VAG) of vehicles.
- **Porsche Doppelkupplung (PDK).** The Porsche term used to describe their dual clutch automatic.
- **Automated manual transmission (AMT).** Original term no longer commonly used. May refer to a single clutch five-speed transaxle (smart car).
- **Twin clutch transmission.** Another variation of the term used for a dual clutch automatic transmission.

PARTS AND OPERATION

A dual clutch automatic transmission/transaxle uses two clutches that are mounted together. One clutch drives the odd number gears (first, third, fifth, and seventh). The other clutch

FIGURE 24-2 Dual clutch automatic transaxles that use two dry clutches. The larger clutch drives the odd number gear ratios (first, third, and fifth) and the smaller clutch drives the even numbered gear ratios (second, fourth, and sixth).

drives the even number gears (second, fourth, and sixth).
● **SEE FIGURE 24-1.**

The shifts occur without interrupting the torque from the engine by applying torque to the clutch while at the same time disconnecting the other clutch. These actions result in a rapid shift without the slight delay usually associated with an automatic transmission.

There are two types of clutches used depending on application.

1. Dual dry clutches are used in low powered vehicles such as small front-wheel-drive vehicles. ● **SEE FIGURE 24-2.**
2. Dual wet clutches are often used in higher powered vehicles.

Vehicles that use a dual clutch automatic-type transmission/transaxle include certain models of Audi, Nissan, Mercedes, BMW, Porsche, Ford, Ferrari, VW, and Mitsubishi.

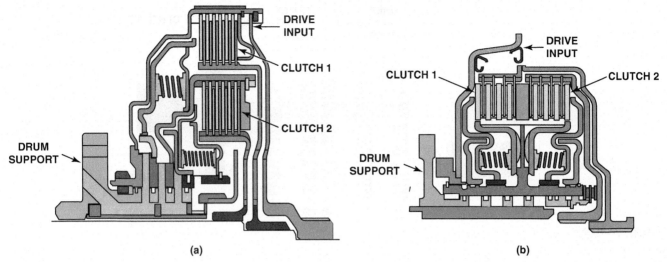

FIGURE 24–3 (a) A concentric (nested) clutch design, the assembly is shorter in length but taller in height. (b) A parallel clutch design is longer but has a smaller diameter drum assembly.

ADVANTAGES The advantages of a dual clutch automatic transmission/transaxle compared to a conventional automatic transmission include the following:

1. Quicker throttle response
2. No drop in engine speed when the driver releases the throttle
3. Instant gear changes
4. Improved fuel economy

DISADVANTAGES The disadvantages of a dual clutch automatic transmission/transaxle compared to conventional or continuously variable automatic transmissions include the following:

1. No torque multiplication advantage of a torque converter
2. Not as fuel efficient as a continuously variable transmission (CVT) or transaxle

DUAL CLUTCH TRANSAXLE

TERMINOLOGY A dual clutch transaxle is essentially two transmissions built into one case. Each portion is driven by one of the clutches, and these clutches are applied, one at a time, to transfer power. A dual clutch transmission is essentially an automatic transmission that uses manual transmission-style gear layout and synchronizers with two countershafts. The shifts can occur vary rapidly, being controlled by how fast each clutch can be applied and with partially engaging one clutch while slipping the other during shifts.

CONCENTRIC AND PARALLEL CLUTCH DESIGNS There are two basic wet clutch designs used in dual clutch automatic transmissions.

1. A **concentric clutch** (also called a *nested-type clutch*) is a design where both plates share the same vertical plane and provides a shorter assembly.
2. A **parallel clutch** design is used in a side-by-side arrangement. ● **SEE FIGURE 24–3**.

GEAR ARRANGEMENTS The 1–3 and 5 synchronizer assemblies are driven by clutch #1 and the 2–4 and 6-reverse synchronizers are driven by clutch #2. Vehicle movement begins with the 1–3 synchronizer shifted to first gear and clutch #1 applied. The 2–4 synchronizer is then shifted into second gear by a hydraulic servo, and the 1–2 upshift will occur when clutch #1 is released and clutch #2 is applied. The remaining upshifts occur in the same manner, with the synchronizer preshifted or shifted early, and the actual shift occurring when the clutches are cycled. ● **SEE FIGURE 24–4**.

The driver can control the transmission/transaxle using a floor-mounted shift lever or one of a pair of paddles mounted on the steering wheel.

- Clutches #1 and #2 are applied by hydraulic pressure, similar to automatic transmission clutches.
- The hydraulic flow to the clutches and servos is controlled electronically by a control module.

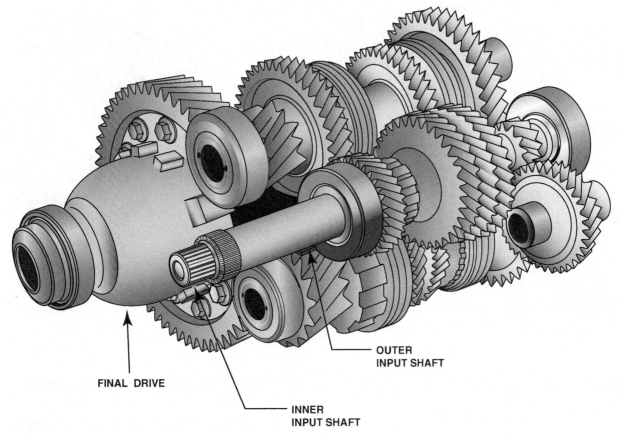

FINAL DRIVE

INNER
INPUT SHAFT

OUTER
INPUT SHAFT

FIGURE 24–4 Notice the two concentric input shafts. Each shaft is splined to a clutch.

GETRAG DCT 450

A Getrag DCT 450 transaxle is a dual clutch automatic trans-axle commonly used in a number of Ford and Volvo vehicles starting in 2008. This is a six-speed unit and uses clutch 1 for the odd-numbered gears (1, 3, 5) and clutch 2 for the even-numbered gears (2, 4, 6).

GEAR CHANGE EXAMPLE Using the DCT 450 as the example, the shift from first to second includes the following actions:

STEP 1 Clutch 1 is on and drives the inner shaft. ● **SEE FIGURE 24–5**.

STEP 2 Second gear control device is pressurized to get ready to shift to second gear.

STEP 3 Clutch 2 is starting to be filled with hydraulic pressure (both clutches work at the same time during shifting).

STEP 4 First gear torque delivery through clutch 1 is being reduced as clutch 2 in being applied and starting to transmit engine torque.

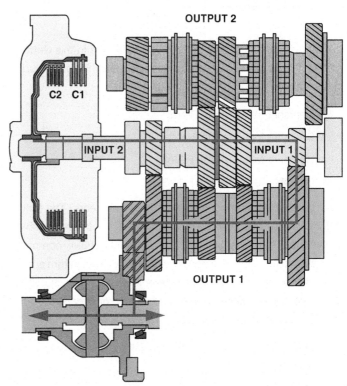

OUTPUT 2

C2 C1

INPUT 2

INPUT 1

OUTPUT 1

FIGURE 24–5 First gear engaged using clutch 1 (C1) to transmit engine torque.

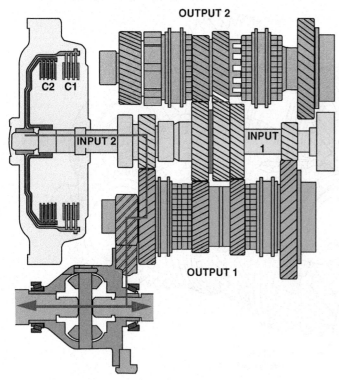

OUTPUT 2

C2 C1

INPUT 2

INPUT 1

OUTPUT 1

FIGURE 24–6 Second gear engaged using clutch 2 (C2) to transmit engine torque. Both output shafts alternately engage the final drive ring gear (refer to Figure 24–4).

STEP 5 Engine torque through clutch 1 is zero and full engine torque is being transmitted through clutch 2. ● **SEE FIGURE 24–6.**

SHIFT FORKS

There are four gearshift forks in this Getrag DCT 450 transaxle. The gear positions per gearshift fork include the following:

- Gearshift fork 1 (odd): R-N-5
- Gearshift fork 2 (odd): 3-N-1
- Gearshift fork 3 (even): 2-N-4
- Gearshift fork 4 (even): P-N-6

The gearshift forks mechanically engage the gears. The forks are moved by hydraulic pistons, which are controlled by shift solenoids. The transmission control module (TCM) operates shift solenoids. The solenoids move pistons, which in turn apply force to the shift forks through lever points to help increase the force applied. Both an even and an odd gear can be commanded at the same time in parallel.

- Fifth gear and neutral are blocked if the reverse gear is engaged
- Neutral and first gear are blocked if third gear is engaged. ● **SEE FIGURE 24–7.**

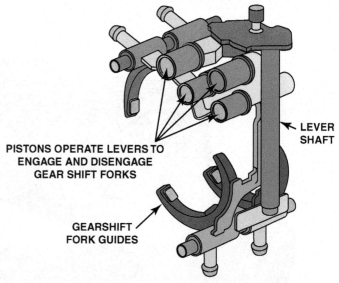

PISTONS OPERATE LEVERS TO ENGAGE AND DISENGAGE GEAR SHIFT FORKS

LEVER SHAFT

GEARSHIFT FORK GUIDES

FIGURE 24–7 The shift forks are similar to those used in a manual transmission but are moved using hydraulic pistons.

? FREQUENTLY ASKED QUESTION

How Does a Dual Clutch-Type Transmission Achieve Better Fuel Economy?

One of the advantages of a dual clutch automatic is that it is able to provide improved fuel economy over a conventional torque converter-type automatic. One strategy is to have the unit go into neutral when the vehicle is stopped by disengaging the clutches. This allows the engine to remain running but reduces the load on the engine, which improves fuel economy and reduces vibrations. The clutch is engaged when the driver releases the brake.

SPEED SENSORS

Speed sensors include the following:

- **Engine RPM sensor.** Inputs the engine RPM to the TCM from the sensor located on the clutch drum housing.
- **Speed sensor input shaft odd gears.** Gives the TCM information on input shaft RPM (after the C1 clutch) for odd gears, 1, 3, 5, and R.
- **Speed sensor input shaft even gears.** Gives the TCM information on input shaft RPM (after the C2 clutch) for even gears, 2, 4, and 6.

TEMPERATURE SENSORS

Temperature sensors include the following:

- **Clutch fluid temperature.** Used to measure the temperature of the fluid leaving the clutches.

- **Transmission fluid temperature.** Used to measure the temperature of the fluid in the transmission.
- **Oil temperature sensor.** Located on the TCM, which provides information on transmission oil temperature.

The TCM uses temperature information to determine correct system pressure, for controlling clutch, for cold starts, and for overheating protection.

PRESSURE SENSORS Pressure sensors give the TCM information on hydraulic pressure of the clutches. The TCM supplies the sensors with 5 volts. The sensors register the oil pressure to control the clutch pressure so that the TCM can control the solenoids to provide correct clutch pressure for each clutch.

POSITION SENSORS Position sensors include the following:

- *Fork position sensors*—These sensors give the TCM information on the position of the four gear shift forks that handle shifting in the transmission. Includes 1-R; 3-5; 2-4; and 6-N.
- *Transmissions Range Sensor (TRS)*—This sensor provides the actual P R N D gear selection.

The transmission electronic control module uses information from the sensors to determine the proper clutch and shift servo operation. Once the TCM determines the required gear range and driving conditions, actuators are turned on or off to control hydraulic pressure, gear selection, clutch control, and shift lock.

 FREQUENTLY ASKED QUESTION

Why Is the TCM Using the Position of the Steering Wheel?

The steering wheel position (SWP) sensor information is sent to the transmission control module (TCM) over the network to prevent the transmission from upshifting when cornering. This helps the driver by allowing the vehicle to be accelerated when exiting a corner. If the steering wheel position was not part of the shift program, the transmission might likely upshift to a higher gear as the vehicle slows then the transmission may have to downshift again when the vehicle exits the corner.

SOLENOIDS

A typical dual clutch automatic transmission/transaxle includes the following solenoids:

- **Line pressure solenoid (LPS)**—Controls system pressure in the transmission by directing the hydraulic oil to clutch, shifting, cooling flow, and then returning the oil to the oil sump.
- **Clutch cooling flow solenoid (CCFS)**—Controls hydraulic oil for cooling of clutches.
- **Shift cooling multiplex solenoid (SHCMS)**—Controls position of gearshift forks as well as cooling of clutch.
- **Clutch shift multiplex solenoid (CSMS1)**—Leads the pressure between odd clutch and shifting, activates odd gears, as well as controls cooling flow for clutches.
- **Clutch shift multiplex solenoid (CSMS2)**—Leads the pressure between even clutch and shifting, controls cooling flow for clutches, and can turn off the valve for dumping clutch pressure.
- **Clutch shift pressure solenoid (CSPS1)**—Controls hydraulic pressure for odd clutch or shifting.
- **Clutch shift pressure solenoid (CSPS2)**—Controls hydraulic pressure for even clutch or shifting.
- **Clutch pressure cut (CPCUT)**—Safety valve that controls pressure dumping in the hydraulic system.
- **Shift select solenoid (SHSS1)**—Controls shifting for gearshift fork 1 and 3.
- **Shift select solenoid (SHSS2)**—Controls shifting for gearshift fork 2 and 4.

SHIFT FORK POSITION The transmission control module (TCM) operates shift solenoids. These pistons apply force to the shift forks through lever points to help increase the force applied. Both an even and an odd gear can be commanded at the same time in parallel. Position sensors are located inside the case and this information is used by the TCM to determine the actual position of each shift fork. ● **SEE FIGURE 24–8.**

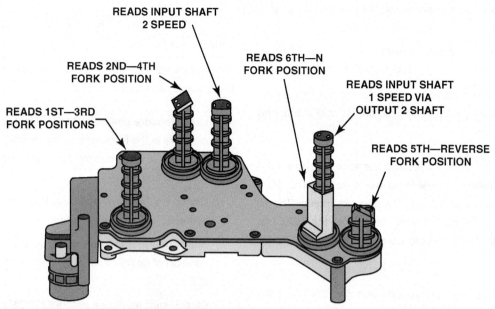

FIGURE 24–8 Fork position and shaft speed sensors are used as inputs to the TCM.

READS INPUT SHAFT
2 SPEED

READS 2ND—4TH
FORK POSITION

READS 6TH—N
FORK POSITION

READS INPUT SHAFT
1 SPEED VIA
OUTPUT 2 SHAFT

READS 1ST—3RD
FORK POSITIONS

READS 5TH—REVERSE
FORK POSITION

DIAGNOSIS AND SERVICE

DIAGNOSTIC PROCEDURES To diagnose faults with dual clutch automatic transmission/transaxle system, follow the recommended procedures found in service information. The usual procedure involves the following steps:

STEP 1 Verify the customer concern (complaint). This step includes trying to duplicate what the customer or driver is concerned about.

STEP 2 Perform a thorough visual inspection, including:

- Checking the level and condition of the fluid
- Checking the drivetrain mounts for damage or faults

STEP 3 Check service information for the specified procedure to follow. Most vehicles require the use of a factory-brand scan tool. ● **SEE FIGURE 24–9**.

STEP 4 Follow the troubleshooting procedure as specified to fix the root cause of the problem. This means following the instructions displayed on the scan tool or service information.

STEP 5 Repair the fault.

STEP 6 Road test the vehicle under the same conditions that were performed to verify the fault to ensure that the repair is completed.

FIGURE 24–9 The use of a factory or a factory-level after-market scan tool is often needed to diagnose the dual clutch transmission system.

TYPICAL DIAGNOSTIC TROUBLE CODES As part of any diagnostics, checking for diagnostic trouble codes is one of the first steps. ● **SEE CHART 24–1** for some examples of dual clutch automatic transmission-related DTCs.

FLUID AND FILTER SERVICE The transmission fluid is usually high-quality synthetic oil which is unique for this type of

P0715	Input shaft 1 (odd number gear axle) speed sensor system (output high range out)
P0716	Input shaft 1 (odd number gear axle) speed sensor system (poor performance)
P0717	Input shaft 1 (odd number gear axle) speed sensor system (output low range out)
P0746	Line pressure solenoid system (drive current range out)
P0753	Shift select solenoid 1 system (open circuit)
P0758	Shift select solenoid 2 system (open circuit)
P0776	Clutch cooling flow solenoid system (drive current range out)
P0842	Clutch 1 pressure sensor system (output low range out)
P0960	Line pressure solenoid system (open circuit)

CHART 24–1

Selected dual clutch transmission-related diagnostic trouble codes.

transmission. Dual clutch transmission fluid is usually green to help identify it as a unique fluid and to help prevent someone from using conventional automatic transmission fluid. Always use the specified fluid.

For example, the Ford Dry Dual Clutch Fluid is specifically formulated for use in the DPS6 power shift twin dry clutch transmission. This fluid is manufactured with synthetic base oils and performance additives, providing improved shifting at all ambient temperatures. This fluid is used only in transmissions requiring a fluid meeting WSS-M2C200-D2.

Most dual clutch automatic transmissions/transaxles use an external filter that is serviceable and an internal filter that is a nonserviceable part unless the unit is totally disassembled. Always follow the vehicle manufacturer's recommended fluid and filter service intervals.

SUMMARY

1. A dual clutch automatic transmission or transaxle uses a manual-type transmission and two clutches that engage either the inner or outer transmission shaft.

2. A dual clutch automatic transmission can also be referred to as direct shift gearbox (DSG), Porsche Doppelkupplung (PDK), automated manual transmission (AMT), or a twin clutch transmission.

3. A dual dry clutch system is mostly used for lower-powered front wheel drive vehicles, whereas dual wet clutches are used for most high-powered front and rear wheel drive vehicles.

4. There are two basic wet clutch designs used in dual clutch automatic transmissions.

  - A concentric clutch (also called a nested-type clutch) is a design where both plates share the same vertical plane and provides a shorter assembly.
  - A parallel clutch design is used in a side-by-side arrangement.

5. Speed sensors are used to measure the speed of the odd gear shaft and the even gear shaft.

6. Position sensors are used to detect the positions of the shift forks.

7. Solenoids are used to make the actual shifts by moving the shift forks.

8. Dual clutch automatic transmissions use a unique fluid.

REVIEW QUESTIONS

1. What are the benefits of using a dual clutch automatic transmission compared to a conventional automatic transmission?

2. What are the disadvantages of a dual clutch automatic transmission?

3. What type of vehicles use two dry clutches?

4. What are the two designs of wet clutches?

5. How is a shift made from first to second on a dual clutch automatic transmission?

6. What sensors are used in a typical dual clutch automatic transaxle?

1. All of the following are advantages of a dual clutch automatic transmission/transaxle *except.*
   a. Instant gear changes
   b. No torque multiplication advantage of a torque converter
   c. Quicker throttle response
   d. Improved fuel economy

2. A dual clutch automatic transmission/transaxle may be called _____.
   a. Direct shift gearbox (DSG)
   b. Porsche Doppelkupplung (PDK)
   c. Automated manual transmission (AMT)
   d. Any of the above

3. A dual dry clutch system is used in what type of vehicle?
   a. Small front-wheel drive
   b. Heavy rear-wheel drive
   c. All-wheel drive trucks and SUVs
   d. High power front-wheel drive

4. A concentric clutch is _____.
   a. A type of wet clutch
   b. A type of dry clutch
   c. Also called a nested-type clutch
   d. Both a and c

5. How does a dual clutch transmission/transaxle achieve better fuel economy compared to a conventional automatic transmission?
   a. By using a high capacity torque converter
   b. By engaging neutral when the vehicle is stopped
   c. By skipping gears
   d. By slipping the clutches to achieve smoother operation

6. In a Getrag DCT 450 transaxle what does gear shift fork 2 control?
   a. R-N-5   c. 2-N-4
   b. 3-N-1   d. P-N-6

7. Why is the steering wheel position sensor used as an input to the TCM?
   a. Used to help determine when to shift when driving straight
   b. Used to help control line pressure based on steering wheel angle
   c. Used to prevent an upshift if the vehicle is turning
   d. Used as a diagnostic input to help retrieve DTCs

8. The fluid used in dual clutch automatic transmissions and transaxles is usually _____.
   a. Dexron VI
   b. Special synthetic fluid often green in color
   c. Mercon V
   d. Any of the above depending on make, model, and year

9. What is the purpose of the clutch shift multiplex solenoid (CSMS2)?
   a. Leads the pressure between even clutch and shifting, controls cooling flow for clutches, and can turn off the valve for dumping clutch pressure
   b. Controls hydraulic pressure for odd clutch or shifting
   c. Safety valve that controls pressure dumping in the hydraulic system
   d. Controls shifting for gearshift fork 2 and 4

10. A P0753 diagnostic trouble code (DTC) means that the TCM has detected a fault with _____.
   a. Input shaft 1 (odd number gear axle) speed sensor system
   b. Line pressure solenoid system (open circuit)
   c. Shift select solenoid 1 system (open circuit)
   d. Input shaft 1 (odd number gear axle) speed sensor system (output high range out)

chapter 25

TRANSMISSION CONDITION DIAGNOSIS

LEARNING OBJECTIVES

After studying this chapter, the reader will be able to:

1. Outline the procedures involved in the first step of the automatic transmission diagnostic process—verifying customer concern.

2. Outline the procedures involved in the second step of the automatic transmission diagnostic process—fluid level and condition.

3. Outline the procedures involved in the third and fourth steps of the automatic transmission diagnostic process—retrieving diagnostic trouble codes and checking for technical service bulletins.

4. Outline the procedures involved in the fifth step of the automatic transmission diagnostic process—scan tool testing.

5. Outline the procedures involved in the sixth step of the automatic transmission diagnostic process—visual inspections.

6. Outline the procedures involved in the seventh step of the automatic transmission diagnostic process—finding the root cause.

This chapter will help you prepare for ASE Automatic Transmission/Transaxle (A2) certification test content area "A" (General Transmission/Transaxle Diagnosis).

KEY TERMS

Clutch volume index (CVI) 418
Powertrain control module (PCM) 413
Recalibration 415
Transmission control module (TCM) 413

GM STC OBJECTIVES

GM Service Technical College topics covered in this chapter are as follows:

1. View and clear stored DTC information from the GM Scan Tool.

2. Perform a special function test using the GM Scan Tool.

3. Describe the proper procedure to verify a customer's concern.

4. Demonstrate the ability to perform preliminary inspections related to the customer concern.

5. Demonstrate how to perform a Diagnostic System Check—Vehicle.

6. Describe the proper road test procedure including all of the steps involved.

7. Diagnose unusual fluid usage, level, and condition concerns to determine necessary repairs.

8. Diagnose hydraulic apply and control components prior to disassembly.

9. Diagnose NVH to determine the suspect components for repair prior to disassembly.

THE DIAGNOSTIC PROCESS

STEPS INVOLVED When diagnosing automatic transmission concerns, perform the following steps:

STEP 1 The first step is to verify the customer complaint. This step usually includes performing a road test to see if the complaint can be duplicated. If the problem cannot be duplicated, then the repair cannot be verified.

STEP 2 Check the fluid level and condition.

STEP 3 Check for stored diagnostic trouble codes (DTCs).

STEP 4 Check for any related technical service bulletins (TSBs).

STEP 5 Check scan tool data including checking the adaptive values.

STEP 6 Visual inspections, including the following:

- Check for obvious faults such as damaged or worn driveshafts or U-joints
- Check for evidence of recent transmission or drivetrain service work
- Check the body and frame for evidence of a collision or recent collision repairs
- Check for leaks

STEP 7 Locate the root cause of the problem. This step involves performing more detailed tests such as pressure testing.

STEP 8 Replace all components that do not meet factory specifications.

STEP 9 Perform an adaptive relearn and drive the vehicle to verify that the repairs corrected the customer concern.

NOTE: Steps 8 and 9 are discussed in Chapter 17 after the transmission/transaxle has been repaired or rebuilt and reinstalled in the vehicle.

STEP 1—VERFIY THE CUSTOMER CONCERN

ROAD TEST A road test is used to verify the customer's concern and check the general overall condition of the transmission. The vehicle should be road tested at the start of the diagnosis and after the repair. The first road test helps the technician understand the customer's concern as well as

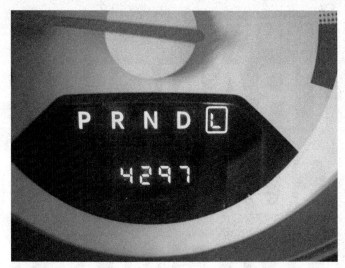

FIGURE 25–1 Selecting all of the shift modes of an automatic transmission/transaxle helps pinpoint the area where the fault is located.

the nature of the problem. The road test after repairs have been completed confirms that the repairs were successful. A road test may involve simply driving the vehicle and mentally reviewing the transmission operation.

ITEMS TO CHECK The following points are normally checked during a road test:

- Quality of the garage shifts (neutral–drive and neutral–reverse) ● **SEE FIGURE 25–1.**
- Engagement time for the garage shifts
- Quality of each upshift and downshift at various loads
- Timing of each upshift and downshift at various loads
- Any hunting between gear ranges
- Operation of the torque converter and torque converter clutch (TCC)
- Slipping in any gear range
- Binding or tie-up in any gear range
- Noise or vibration in any gear range
- Engine (compression) braking during deceleration in drive and manual gear ranges
- Speedometer operation (shows output from the vehicle speed [VS] sensor)
- Proper engine operation

There are many shift quality and timing problems that can occur. The common terms used to describe abnormal shifts are described in ● **CHART 25–1.**

TERM	MEANING
Binding	A very noticeable drag that causes the engine to slow down and labor.
Bump	A sudden, harsh application of a clutch or band.
Chuggle	A bucking or jerking condition, similar to the sensation of clutch chatter or acceleration in too high of a gear with a standard transmission (could be engine related).
Delayed or late shift	The shift occurs some time after normally expected.
Double bump	Two sudden, harsh applications of a clutch or band, also called "double feel."
Dropout	An unexpected shift to neutral or a lower gear, also called "fallout."
Early	The operation occurs before normally expected. An early shift results in a laboring engine, poor acceleration, and sometimes a chuggle.
End bump	A shift feel that becomes noticeably firmer as it is completed, also called "end feel" or "slip bump."
Firm shift	A quick, easily felt shift that is not harsh or rough.
Flare	A rapid increase in engine speed, usually caused by slippage.
Harsh or rough shift	An unpleasantly firm band or clutch application.
Hunting	A repeated up-and-then-down shifting sequence that produces noticeable repeated engine RPM changes.
Shudder	A more severe form of chuggle.
Slipping	A noticeable loss of power transfer that results in an increase in engine RPM.
Soft shift	A very slow shift that is barely noticeable.
Stacked shifts	An upshift that occurs immediately after a prior upshift.

CHART 25–1

Typical automatic transmission/transaxle fault descriptions and their meaning.

THROTTLE POSITION VERSUS SHIFT POINTS The technician operates the vehicle at various throttle positions during the road test. Light-, medium-, full-throttle, and through detent or wide-open throttle (WOT) upshifts are made to check shift quality and timing under each of these conditions. The vehicle is also operated under different closed-throttle conditions. The various throttle positions used are defined as follows:

- Minimum—the least throttle opening that produces acceleration
- Light—when the throttle is about one-fourth open
- Medium—when the throttle is about one-half open
- Heavy—when the throttle is about three-fourths open
- Wide-open throttle (WOT)—fully opened throttle without forcing a downshift
- Closed—a complete release of the throttle, which results in coasting
- Engine braking—a closed-throttle manual downshift to produce a condition where engine compression slows the vehicle

Manufacturers publish shift points. These are the vehicle speeds at which upshifts and downshifts should occur relative to the different throttle openings. To check the shift points, accelerate the vehicle using different throttle openings, and watch the tachometer or listen for the engine speed change that indicates a shift. Have an assistant record the speed for comparison with the specifications. If no specifications are available, the approximate shift points are shown in **CHART 25–2**.

STEP 2—FLUID LEVEL AND CONDITION

The driver of a vehicle should periodically check the fluid level in an automatic transmission. A good time to check this is at every engine oil change. If the level is low, fluid of the correct type should be added. It usually takes 1 pint (0.5L) to move the fluid level from low to the full mark on the dipstick.

Most transmission dipsticks are marked for both cold and *hot fluid* temperatures. **SEE FIGURE 25–2**.

The most obvious markings are for the hot level, which is the normal operating temperature, about 150°F to 170°F (66°C to 77°C). Room temperature of about 65°F to 85°F (18°C

MINIMUM THROTTLE	SPEED MPH (km/h)	PART THROTTLE	SPEED MPH (km/h)	WOT	SPEED MPH (km/h)
1–2	5–10 (8–16)	1–2	15–30 (24–48)	1–2	35–45 (56–72)
2–3	15–25 (24–40)	2–3	25–45 (40–72)	2–3	55–65 (89–105)
3–4	30–45 (48–72)	3–4	40–55 (64–90)	3–4	Above 60/100
4–3	30–40 (48–64)	4–3	35–45 (56–72)	4–3	Above 60/100
3–2	10–15 (16–24)	3–2	30–40 (48–64)	3–2	55–65 (89–105)
3–1	5–10 (8–16)	2–1	10–20 (16–32)	2–1	25–40 (40–64)

CHART 25–2

Typical shift points for a four-speed automatic transmission/transaxle. Always observe all speed limits and traffic regulations during a road test.

FIGURE 25–2 A typical automatic transmission dipstick (fluid level indicator). Many use a clip to keep it from being forced upward due to pressure changes inside the automatic transmission. A firm seal also helps keep water from getting into the fluid, which can cause severe damage to the clutches and bands.

to 29°C) is considered cold for transmission fluid. If the fluid at the end of the dipstick is too hot to hold, then the fluid is hot. When the fluid is cold, use the cold markings on the dipstick. Some transaxles use a thermostatic valve to raise the fluid level in the upper valve body pan as the transaxle warms up. These units have a lower hot level and a higher cold level. The exact procedure for checking the fluid level can be found in the vehicle owner's manual, or occasionally it is printed on the dipstick.

OVERFILLED OR UNDERFILLED
It is never a good idea to operate a transmission with the fluid level too high (an *overfill* condition) or too low (an *underfill* condition).

- An underfill is below the low, cold level on the dipstick and it is sometimes marked "Do not drive." An underfill

condition can allow air to enter the filter and pump intake, which can cause mushy operation. It may go into neutral, may slip, or the torque converter clutch (TCC) may fail to lock and unlock properly.

- Overfilling can cause slippage and mushy operation because of the air in the foamy fluid. An overfill condition can bring the fluid level up to the point where it contacts the spinning gear sets. This in turn causes foaming of the fluid and fluid may flow out through the vent or filler pipe. There have been cases of vehicle fires caused by the fluid spilling out of the filler pipe and onto a hot exhaust manifold.

CHECKING FLUID LEVEL WITH A DIPSTICK
To check transmission fluid with a dipstick, check the procedure stamped on the dipstick. The usual procedure includes the following steps:

STEP 1 Park the vehicle on a level surface, apply the parking brake securely, and place the gear selector in park or neutral as recommended by the manufacturer. Start the engine, and let the temperature of the transmission come up to operating temperature.

STEP 2 Apply the service brakes firmly and move the gear selector to each of the operating ranges. Leave the selector in each position long enough for each gear to become completely engaged.

STEP 3 Return the selector lever to park or neutral, depending on the transmission. Leave the engine running at idle speed.

STEP 4 Clean any dirt from the dipstick cap and remove the dipstick.

STEP 5 Wipe the dipstick clean and return it to the filler pipe, making sure that it is fully seated.

FIGURE 25–3 The "add" mark on most automatic transmission dipsticks indicates the level is down 0.5 quart (0.5L). Always follow the instructions stamped or printed on the dipstick.

STEP 6 Pull the dipstick out again and read the fluid level. ● **SEE FIGURE 25–3**.

Carefully grip the end of the dipstick between two fingers to get an indication of the fluid temperature.

a. If it feels cold, use the COLD marks.

b. If it feels warm, the correct fluid level will be between the HOT and COLD marks.

c. If it is too hot to hold onto, use the HOT marks.

STEP 7 Replace the dipstick completely into the filler tube.

CHECKING FLUID LEVEL WITHOUT A DIPSTICK

Some units do not use dipsticks. Fluid level is checked by following the procedure stated in the service information. When checking sealed units, a general procedure is to bring the transmission to operating temperature, and then remove the fluid level plug. Fluid will trickle or weep out of the plug if the level is correct.

- If it runs out, the level is high.
- If there is no fluid, the level is low.

Some manufacturers require a special procedure or tool in order to check the fluid level of their sealed transmissions, so it is wise to review their fluid-checking procedures. A general procedure follows.

To check transmission fluid level on a vehicle without a dipstick, perform the following steps:

STEP 1 Check service information for the correct checking procedure.

STEP 2 Check the transmission temperature using a scan tool. This is very important and the vehicle will usually need to be driven for several miles before the specified fluid temperature is achieved. ● **SEE FIGURE 25–4**.

STEP 3 Locate and carefully remove the fluid level plug. Note that the level plug can be small, like a pressure check plug, or large, like a conventional plug. The plug can be located in the transmission case or on the bottom or side of the pan. ● **SEE FIGURE 25–5**.

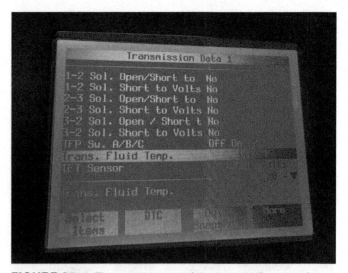

FIGURE 25–4 The temperature of the automatic transmission fluid is displayed on a factory or factory-level scan tool. It may require that the vehicle be driven under a load for the fluid to reach the specified temperature and can often be achieved by allowing the engine to idle.

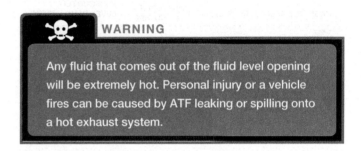

WARNING

Any fluid that comes out of the fluid level opening will be extremely hot. Personal injury or a vehicle fires can be caused by ATF leaking or spilling onto a hot exhaust system.

STEP 4 If fluid drips or seeps from the hole, the level is correct. If fluid runs out, the level is too high, allowing the excess fluid to drain out. Some transmissions use a stand pipe. ● **SEE FIGURE 25–6**.

If no fluid comes out, the level is low. Add additional fluid of the correct type until the level is correct. If necessary, add additional fluid by pumping it into the fill port located at the side of the case or up through the fluid level checking plug opening.

FLUID CONDITION Fluid condition should always be checked when checking fluid level. A transmission technician will normally smell the fluid and check the color for unusual characteristics. The fluid should be a bright reddish color with a smell that is similar to new fluid. It should be noted that some fluids will normally darken and take on a definite odor after a few hundred miles. One manufacturer states that a smoky odor with light brown color is normal. ● **SEE FIGURE 25–7**.

(a)

(b)

FIGURE 25–5 (a) The fluid level indicator is reached from under the vehicle on this rear-wheel-drive transmission. (b)The level indicator can be removed after removing the plug, and then the fluid level can be read on the stick.

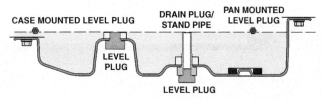

FIGURE 25–6 This drawing shows four possible fluid level check points. Fluid level is checked by removing the level plug, which can be mounted in the bottom or side of the pan or in the case. It is normal for some fluid to drip from this type of level indicator because normal operation of the transmission causes fluid to fill the stand pipe.

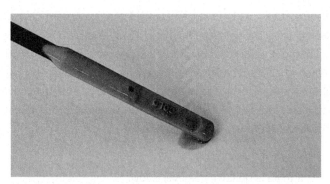

FIGURE 25–7 Fluid condition can be checked by placing a sample on clean, white, absorbent paper. Clean fluid will spread out and leave only a wet stain. Dirty fluid will leave deposits of foreign material.

 REAL WORLD FIX

NO DIPSTICK

A shop drained the dirty transmission fluid and replaced the filter in an automatic transmission and then noticed that there was no dipstick to check the fluid level. The problem was how to properly adjust the fluid level.

On this vehicle, the recommended fluid level is to install 2 quarts of the proper fluid, start the engine, and monitor the transmission fluid temperature. At 96°F (35°C), fluid should flow from the fluid level port. If no fluid flows, the level is low and more should be added. The exact procedure published by the manufacturer for each transmission should be followed.

Following are indications of fluid breakdown:

- Dark brown or black color indicates dirt or burned friction material.

NOTE: **Some highly friction-modified ATFs do tend to turn light brown after a short period of time and this should not be used as a sign of fluid breakdown.**

- A definite burned odor indicates slippage or overheating.
- Pink fluid or a milky color indicates a coolant leak at the heat exchanger in the radiator.
- A varnish-like odor indicates fluid oxidation and breakdown. This is often accompanied by a gold-brown varnish coating on the dipstick.

EXAMPLE: P0302 = CYLINDER #2 MISFIRE DETECTED

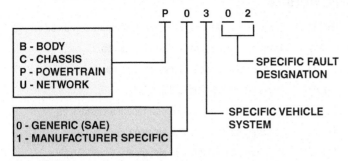

FIGURE 25-8 OBD-II DTC identification format.

- Metallic appearance or very fine metal particles indicate wear.
- Foam might indicate a leak in the pump intake system or incorrect fluid level.

STEP 3—RETRIEVE DIAGNOSTIC TROUBLE CODES

HOW THE PCM/TCM SETS CODES One of the roles of the **powertrain control module (PCM)** and/or the **transmission control module (TCM)** is to monitor transmission operation and determine if malfunctions may be occurring. The PCM/TCM will run frequent self-tests of the electrical circuitry and will also analyze the sensor data to look for transmission slippage, overheating, or other problems. When a problem has been detected, the PCM will generate a diagnostic trouble code (DTC) and may also place the transmission in limp-home mode, depending on what sort of problem has been detected. Limp-home mode is when the transmission stays in one gear only (second gear is a common option) and gives the driver the ability to take the vehicle to the closest service center without having to call a tow truck.

If a diagnostic trouble code (DTC is present in the PCM/TCM memory, it may illuminate the malfunction indicator lamp (MIL), commonly labeled "check engine" or "service engine soon." Any code(s) that is displayed on a

 TECH TIP

Look for DTCs in "Body" and "Chassis"

Whenever diagnosing a customer concern with a transmission, transfer case, or other driveline components, check for diagnostic trouble codes (DTCs) under chassis and body systems and do not just look under engines. Engine or emission control type codes are "P" codes, whereas module communications are "U" codes. These are most often found when looking for DTCs under chassis or body systems. Chassis-related codes are labeled "C" and body system-related codes are labeled "B" codes and these can cause drivetrain issues if they affect a sensor that is also used by the HVAC system for example. ● **SEE FIGURE 25-9**.

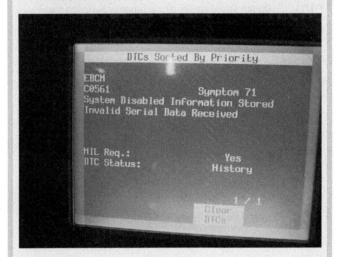

FIGURE 25-9 A "C" diagnostic trouble code was stored along with a note "symptom 71" which gives additional information about the possible cause of this serial data fault code being set.

scan tool when the MIL is *not* on is called a pending code or a transmission code for a fault that would not result in an increase in exhaust emissions. Although this pending code is helpful to the technician to know that a fault has, in the past, been detected, further testing will be needed to find the root cause of the problem. ● **SEE FIGURE 25-8**. ● **SEE CHART 25-3** for transmission-related diagnostic trouble codes.

TRANSMISSION-RELATED DTCs		
P0703	Brake switch input circuit	
P0705	Transmission range sensor circuit problem (PRNDL input)	
P0706	Transmission range sensor circuit range or performance	
P0707	Transmission range sensor circuit low input	
P0708	Transmission range sensor circuit high input	
P0710	Transmission fluid temperature sensor problem	
P0711	Transmission fluid temperature sensor range or performance	
P0712	Transmission fluid temperature sensor low input	
P0713	Transmission fluid temperature sensor high input	
P0715	Input or turbine speed sensor circuit problem	
P0716	Input or turbine speed sensor circuit range or performance	
P0717	Input or turbine speed sensor circuit no signal	
P0720	Output speed sensor circuit problem	
P0721	Output speed sensor circuit range or performance	
P0722	Output speed sensor circuit no signal	
P0725	Engine speed input circuit problem	
P0726	Engine speed input circuit range or performance	
P0727	Engine speed input circuit no signal	
P0728	Gear 6 incorrect ratio	
P0730	Incorrect gear ratio	
P0731	Gear 1 incorrect ratio	
P0732	Gear 2 incorrect ratio	
P0733	Gear 3 incorrect ratio	
P0734	Gear 4 incorrect ratio	
P0735	Gear 5 incorrect ratio	
P0736	Reverse incorrect ratio	
P0740	Torque converter clutch system problem	

P0741	Torque converter clutch system performance or stuck off	
P0742	Torque converter clutch system stuck on	
P0743	Torque converter clutch system electrical	
P0745	Pressure control solenoid problem	
P0746	Pressure control solenoid performance or stuck off	
P0747	Pressure control solenoid stuck on	
P0748	Pressure control solenoid electrical	
P0750	Shift solenoid A problem	
P0751	Shift solenoid A performance or stuck off	
P0752	Shift solenoid A stuck on	
P0753	Shift solenoid A electrical	
P0755	Shift solenoid B problem	
P0756	Shift solenoid B performance or stuck off	
P0757	Shift solenoid B stuck on	
P0758	Shift solenoid B electrical	
P0760	Shift solenoid C problem	
P0761	Shift solenoid C performance or stuck off	
P0762	Shift solenoid C stuck on	
P0763	Shift solenoid C electrical	
P0765	Shift solenoid D problem	
P0766	Shift solenoid D performance or stuck off	
P0767	Shift solenoid D stuck on	
P0768	Shift solenoid D electrical	
P0770	Shift solenoid E problem	
P0771	Shift solenoid E performance or stuck off	
P0772	Shift solenoid E stuck on	
P0773	Shift solenoid E electrical	

CHART 25–3

Transmission/transaxle-related diagnostic trouble codes (DTCs). For transmission-related diagnostic trouble codes for vehicles older than 1996, check service information on how to retrieve and read the codes.

STEP 4—CHECK FOR TECHNICAL SERVICE BULLETINS

Check for corrections or repair procedures in technical service bulletins (TSBs) that match the symptoms. According to studies performed by automobile manufacturers, as many as 30% of vehicles can be repaired following the information, suggestions, or replacement parts found in a technical service bulletin. DTCs must be known before searching for service bulletins, because bulletins often include information on solving problems that involve a stored diagnostic trouble code. ● SEE FIGURE 25–10

What Is Meant by Flashing a Module?

Flashing a module is the updating of the programming of an electronic control module such as the PCM or TCM to solve an issue or customer concern. Flashing a PCM/TCM, also called *programming*, *reprogramming*, and *calibrating*, can be done to correct possible software problems. Occasionally there is a concern that a transmission has improper shift points, delayed shifts, or just does not work right, and a thorough diagnosis fails to locate any problems. TCMs use an electronically erasable programmable read-only memory (EEPROM) that determines the operating parameters of the TCM. The TCM determines when the transmission upshifts or downshifts, when the TCC applies or releases, and the hydraulic system pressures in some transmissions. This memory function can be changed by connecting a computer interface to the TCM that will erase the old instructions and send new instructions to the vehicle TCM. Flashing will remove adaptive learned values.

Recalibration is often necessary when a new TCM is installed. The process must be performed exactly as directed by the manufacturer. The TCM can be recalibrated outside of the vehicle in some cases. The TCM in some vehicles has a learn strategy that can compensate for some transmission faults such as low line pressure. These units should be recalibrated after a major repair or overhaul.

FIGURE 25–10 After checking for stored diagnostic trouble codes (DTCs), check service information for any technical service bulletins (TSBs) that may relate to the vehicle being serviced.

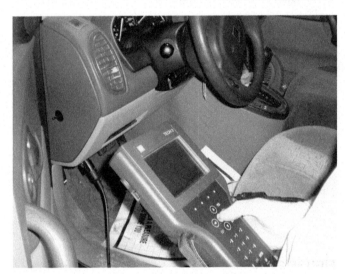

FIGURE 25–11 A TECH 2 scan tool is the factory scan tool used on General Motors vehicles.

STEP 5—SCAN TOOL TESTING

TYPES OF SCAN TOOLS Scan tools are the most important tools for any diagnostic work on all vehicles. Scan tools can be divided into the following three basic groups:

1. **Factory scan tools.** These are the scan tools required by all dealers that sell and service a specific brand of vehicle. Examples of factory scan tools include the following:

   On General Motors vehicles the required scan tools are as follows:

   ▪ Tech 2 (1996 to 2010, depends on model). ● **SEE FIGURE 25–11**.

   ▪ Tech 2 and Candi module (2005 to 2012, depending on model).

   ▪ Tech2Win and multiple diagnostic interface (MDI) ● **SEE FIGURE 25–12**

   ▪ Global Diagnostic System 2 (GDS2) and multiple diagnostic interface (MDI) (2009 and later, depending on model) ● **SEE FIGURE 25–13**

All factory scan tools are designed to provide bidirectional capability, which allows the service technician the opportunity to operate components using the scan tool, thereby confirming that the component is able to work when commanded. Also, all factory scan tools are capable of displaying all factory parameters.

FIGURE 25–12 The Tech 2 Win program runs on a laptop using the MDI as an interface. (Courtesy of Jeffrey Rehkopf)

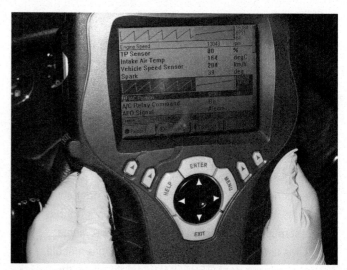

FIGURE 25–14 An OTC Genisys being used to troubleshoot a vehicle. A scan tool like this can be useful when diagnosing non-General Motors vehicles.

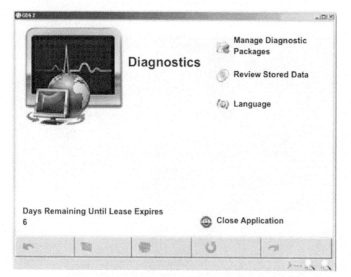

FIGURE 25–13 Global Diagnostic System 2 is required for the latest GM vehicles. (Courtesy of General Motors)

2. **Aftermarket scan tools.** These scan tools are designed to function on more than one brand of vehicle. Examples of aftermarket scan tools include the following:

   - Snap-on (various models, including the Ethos, Modis, Versus, and Solus).
   - OTC (various models, including Pegasus, Genisys, EVO, Nemisys, and Task Master). ● **SEE FIGURE 25–14**.
   - AutoEnginuity and other programs that use a laptop or handheld computer for display.

   While many aftermarket scan tools can display most if not all of the parameters of the factory scan tool, there can be a difference when trying to troubleshoot some faults.

3. **Global scan tools.** The vehicle diagnostic trouble codes (DTCs) and data can be acquired by looking at the global

(generic) part of the PCM and does not need to have the vehicle information entered into the scan tool. All global scan tools display only emission-related data stream information and do *not* display faults or codes for any other system or transmission.

SENSOR VALUES A scan tool can display information about the various sensors and components that can assist the service technician in determining the cause of many automatic transmission/transaxle problems. ● **SEE FIGURE 25–15**.

A properly operating engine should display the following readings with the engine at idle and operating in closed loop.

- **Engine coolant temperature (ECT)**—between 180°F and 215°F (82°C and 102°C)
- **Throttle position (TP) sensor**—usually between 0.5 and 4.5 volts and varying directly with throttle movement.
- **Accelerator pedal position sensor (APPS)**—usually two or more sensors on differing scales (0.4 to 4.6 volts) and varying with accelerator pedal movement
- **Fuel injector pulse width**—1.5 to 3.5 ms.
- **Upstream oxygen sensor (O2S)**—voltage varying between 200 and 800 mV
- **Air–fuel ratio sensor(s)** (if equipped)—scan tool to read fairly low and steady
- **Transmission fluid temperature (TFT)**—less than 275°F (135°C)
- **Brake switch**—scan data to show a change when brake pedal is pressed and released
- **Manifold absolute pressure (MAP) sensor**—with the engine idling in park or neutral, the voltage should be

Data Display

| Diagnostic Data Display | Graphical Data Display | Line Graph | DTC Display |

Solenoid Valve Data

Parameter Name	
Shift Solenoid Valve 1	Transmissio
Shift Solenoid Valve 1 Control Circuit Low Voltage Test Status	Transmissio
Shift Solenoid Valve 1 Control Circuit Open Test Status	Transmissio
Shift Solenoid Valve 1 Control Circuit High Voltage Test Status	Transmissio
Shift Solenoid Valve 2	Transmissio
Shift Solenoid Valve 2 Control Circuit Low Voltage Test Status	Transmissio
Shift Solenoid Valve 2 Control Circuit Open Test Status	Transmissio
Shift Solenoid Valve 2 Control Circuit High Voltage Test Status	Transmissio
Calculated Line Pressure	Transmissio
Line Pressure Control Solenoid Valve Pressure Command	Transmissio
Line Pressure Control Solenoid Valve Performance Test Status	Transmissio
Line Pressure Control Solenoid Valve Control Circuit Low Voltage Test Status	Transmissio
Line Pressure Control Solenoid Valve Control Circuit High Voltage Test Status	Transmissio
Pressure Control Solenoid Valve 2 Pressure Command	Transmissio
Pressure Control Solenoid Valve 2 Pressure Command	Transmissio
Pressure Control Solenoid Valve 2 Performance Test Status	Transmissio
Pressure Control Solenoid Valve 2 Control Circuit Low Voltage Test Status	Transmissio
Pressure Control Solenoid Valve 2 Control Circuit High Voltage Test Status	Transmissio
Pressure Control Solenoid Valve 3 Pressure Command	Transmissio
Pressure Control Solenoid Valve 3 Pressure Command	Transmissio

 Back

GDS 2 v.12.0.00835 ● GM Global v2014.12.1 ● VIN: 1GYDE637040118726 ● 2014,Cadillac,CTS,D

FIGURE 25–15 Global diagnostic system 2 (GDS2) is used when diagnosing late model transmission concerns. (Courtesy of General Motors)

between 0.88 and 1.62 volts or between 102 and 109 Hz for a Ford MAP sensor.

- **Mass airflow sensor (MAF)**—warm engine in park with no load typically reads grams per second within 20% of the engine's liters of displacement with a 3.5 L engine will show fairly close to 3.5 g/s of airflow at idle

- **Vehicle speed (VS) sensor**—source can vary: derived from ABS wheel speed sensors, output speed sensor of transmission, or a dedicated sensor on transmission or transfer case.

- **Idle speed**—check for normal idle speed. Vehicles with electronic throttle control will display 2% to 3% open at warm idle in park and vehicles with IAC (idle air control) valves will display 10 to 30 steps or counts on a scan tool.

- **Shift solenoids**—check for the proper voltage and current of the shift solenoids using a factory or factory-level scan tool.

Observe the operation of the command for the shift solenoids and the TCC solenoid while driving the vehicle. This information confirms that the PCM is commanding the operation and it does not mean that the solenoids are working correctly. Therefore, if the scan data indicate that a particular solenoid is

TECH TIP

Use All Resources

An experienced technician will check all available diagnostic service information from technical service bulletins (TSBs) for the vehicle. Some vehicles have known problems, and their repair is described in a TSB. These are called *pattern failures*. Diagnostic information is also available on the Internet through various organizations, such as the Automatic Transmission Rebuilders Association (ATRA), Automatic Transmission Service Group (ATSG), Identifix, and International Automotive Technicians Network (iATN).

being commanded on and nothing occurs, then the problem could be caused by a defect with the following:

1. Hydraulic component (clutch, band, etc.)
2. Solenoid
3. Fault in the wiring to the solenoid or from the solenoid to the PCM or TCM.

CLUTCH VOLUME INDEX Some vehicles include a code for **clutch volume index (CVI),** also called *transmission adapt pressure (TAP)* or *clutch fill volume index.* The index monitors the time needed to fill a clutch as it applies. Each clutch should fill and stroke the clutch in a specified time. This time period usually increases with normal wear.

The TCM determines CVI from the speed differential between the input and output speed sensors. The TCM can determine the actual ratio and how long it takes to complete a shift from the speed differential of the two speed sensors. A high CVI usually indicates a clutch with excessive slippage.

STEP 6—VISUAL INSPECTIONS

ITEMS TO CHECK The diagnostic procedure should determine if the problem is *inside the transmission* (faulty hydraulic or mechanical operation) or *outside the transmission* (linkage or electrical problems).

Many technicians begin their diagnosis by making a visual check of the battery and wiring. Green corroded battery terminals or loose terminals can easily cause improper electrical operation. Modified or altered wire connections also lead to unsuspected problems.

- The shifts can be forced electrically by providing the proper electrical signal to operate the solenoids using a special diagnostic tool or a factory level scan tool.

- Try removing the fuse that supplies power to the transmission control unit, and conduct a second road test. Without power, the TCM will shut down, causing the transmission operation to revert to a limp-in mode. In this mode, forward operation in the drive range is limited to a single gear, usually second or fourth. Gear operation is controlled by the manual valve, and there will be no automatic upshifts or downshifts. The transmission's operation will be purely hydraulic and mechanical, so it will start in a higher gear than first, and not upshift. If the second road test has the same problems as the first, then this confirms that the problem is not in the electronic controls.

SOURCES OF NOISE The three most common sources of transmission noise are the following:

1. Bearings
2. Gears
3. Hydraulic system

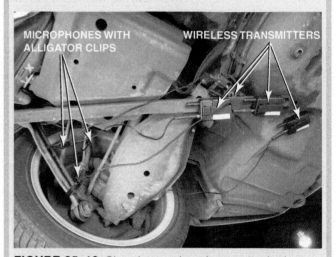

FIGURE 25–16 Chassis ear microphones attached to various under vehicle components using the integral clamps. The sound is transmitted wirelessly to the receiver inside the vehicle where an assistant technician can listen for noises while the vehicle is being driven.

Bearings, both ball and roller, consist of three parts: the bearing element (rollers or balls with cage), and the inner and outer races. The races can be separate parts or a hardened portion of a shaft, gear, or carrier. Bearing noise, often described as a *whine,* is caused by damage, pits, or scoring that makes the bearing surface rough.

Gear noise is usually the result of a rough gear surface or a worn bearing that allows the gear to change position. Gear noise usually shows up as a whine in a certain gear or multiple gears. Another type of gear noise is a *clack* or *clunk* that occurs when there is a change in power flow; it is the result of excessive clearance in the gear train. Worn differential gears and differential pinion shaft are a major cause of neutral-to-drive or neutral-to-reverse clunk.

Hydraulic noise, often described as a "buzz," is the result of rapid fluid pressure pulsations. With many transmissions, it will occur for a short time period while the fluid is cold and then go away.

When troubleshooting noise problems, it helps to determine how the noise fits into the following categories.

- **Speed relation**—related to engine or vehicle speed
- **Gear range**—related to gear range
- **Pitch/frequency**—low (rumble), medium (growl), or high (squeal)
- **Load sensitive**—heavy throttle, light throttle, or coast
- **Direction**—straight or right or left turn

LOCATING THE SOURCE OF THE NOISE

To locate the cause of a transmission noise, perform the following steps:

STEP 1 Raise the vehicle so you have access to the transmission mounts. Visually check their condition, and if the mounts appear weak, pry upward on the transmission to check for possible separation of the mounts.

STEP 2 Start the engine and shift the transmission through its gear ranges while observing for any mount problems.

STEP 3 With the engine running and the gear selector in P or N, listen for the noise. Shift into D, and with the brake firmly applied, listen for the noise. A torque converter problem is indicated if the noise occurs with the transmission in gear but not in P or N. A pump problem is indicated if the noise occurs in both D and P or N. A faulty input drive chain and sprockets can also cause this problem.

STEP 4 With the engine running, shift from N to R while listening for the noise. A hydraulic problem is indicated if the noise increases when shifted into R. Shift into D and alter the signal to the EPC solenoid using a scan tool to boost line pressure. A hydraulic problem is indicated if the noise increases.

STEP 5 Perform a road test and listen for noise changes as the transmission shifts through the gear ranges. A transmission gear set problem is indicated if the noise changes depending on the gear range, especially if it is quiet during the range with a 1:1 ratio.

STEP 6 Repeat step 5 and listen for a noise that increases as the vehicle speed increases. A final drive problem is indicated if the noise intensity or frequency increases with vehicle speed. Note that the final drive can include transfer gears or chain drives depending on the transaxle.

Transmission noise problem areas usually fit into the categories shown in ●**CHART 25–4**.

NOISE	PROBABLE CAUSE
Chain noise	A whine or growl that increases in frequency and amplitude with vehicle speed. Most noticeable under light acceleration. Input chain noise can be heard in park and neutral.
Final drive	A hum related to vehicle speed. Usually torque sensitive.
Gear noise	A whine or growl related to vehicle speed. Usually torque and gear-range sensitive.
Pump noise	A high-pitched whine that increases in amplitude with engine speed. Most noticeable in park or neutral with cold transmission fluid.

CHART 25–4

Typical noise problem descriptions.

VIBRATION CHECKS

Torque converter problems cause an engine-speed-related vibration problem. Output shaft vibration problems are vehicle-speed related. These are often accompanied by driveline clunk. FWD output shaft problems will usually be most noticeable on turns because of the increased differential and CV joint action.

- Engine-speed-related vibrations occur during particular engine speed ranges and these vibrations change when the transmission shifts gears. There are several causes leading to this, for example, belt-driven accessories such as the fan, alternator, air-conditioning compressor, or internal engine unbalance. Belt-driven problems can be identified by running the engine with the belt removed. If the vibration is gone, then the source of the vibration is one of the units being driven by the accessory drive belt.

- Identifying a torque converter problem begins with removing the converter cover and carefully inspecting the torque converter and flex plate. Look for a wobble (runout) of the converter during engine rotation. Torque converter runout can be caused by the following:

  - Improper tightening of the torque-converter-to-flex plate bolts

  - A damaged flex plate. ●**SEE FIGURE 25–17**.

  - Improper mounting of the torque converter into the crankshaft. If there is no runout, then replace the torque converter.

FIGURE 25-17 A broken flexplate that made a lot of noise and then the engine would not crank when it finally broke.

FIGURE 25-18 This is a normal amount of wear material in the bottom of an automatic transmission pan.

STEP 7—FIND THE ROOT CAUSE

OIL PAN DEBRIS CHECK When it has been determined something is wrong with the transmission/transaxle, the next step is to drain the oil and remove the pan for inspection. The debris in the pan can give a good indication of what is occurring in the transmission.

- A small amount of debris with a blackish oil film is normal. A small amount of metal can be attributed to the wear that occurs during break-in and normal operation. ● **SEE FIGURE 25–18**.

- An excess of loose black material is burned lining material from a slipping band or clutch. It usually has a burned smell.

- A heavy golden brown coating is from badly oxidized, old fluid. The lower part of the case and valve body will also have this varnish coating. It usually has a strong odor similar to varnish and indicates that the transmission ran hot.

- An excess of metal is from a gear set, thrust washers, bushings, or the transmission case. Steel and iron are usually from the gears, needle bearings, a spring, or a spring retainer. Aluminum is from the case, a carrier, or a clutch piston. Brass or bronze is from a bushing or thrust washer.

- Any plastic debris (broken or melted) is from a thrust washer, spacer, or clutch spring retainer.

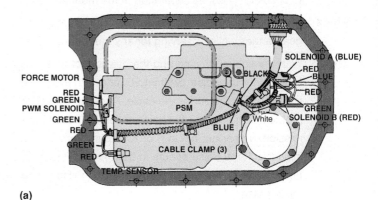

(a)

(b)

FIGURE 25-19 A visual inspection of the transmission electrical connector ensures that the terminals are clean and in good condition as well as being completely engaged.

ELECTRICAL SYSTEM CHECKS An electronic system cannot function without adequate power or a good ground. The power and ground connections are often overlooked by the technician who is eager to solve a transmission problem. The case connector should be checked, since it is exposed to road hazards as well as water, snow, and mud. ● **SEE FIGURE 25–19**.

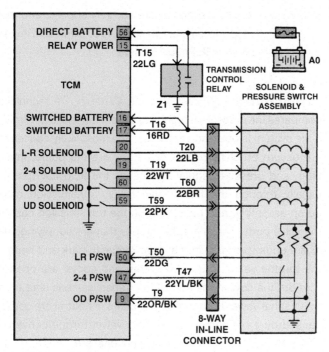

FIGURE 25–20 TCM terminals 16 and 17 receive B+ when the transmission relay is energized.

FIGURE 25–21 The locations (taps) for connecting a pressure gauge to measure the pressure of the various hydraulic circuits are usually found on the side of the automatic transmission/transaxle. Check service information for the exact locations for the vehicle being tested.

After determining there is a problem in the electronic system, an experienced technician will check B+ voltage at the battery and then at the TCM and transmission power relay if there is one. There should be at least 12.6 volts with the engine off and 13.6 to 15 volts with the engine running. There should also be a minimum voltage drop between the TCM ground (B–) terminal and ground, 0.2 volt or less. ● SEE FIGURE 25–20.

- When checking a circuit, make sure that all connectors are properly latched. Disassemble the connector and check for loose, bent, or pushed-back pins, cracked connectors, and water intrusion that will cause corrosion.

- A signal generator can be used to input ISS and OSS signals, and if the TCM responds properly, the speed sensor in question must be faulty.

HYDRAULIC SYSTEM PRESSURE TESTS The operation of an automatic transmission is dependent on hydraulic pressure. A technician uses a pressure gauge to check the condition of the hydraulic system. Some hydraulic system problems can be cured with the transmission still in the vehicle. For example, it is not a good business practice to remove and replace (R&R) a transaxle if the problem was caused by a loose valve body, faulty governor, or electrical problems.

 REAL WORLD FIX

The Case of the Drips

A vehicle came in with a complaint of fourth-gear dropout. This occurs when it is hot with the A/C on. Normal operation returns after the car is shut off for a while. The technician checked the A/C evaporator drain and found that it was dripping water onto the transmission harness connector. Sealing/waterproofing this electrical connector fixed this problem.

All transmissions have a pressure test port, and some have more than one. If there is only one port, it will usually be for line pressure. The additional ports provide the apply or release pressure of a particular clutch. Service information includes illustrations to identify these test ports. ● SEE FIGURE 25–21.

PRESSURE GAUGES A common analog hydraulic pressure gauge is normally dampened, so minor pressure fluctuations are lost. The electrical transducer of an electronic gauge can be connected to a scope, which can be used to watch small pressure changes and find an important clue to the cause of a problem. When using a hydraulic pressure gauge, it is recommended that the range of the gauge be 0 to 300 PSI (0–2 kPa) to prevent gauge damage while testing reverse gear pressure.

FIGURE 25–22 Six pressure gauges are installed on this vehicle to show students how the pressures vary and how the gauges can be used to find faults or possible problem areas before the unit is removed and disassembled.

To test transmission hydraulic pressures, perform the following steps:

STEP 1 Raise and securely support the vehicle on a hoist or jack stand.

STEP 2 Locate the pressure ports, remove the plugs, and connect the gauge(s) to the ports. Note that most domestic transmission ports use female, 1/8-in. National Pipe Threads (NPT). Always double-check that the fitting has the same threads as the transmission port by turning the adapter inward several turns using hand force only.

STEP 3 Connect a scan tool to the vehicle to monitor engine speed.

STEP 4 Route the various lines and wires so they can be read while the vehicle is operated. Be sure to keep them away from the hot exhaust system and rotating parts. Do not run the hydraulic lines or gauge inside the vehicle.

STEP 5 Place the gear selector in park, securely apply the brakes, start the engine, and note the readings on the various gauges.

STEP 6 Run the engine at idle speed, and then shift the gear selector through each of the gear ranges and record the pressure readings. While testing pressure during a road test, watch the gauge pressure before, during, and after a shift. The pressure should drop and then come back. A lower pressure after a shift indicates a leaking fluid circuit.

STEP 7 Make sure the brakes are securely applied, and then increase the engine speed to 1000 RPM and repeat step 6. ● **SEE FIGURE 25–22**.

INTERPRETING PRESSURE READINGS A technician compares the pressure readings to specifications to determine if the system is operating correctly. The most likely causes for a pressure problem in park or neutral are the pump, intake filter, and pressure regulator because the fluid flow path is usually through the filter, valve body, transmission case, pump assembly, and back through the transmission case to the valve body. These are the circuits that are supplying fluid or are under pressure in that gear range. In park and neutral, the throttle valve, torque converter, and cooler are open to flow but the flow to the rest of the transmission is shut off at the manual valve. High or low pressures in neutral are usually caused by a problem in the throttle valve, torque converter, and cooler circuits. If no specifications are available, the approximate pressures in most transmissions will be as follows:

- Neutral, park, and drive at idle: 50 to 60 PSI (350 to 400 kPa)
- M1 and M2: 50 to 60 PSI; in some transmissions: 100 to 125 PSI
- Reverse: 150 to 250 PSI

Increase the engine speed to 2000 RPM, observe the pressure gauge, and switch the ignition off. If the pressure increases to normal or above as the engine stops, there is a problem in the electronic pressure control (EPC) circuit. Any transmission that develops normal pressure in reverse is sure to have a good pump and pressure control circuit.

Control pressure test results are as follows:

- If normal in any range, the pump and pressure regulator pressure control solenoid and circuit are normal.
- If normal in reverse, the pump and pressure regulator valve or pressure control solenoid and circuit are normal.
- If low in all ranges, there is probably a clogged filter, defective pump, or defective pressure regulator valve, or faulty pressure control solenoid or circuit.
- If low in any gear range, there is a problem in that circuit, probably defective seals or sealing rings.

Clutch and band apply pressures are checked by moving the gear selector to the different gear ranges. For example,

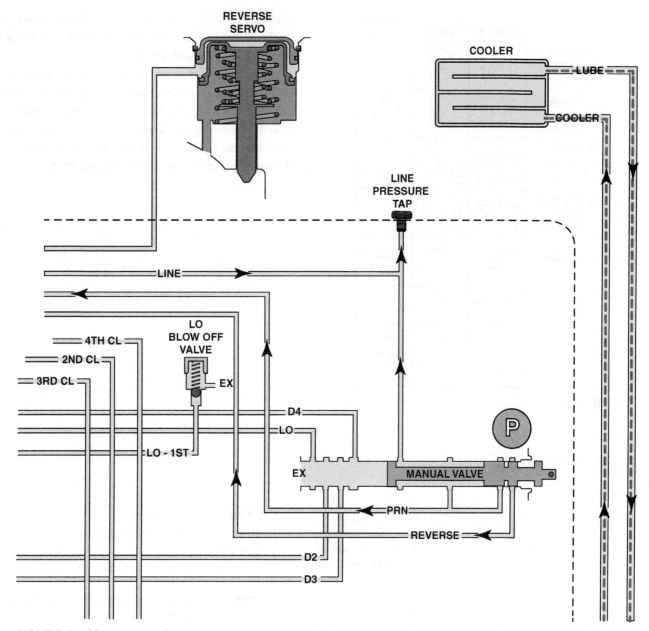

FIGURE 25-23 A portion of a typical hydraulic schematic showing part of the hydraulic system and pressure tap.

normal pressure in every range except drive-3 and reverse indicates leakage in the clutch that is applied for the drive-3 and reverse circuits. This pressure loss can cause slippage in high and reverse.

INDIVIDUAL CIRCUIT TEST PORTS When a transmission has test ports for individual apply circuits as well as line pressure, the condition of that circuit can be easily determined by comparing its pressure with line pressure. For example, if line pressure is 75 PSI (520 kPa) and third-gear pressure is also 75 PSI, then the third-gear circuit, and all of the piston seals, and sealing rings are in good condition. If any circuit is more than 10 PSI (70 kPa) lower than line pressure, there is a sealing problem in that gear circuit that must be corrected.

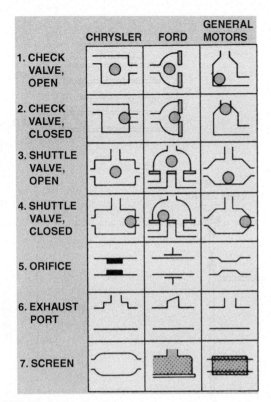

	CHRYSLER	FORD	GENERAL MOTORS
1. CHECK VALVE, OPEN			
2. CHECK VALVE, CLOSED			
3. SHUTTLE VALVE, OPEN			
4. SHUTTLE VALVE, CLOSED			
5. ORIFICE			
6. EXHAUST PORT			
7. SCREEN			

FIGURE 25–24 Hydraulic symbols used by domestic vehicle manufacturers.

FLUID FLOW DIAGRAMS Manufacturers provide hydraulic schematics/fluid diagrams of the fluid passages and valves. ● **SEE FIGURE 25–23**.

They are used to locate the cause of a problem such as low fluid pressure or no upshift. The diagrams are used to trace the fluid flow through a circuit in the same way that you would use a street map to locate the roads between two points. The symbols (such as for check valves or exhaust ports) vary between manufacturers. ● **SEE FIGURE 25–24**.

SUMMARY

1. The diagnostic process includes the following steps:
   - **STEP 1** The first step is to verify the customer complaint. This step usually includes test-driving the vehicle to see if the complaint can be duplicated. If the problem cannot be duplicated, then the repair cannot be verified.
   - **STEP 2** Check the fluid level and condition.
   - **STEP 3** Check for stored diagnostic trouble codes (DTCs).
   - **STEP 4** Check for any related technical service bulletins (TSBs).
   - **STEP 5** Check scan tool data including the adaptive values.
   - **STEP 6** Visual inspections.
   - **STEP 7** Locate the root cause of the problem.
   - **STEP 8** Replace all components that do not meet factory specifications and clear all codes and reset all adaptive factors.
   - **STEP 9** Test-drive the vehicle to verify that the repairs corrected the customer concern.

2. A road test is used to verify the customer's concern and check the general overall condition of the transmission.

3. To check transmission fluid with a dipstick, check the procedure stamped on the dipstick.

REVIEW QUESTIONS

1. What is the diagnostic procedure that most vehicle manufactures suggest be followed when diagnosing an automatic transmission/transaxle customer concern?

2. How is the automatic transmission fluid level checked on an automatic transmission/transaxle that does not have a dipstick?

3. What is the difference between a factory scan tool and an aftermarket scan tool?

4. What does a high CVI indicate on a scan tool display?

5. How are pressure gauges attached to an automatic transmission/transaxle?

1. Why should the transmission control system be checked for diagnostic trouble codes (DTCs), before checking for technical service bulletins (TSBs)?
   a. Some TSBs refer to stored DTCs
   b. If there are no DTCs, then there will not be any TSBs
   c. The two are not related so it does not matter in which order they are checked
   d. TSBs refer to fluid level checking only

2. Why does the customer concern need to be verified?
   a. To make sure that there is a real concern
   b. To be able to verify the repair
   c. To determine under what conditions the fault is noticed or occurs
   d. All of the above

3. An "end bump" is best described as _____.
   a. The operation occurs before normally expected
   b. A shift feel that becomes noticeably firmer as it is completed
   c. A repeated up-and-then-down shifting sequence that produces noticeable repeated engine RPM changes
   d. The shift occurs sometime after normally expected

4. An automatic transmission or transaxle that is underfilled may experience which symptom?
   a. Mushy operation
   b. Goes into neutral
   c. Slipping
   d. Any or all of the above

5. What is needed to properly check the ATF level on an automatic transmission or transaxle NOT equipped with a dipstick?
   a. A special tool
   b. A scan tool to determine ATF temperature
   c. A scan tool to check the fluid level sensor reading
   d. A high-pressure gauge

6. A vehicle's transmission fluid is pink when checked. What could be the cause?
   a. It is a synthetic ATF
   b. The fluid has been aerated (filled with air)
   c. Indicates a coolant leak at the heat exchanger in the radiator
   d. The fluid has been oxidized

7. A high CVI reading on a scan tool usually indicates _____.
   a. A worn clutch pack
   b. A defective one-way clutch
   c. Low ATF level
   d. Incorrect gear ratio detected

8. A factory or factory-level scan tool can _____.
   a. Read DTCs
   b. Read TSBs
   c. Command shifts
   d. Both a and c

9. During oil pan debris check, what is considered to be normal?
   a. Loose black material
   b. Heavy golden brown coating
   c. A small amount of debris with a blackish oil film
   d. Plastic debris

10. If no specifications are available, the approximate pressures in most transmissions will be _____.
    a. Neutral, park, and, drive at idle: 50 to 60 PSI (350 to 400 kPa)
    b. Neutral, park, and, drive at idle: 100 to 120 PSI (690 to 827 kPa)
    c. Neutral, park, and, drive at idle: 120 to 160 PSI (827 to 1100kPa)
    d. Neutral, park, and, drive at idle: 160 to 200 PSI (1100 to 1380 kPa)

SERVICE

Test Drive Before and After Every Service

The wise technician test drives any vehicle being serviced, especially one where a routine automatic transmission service is being requested. Sometimes, a vehicle owner will ask that a service be performed hoping that it will fix an issue that has been noticed. To help avoid misunderstandings and to insure good customer relations, test drive the vehicle and let the customer know if any transmission-related issues are discovered before performing a routine transmission service. Then, of course, test drive the vehicle after the service has been performed to verify that everything is normal and operating properly.

FLUID LIFE (miles/km)	TEMPERATURE (F/C)
100,000/160,000	175°/80°
50,000/80,000	195°/90°
25,000/40,000	215°/100°
12,550/20,000	235°/113°
6,250/10,000	255°/124°
3,125/5,000	275°/135°
1,560/2,500	295°/146°
780/1,250	315°/157°

CHART 26–1

The higher the ATF temperature, the shorter the life expectancy of the fluid.

- Commercial use such as taxi or delivery service
- Police or ambulance usage

The fluid should be changed when it starts to break down, which is best indicated by the fluid appearance and smell. It is wise to change the fluid early, before transmission damage occurs. Dirty fluid may cause the shift valves and solenoids to start sticking, which in turn can cause sluggish shifts and slippage and thus more fluid heat, breakdown, contamination, and damage.

ATF TEMPERATURE AND LIFE EXPECTANCY The main factor that determines transmission fluid life is heat or how hot the fluid is during vehicle operation. If the fluid temperature is kept below 175°F (79°C), the fluid should easily last 100,000 miles. At higher temperatures the fluid oxidizes, causing it to break down at a rate one-half its expected life for every increase of 20°F (11°C).

- Varnish begins forming at temperatures above 240°F (116°C)
- Rubber seals start hardening at temperatures above 260°F (127°C).

See transmission fluid life relative to temperature in ● **CHART 26–1**.

IN-VEHICLE SERVICE ITEMS

OVERVIEW Automatic transmissions and transaxles can operate properly for many miles. Some that fail could have had a longer service life had they been properly maintained. Several surveys of transmission shops have shown that over 80% of transmission failures were the result of neglecting to change the fluid. Maintaining the correct fluid level and changing the fluid are primary maintenance tasks.

FLUID CHANGES

RECOMMENDED INTERVAL Most manufacturers recommend fluid changes every 100,000 miles (160,000 km) under normal driving conditions. Some recommend a **fluid change** at 50,000 miles (80,000 km). Fluid change recommendations are usually accompanied with a recommendation that the change interval be shortened to as low as 15,000 miles (24,000 km) when the vehicle is used under severe driving conditions. Such severe driving conditions include the following:

- Frequent trailer pulling
- Heavy city traffic, especially in areas where the temperature exceeds 90°F (32°C)
- Very hilly or mountainous conditions

OLD FLUID CHANGE ISSUES If the old transmission fluid is extremely dirty, be aware that when the fluid is changed, the new ATF contains a fresh supply of detergents and dispersants that could result in the following:

- Loosen varnish and other deposits that have accumulated inside the transmission
- Carry this material throughout the transmission, including valves and solenoids

FIGURE 26–1 Draining the fluid from an automatic transaxle by allowing the fluid to flow into a container after most of the retaining bolts have been removed.

- Possibly remove varnish that has formed over worn seals and open up a leak.
- The supply of new friction modifier will increase the "slippery" level of the fluid, which might increase slipping on upshifts.

SAFETY ISSUES The material safety data sheets (MSDS) (SDS) for most transmission fluids indicate that there are few safety hazards when working with new fluid. Some indicate a possible skin reaction. Used fluid, however, goes through an unknown change inside the transmission that might cause it to be more of a hazard. Experts usually recommend the following precautions:

- Wear goggles or a face shield.
- Wear gloves or barrier cream for skin protection.
- Clean any skin contact with ATF using soap and water.
- Change clothing that has contacted ATF.
- Wash any clothing that has contact with ATF.
- If ATF under pressure breaks the skin, medical attention should be sought.

FLUID CHANGING, DROPPING THE PAN

PROCEDURE The procedure for changing the fluid in a specific vehicle can be found in service information. To be specific, the procedure usually includes the following steps:

Fluid Change Tips

Here are some tips about fluid changes:

1. Before draining the fluid, check the level according to service information (use a scan tool to monitor fluid temperature).
   - If the level is too low, where did it go? There is a leak.
   - If the level is too high, ask why. Someone added fluid.
   - If the level is OK, proceed with the fluid change.
2. Drain the fluid into an empty, clean drain pan.
3. How much to put back in? Measure how much was drained out; that is how much you put back in.

STEP 1 Safely hoist the vehicle.

STEP 2 Select the best direction for fluid to spill from the pan. Place a large drain pan in this area and remove all but two of the pan bolts. The remaining two bolts should be at the end away from the drain pan and they serve as the "hinge" for lowering the pan. ● SEE FIGURE 26–1.

STEP 3 When the pan lowers to an angle of about 30° to 45°, support it by hand, and then remove the remaining two bolts and finish draining the pan.

STEP 4 Remove the filter, which is usually attached to the valve body. Watch for any small parts that may come loose with the filter. Set aside the old filter for comparison with the new filter.

STEP 5 Inspect the pan, filter, and pan magnet for debris and varnish buildup. The magnet in most automatic transmission pans is used to collect steel particles to keep them from getting circulated throughout the transmission/transaxle. A few metal particles are considered normal. These result from wear and transmission break-ins. Inspect the inside of the transmission for any visible damage or varnish buildup.

STEP 6 Install a new filter using a new gasket or O-ring and tighten the mounting bolts to the correct torque, if equipped. If an O-ring is used, it should be lubricated with transmission assembly lube, petroleum jelly, or automatic transmission fluid (ATF) before installation. ● SEE FIGURE 26–2.

STEP 7 Clean the oil pan and check and straighten if needed any bends at the pan bolt holes.

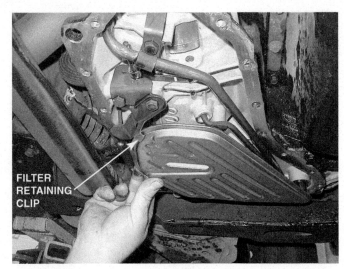

FIGURE 26–2 Always check that the filter is secured by a clip or other fastener to keep it from dropping out of its position.

FIGURE 26–3 In this case, the cork-rubber gasket is glued to the pan and is ready to be installed. The retaining bolts need to be tightened in sequence, but be aware that over tightening will cause a leak. Also, some manufacturers recommend using only an RTV sealer, but never use an RTV sealer and a gasket together.

STEP 8 Install a new gasket on the pan and install the pan on the transmission. ● **SEE FIGURE 26–3.**

STEP 9 The bolts should be tightened in a back-and-forth, across-the-pan sequence to the specified torque.

STEP 10 Lower the vehicle and add the proper amount of fluid. A rule of thumb is 4 quarts. Start the engine and check the fluid level. Add additional fluid to correct the level if necessary.

STEP 11 Dispose of the old transmission fluid according to federal, state, and local laws and regulations.

NOTE: This procedure only changes the fluid in the pan, which is about one-quarter to one-third (1/4 to 1/3) of the total fluid capacity still in the transmission. The remaining fluid stays in the torque converter, clutches and band servos, accumulators, cooler, and fluid passages.

FLUID EXCHANGE AND FLUSH UNITS

TERMINOLOGY Fluid flushing typically uses a chemical to dissolve varnish and other deposits. **Fluid exchange** usually means taking out the old fluid and replacing it with new fluid of the correct type. By using a fluid exchange machine, all of the fluid in the system is replaced.

If the flush is needed to remove solid debris, there must be enough flow velocity to break the material loose and carry it out of the component. More efficient flush machines will pulsate the flow to increase the cleaning power. In severe cases, such as a plugged cooler, the flush can be set up to pump the solvent into the cooler outlet and remove it from the inlet.

TRANSFLOW MACHINE General Motors requires the use of a cooler flushing machine (J-45096, Transflow machine) whenever transmissions are replaced of rebuilt. In the flush mode, transmission fluid is cycled through the transmission oil cooling system. High-pressure air is automatically injected into the fluid stream adding agitation to the ATF oil to enhance the removal of contaminated ATF oil and debris. In the flow mode, an electronic flow meter is used to measure the flow capability of the ATF oil cooling system. A digital display indicates the ATF oil flow rate in gallons per minute (GPM). ● **SEE FIGURE 26–4.**

TYPICAL PROCEDURE Fluid exchange machines are usually connected into the transmission cooler lines so that the machine can pump new fluid to the return line as it captures the fluid leaving the transmission. ● **SEE FIGURE 26–5.**

Running the engine will pump the old fluid out of the transmission, and a pump in the fluid exchange machine will pump new fluid into the return line. When new clean fluid starts leaving the transmission, the fluid exchange is complete.

Always follow the manufacturer's instructions when using a fluid exchanger, which usually includes the following steps:

STEP 1 Identify which cooler line is the return line.

STEP 2 Disconnect the return line from the cooler and connect the line to the NEW FLUID connector of the machine.

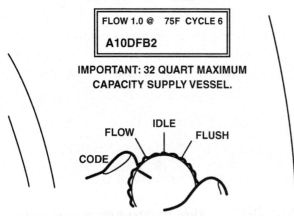

IMPORTANT: TO OPERATE MACHINE, SUPPLY
ATF MUST BE GREATER THAN 65 F.

FLOW 1.0 @   75F CYCLE 6
A10DFB2

IMPORTANT: 32 QUART MAXIMUM
CAPACITY SUPPLY VESSEL.

IDLE
FLOW   FLUSH
CODE

FIGURE 26–4 After flushing and flow testing the cooler a code is produced to verify that the cooler is OK and that the test was done. The flow test must run for a minimum of 8–10 seconds and be above 0.5 GPM for a code to be generated. (Courtesy of General Motors)

FIGURE 26–5 The lines from the fluid exchange machine can often be connected to the cooling lines from underneath the vehicle as on this front-wheel-drive General Motors vehicle.

Connect the USED FLUID connector of the machine to the cooler.

STEP 3 Apply the parking brake and shift the transmission into park. Start the engine and observe the fluid flow in the machine. To prevent starving the transmission of fluid, new fluid should enter the machine at the same rate that used fluid leaves.

STEP 4 When the used fluid has the same appearance as new fluid, stop the engine.

STEP 5 Disconnect fluid connections to the machine, and reconnect the cooler return line.

FIGURE 26–6 This seal is being removed using a seal puller.

STEP 6 Start the engine and check the line connection for leaks.

STEP 7 Check the transmission fluid level and adjust as necessary.

STEP 8 Dispose of the used transmission fluid in an approved manner.

SEAL REPLACEMENT

TWO SEALING SURFACES   A standard metal-backed lip seal must seal against two different surfaces:

1.   A dynamic seal with the movable shaft at the inner bore.

2.   A static seal where it fits into its bore. The static seal is made when the slightly oversize seal backing is driven into the bore.

GENERAL REPLACEMENT PROCEDURE   A chisel, slide hammer, or seal puller can be used to remove a seal after the shaft has been removed. ● **SEE FIGURE 26–6.**

Be careful when installing the seal over a shaft or a shaft into a seal. The sharp lip of the seal is easily cut or torn.

▪ When installing a seal over a shaft, it is good practice to protect the sealing lip with a seal protector, especially if there are any rough or sharp edges on the shaft. A piece of slick paper wrapped around the shaft will work as a seal protector in many cases.

▪ The lip of the seal should always be lubricated to prevent wear. Automatic transmission assembly lube, petroleum jelly, or automatic transmission fluid (ATF) can be used for a lubricant.

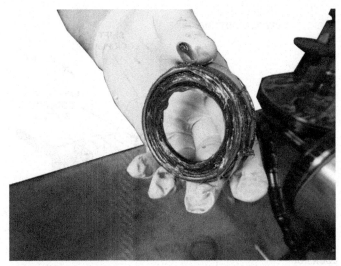

FIGURE 26–7 The lip of the seal around the garter spring is packed with assembly lube to help keep the spring from falling out when it is driven into the transmission housing.

FIGURE 26–8 Using a plug helps prevent fluid loss when the driveshaft is removed.

■ Some seals include a garter spring to increase sealing lip pressure. This garter spring can be dislodged as the seal is driven into position. Filling the recess with assembly lube or petroleum jelly will keep the garter spring in place during installation. ● SEE FIGURE 26–7.

EXTENSION HOUSING SEAL To remove and replace a transmission extension housing seal, perform the following steps:

STEP 1 Raise and support the vehicle on a hoist that allows access to the transmission and driveshaft.

STEP 2 Place alignment marks on the rear universal joint and rear-axle pinion flange.

STEP 3 Disconnect the driveshaft from the rear axle. ATF will begin leaking out of the driveshaft opening. You should either raise the rear of the vehicle enough to stop the flow or place a container to catch the flow. A **stop-off tool** or old U-joint slip yoke can be used to stop the fluid leak. ● SEE FIGURE 26–8.

STEP 4 Pull or pry out the rear seal using a suitable tool.

STEP 5 If necessary, remove the rear bushing using a suitable tool.

STEP 6 If the bushing is removed, use a suitable tool to drive the new bushing completely into place.

STEP 7 Use a correctly sized driver to drive the new seal into place. If the replacement seal does not have an outer sealant coating, a film of sealant should be spread around the outer surface of the seal case.

NEED TO CHECK ADJUSTMENT The manual linkage is adjustable on most automatic transmissions. This ensures the manual valve is positioned correctly relative to the gear selector.

Detents are internal to the transmission and keep the manual valve aligned with the selected position. Because the detents act on the internal linkage, they normally stay correctly aligned with the valve position.

CHECKING MANUAL LINKAGE ADJUSTMENT To check manual linkage adjustment, the specified procedure usually includes the following steps:

STEP 1 Firmly set the parking brake and leave the engine off.

STEP 2 Move the selector level through the ranges and observe the range pointer and the position of the internal detents. The detents engage as the pointer aligns with the gate for each gear position indicator.

STEP 3 Move the selector lever to park, and the parking pawl should freely engage to lock the transmission.

STEP 4 Check that the starter operates in park and neutral but not in other gear positions.

Always check service information for the proper procedure. ● SEE FIGURE 26–9.

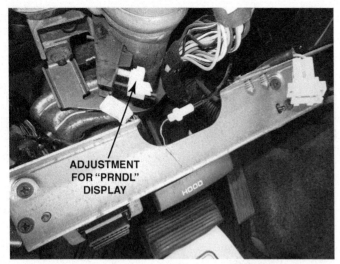

FIGURE 26–9 The position for the pointer ("PRNDL" display) on this truck is adjustable.

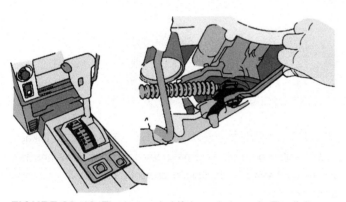

FIGURE 26–10 The manual shift lever is in park. The linkage is being tightened to lock the adjustment in after making sure that the transmission is in park.

MAKING A MANUAL LINKAGE ADJUSTMENT The manual linkage should be adjusted if the starter engagements occur in the wrong position or the transmission detents do not align correctly relative to the gear range pointer. The procedure will vary with vehicle makes and models. Check service information for the exact procedure for a particular vehicle. ● **SEE FIGURE 26–10**.

SHIFT INTERLOCK MECHANISM The shift interlock mechanism locks the shifter in park position when the ignition key is removed. On most vehicles, the brake pedal must be depressed before the shifter can be moved, and the ignition key cannot be removed unless the lever has been shifted into park. These systems operate either electrically or through a mechanical linkage. The mechanical systems usually have an adjustment to ensure proper positioning. These systems

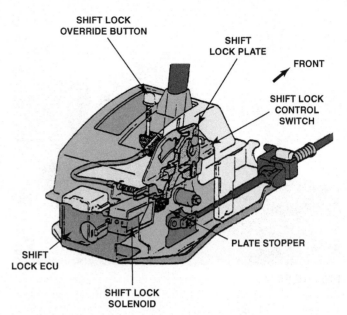

FIGURE 26–11 This shift lock mechanism includes a solenoid that can mechanically hold the shift lock plate. Note the shift lock override button that can be used to release the shift lock.

vary, so service information for that particular vehicle should be consulted when diagnosing problems or checking adjustments.

A shift interlock can get out of adjustment or fail to release. Vehicle manufacturers have incorporated a fail-safe mechanism so the vehicle can be operated. Located near the shift lever is a small lever or button that can be used to override the shift lock and release the lever. The release is often located under a cover that must be removed for access. This procedure is normally described in the vehicle owner's manual. ● **SEE FIGURE 26–11**.

POWERTRAIN MOUNTS

REPLACING MOUNTS Powertrain mounts often require replacement due to damage or wear. Defective powertrain (engine and transmission) mounts are replaced by lifting the engine and/or transmission slightly to remove the weight, and then removing the mounting bolts. The old mount is then removed and the new mount is installed.

The mount for a rear-wheel-drive (RWD) transmission is aligned by the bolts through slotted holes in the mount. Alignment is required so the engine, transmission, and exhaust system do not contact the frame or body.

Bad Transmission When Accelerating

The owner of a front-wheel-drive vehicle complained of a transmission concern that seemed to occur only when accelerating rapidly. The vehicle would shake and a loud knock sound was heard when decelerating, but everything seemed to be normal if the vehicle was accelerated slowly. Everything seemed to be fine when driven in reverse. The technician was able to confirm the situation. A visual inspection confirmed that an engine mount was broken. Replacing the mount solved the "transmission" problem. ●SEE FIGURE 26–12.

(a)

(b)

FIGURE 26–12 (a) The old front engine mount contained hydraulic fluid. The oil was leaking from the split in the mount. (b) The new original equipment (OE) mount ready to be installed.

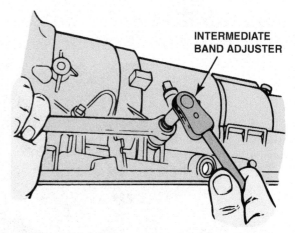

FIGURE 26–13 Adjusting the intermediate band on a rear-drive transmission.

BAND ADJUSTMENTS

The band in many transmissions is used only in manual ranges for engine compression braking and is expected to last the life of the transmission. Most recent transmissions have no provision for in-vehicle adjustments.

- Some older transmissions have threaded adjusters extending through the case to allow an easy readjustment of the band.

- Some band adjustments are made inside the transmission and it is necessary to drop the pan to gain access to the adjuster.

ADJUSTMENT PROCEDURE Service information should be checked to determine the exact adjustment procedure for each particular vehicle.

To readjust a band, the usual procedure includes the following steps:

STEP 1 Loosen the lock nut on the adjuster screw several turns. ●SEE FIGURE 26–13.

STEP 2 Tighten the adjuster screw to the specified torque. Special adjuster wrenches with preset torque settings are available for this operation.

STEP 3 Mark the adjusting screw position and then back it off the specified number of turns. Hold the adjuster screw stationary and retighten the lock nut to the specified torque.

STEP 4 Road-test the vehicle to check the adjustment.

TRANSMISSION PAN REPLACEMENT

1 The owner of this truck complained that automatic transmission fluid was leaking from the pan gasket.

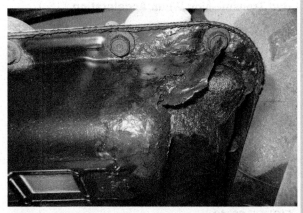

2 The transmission fluid leak is found to be from small holes that had rusted through the steel pan.

3 The retaining bolts being removed from the pan.

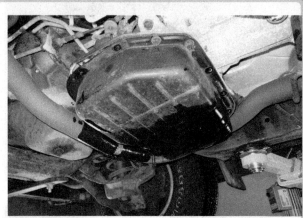

4 The retaining bolts on one side are kept attached and then loosened to allow fluid to drain from one side of the pan.

5 The pan is then gently lowered and the ATF is caught dripping from the valve body.

6 The pan is then emptied into an oil drain unit.

7 The old filter is removed.

8 The shop purchased a new original equipment filter and a new, improved transmission pan gasket.

9 The new filter is installed.

10 The replacement pan is installed and the fasteners tightened to factory specifications. The new pan is galvanized steel compared to painted steel on the original.

11 The specified ATF is installed.

12 The level is checked with the engine running and the gear selector in neutral as per the instructions on the dipstick.

1. Maintaining the correct fluid level and changing the fluid are primary maintenance tasks.

2. Most manufacturers recommend fluid changes every 100,000 miles (160,000 km) under normal driving conditions.

3. Fluid flushing typically uses a chemical to dissolve varnish and other deposits. Fluid exchange usually means taking out the old fluid and replacing it with new fluid of the correct type.

4. The material safety data sheets (MSDS) (SDS) for most transmission fluids indicate that there are few safety hazards when working with new fluid. Some indicate a possible skin reaction. Used fluid, however, goes through

an unknown change inside the transmission that might cause more hazards.

5. A chisel, slide hammer, or seal puller can be used to remove a seal after the shaft has been removed.

6. The manual linkage should be adjusted if the starter engagement occurs in the wrong position or the transmission detents do not align correctly relative to the gear range pointer.

7. Defective powertrain (engine and transmission) mounts are replaced by lifting the engine and/or transmission slightly to remove the weight, and then removing the mounting bolts. The old mount is then removed and the new mount is installed.

REVIEW QUESTIONS

1. What are severe driving conditions that may require the automatic transmission fluid to be changed more often than when driven under normal conditions?

2. What issues may be the result of replacing fluid in a vehicle that has not had the specified fluid changes?

3. What is the difference between a fluid flush and a fluid exchange?

4. What is the general seal replacement procedure?

5. What are the typical steps involved with a band adjustment?

CHAPTER QUIZ

1. Most manufacturers recommend fluid changes every _____.
   a. 10,000 miles (16,000 km)
   b. 25,000 miles (40,000 km)
   c. 50,000 miles (80,000 km)
   d. 100,000 miles (160,000 km)

2. Severe service includes _____.
   a. Extensive highway driving
   b. Commercial use, such as police or taxi use
   c. A combination of city and highway driving
   d. Driving in temperatures below freezing

3. The life of ATF is reduced if the temperature of the fluid is above _____.
   a. 32°F (0°C)   c. 175°F (80°C)
   b. 100°F (38°C)   d. None of the above

4. The material safety data sheets (MSDS) (SDS) for most transmission fluids indicate which safety hazards when working with new fluid?
   a. Possible skin reaction
   b. Possible skin cancer
   c. Possible exposure to HIV
   d. Possible swelling of spots exposed to the fluid

5. When being exposed to ATF, what should a technician do?
   a. Wear goggles or a face shield
   b. Wear gloves or barrier cream for skin protection
   c. Clean any skin contact with ATF using soap and water
   d. All of the above

6. Fluid flushing typically _____.
   a. Uses a chemical to dissolve varnish and other deposits
   b. Another name for fluid exchange
   c. Pulsates the flow to increase the cleaning power
   d. Both a and c

7. Why is there a magnet in the bottom of many automatic transmission pans?
   a. To keep the pan in place as it is being installed
   b. To attract any steel particles and keep them from flowing through the transmission
   c. Used in assembly only
   d. Any of the above depending on make and model

8. A lip seal requires what type of tool to remove?
   a. A chisel or slide hammer and/or a seal puller
   b. A plastic trim removing tool
   c. A large ball peen hammer
   d. A clutch installation tool

9. What is the purpose of the shifter interlock system?
   a. Keep the transmission from being forced into reverse when the vehicle is moving forward
   b. Allows for the selection of all forward gears and reverse when the vehicle is stopped
   c. Prevents the shifter from being moved into drive or reverse unless the brake pedal has been depressed
   d. Prevents the vehicle from rolling backwards on a hill if in the drive position.

10. Which statement(s) is/are true about band adjustments?
    a. The band in many transmissions is used only in manual ranges for engine compression braking and is expected to last the life of the transmission
    b. Most recent transmissions have no provision for in-vehicle adjustments
    c. Some older transmissions have threaded adjusters extending through the case to allow an easy readjustment of the band
    d. All of the above are correct

chapter 27

TRANSMISSION/ TRANSAXLE REMOVAL AND DISASSEMBLY

LEARNING OBJECTIVES

After studying this chapter, the reader will be able to:

1. Describe automatic transmission repair options.
2. Describe the automatic transmission/transaxle inspection process.
3. List the steps need to be followed to remove an automatic transmission/transaxle.
4. Explain the procedure for disassembling a transmission/transaxle.

This chapter will help you prepare for ASE Automatic Transmission/Transaxle (A2) certification test content area "C" (Off-Vehicle Transmission/Transaxle Repair).

KEY TERMS

Aftermarket 441
Hard parts 441
Overhaul 439
Rebuild 439
Remanufactured transmission/ transaxle 439

Retaining bracket 441
Selective 446
Soft parts 441

GM STC OBJECTIVES

GM Service Technical College topics covered in this chapter are as follows:

1. Remove a transmission/transaxle assembly.
2. Remove torque converter assembly.
3. Disassemble clean, and inspect all automatic transmission/transaxle internal components.
4. Disassemble a transaxle differential.
5. Use of press and special press tools to disassemble a clutch apply pistons and return springs.

REPAIR OPTIONS

REPAIR A repair is an operation that replaces faulty parts and performs the needed labor to correct a transmission fault. Most transmission shops are equipped to perform all repairs needed to the vehicle's transmission. Repairing the original transmission ensures that the transmission will be the proper one for the vehicle.

REPLACEMENT A replacement is the removal and installation of the automatic transmission/transaxle. The replacement may be new, remanufactured, or wrecking (recycling) yard unit. For example, many shops install remanufactured transmissions because they are often less expensive than rebuilding or updating the original transmission. A **remanufactured transmission/transaxle** is a unit that has been disassembled, cleaned, inspected, and reassembled using new or like-new parts. It will have any necessary modifications and updates required for proper operation of the transmission. These units are commonly used by dealers to repair transmission problems that occur while a vehicle is still under its new-vehicle or extended warranty. Remanufacturing is done on a production line, with many transmissions of the same model being rebuilt at the same time. Many smaller shops will use remanufactured transmissions when the vehicle's unit is so badly damaged that the cost of the parts comes close to or exceeds the cost of a remanufactured unit.

COMPLETE OVERHAUL A complete overhaul includes disassembling the entire transmission/transaxle and replacing all needed parts, gaskets and seals to restore the transmission to perform like a new unit. A defective transmission with considerable mileage, damage, or wear is a candidate for overhaul or replacement. An **overhaul** implies a **rebuild**, which is generally considered to include the following steps:

- Transmission disassembly
- Replacement of all gaskets and seals
- Replacement of all friction materials
- Replacement of worn bushings
- Replacement of the filter and modulator, if equipped
- Cleaning and inspection of the planetary gears
- Cleaning and inspection of the valve body and all related components
- Cleaning and inspection of the torque converter
- Reassembling with a check of all necessary clearances

Some states have rules and regulations that define what an automatic transmission rebuild or overhaul must include. The California Bureau of Automotive Repair (BAR) states that a rebuilt, remanufactured, reconditioned, or overhauled transmission must include the following steps:

- Cleaning and inspection of all internal and external parts
- Valve body disassembly, cleaning, and inspection
- Front and intermediate bands replaced with new or relined units
- Replacement of the following parts: lined frictions, internal and external seals, rotating metal sealing rings, gaskets, and organic media filters
- All worn or defective parts repaired or replaced with new, rebuilt, or good parts
- Torque converter inspected or replaced with a new or rebuilt unit

NOTE: The California Bureau of Automotive Repair (BAR) regulations require that if a transmission is "exchanged," a descriptive term such as *new, used, rebuilt, remanufactured, reconditioned,* or *overhauled* shall accompany the exchange.

VERIFY THE NEED FOR UNIT REPAIR

VERIFY THE FAULT It is not unusual for a transmission or transaxle to be removed from the vehicle when the fault could have been repaired with the unit still in the vehicle. The fault could also be due to an electrical or engine-related fault outside the transmission/transaxle. Check with all of the following to be sure that the unit needs to be removed from the vehicle.

- A knowledgeable technician
- The archives at www.iatn.net
- A hotline service provider, such as Identifix (www.identifix.com)

Use these resources to verify that the fault is inside, not outside, the unit.

IN-VEHICLE REPAIRS Not all mechanical faults require that the automatic transmission/transaxle be removed from the vehicle. Faults that can usually be repaired with the unit still in the vehicle include any valve-body-related concerns. ● **SEE FIGURE 27–1**.

(a)

(b)

(c)

FIGURE 27–1 (a) This Saturn did not shift correctly and one technician was ready to replace the unit. However another technician thought that the problem could be due to a fault in the valve body. (b) Removing the valve body shows the non-planetary gears used in the Saturn automatic transaxle. (c) The valve body was disassembled and a broken pressure regulator spring was found to be the cause of the customer concern.

Depending on the transmission/transaxle, it may be possible to disassemble and repair many mechanical components of the unit while it remains in the vehicle. Parts and components that may be replaced with the transmission/transaxle still in the vehicle include the following:

- Pressure switches
- Transmission range switch
- Turbine and output speed sensors
- Extension housing gasket
- Drive axle seals
- Valve body replacement

Check service information for details on what can be replaced with the unit in the vehicle.

IDENTIFY THE UNIT Before removing the transmission/transaxle for replacement or repair, be sure that the unit is properly identified. This identification is critical because of the following:

1. The final drive ratio in transaxles can vary depending on the application; and using the wrong unit can cause shifting and other issues such as gear ratio–related diagnostic trouble codes.

2. The internal gear ratios can vary depending on exact application of the unit.

3. Sometimes the vehicle identification number (VIN) is needed to obtain the correct parts, but more often the transmission/transaxle identification number, also called the *tag number*, is the identification needed to be assured of ordering and receiving the proper parts. ● **SEE FIGURE 27–2.**

REMOVING THE AUTOMATIC TRANSMISSION/ TRANSAXLE

STEPS INVOLVED Removing an automatic transmission/transaxle from a vehicle includes many steps to avoid, which would otherwise cause damage to the vehicle or harm the personnel working on it. Always follow the vehicle manufacturer's recommended procedures. Most procedures include the following steps.

STEP 1 Disconnect the negative (–) battery cable from the battery. This prevents the possibility of an accidental

FIGURE 27–2 A transmission identification number on the side of the unit. The information on this tag is needed when ordering parts, as there are often several versions of the same transmission used in similar vehicles and the differences could affect the parts needed.

short circuit that could damage the vehicle or cause a spark that could start a fire.

STEP 2 Hoist the vehicle safely and drain the fluid from the unit.

STEP 3 Disconnect the driveshaft or drive axle shafts.

STEP 4 Disconnect all cooler lines, linkage, and electrical connections. Be sure to label each to ensure proper reinstallation.

STEP 5 Disconnect the torque converter from the flex (drive) plate of the engine.

STEP 6 Support the engine before disconnecting the automatic transmission/transaxle. ● **SEE FIGURE 27–3.**

STEP 7 Remove the transmission/transaxle mounting fasteners.

STEP 8 Support the transmission/transaxle on a jack and remove the attaching bolts at the bell housing of the engine. ● **SEE FIGURE 27–4.**

STEP 9 Remove the transmission/transaxle from the vehicle.

CAUTION: There is a possibility that the converter can slide off its splines and fall as the transmission is being removed. It is heavy and can cause injury or damage if it falls. Some manufacturers recommend installing a converter retaining bracket. ● SEE FIGURE 27–5.

AUTOMATIC TRANSMISSION PARTS

HARD PARTS Major transmission components such as pumps, clutch drums, or gear sets are called **hard parts**. New hard parts are generally available only from the manufacturer or an aftermarket supplier of automatic transmission parts. Some aftermarket companies specialize in used or rebuilt hard parts.

SOFT PARTS On the other hand, **soft parts** are those parts that are normally replaced during an overhaul. These include the gaskets, seals, and friction material.

The parts needed to overhaul a transmission are available from various sources. The vehicle manufacturer can supply all parts needed to repair or overhaul a transmission. Soft parts can be purchased from **aftermarket** sources (a supplier other than the vehicle manufacturer). These parts are usually available as individual components or as part of a kit. Kits are available in several forms, and the contents of a kit will vary between suppliers.

KITS A kit is more convenient and often less expensive than buying individual parts. A variety of kits is available to fit the needs of the particular job. Some of the kits available include the following:

- *Banner kit*—an overhaul kit plus the friction clutch plates
- *Bearing kit*—all bearings for the transmission
- *Compliance kit*—includes all parts that must be replaced as required for a rebuilt transmission in particular states
- *Deluxe or super kit*—a master kit plus filter, band(s), bushings, modulator (if used), and bonded pistons as required for the transmission
- *Filter kit*—the filter and pan gasket
- *Master kit*—an overhaul kit plus the friction and steel clutch plates
- *Overhaul kit*—all gaskets, O-rings, metal-clad seals, and lip seals
- *Sealing ring kit*—all seals made from Teflon, metal, or other materials
- *Solenoid kit*—shift, PWM, and force motor solenoids, which may include the wiring harness
- *Valve body kit*—additional parts needed for replacing worn valve body parts, including check balls, filters, springs, valves, and other needed parts. ● **SEE FIGURE 27–6.**

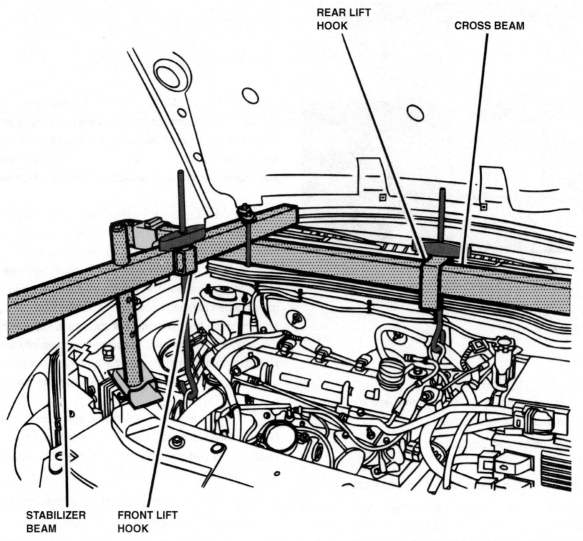

FIGURE 27-3 A support fixture is used to hold the engine while the transaxle is removed. (Courtesy of General Motors)

REAR LIFT HOOK

CROSS BEAM

STABILIZER BEAM

FRONT LIFT HOOK

FIGURE 27-4 A transaxle being supported by a transmission jack prior to removal of the unit from underneath the vehicle.

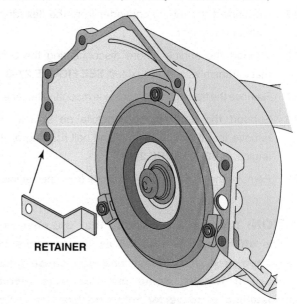

RETAINER

FIGURE 27-5 When the transmission/transaxle is being removed from the vehicle, either remove the torque converter or install a retaining bracket to keep it from falling off the splines.

(a)

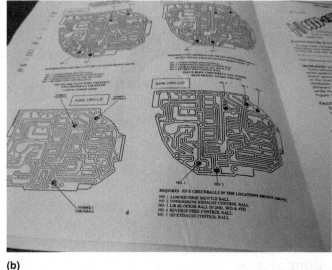

(b)

FIGURE 27–6 (a) A typical automatic transaxle overhaul kit. (b) The kit includes instructions and diagrams to help identify the unit being overhauled so that the correct parts are used from the kit.

TRANSMISSION/ TRANSAXLE DISASSEMBLY

PRE-DISASSEMBLY CLEANUP Cleanliness is a must during a transmission overhaul. Many shops steam clean or pressure wash the outside of the transmission as soon as it is removed from the vehicle. Pre-cleaning removes all exterior dirt and other debris and helps keep the work area clean. An alternate cleanup method is to use solvent or an engine degreaser with a parts-cleaning brush and scraper. Always dispose of hazardous waste following the appropriate disposal procedures and requirements. ● **SEE FIGURE 27–7**.

DISASSEMBLY BENCH AND HOLDING FIXTURES Many shops use a disassembly bench that has a steel top designed to catch the fluid and drain it into a catch pan. During disassembly, the transmission is placed on the bench and torn down. It is usually placed upside down and rolled over as needed. Some shops use transmission holding fixtures during overhaul. Holding fixtures allow the unit to be easily rotated to the best working position, which makes the work faster and easier. When using a holding fixture, a drain pan should be placed under the transmission to catch the dripping fluid. ● **SEE FIGURE 27–8**.

FIRST THINGS FIRST The first disassembly step is to remove the oil pan, filter, and valve body. The procedure is

FIGURE 27–7 A power washer being used to remove the road grime from the unit before it is disassembled.

to remove the pan, inspect the debris (if it has not been done already), wash the pan in solvent, and air dry it. Next, the filter and gasket are removed and set aside for comparison with the new filter. The valve body is then removed and set aside for cleaning and inspection. ● **SEE FIGURE 27–9**.

CAUTION: Valve body bolts are often of different lengths. Either identify where they belong or leave them in the valve body holes after they are loosened.

FIGURE 27–8 Using a holding fixture is the preferred method to use when disassembling and assembling an automatic transmission/transaxle. It allows the unit to be tilted and rotated as needed to get access to the internal and external components.

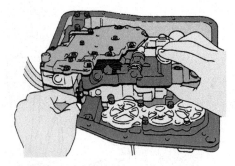

FIGURE 27–9 The valve body can be removed after the pan has been removed.

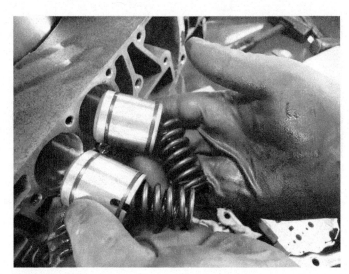

FIGURE 27–10 The accumulators used in some transmissions look the same but use different springs.

FIGURE 27–11 A round retaining ring being removed after the accumulator piston plate/cover has been compressed using a compressing tool.

Inspect for check balls as the valve body is removed and note their location. Save the valve body gasket (if used) so it can be compared with the replacement gasket. Remove any check balls and screens under the valve body.

The valve body of some transmissions can serve as the cover for the accumulator or servo piston(s). Note the position of the piston(s) and spring (if used) and remove them. In other transmissions, a separate cover is used for the accumulator or servo. Each accumulator has its own spring and piston configuration. They may look alike, but there are slight differences. Improper assembly will cause shift timing and quality problems. ● SEE FIGURE 27–10.

RETAINING RINGS   Retaining rings are used to hold many parts in the proper position. One example is like a standard snap ring and another looks like a round wire. The two types of retaining rings are external and internal. External rings fit over a shaft and need to be expanded for removal or installation. Internal rings fit into a bore and are contracted or compressed for removal or installation. ● SEE FIGURE 27–11.

Snap-ring pliers are often used to remove and install retaining rings and specially designed snap-ring pliers are sometimes required for snap rings that are hard to remove.

Magnetic Trays

Many shops use magnetic trays to help keep bolts and nuts organized. For example, one tray can be used just for the oil pan bolts and another for valve body bolts. When not being used, they should be stored attached to a metal workbench or tool box. If a magnetic tray is stored on a wooden workbench, the magnet can lose some of its holding power. ● **SEE FIGURE 27–12**.

FIGURE 27–12 Magnetic trays are an excellent tool to use to help keep fasteners organized so they do not get misplaced. Some technicians use a separate tray for the fasteners from each major component such as the valve body bolts.

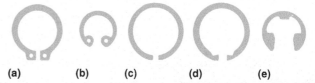

FIGURE 27–13 The most common types of retaining rings are (a) external pin type, (b) internal pin type, (c) plain external, (d) plain internal, and (e) E-clip.

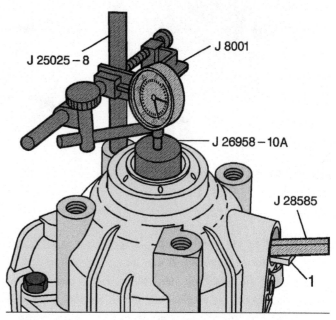

FIGURE 27–14 Using a dial indicator and special tools to check input or output shaft end-play. (Courtesy of General Motors)

☠ **WARNING:**

Use caution during servo cover removal because some servos use a strong piston spring.
These require a special tool to hold the spring compressed during retainer ring removal and then allow the spring to be safely extended.

The correct type and size of snap-ring pliers must be used. Once removed, it is recommended that the retaining ring be replaced with a new one. ● **SEE FIGURE 27–13**.

END-PLAY CHECK

It is standard practice to measure the input shaft end play before removing the pump. End play is the in-and-out movement of the shaft.

■ If there is no end play, there will be drag and a possible binding of the internal components.

■ Too much end play allows misalignment of the internal parts, which could cause damage from the excess movement.

■ If the end play is correct, the internal thrust washers are probably in good shape. If the end play is excessive, there is internal wear, which must be corrected during the rebuild. End play is normally measured using a dial indicator.

To measure input or output shaft end play, the usual method includes the following steps:

STEP 1 Place the transmission in a vertical position with the input shaft pointing up. Some transmissions require that a special fixture be used to hold the output shaft during end-play checks.

STEP 2 Attach a dial indicator onto the case or front pump and position the measuring stylus against the end of the input shaft.

STEP 3 Pull the shaft slightly upward and then push it inward as far as it goes. Now adjust the indicator to read zero. ● **SEE FIGURE 27–14**.

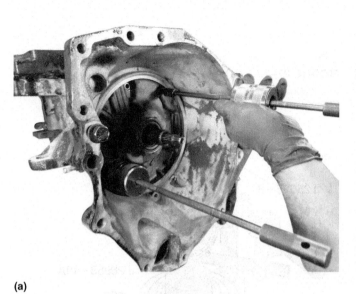

(a)

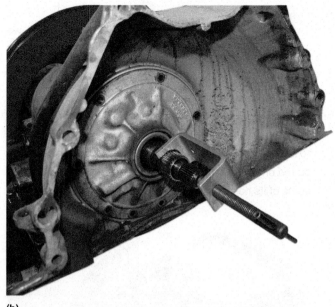

(b)

FIGURE 27–15 (a) Two slide hammers are used to removed the pump in some transmissions/transaxles. (b) A special puller being used to remove the pump.

NOTE: On some transmissions, the input shaft is not attached and can be easily pulled out of the transmission. On these units, end play is checked by measuring the distance from the end of the stator support to the end of the turbine shaft. End play on some of these units can be measured by prying upward on the gear train or specifying that the tailshaft (output) be lifted up and allowed to fall when checking total end play. This allows the entire stacked unit to be checked.

STEP 4 On most transmissions, pull up on the shaft and read the movement on the dial indicator. This is the amount of shaft end play.

STEP 5 Repeat steps 3 and 4 until you get consistent, reliable readings. Then make three more measurements, and if there is a slight difference, average them.

STEP 6 Record your reading and compare it to the specification.

Some manufacturers specify gear train end-play checks at the output shaft or other locations or require additional end-play checks. This helps locate excessive wear in specific areas or determine if the correct selective thrust washers or spacers are being used. For example, a transmission with a center support should have end play on each side of the center support. Manufacturers specify end-play checks between various components of the gear train. **Selective** washers or snap rings are produced in various sizes. This lets the technician select the proper size thrust washer for the best end play or clearance.

PUMP REMOVAL The pump assembly is the front cover that holds the gear train inside the case on RWD transmissions. Its removal allows the disassembly of the rest of the internal parts. The pump is held in place by a set of bolts. The close fit between the outer pump diameter and the case plus a rubber sealing ring and/or gasket makes pump removal a little difficult. Several methods can be used to remove the pump. These include the following:

- Slide hammers
- Special screw-type pullers. ● **SEE FIGURE 27–15.**

TRANSAXLES USING INPUT CHAIN DRIVE Some transaxles use a chain and sprockets for gear train input. The main gear train is behind the valve body. Removal of these parts provides access to the driven sprocket support, which supports the input end of the gear train.

The drive chain and sprockets are exposed after the valve body and case cover/channel plate assembly have been removed. The chain should be checked for the following:

- Wear/link stretch—If the chain has stretched, it should be replaced.
- The master link—It may be a different color. Also note which side is up or down. ● **SEE FIGURE 27–16.**

FIGURE 27–16 The master link in this GM 4T65-E is facing upward and is colored black.

FIGURE 27–17 A snap ring being removed after the clutch piston has been compressed to allow access to the snap ring on this GM 4T65-E transaxle.

NOTE: If the chain is replaced with the master link in the opposite position, it can be noisy. This noise will occur whenever the engine is running, even in park and neutral.

CASE DISASSEMBLY Service information should be followed for the disassembly procedure. To complete transmission disassembly, the usual procedure includes the following steps:

STEP 1 To remove a band, carefully note the position of the band struts, loosen the band adjusting screw, and remove the servo cover and piston. Remove the band struts and band. On transmissions using a clutch mounted next to the pump, remove the clutch friction, steel, and pressure plates. Be sure to note the position of the various clutch plates.

STEP 2 Remove the driving clutch assemblies. ● **SEE FIGURE 27–17.**

STEP 3 Remove the bolts retaining the extension housing, if equipped. It may be necessary to remove the snap ring and the extension housing.

STEP 4 The planetary gear train can be slid out of the case as one assembly on some transmissions. The condition of each part should be checked as it is removed.

STEP 5 If the transmission uses a center support, remove the retainer, usually a large snap ring, and lift the center support out of the case.

FIGURE 27–18 Witness marks are sometimes hard to see but there is often wear when two parts operate together, thus should be reinstalled in the same position.

> ### TECH TIP
>
> **Look for Witness Marks**
>
> Many transmissions use a drive shell that is connected to a clutch through a set of lugs, and a wear pattern will be established between them. These wear patterns are commonly referred to as *witness marks*. While reassembling, it is important to assemble them in the original position. While disassembling, it is a good practice to place index marks on both parts. ● **SEE FIGURE 27–18.**

FIGURE 27–19 The final drive assembly on a GM 4T65-E.

STEP 6 As the park gear is removed, the gear and park pawl should be inspected for wear and damage. Also, the pawl return spring should be checked to ensure that the park pawl is moved completely away from the gear when released.

STEP 7 On rear-wheel-drive (RWD) transmissions, remove any remaining parts as required by the manufacturer's instructions. On transaxles, remove the final drive gears and differential plus any other remaining parts.
● **SEE FIGURE 27–19.**

1 For safety purposes, remove the negative battery cable before starting the transaxle removal procedure.

2 Remove engine bay cross members that may interfere with access to the transaxle fasteners.

3 Remove the air intake and air filter assembly, which is covering the transaxle in this vehicle.

4 Install a support for the engine.

5 Safely hoist the vehicle and remove the wheels.

6 Remove the retaining nut from the drive axle shaft.

CONTINUED ▶

7 Disconnect the lower ball joint on the front-wheel-drive vehicle to allow removal of the drive axle shaft.

8 Remove the drive axle shaft from the transaxle using a pry bar.

9 Disconnect the cooler lines from the transaxle using a line wrench.

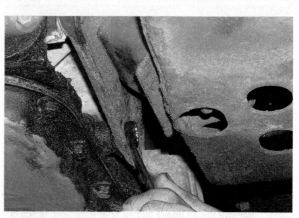

10 Unbolt the torque converter from the flexplate, then remove the transaxle mounts.

11 With the transaxle supported on a transmission jack, remove the retaining bolts from the bell housing.

12 Carefully remove the transaxle from the vehicle.

1 The first step before disassembling, it is preferred that the unit be mounted on a holding fixture.

2 The unit is tipped and fluid drained. The fluid looked burned and watery.

3 After removing the pan, the filter is removed.

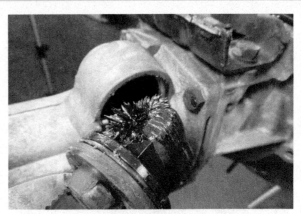

4 When the magnetic vehicle speed sensor was removed, it showed lots of metal fillings which indicates that something is worn or damaged inside the unit.

5 The pressure switch manifold being removed prior to removing the valve body.

6 The pump assembly is being removed from the unit.

CONTINUED ▶

7 Removing the input housing and shaft assembly.

8 The cause of the metal shavings was found to be an excessively worn planet carrier.

9 The reaction carrier and shaft with internal bushing being removed.

10 Removing a snap ring used to retain the low-reverse clutch assembly.

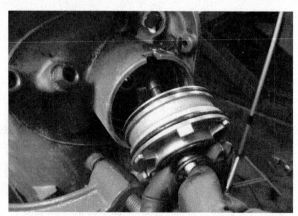

11 Removing the second gear apply piston assembly from the side of the case.

12 Visual inspection of the fluid in this unit shows that it has been overheated and, of course, there are hard parts needed to return this unit to useful service.

SUMMARY

1. Transmissions are removed to make repairs, for overhaul, or for replacement.

2. The removal procedures are similar for most transmissions and transaxles.

3. Always check the service information before removing an automatic transmission/transaxle as per the required tools and procedures that are specified.

REVIEW QUESTIONS

1. What is the difference between a transmission repair and an overhaul?

2. What parts and components may be replaced with the transmission/transaxle still in the vehicle?

3. Why is the proper identification of the automatic transmission/transaxle critical?

4. What are the steps involved in removing an automatic transmission/transaxle from a vehicle?

5. What is the difference between hard parts and soft parts?

6. How is end play measured?

CHAPTER QUIZ

1. What component or part cannot be replaced with the transmission/transaxle in the vehicle?
   a. Torque converter
   b. Shift solenoids
   c. Valve body
   d. Output speed sensor

2. What is the first step usually specified by vehicle manufacturers when removing an automatic transmission (rear-wheel drive) from the vehicle?
   a. Remove the driveshaft
   b. Remove the torque converter inspection cover
   c. Disconnect the negative battery cable
   d. Hoist the vehicle

3. What parts can usually be removed with the automatic transmission/transaxle still in the vehicle?
   a. Pressure switches
   b. Transmission range switch
   c. Turbine and output speed sensors
   d. Any of the above

4. What information is often needed when ordering parts for an automatic transmission/transaxle?
   a. Number of bolts used on the pan
   b. VIN/Tag number
   c. The length of the extension housing
   d. The diameter of the torque converter

5. Some states have rules and regulations that define what an automatic transmission rebuild or overhaul must include when performing which service or repair?
   a. Fluid exchange service
   b. Filter replacement
   c. Overhaul
   d. Extension housing seal replacement

6. What can be used to prevent the converter from sliding off its splines and falling as the transmission is being removed?
   a. Keep the torque converter attached to the flexplate
   b. Pack assembly lube into the splines
   c. Use a retaining bracket
   d. Tilt the transmission upward at the rear

7. An overhaul kit may be called _____ depending on the parts that are included.
   a. Compliance kit   c. Overhaul kit
   b. Master kit   d. Any of the above

8. After the automatic transmission/transaxle has been removed from the vehicle, many service technicians use _____ to clean the road grime and dirt from the unit before starting disassembly.
   a. A power washer
   b. Hot soapy water and a steel wire brush
   c. An acid bath
   d. A scraper and a used tooth brush

9. It is standard practice to _____ before removing the pump assembly.
   a. Remove the extension housing
   b. Remove the direct (forward) clutch assembly
   c. Check end play
   d. Loosen the band adjustment

10. What is the preferred tool to use when removing a pump?
    a. A chain
    b. Slide hammers
    c. Special screw-type puller
    d. Either b or c

chapter 28

VALVE BODIES AND VALVE BODY SERVICE

FIGURE 28–1 A typical valve body as installed on a GM 4T65E transaxle.

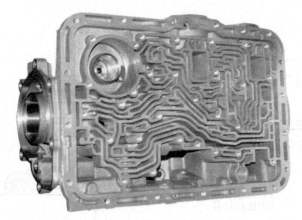

FIGURE 28–2 A typical upper valve body showing the fluid passages ("worm holes").

VALVE BODY

PURPOSE AND FUNCTION The **valve body** enables an automatic transmission/transaxle to operate automatically and is often referred to as the "brain" of the transmission. It supplies the force to apply the clutches, bands, and the valves that control pressure and direct the fluid for automatic shifts. A valve body is where most of the hydraulic valves in a transmission/transaxle are located, and is attached to the case with bolts. Valve bodies can be made of either cast aluminum or cast iron. The valve body in most rear-wheel-drive transmissions is located inside the transmission oil pan at the bottom of the case. A transaxle valve body may be at the bottom of the case, on the backside of the torque converter housing, or on the top or side of the transaxle housing depending on the specific application. ● **SEE FIGURE 28–1.**

FUNCTIONS OF A VALVE BODY The basic functions of the valve body assembly include the following:

- Schedule shifts to optimize engine performance
- Safely shift into reverse when requested
- Provide driver control of the operating ranges
- Provide for proper shift timing
- Provide engine braking to help control vehicle speed on downgrades
- Lock or unlock the torque converter clutch

PARTS Valve bodies have many fluid passages for the various transmission hydraulic circuits cast into them.

These are sometimes called **worm tracks** or *worm holes.* ● **SEE FIGURE 28–2.**

Some of these passages may be widened to form pockets that contain steel, nylon, or rubber check balls. Most valve bodies consist of two cast sections that bolt together with a flat metal separator plate between them.

- The upper section of the valve body is part of the transmission case and is often called the case side.
- The **separator plate**, also called a *transfer plate*, *restrictor plate*, or *spacer plate*, is located between the case side and the valve body side of the valve body assembly. It provides rigidity and contains calibrated drilled holes and openings that help manage fluid flow.
- The lower part of the valve body is located in the valve body itself and is often called the valve body side.
- Valve bodies contain specialized valves and circuits that are particular to a specific transmission.

Electronic solenoids are used in place of some valves on electronically controlled transmissions/transaxles. Some transmissions/transaxles incorporate the transmission control module (TCM) right on the valve body. This eliminates the wiring harness between the TCM and the solenoids, which in turn eliminates connector problems.

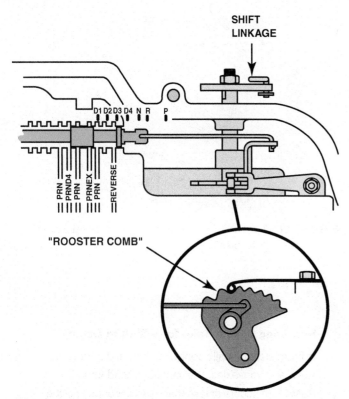

SHIFT LINKAGE

"ROOSTER COMB"

FIGURE 28–3 A rooster comb is the detent that helps retain the manual valve in the various positions in the valve body.

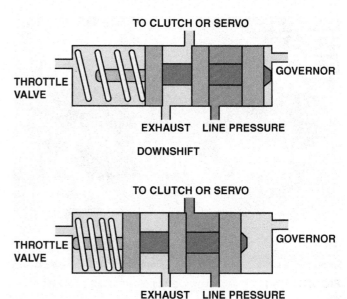

TO CLUTCH OR SERVO

THROTTLE VALVE

GOVERNOR

EXHAUST   LINE PRESSURE

DOWNSHIFT

TO CLUTCH OR SERVO

THROTTLE VALVE

GOVERNOR

EXHAUST   LINE PRESSURE

UPSHIFT

FIGURE 28–4 A typical shift valve has a spring to move the valve to a downshift position where the throttle pressure works with this spring. When governor pressure gets high enough, the valve will move to an upshift position.

MANUAL VALVE

PURPOSE AND FUNCTION The **manual valve** is the only hydraulic valve in the transmission that is "manually" controlled by the driver, and therefore, it is called a "manual valve" or sometimes *selector valve*. It controls the fluid flow to the band servos and to clutch apply pistons for drive, low, and reverse gears plus to the shift valves. It receives the fluid from the pump at line pressure. This valve is connected to the shift lever in the driver's compartment.

OPERATION The manual valve is moved by mechanical linkage when the driver moves the shift lever. The valve is held in position by the detent cam at the valve body. This detent is a spring-loaded roller or ball that drops into notches in the cam to position the manual valve properly in its bore. The detent cam is commonly called a "**rooster comb**". ● SEE FIGURE 28–3.

When the gear selector is in neutral or park, fluid flow through the manual valve is blocked by a land or trapped between two lands. In the other gear selector positions, the valve is moved to allow fluid flow through the valve to various valves and friction-apply circuits. Most three- and four-speed transmissions have six gear selector positions. Some four-speed transmissions have seven positions that allow

fourth-gear operation in overdrive and limit the transmission to first- through third-gear operation in drive.

Nearly all transmissions also have one *shift valve* for each automatic upshift. ● SEE FIGURE 28–4.

The largest volume of fluid flow is to the **actuator**, which is usually a hydraulic piston. The hydraulic actuators of an automatic transmission are the servos that apply and release the bands and the pistons that apply the clutches.

In automatic transmissions, the valves are positioned so that fluid pressure is exerted on the actuator piston all the time that the actuator is applied. When the actuator is released, fluid pressure is exhausted. ● SEE FIGURE 28–5.

CONTROL VALVES

CHECK BALLS A **check ball** is the simplest device for controlling fluid flow. A *one-way check valve* resembles a steel bearing or plastic ball located over a hole in the separator plate. ● SEE FIGURE 28–6.

An upward fluid flow moves the ball aside and fluid flows around it. A downward fluid flow forces the ball against the hole and stops the flow. The flow of fluid is possible in only one direction, upward. Often there are check balls in both the case side and valve body side of the valve body assembly. ● SEE FIGURE 28–7.

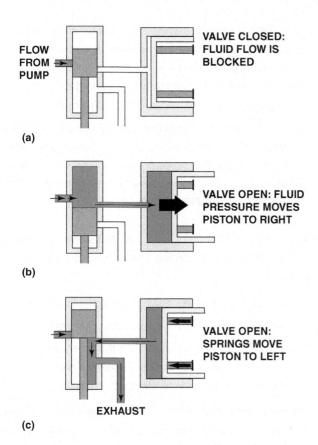

FIGURE 28–5 Operation of the valve controls fluid flow to the actuator. It can (a) block operation, (b) cause apply, or (c) cause release.

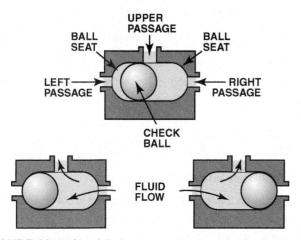

FIGURE 28–7 Check balls are used in the valve body to allow hydraulic circuits to share a common passage.

Check balls are usually made from steel, but they can be made of nylon, rubber, or some composite material as well. The type of material used depends on the manufacturer and application. Steel balls generally hold up better, but cause greater seat wear because of their hardness. The softer composite balls are easier on seats and they cannot be magnetized.

Some transmissions use a *two-way check valve*, also called a *shuttle valve*. The ball is positioned above two side-by-side

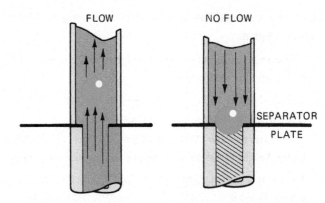

FIGURE 28–6 A check valve is opened by fluid flow in one direction (left) and closes when the fluid tries to flow in the reverse direction.

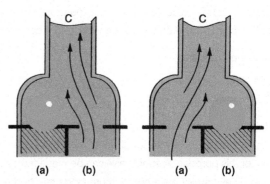

FIGURE 28–8 When fluid flows through this shuttle valve from port B to port C, the check ball moves over to close port A (left). Fluid flow from port A will close port B (right).

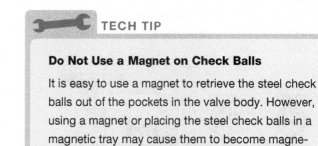

TECH TIP

Do Not Use a Magnet on Check Balls

It is easy to use a magnet to retrieve the steel check balls out of the pockets in the valve body. However, using a magnet or placing the steel check balls in a magnetic tray may cause them to become magnetized. If the balls become magnetized, they may be attracted to the steel separator plate and not be free to move to block passages as designed.

holes with another flow passage extending upward or to the side. Upward flow through one of the holes in the plate causes the ball to move over and seal the other hole. Fluid flow upward through the second hole causes the ball to move over and seal the first hole. ● **SEE FIGURE 28–8.**

ORIFICES An **orifice** is simply a small hole, usually in the separator plate. An orifice produces a resistance to fluid flow and therefore causes a pressure drop as long as fluid is flowing through it.

- The amount of pressure drop is relative to the size of the orifice and the flow volume.
- The smaller the orifice size, the greater resistance to flow and the larger the drop in fluid pressure.
- As soon as the flow stops, the orifice no longer has an effect on the flow, and the pressure on both sides becomes equal.
- An orifice is also used to dampen fluid flow to the control valves. There is usually one in the passage between the pump and reaction land of the pressure regulator valve and this orifice helps soften pressure pulses from the pump that can cause the valve to overreact. ● SEE FIGURE 28–9.

SPOOL VALVES
The fluid flow from the pressure regulator valve to the manual valve and into the control circuit can be called

- Mainline pressure
- Line pressure
- Control pressure.

Flow to and from a transmission hydraulic actuator is controlled by one or more valves. Spool valves sliding in a round bore are used for this purpose. A spool valve can be made from steel or aluminum. They usually have two or more lands that fit the valve bore tightly enough so that fluid cannot escape past the valve land but loosely enough so that the valve can slide freely in the bore.

- The valleys or grooves between the lands serve as fluid passages. Typically the valve-to-bore clearance is about 0.003 to 0.004 inches (80 to 100 μm). The close fit

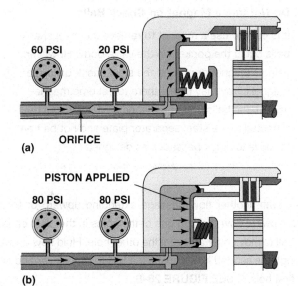

FIGURE 28–9 (a) An orifice will cause a pressure drop as fluid flows through; (b) when the flow stops, the pressure on both sides of the orifice will be the same.

requires the valve to expand and contract at the same rate as the valve body. This prevents the valve from sticking or having excessive leakage. The outer edges of the lands have sharp corners to help prevent debris from wedging between the land and the valve bore.

- The faces serve as pressure surfaces, also called *reaction surfaces*, to produce valve movement. Some valves are relatively long with a series of lands and grooves so fluid flow through two or more passages are controlled at the same time. ● SEE FIGURE 28–10.

HYDRAULIC SHIFT VALVES
A **shift valve** is a spring-loaded spool valve that controls the transmission upshift and downshift circuits.

- Throttle pressure works against one side of the valve.
- Governor pressure works against the other side.
- When one pressure is greater than the other, the valve moves to the upshift or downshift position and the valve lands uncover the ports to the relative circuits.

Transmission shift valves may be referred to as "snap valves" because they shift almost instantly in response to pressure differential changes. Since these valves cause upshifts and downshifts, they are also known as "event-causing valves." There are only two positions for a shift valve:

- Fully to one end of the stroke or
- Fully to the other end of the stroke

Otherwise, hydraulic pressure could apply control devices for two gears at once and damage the transmission. ● SEE FIGURE 28–11.

 FREQUENTLY ASKED QUESTION

What Does an Accumulator Do?

An **accumulator** is a piston or valve that is not attached to anything because all it does is move in its own bore and is usually located in the valve body. An accumulator is tied to an apply piston by a branch of the fluid passage used for apply pressure. It is designed to move at a pressure just above that needed to move the apply piston. Just after the apply piston takes up the clutch or band clearance and the fluid pressure starts to increase, the accumulator piston moves and absorbs some of the fluid flow. This causes a lag in the pressure increase at the band servo and clutch. The effect is a slightly longer and smoother (cushioned) shift.

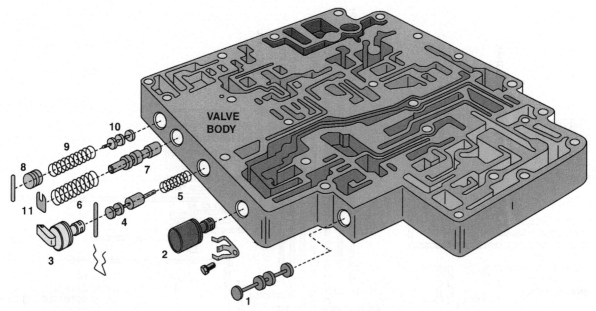

FIGURE 28–10 A typical valve body showing some of the valve and solenoids as well as the clips and pins used to retain the parts in the valve body.

1 VALVE, MANUAL

2 VALVE ASSEMBLY, PRESSURE CONTROL SOLENOID

3 VALVE ASSEMBLY, TCC PWM SOLENOID

4 VALVE, TCC REGULATOR APPLY

5 SPRING, TCC REGULATOR APPLY VALVE

6 SPRING, ACTUATOR FEED LIMIT VALVE

7 VALVE, ACTUATOR FEED LIMIT

8 PLUG, ACCUMULATOR VALVE BORE

9 SPRING, ACCUMULATOR VALVE

10 VALVE, ACCUMULATOR

11 RETAINER, ACCUMULATOR FEED LIMIT VALVE SPRING

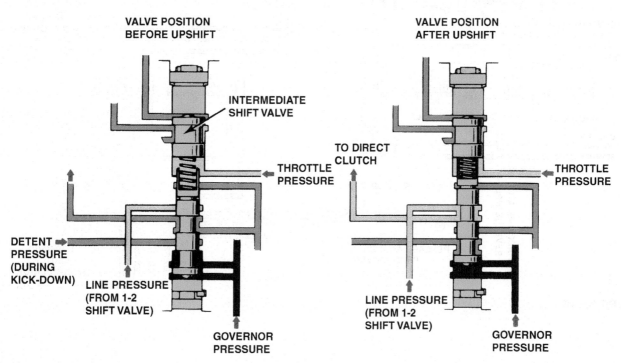

FIGURE 28–11 Shift valves move when there is a difference in pressure. In a hydraulically controlled automatic transmission/transaxle, the shift valves compare governor pressure force against throttle valve (TV) pressure force to determine when to upshift or downshift.

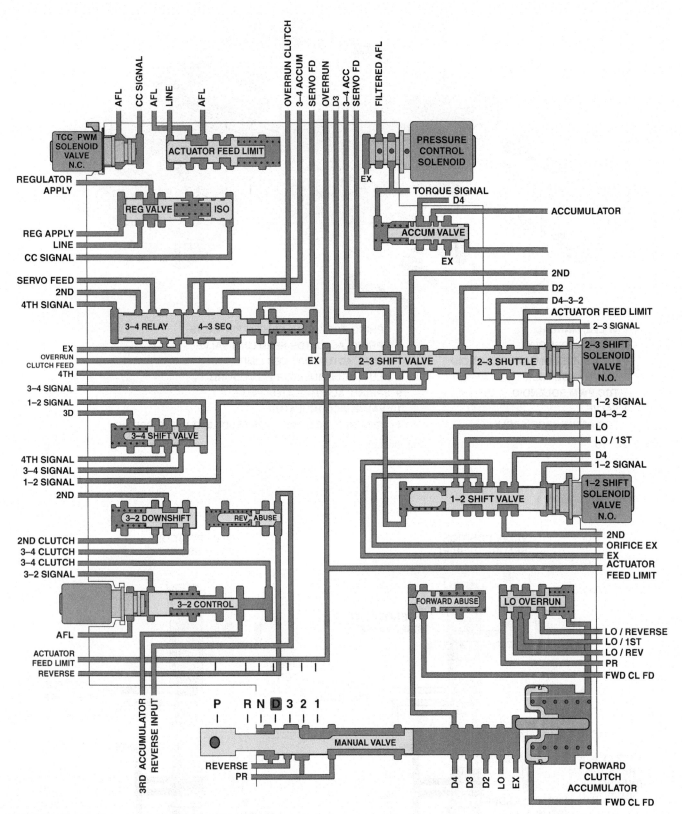

FIGURE 28-12 The shift valves and shift timing are controlled by solenoids. The accumulator (lower right) cushions the application of the forward clutch.

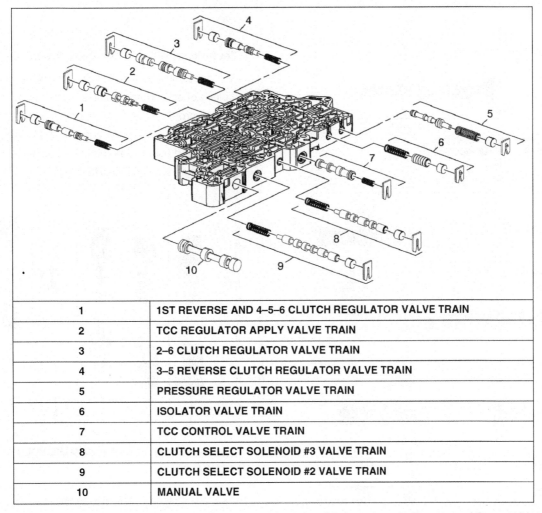

1	1ST REVERSE AND 4–5–6 CLUTCH REGULATOR VALVE TRAIN
2	TCC REGULATOR APPLY VALVE TRAIN
3	2–6 CLUTCH REGULATOR VALVE TRAIN
4	3–5 REVERSE CLUTCH REGULATOR VALVE TRAIN
5	PRESSURE REGULATOR VALVE TRAIN
6	ISOLATOR VALVE TRAIN
7	TCC CONTROL VALVE TRAIN
8	CLUTCH SELECT SOLENOID #3 VALVE TRAIN
9	CLUTCH SELECT SOLENOID #2 VALVE TRAIN
10	MANUAL VALVE

FIGURE 28–13 Valve body and valves; the valves are actuated by solenoids (not shown). (Courtesy of General Motors)

ELECTRONIC SHIFT VALVES In an electronically controlled transmission, the shift valves are controlled by turning solenoids on or off. Depending on the design, the shift solenoids hold or release pressure, causing the related valve to move in the valve body. ● **SEE FIGURE 28–12**.

VALVE BODY SERVICE

PURPOSE Despite its complexity, the valve body is one of the more reliable parts in a transmission, probably because the valves are so well lubricated. In a way, valves do little, as they move only slightly and only once in a while. The biggest "enemies" of a valve body include

1. Dirt (from dirty fluid or dirt getting into the fluid through the dipstick tube or opening).

2. Overheated fluid, which can cause varnish buildup on the valves and bores.

3. Solenoids can fail and, being magnetic, can attract iron and steel particles which can restrict their flow and prevent them from working properly in many cases.

4. All filter screens should be replaced and are usually included in most overhaul kits.

Most valve body service operations consist of the following:

- disassembly
- cleaning
- checking for free movement
- replacing defective solenoids
- replacing all filter screens
- reassembly. ● **SEE FIGURES 28–13 AND 28–14**.

VALVE RETAINING METHODS Several methods are used to retain the valve(s) in a bore.

- Many units use a cover plate that holds one or more valves. Removal of the retaining screws allows removal of the plate, valve(s), and spring(s).

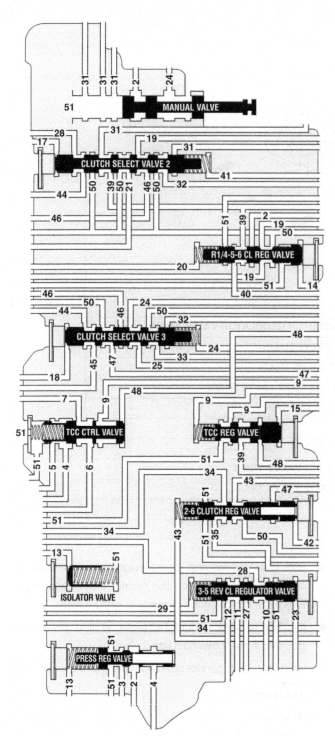

FIGURE 28–14 A 6T70 upper valve body, showing the location of the valve trains and some of the fluid passages. (Courtesy of General Motors)

■ Many valves use a plug or sleeve at the end of each bore. The plug/sleeve is retained with a keeper, which can be a pin, plate, or key. Some valve bodies use a coiled spring pin (roll pin) to hold the valve plug/sleeve in place. In some cases, this coiled pin can be pulled out by gripping it with a pair of pliers or using an extractor tool.

Technician-Made Valve Body Organizer

Some technicians make a valve organizer by folding a piece of cardboard into an accordion shape. The biggest problem during valve body repair is getting it back together with everything in the right order and location and using something like this helps with the organization. ● **SEE FIGURE 28–15.**

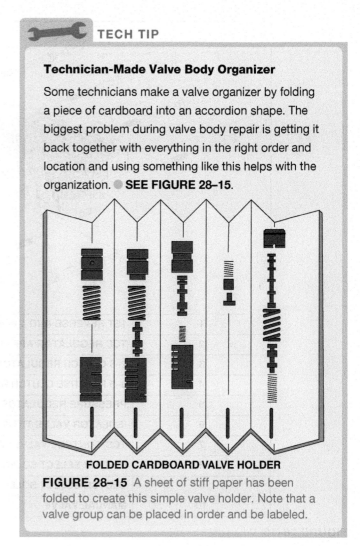

FOLDED CARDBOARD VALVE HOLDER

FIGURE 28–15 A sheet of stiff paper has been folded to create this simple valve holder. Note that a valve group can be placed in order and be labeled.

VALVE BODY CHECKS AND TIPS Most technicians place a lint-free shop cloth(s) or a carpet scrap under the valve body while disassembling it. The cloth helps keep the check balls, screws, and pins from rolling away and might prevent a nick or dent in a valve if one happens to drop.

The **free fall test** is a standard check for a sticking valve. Hold the valve body so the bore is vertical. In this position, a steel valve should fall freely from one end of the bore to the other and it should at least fall through the area of normal valve movement. Any valve that does not fall freely is sticking, which can be a fault of the valve, the bore, or both. ● **SEE FIGURE 28–16.**

■ Aluminum valves and valve bodies should be checked for wear. Position the valve as deep in the bore as possible. Some valves can be inserted into the bore backward for this check. Next, try to move the valve vertically, and note the amount of movement. Vertical movement should be very small. Compare the amount of movement to a new or known-good valve body.

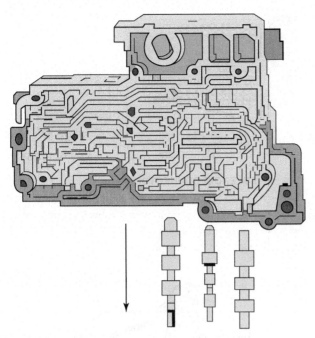

FIGURE 28–16 If the valve body is moved to a vertical position, steel valves should slide freely from the bore. Be prepared to catch the valves when making this check.

- A wet air test can also be used to check for wear. Valve body wear can also be checked using a vacuum test; more information for this test can be found at www.sonnax.com/

- Short valves that are located between fluid pressure and a spring tend to tip in the valve bore. This can cause ridges in the bore, leading to jamming of the valve.

- Carefully inspect the valve and valve body for varnish, which can be a light brown or golden brown coating. It can be cleaned off with brake cleaner. ● SEE FIGURE 28–17.

- If a valve is smooth but still sticks in the bore, carefully examine the bore for debris or nicks that might cause raised metal.

- A valve that has excessive movement, such as a pressure regulator valve, can wear into the bore and cause excess leakage.

TESTING SHIFT SOLENOIDS
Shift solenoids control the pressure force, which in turn controls the position of the shift valve.
To test a solenoid, perform the following steps:

STEP 1 Disconnect the solenoid connector and connect one ohmmeter lead to each of the solenoid electrical terminals.

STEP 2 Read the resistance and compare the reading to the specifications.

FIGURE 28–17 A valve body being washed and air dried in a parts washer. It will be cleaned again when the two major parts are separated.

STEP 3 Move one of the leads to the solenoid body or base to check the ground circuit.

NOTE: A two-wire solenoid should not have continuity to ground. A single-wire solenoid will be grounded through the solenoid case, and it should have continuity when one of the ohmmeter leads is connected to the case and the other to the solenoid terminal.

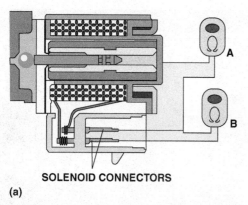

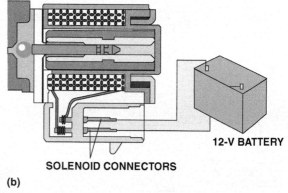

(a)   (b)

FIGURE 28–18 (a) Ohmmeter A is checking for a grounded solenoid coil; the reading should be infinite. Ohmmeter B is measuring the coil resistance; it should be within the specifications for this solenoid. (b) Connecting a solenoid to a 12-V battery should cause it to operate. Make sure the battery is connected using the correct polarity in case the solenoid has an internal diode.

 **TECH TIP**

Solenoids Are Wear Items

Many technicians consider solenoids, especially PWM solenoids, to be "wear items" and automatically replace them if the transmission experiences problems after about 90,000 miles (150,000 km).

STEP 4 A quick solenoid check is to apply power to the solenoid and listen for a click. This is done by connecting a jumper wire from the solenoid lead to the battery for a single-wire solenoid. A two-wire solenoid will also need to be grounded. The solenoid should click indicating the coil windings are complete and the plunger is moving. ● **SEE FIGURE 28–18.**

CAUTION: Do not perform this quick check on a PWM solenoid because the lower coil resistance will allow excessive current flow that can damage the solenoid.

STEP 5 The mechanical operation of a solenoid also should be checked. Because solenoids are basically electromagnets operating in an area that might have some metal debris, they tend to attract metal particles. These can cause sticking or binding of the solenoid plunger or blocking of the fluid passage. Test the solenoid by blowing air into the fluid passage while energizing and de-energizing the coil. ● **SEE FIGURE 28–19.**

REASSEMBLY After all the valves, springs, and valve body are cleaned and the valves move freely in their bores, the valve body can be reassembled.

- The springs should be checked to make sure they are not damaged and do not have distorted coils.

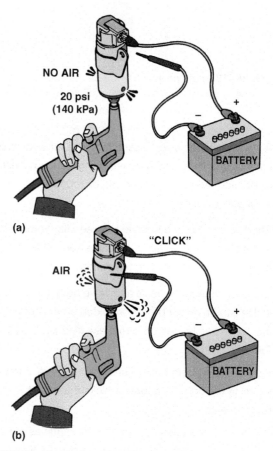

(a)

(b)

FIGURE 28–19 Air should not be able to flow through this solenoid if it is not activated. If it is connected to a 12-V battery, it should make a "click," and air should be able to flow through it.

- Each valve should be dipped in ATF before installation. The reassembly procedure is generally the reverse of the disassembly procedure. As each valve is installed, make sure that it moves freely in its bore.

- Ensure that all check balls and filter screens are replaced in their proper locations. ● **SEE FIGURE 28–20.**

- Be sure to tighten each fastener to the correct torque. ● **SEE FIGURE 28–21.**

FIGURE 28-20 Using assembly lube is a great way to keep check balls in place during the reassembly of the valve body.

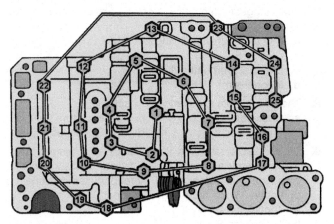

FIGURE 28-21 The valve body bolts should be tightened in order, starting from the center and working in an outward spiral.

TECH TIP

The Shop Light Trick

If a faulty check ball–transfer plate seat is suspected, place the ball on its seat and hold a flashlight behind the transfer plate. Light shining between the ball and the transfer plate indicates a problem. ● **SEE FIGURE 28-22**.

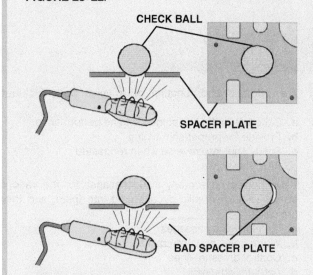

FIGURE 28-22 A check ball should seal off light from coming through the spacer plate. A problem is indicated if light shines through an opening alongside of the check ball.

SUMMARY

1. The valve body is often referred to as the brain of the automatic transmission because the valves in the valve body are used to apply and release clutches and bands.

2. Various types of valves are used to direct the fluid flow and regulate the pressures used to operate the transmission, including spool valves and check balls.

3. Most valve body service operations consist of the following:

   - disassembly
   - cleaning
   - checking for free movement
   - replacing defective solenoids
   - replacing all filter screens
   - reassembly.

4. All solenoids used in electronically controlled automatic transmissions and transaxles should be tested for proper operation during valve body service.

1. What is the purpose and function of a valve body?
2. Where is the separator plate located?
3. What does an accumulator do?
4. What is the purpose and function of orifices and check balls?
5. What is the free fall test?
6. What steps are needed to be performed to test solenoids?

1. The purpose and function of a valve body includes _____.
   a. Schedule shifts to optimize engine performance
   b. Provide for proper shift timing
   c. Safely shift into reverse when requested
   d. All of the above

2. Valve bodies have many fluid passages for the various transmission hydraulic circuits cast into them, and they are called _____.
   a. Manual valve passages
   b. Worm holes or worm tracks
   c. Control pressure lines
   d. Actuator channels

3. What part separates the lower valve body from the upper valve body?
   a. Separator plate
   b. Divider
   c. Valve body channel
   d. Valve springs

4. Where are most orifices located?
   a. In the valve body channel
   b. Under the valve springs
   c. In the separator plate
   d. Between the gaskets

5. An accumulator _____.
   a. Cushions a shift
   b. Applies fluid pressure to a clutch or band
   c. Releases fluid pressure from a clutch or band
   d. Increases fluid pressure

6. What valve body service operations are usually performed?
   a. Disassembly
   b. Cleaning
   c. Replacing all filter screens
   d. All of the above

7. The biggest "enemies" of a valve body include _____.
   a. City and highway driving
   b. Cold ATF
   c. Dirt and overheated fluid
   d. Magnetism

8. The free fall test is a standard check for _____.
   a. Check balls
   b. Shift valves
   c. Accumulators
   d. Shift solenoids

9. Technician A says that if a check ball is magnetized, it may not work as designed. Technician B says a solenoid is magnetic and can attract metal particles and affect its operation. Which technician is correct?
   a. Technician A only
   b. Technician B only
   c. Both technicians A and B
   d. Neither technician A nor B

10. What can be used to make sure that a check ball is properly seated to a spacer plate?
    a. A magnet
    b. A light
    c. Low pressure air from an air nozzle
    d. ATF from a squirt can

chapter 29

TRANSMISSION/ TRANSAXLE ASSEMBLY AND INSTALLATION

LEARNING OBJECTIVES

After studying this chapter, the reader will be able to:

1. Identify the different methods of component cleaning.
2. Explain bushing, bearing, and thrust washer service.
3. Discuss friction material service.
4. Explain internal seal and ring service.
5. Describe the procedure for performing case and pump service.
6. Explain the procedure for clutch assembly and disassembly.
7. Discuss gear set service and air testing.
8. Explain the procedure to perform a final transmission assembly.
9. List the steps involved in installing a transmission/transaxle.

This chapter will help you prepare for ASE Automatic Transmission/Transaxle (A2) certification test content area "C" (Off-Vehicle Transmission/Transaxle Repair).

GM STC OBJECTIVES

GM Service Technical College topics covered in this chapter are as follows:

1. Reassemble an automatic transmission/transaxle case.
2. Clean, inspect, and reassemble all automatic transmission/transaxle internal components.
3. Reassemble a transaxle differential.
4. Reassemble input shaft and output shafts using the appropriate special tools.
5. Reassemble automatic transmission/transaxles using the appropriate sealers and correct amounts as necessary per Service Information.
6. Properly use a dial-and-click-type torque wrench for fastener and preload specifications.
7. Properly use press and special press tools to reassemble clutch apply pistons and return springs.
8. Perform end-play measurements to determine correct selective components.
9. Inspect, measure, and replace thrust washers and bearings.
10. Perform differential preload measurements and select proper shims.
11. Perform individual shaft end-play measurement to determine correct selective components.

KEY TERMS

Adaptive learning 487
Aqueous-based solutions 468
Bearings 469
Bushings 469
Clutch pack clearance 480
Cross leak 475

Scarf-cut 474
Selective 470
Subassemblies 474
Torrington 469
Thrust washers 469
Warpage 475

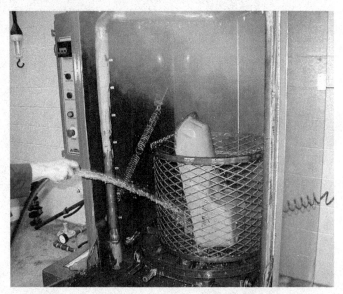

FIGURE 29–1 A pressure jet washer is similar to a large industrial-sized dishwasher. This type of cleaning unit can be used for most automotive components including engines and transmissions. Each part is then rinsed with water to remove chemicals or debris that may remain there while it is still in the tank.

FIGURE 29–2 Transmission parts being cleaned in a water-based solvent cleaning tank.

 WARNING

The petroleum solvent–air mixture from drying the parts is highly flammable. Never use cleaning solvent around an open flame, spark, or source of ignition.

COMPONENT CLEANING

CLEANING OPTIONS The internal parts, case, and extension housing are cleaned after disassembling. Some technicians set major components aside to be thoroughly cleaned as they are disassembled and serviced. Cleaning methods that are commonly used include the following:

- Hot spray wash
- Solvent wash
- Water (aqueous) solution wash
- Microbe cleaning

The parts should be dried using compressed air after washing. Each technician or shop has a preferred method of cleaning.

HOT SPRAY WASHING A hot spray wash cabinet resembles a large dishwasher. The parts are placed inside the cabinet, and the washer sprays the parts with a hot-water-based detergent solution as the parts are rotated. It is an effective and quick cleaner. Newer machines are designed to trap the sludge and dirt to make waste disposal easy and inexpensive. The used cleaning solution, sludge, and dirt waste is an identified hazardous waste that is carefully monitored in many areas. ● **SEE FIGURE 29–1.**

SOLVENT WASHING Solvent washing is usually done for small parts. Rubber seals, Teflon thrust washers, bands, and lined friction plates should not be cleaned in petroleum solvent because the solvent can destroy the seals and other friction materials. This method of cleaning parts is labor intensive. The parts are brushed as they are dipped or sprayed with a petroleum- or water-based solvent. Petroleum solvents are flammable and can cause redness and soreness of the skin. They are also considered pollutants because of the emissions released into the atmosphere and are treated as a hazardous waste when disposed.

WATER-BASED CHEMICAL CLEANING Because of environmental concerns, most chemical cleaning is now performed using water-based solutions (also called **aqueous-based solutions**). Most aqueous-type chemicals are silicate based and are mixed with water. Aqueous-based solutions can be used in one of two ways.

- Sprayed on
- Used in a tank for soaking parts. ● **SEE FIGURE 29–2.**

MICROBIAL CLEANING Microbial cleaning uses microbes that are living organisms (single-celled bacteria) that

FIGURE 29–3 A microbial cleaning tank uses microbes to clean grease and oil from parts.

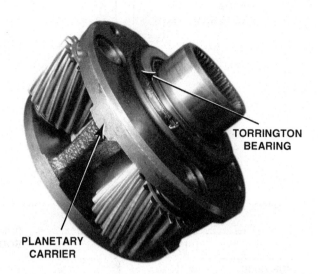

TORRINGTON BEARING

PLANETARY CARRIER

FIGURE 29–4 A Torrington bearing used to absorb thrust loads on a planetary gear set.

literally "eat" the hydrocarbons (grease and oils) off the parts being cleaned. The typical microbial cleaning system includes three steps.

1. A liquid assists the microbes by breaking the hydrocarbons to a smaller (molecular) size.

2. The microbes, stored in a dormant phase until ready for use, give an indefinite shelf life to the product. Once the microbes come into contact with the liquid, they wake up from the dormant state and begin to feed.

3. A third part is a blend of nutrients to ensure that the microbes start to multiply in the shortest possible time to help speed the cleaning time needed.

Microbial cleaning is environmentally friendly, but is slower to clean parts. ● **SEE FIGURE 29–3.**

BUSHING, BEARING, AND THRUST WASHER SERVICE

DESCRIPTION **Bushings** and **bearings** are used to support rotating shafts. **Thrust washers** are used to separate rotating parts from each other or from stationary parts. Bushings are plain metal bearings that require a flow of ATF lubricant to reduce friction. Bearings have much less friction because they have rolling members, either balls or rollers, as well as a lubricant to reduce friction. Bushing, bearing, or thrust washer failure causes wear as the hard parts turning at different speeds rub against each other.

Thrust washers can be made from plastic, fiber, or bronze- or tin-lined iron. When end-play positioning is critical or thrust loads are very high, a radial needle bearing commonly called a **Torrington** is used. This bearing type uses needle bearings to absorb the loads. These bearings must run against a very smooth, hard surface—either the face of a gear or a race. A bushing or thrust washer must have an operating clearance of about 0.003 to 0.005 inches (0.076 to 0.157 mm) to allow a good oil flow across the bearing surface. The condition of a Torrington is checked by feeling for rough operation under load. ● **SEE FIGURE 29–4.**

BUSHING REMOVAL A bushing is a metal sleeve that is lined with a soft bearing material, usually bronze, tin, or both. Any scoring, galling, flaking, excess wear, or rough operation is cause for replacement. A bushing is relatively inexpensive, but the damage caused by a worn bushing is very expensive to repair. The front (pump) and rear (extension housing) bushings are usually replaced during every transmission rebuild. If the bore is straight, the bushing is normally pressed or driven straight out the other end of the bore. The driving tool is usually a stepped disk that fits into the bushing bore and has a raised shoulder to press against the end of the bushing. Most manufacturers do not publish clearance or size specifications for bushings. Generally, anything over 0.006 inch (0.15 mm) clearance is excessive. ● **SEE FIGURE 29–5.**

BUSHING INSTALLATION Replacement bushings are available as individual items or as part of an overhaul kit.

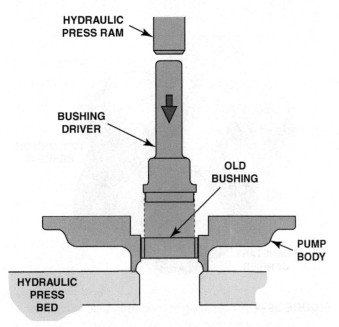

FIGURE 29–5 Worn pump bushings can be removed using a hydraulic press and a tool that applies force only to the bushing.

A bushing installer should be used to push the new bushing into its bore to prevent damaging it or the bore. This is often the same tool that was used to remove the bushing. In most cases, the bushing is placed on the tool and pressed or driven into the bore to the correct depth. Some bushing drivers have steps so they "bottom out" and stop at the correct depth. A bushing with a groove or oil passage should be aligned in the original position.

After staking a bushing (making a dent at the end using a blunt chisel), remove any raised metal with a scraping tool or sharp knife. Some bushings have a hole that must be aligned with an oil passage to permit lubrication of other parts. It is recommended to use a locking compound such as Loctite® to prevent the bushing from rotating in its bore and shutting off the lube flow.

TAPERED ROLLER BEARING SERVICE

Some transaxles use tapered roller bearings. The bearing consists of the *inner race*, *rollers*, *cage*, and *cup*. ● SEE FIGURE 29–6.

These bearings are checked by visual inspection and by rotating the cleaned and lubricated bearing with a pressure between the bearing and the cup. Any scoring or flaking of the cup or roller surfaces, or a rough feel is cause for replacement. These bearings are often press-fit onto the shaft, and the cup is press-fit into the bore. Special tools are usually required to

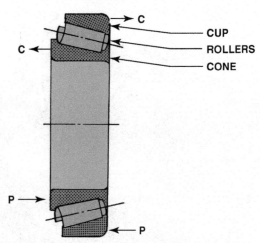

FIGURE 29–6 The cup, rollers, and cone of a tapered roller bearing are machined at an angle as shown. This allows them to resist a thrust in the direction indicated by the P arrows. The bearing is preloaded in this direction; any clearance at the sides of the bearing (C arrows) is called free play.

FIGURE 29–7 The selective spacer used at the final drive support bearings. This unit uses two tapered roller bearings facing each other to support the final drive.

remove and replace the bearing and its cone. If a bearing or its cup is damaged, both should be replaced. If the bearings and cups are to be reused, they should be marked or tagged so a bearing will be installed with the original cup.

Tapered roller bearings must be adjusted to get the correct end play or preload. This adjustment is normally accomplished by changing **selective**-sized shims that can be positioned under the cup. A shim of the proper size is selected to provide the correct end play or preload. The procedure for this adjustment varies between manufacturers. ● **SEE FIGURE 29–7.**

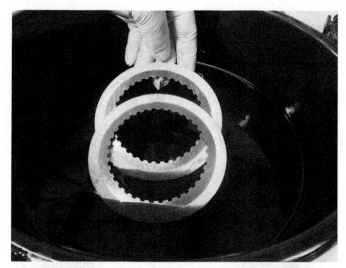

FIGURE 29–8 All lined friction material should be submerged in a shallow pan of ATF and allowed to soak before being installed in the automatic transmission/transaxle.

FIGURE 29–9 Steel plates can usually be reused if no faults are found during a visual inspection.

FRICTION MATERIAL SERVICE

LINED PLATE SERVICE   If lined plates are to be reused, they should be carefully inspected. The requirements for reuse of a lined plate include the following:

- The lining wear is minimal.
- There must be no breaking up or pock marks in the lining.
- There must be no metal particles embedded in the lining.
- The lining must not come apart when scraped with a coin, fingernail, or knife blade.
- The lining must not have a glazed, shiny appearance.
- The lining material must not be severely discolored.
- The plate must be flat.
- The splined area must be flat and even.

New lined material should be soaked in ATF for at least 20 minutes before installation and some shops soak the plates overnight. ● **SEE FIGURE 29–8.**

STEEL PLATE SERVICE   Unlined steel plates are often reused. They must be carefully inspected before reuse for the following:

- The plate must be flat (except for wave or Belleville plates).
- There must be no sign of surface irregularities.

TECH TIP

A Stack of Plates Test

A quick way to check the plates for flatness is to stack the plates and look for any gaps between them. Overheated plates tend to warp into either a slightly conical or a "potato chip" shape. Gaps indicate warped, unusable plates. Restack the plates, turning every other one upside down, and recheck for gaps. Any gaps indicate faulty, unusable plates.

- The notches must be flat and even.
- Slightly burned plates must be replaced or reconditioned.

A "good" steel plate is reusable. Other than cleaning, no further preparation is needed. The friction surface of the lined plate has to wear slightly until it matches the surface of the unlined plate. Too rough a steel plate surface produces severe operation and rapid friction material wear. The ideal surface finish for a used steel plate is a tumbled-finish, smooth, very flat surface like that of a new steel plate. ● **SEE FIGURE 29–9.**

BAND SERVICE   If a band is to be reused, it should be checked to ensure the following:

- The lining material is sound with no breaking up or pock marks. ● **SEE FIGURE 29–10.**
- The lining material does not come apart when scraped with a thumbnail or knife blade.

FIGURE 29–10 A badly chipped and pitted band. This band requires replacement.

- The lining thickness is almost the same as that of a new band.
- The lining material is not badly discolored or does not appear burned.
- There are no metal particles embedded in the friction material.
- The end lugs appear tight and unworn.

The drum surface for a band must also be in good condition. The drum surface should be very smooth and flat. A rough, badly scored drum should be replaced.

INTERNAL SEAL AND RING SERVICE

RUBBER SEALS An O-ring seal (round or square-cut) is first checked by placing it in the bore by itself. The seals can be checked for size by placing them one at a time in their operating position. A round O-ring should produce some drag and a square-cut seal is normal if it produces a barely noticeable drag. A lip seal is checked the same way. Just like an O-ring seal, it must produce a drag on the way into the drum, but it is okay if it falls outward when turned over. On a

(a)

(b)

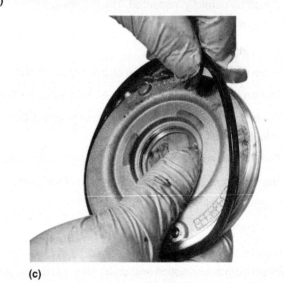

(c)

FIGURE 29–11 (a) Piston seals as supplied in an overhaul (OH) kit. (b) These seals are being lubricated in ATF before installation. (c) Installing a lip seal.

piston that uses three lip seals, each one should be checked, one at a time. A seal should never be installed dry. Both the bore and the seals should be lubricated with ATF, transmission assembly lubricant, or petroleum jelly. ● **SEE FIGURE 29–11.**

FIGURE 29–12 A round flat plastic disc is often included in overhaul kits and makes seal installation easier.

FIGURE 29–13 A dial indicator is set up to measure clutch pack clearance and then it is air checked to verify proper operation.

INSTALLING PISTONS WITH LIP SEALS

The clutch piston should be inspected before seal installation. A piston that is manufactured from sheet metal stampings should be checked for broken welds or cracks. Also make sure that the check ball moves freely in its cage and seals properly.

During installation, a lip seal often catches the edge of the bore and will roll outward. This will probably cut the seal lip and cause a fluid leak. Several procedures can be used to ease installation and produce a reliable clutch: use a wax lubricant, an installing tool, a seal guide, and compress the seal lip.

- Seal installation tools are commercially available. As the piston is being installed, use this tool to coax the seal lip into the bore. ● **SEE FIGURE 29–12.**

- Seal guides are available for some clutch units. These are smooth steel bands with a slight funnel or cone shape. They are placed in the drum and lubricated. As the piston is being installed, the guides prevent the seal lips from catching on the edge of the bore.

After the clutch is completely assembled, it should be air checked to ensure that the seals are good, the piston strokes properly, and the clutch applies and releases. ● **SEE FIGURE 29–13.**

FITTING SEALING RINGS

A sealing ring has to make a seal on one of its sides and at the outer diameter. Fluid pressure plus the elasticity of the ring pushes the ring outward, where it engages the bore. If the bore is rotating, the sealing ring rotates with the bore. Rubbing action should always take place between one side of the sealing ring and the groove. Some sliding action takes place between the ring and the bore.

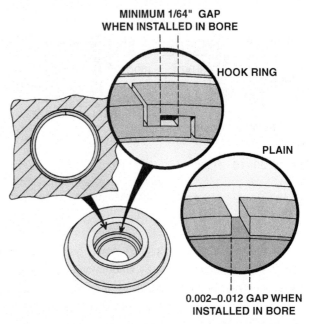

MINIMUM 1/64" GAP
WHEN INSTALLED IN BORE

HOOK RING

PLAIN

0.002–0.012 GAP WHEN
INSTALLED IN BORE

FIGURE 29–14 A metal sealing ring has been hooked and placed into its bore. It should enter with a slight pressure and make full contact with the bore. There should be a slight gap at the ends of the ring as shown.

End play allows the bore along with the drum to move forward and backward.

A metal sealing ring, either *open/plain end* or *hook ring*, should be checked by placing it in its bore. There should be a tight and close fit between the outer diameter of the ring and the bore. Open-end metal rings should have a slight gap, about 0.002 to 0.015 inches (0.05 to 0.3 mm), between the ends of the ring to allow for expansion of the ring metal. ● **SEE FIGURE 29–14.**

Next, check the ring in the groove. A hook- or interlock-type ring should be hooked after installation. There should be

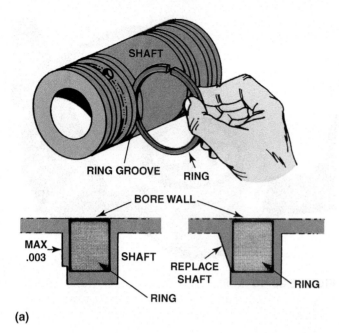

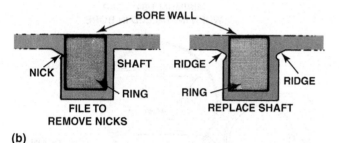

(a)

(b)

FIGURE 29–15 (a) Side clearance of a metal sealing ring is checked by placing the ring into the groove and measuring the clearance using a feeler gauge. (b) While making this check, look for damage to the seal groove.

a maximum of about 0.003 inch (0.07 mm) of groove wear, and the sides of the groove should be smooth and straight. Small imperfections can be smoothed using a small file. Excessive or tapered wear requires shaft or clutch support replacement. ● **SEE FIGURE 29–15.**

INSTALLING TEFLON SEALING RINGS   **Scarf-cut**, Teflon sealing rings are installed by placing them in the groove with the ends lapped in the correct direction. ● **SEE FIGURE 29–16.**

Uncut Teflon rings require two special tools for installation:

1. An installing tool
2. Resizing tool.

To install a Teflon ring,

- place the installing tool over the shaft
- adjust it to the correct depth if necessary
- lubricate the ring and the tool
- slide the ring over the tool and into its groove

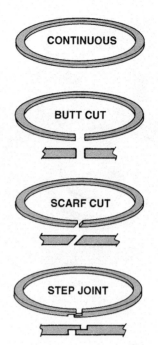

FIGURE 29–16 Four styles of Teflon rings; the uncut, continuous ring requires special tools for installation. The other styles are placed into the groove with overlapping ends positioned properly.

The ring will stretch during installation. Next, lubricate the ring and the resizing tool, and work the resizing tool over the ring, being sure the ring enters its groove correctly. The resizing tool will compress the ring to the correct diameter. Once the transmission operates and the ring gets hot, it will take the shape of the bore. ● **SEE FIGURE 29–17.**

SUBASSEMBLIES

TYPICAL PROCEDURES   Inspection, service, and repair operations are done to each of the transmission **subassemblies** as part of the transmission overhaul. Subassemblies include clutch packs, the pump, and the valve body. Most technicians disassemble the transmission and then service each of the subassemblies separately before starting to reassemble the transmission.

CASE SERVICE

FLUID PASSAGES   Several areas of the case should be checked or serviced after it has been cleaned. These include the bushings, all fluid passages, the valve body worm tracks (grooves for the valve body fluid flow), all bolt threads, the clutch plate lugs, and the governor bore, if equipped.

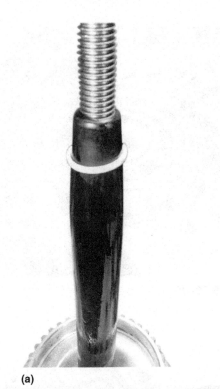

(a)

(b)

(c)

FIGURE 29–17 (a) Using a seal installation tool allows the seal to slide down over the shaft without harming the seal. (b) After the seal has been placed in the groove, use a sizing tool to reduce the size of the seal. (c) The seal after it has been sized.

 TECH TIP

Sealing Ring Tip

Warming the ring in hot water will soften the material and make installation and resizing easier. It is helpful to leave the seal-resizing tool on the seal until ready to install the shaft. ● **SEE FIGURE 29–18**.

FIGURE 29–18 Using water that has been heated in a microwave to help soften a Teflon sealing ring before installing it on the shaft.

Some cases have an output shaft bushing, and it should be checked and replaced if it is worn or scored. Occasionally a bushing will seize and spin with the shaft, which can ruin the case. The repair procedure is to ream the bore oversize and install an oversized bushing.

Every fluid passage in the case must be clean and open. It is a good practice to follow these steps:

- Blow air into each passage and make sure that it comes out through the other end.

- Next, plug off one end of the passage while air pressure is applied and if air is escaping, there is a leak.

WARPAGE Check for **warpage** in the worm track area. Warpage can produce a **cross leak**, which is a leak from one passage to another. A cross leak can cause an unwanted, partial application of a clutch or band that can lead to an early failure. Case warpage is checked by placing a precision straightedge over the area to be checked and trying to slide a feeler gauge between the case and straightedge. Check service information for the specified maximum warpage, which is usually less than 0.002 inch (0.05 mm).

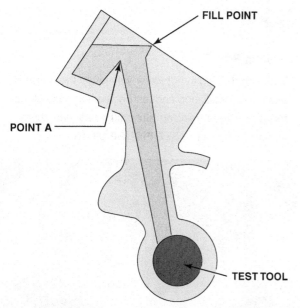

FIGURE 29–19 Filling the passage with ATF and then seeing how long it takes for the fluid to leak down to point A. A test tool instead of the component can be used to check for leakage around a bore if available.

CHECK BORES Check all bores in the case.

1. Accumulator bore size can be checked by placing the accumulator into its bore and filling the passages with ATF. The bore should be repaired if the fluid leaks out too quickly (to point A in less than 30 sec.). ● SEE FIGURE 29–19.

2. Some accumulator bores tend to wear because of repeated accumulator piston oscillation. This produces leakage at the accumulator piston and will ruin the case. A repair sleeve can be installed into the accumulator bore, and this sleeve along with a matching piston will allow the case to be reused.

BOLTS Most faulty bolt threads are found during disassembly. It is good practice to check all bolt threads visually to make sure they are in good shape. Always replace questionable bolts. The telltale sign of failure is when the bolts come out with aluminum on the threads. If aluminum is found to be on the treads of a bolt, the threaded hole has to be repaired using a Heli-coil® or other type of thread insert.

PUMP SERVICE

STEPS INVOLVED Servicing most pumps involves the following operations:

- Disassembly
- Inspection of the pumping members, stator support shaft, front bushing, clutch support surface, and sealing ring grooves

FIGURE 29–20 A pump assembly after the cover has been removed.

FIGURE 29–21 The pump housing should be inspected for wear and replaced if grooved or damaged.

- Checking of all valves
- Cleaning of all fluid passages, including the drain back hole
- Replacement of the front seal and bushing
- Reassembly

To disassemble a pump, simply remove the bolts that secure the cover onto the body. ● SEE FIGURE 29–20.

VISUAL INSPECTION Carefully check the areas where wear normally occurs. The pump has a high-pressure area, and this high pressure tries to force the gears outward. Inspect the following areas for wear.

- Sides of the gears or rotors
- Body and cover where the gears move. ● SEE FIGURE 29–21.

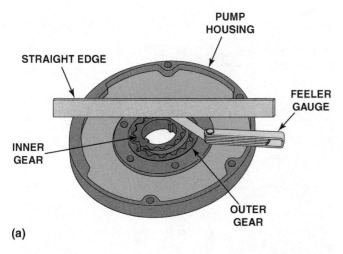

(a)

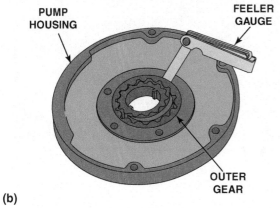

(b)

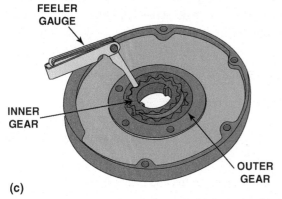

(c)

FIGURE 29–22 Clearance checks of the pump gears include (a) end clearance, (b) gear-to-housing clearance, and (c) gear-tooth clearance.

- Flanks of the gear teeth/rotor lobes for score marks
- Pump bushing

Manufacturers sometimes publish clearance specifications for the pump wear locations. These clearances can be checked using a feeler gauge. A worn pump requires replacement with a new or rebuilt unit. ● **SEE FIGURE 29–22.**

Vane-type pumps are also checked by visual inspection by checking the following:

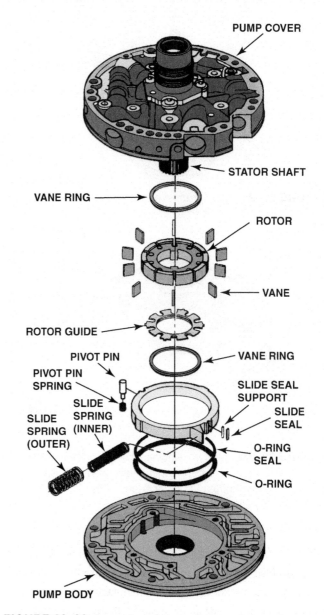

FIGURE 29–23 An exploded view of a vane-type pump. Wear checks include the rotor, vanes, slide, pump body, and pump cover.

- pump guide rings
- vanes
- rotor
- pump guide
- slide
- slide seals
- seal support
- slide pivot pin
- spring
- slide sealing ring
- backup seal. ● **SEE FIGURE 29–23.**

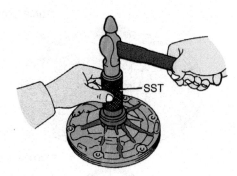

FIGURE 29-24 A new front seal is being installed using a seal driver which is a special service tool (SST).

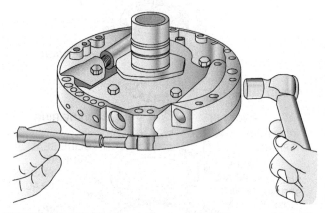

FIGURE 29-25 Using an alignment band to assemble both pump halves to ensure proper alignment. Many experts recommend lightly tapping the outer edges of the pump while tightening the clamp.

FRONT SEAL INSTALLATION The pump is usually disassembled if the front seal and bushing are to be replaced. It should be noted that some manufacturers recommend replacing the pump assembly if the front bushing is damaged. A seal driver should be used when installing the new front seal. ● **SEE FIGURE 29-24.**

ASSEMBLING THE PUMP After the pump has been cleaned, thoroughly checked, and the bushings and seal replaced, it can be reassembled. The gears or rotor and slide assembly should be well lubricated and placed in the pump body.

On some pumps, the cover has a smaller diameter than the body. In this case, the cover is placed in position and the bolts are installed and tightened to the correct torque. Other pump covers and bodies have the same outer diameter. These diameters are only slightly smaller than the bore in the transmission case. The two outer diameters have to be exactly aligned before tightening the bolts. Pump cover alignment can be

FIGURE 29-26 A compressor tool is usually necessary to compress the springs of the clutch piston to remove the snap ring.

accomplished by using various commercially available band-type aligning tools or a large screw-type hose clamp. ● **SEE FIGURE 29-25.**

CLUTCH ASSEMBLY

TYPICAL PROCEDURE The service procedure for most clutch assemblies is as follows:

- Remove the clutch plates and disassemble the return spring(s) and piston using the specified clutch compressor. ● **SEE FIGURE 29-26.**
- Thoroughly clean the parts.
- Inspect the drum, piston, and check ball as well as the bushing and seal ring area.
- Install new seals on the piston.
- Install the piston and return spring(s).
- Soak all new friction plates in ATF.
- Install the clutch plates.
- Check the clutch clearance.

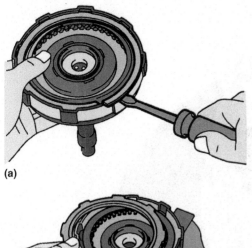

(a)

(b)

FIGURE 29–27 (a) The large snap ring can usually be removed using a screwdriver or a seal pick, and then (b) the pressure plate and clutch plates can be removed.

CLUTCH PACK DISASSEMBLY Clutch plate removal first requires taking the snap ring out of its groove using a screwdriver or a seal pick. The pressure plate and clutch plates are removed next. ● **SEE FIGURE 29–27.**

A spring compressor is usually required to remove the piston return spring(s) and retainer. There is a large variety of spring compressors, and no one unit will work best for all clutches, because some have a bore in the center, a shaft in the center, or are in the case. Many shops use bench- or floor-mounted spring compressors because these are usually faster.

Some clutch pistons almost fall out of the bore when the springs and retainer are removed. Other pistons have to be

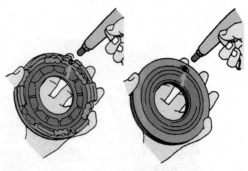

FIGURE 29–28 The check ball should be free to move inside its cage. It should also seal low-pressure airflow in one direction (left) and leak in the other (right).

coaxed with air pressure in the clutch apply oil hole or by tapping the clutch drum piston side down onto a block of wood. With the piston out, remove the old seals, wash the parts in solvent, and dry them using compressed air.

The clutch check ball should be captured in its cage but still be free to rattle when shaken. It should move with either an air blast or with the use of a seal pick. Fill the drum with ATF and check that it does not leak. The check ball assembly can be removed and replaced in stamped steel drums. ● **SEE FIGURE 29–28.**

ASSEMBLING A CLUTCH PACK When the clutch parts check out and are thoroughly clean, perform the following operations:

- Soak all frictions plates in ATF. ● **SEE FIGURE 29–29.**
- Install the new seals.
- Thoroughly lubricate the seals and bore.
- Carefully install the piston completely into the bore.
- Replace the return springs and retainer.

If three piston seals are used, be sure they all face in the proper direction.

A clutch is assembled by stacking the parts in the correct order. Some units use a thick apply plate next to the piston to distribute the apply force onto the plates. The stack is an alternating series of lined and unlined plates followed by a backing/pressure plate. Some units use a wave, Belleville, or selective plate under the backing plate.

When a clutch pack is assembled, the clearance should always be checked and adjusted if necessary. The clearance check ensures that the clutch is assembled correctly and will produce a smooth shift. Depending on the transmission and

FIGURE 29–29 All new friction plates should be soaked in ATF for at least 20 minutes or until bubbles no longer rise to the surface of the shallow pan of ATF.

the particular clutch, different selective parts may be used to adjust clutch clearance. The parts that can be of variable (selective) thickness are the piston, pressure plate, snap ring, apply ring, steel plate, and lined plate. Typically, a selective snap ring is used. Most manufacturers publish clearance specifications for some, if not all, of the clutches used in their transmissions. If clearance specifications are not available, use the rule of thumb that the clearance should be 0.010 inch (0.5 mm) for each lined plate.

Clutch pack clearance, also called *piston travel*, is normally measured using a feeler gauge placed between the pressure plate and the snap ring. If a waved snap ring is used, position the feeler gauge in the widest area under a wave portion. ● **SEE FIGURE 29–30.**

Clearance can also be measured using a dial indicator. Position the dial indicator and raise and lower the backing plate to measure its vertical travel, which is the clutch clearance. If a wave or Belleville plate is used, the pressure plate should be pushed downward with a light, even pressure so the cushion plate(s) is not distorted.

The clutch is ready for installation at this point. If the selective parts do not correct the clearance or are not available,

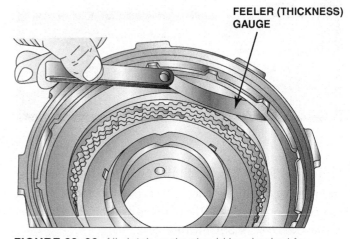

FEELER (THICKNESS) GAUGE

FIGURE 29–30 All clutch packs should be checked for proper clearance. Here, a feeler (thickness) gauge is used to check the clearance to make sure it is within factory specifications.

clutch clearance can be reduced by using extra-thick steel plates or by adding an extra unlined steel or lined friction plate. ● **SEE FIGURE 29–31.**

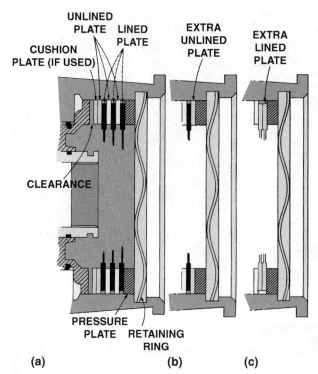

FIGURE 29–31 (a) and (b) Clutch clearance can be reduced by adding an extra unlined plate, or (c) lined plate. If two lined plates are next to each other as in (c), clearance can be increased by shaving the lining off one or both adjacent sides of the two lined plates.

ONE-WAY CLUTCH SERVICE

TYPICAL PROCEDURES One-way clutches (OWCs) are visually inspected during transmission disassembly and reassembly. The commonly encountered problems are severe wear from poor lubrication or metal fragments peeling from a failed part or wear or scoring of the race(s), rollers, or sprags. One-way clutches should always be lubricated using assembly grease, petroleum jelly, or ATF during assembly. After assembly, they should be tested to ensure that they rotate freely in the proper direction and lock up in the opposite direction. ● SEE FIGURE 29–32.

GEAR SET SERVICE

VISUAL INSPECTION Servicing gear sets is primarily a visual inspection of the various gears and a side play and rotation check of the planet gears. In some cases there

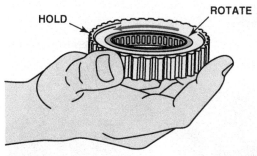

FIGURE 29–32 Service information states that this one-way roller clutch should be installed as shown. Check by holding the outer race so that the inner race is free to rotate counterclockwise as shown.

FIGURE 29–33 This planetary gear set is excessively worn and wear metal form this failure has likely contaminated many other parts in the transmission.

is also an end-play check of the assembled gear train to ensure the thrust washers are not worn excessively. ● SEE FIGURE 29–33.

In many transmissions, the gear set comes out one part at a time. After cleanup, the parts are carefully inspected again. Parts to rebuild a planetary are available from aftermarket sources. All ring and sun gears should be checked for chipped or broken teeth and worn or stripped drive splines. The thrust surfaces at the sides of the gears and any support bushings or bushing surfaces should be checked for scores, wear, or other damage. Drive shells should be checked for stripped splines, damaged lugs, or cracks.

When checking a carrier, the pinion gears must be undamaged and turn freely. Check for worn or missing pinion thrust bushings and measure the pinion gear end play and/or side clearance. ● SEE FIGURE 29–34.

Some manufacturers provide pinion gear side clearance specifications, but if no specifications are available, use the rule

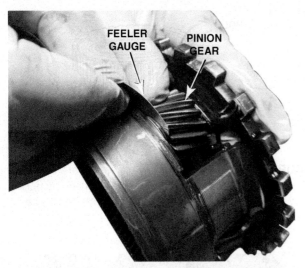

FIGURE 29-34 Using a feeler gauge to measure the pinion gear side clearance.

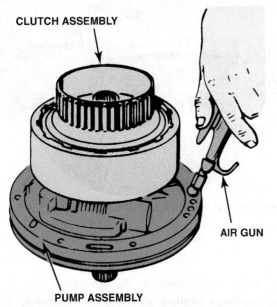

FIGURE 29-35 Air testing a clutch pack before installing it into an automatic transmission or transaxle.

of thumb of 0.005 to 0.025 inches (0.167 to 0.635 mm). In some cases, the pinion gear assembly can be removed from the carrier to replace the bearings, gear, or thrust washers. Shims are available to tighten the side clearance on some carriers.

AIR TESTING

PURPOSE OF THE TEST Air testing is a valuable diagnostic tool, which is also used as a final quality-control check during transmission assembly. Air tests are used to tell if a clutch or band servo operates, and if the passages are properly sealed. ● SEE FIGURE 29-35.

FIGURE 29-36 Using a rubber-tipped air nozzle in a passage to check the operation of a clutch or band.

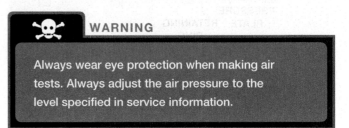

WARNING

Always wear eye protection when making air tests. Always adjust the air pressure to the level specified in service information.

Many manufacturers provide illustrations in their service information that identifies these passages. A rubber-tipped air gun pushed against the end of the passage to make a seal is normally used when making air tests. ● SEE FIGURE 29-36.

It is possible to air check the whole transmission or an individual circuit by blowing air into the pressure test ports. If checking the whole transmission, insert the rubber tip of the air gun into the "line" test port, set the air pressure to about 90 PSI (620 kPa), and apply air pressure. Depending on the location of the test port in the hydraulic circuit, the airflow can be controlled using the manual valve. In some cases with the transmission on the bench, the pump will rotate, but it can be held stationary by installing the torque converter. If the transmission has pressure test ports for the different circuits, each of these circuits can be checked by pressurizing each port. While performing these checks, be sure to listen for escaping air, which indicates leaks.

As different components are air tested, the results can vary.

- **Band servos**—When air is applied, the band should apply with a very small amount of air leakage. Removal of the air gun from the passage should result in band release. Some bands require that air be used to apply the

Air Testing Tricks

Some technicians use an air gun that is modified with a piece of rubber tubing for hard-to-reach locations. An eraser with a hole drilled through the center can be used to seal passages. This makes air testing at the valve body easy. ● **SEE FIGURE 29–37.**

(a)

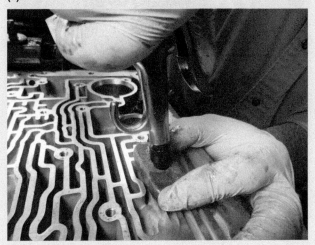

(b)

FIGURE 29–37 (a) An eraser with a hole drilled through it used to seal passages during an air test. (b) Using an air nozzle and the eraser to test hydraulic circuits at the valve body.

band and a second air nozzle position be used to release the band. When the second air nozzle is removed, the band will reapply, and when the first air nozzle is removed, spring pressure will release the band.

- **Clutches**—When air is applied to a clutch, a "kachunk" noise indicates the clutch applied. Removal of the air

FIGURE 29–38 Using an electronic torque wrench to tighten the pump retaining bolts to factory specifications.

gun should result in the sound of a clutch release. If the air nozzle is kept in place, good clutch seals should hold air pressure for about 5 seconds or more after the air is turned off.

FINAL ASSEMBLY

ASSEMBLE THE UNIT The following parts are installed into the case according to the prescribed procedure found in service information:

- Planetary gear sets
- Clutch packs
- Bands

PUMP INSTALLATION After the planetary gear sets, clutches, and bands are assembled, the pump is installed and the retaining bolts torqued to factory specifications. Always follow the vehicle manufacturer's specified assembly procedures and final checks. ● **SEE FIGURE 29–38.**

END PLAY CHECK Perform all end-play checks during assembly to ensure that the unit was properly assembled and that the proper internal clearances are achieved. ● **SEE FIGURE 29–39.**

TRANSAXLE DIFFERENTIALS/CHAINS Transaxle differentials should be checked to make sure that the differential gears, thrust washers, and the differential pinion shaft are in good condition. A differential can usually be disassembled by removing the lock pin and driving the differential pinion shaft

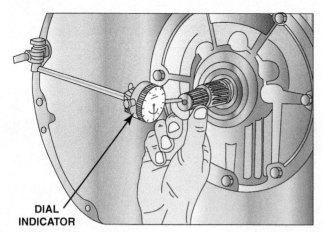

FIGURE 29–39 A dial indicator being used to measure the end play of an input shaft. If the end play is not within factory specifications, the unit may not have been assembled correctly.

FIGURE 29–40 Checking differential gear clearance using a dial indicator on the final drive assembly of a transaxle.

out. This allows removal of the gears and thrust washers. The gears should be inspected for chipped or broken teeth and scoring on the bearing surfaces. The thrust washers and differential pinion shaft should be checked for wear and scoring.

Some differentials are combined with a planet carrier that includes a set of planet pinions along with the differential. Like those inside the transmission, these pinion gears must turn freely on their shafts and not have excessive end play. The thrust washers and needle bearings can be replaced. If differential clearance is excessive, replace the thrust washers. In many cases, the new thrust washers will correct the clearance. ● **SEE FIGURE 29–40.**

Some transaxles use a chain/sprockets and need to be installed with the black link of the chain in the same direction (usually up) as when it was disassembled. Check service information for the specified procedure to follow.

TECH TIP

Avoid Using Red Assembly Lube

Assembly lube is used during the reassembly of automatic transmissions. If red assembly lube is used on seals, it may look like an automatic transmission fluid leak when the transmission gets hot and the lube melts. If you use blue, green, brown, or clear assembly lube, then the color will immediately identify it as assembly lube. ● **SEE FIGURE 29–41.**

Many transmissions have been disassembled because the service technician thought that the red liquid dripping from parts of the transmission was automatic transmission fluid when, in fact, it was only assembly lube that melted and ran when the transmission reached normal operating temperature.

FIGURE 29–41 Blue assembly lube.

VALVE BODY, FILTER, AND PAN INSTALLATION After completing all of the end-play checks and air tests, the valve body can be installed. ● **SEE FIGURE 29–42.**

FINAL COMPONENTS INSTALLATION After the valve body and filter have been installed, the final components need to be installed:

- Turbine shaft seal
- Accumulators and transmission range switch
- Solenoid blocks
- Internal wiring harness
- Speed sensors. ● **SEE FIGURE 29–43.**

(a)

INTERIOR WIRING HARNESS

CASE CONNECTOR

(b)

FIGURE 29–42 (a) The oil pump/valve body retaining bolts being torqued to factory specifications. (b) After the valve body has been installed, the interior wiring harness and case connector are installed.

 REAL WORLD FIX

The Case of the Broken Flex Plate

The 5.7-L engine in a 2005 Suburban was replaced at 185,000 miles with a reputable remanufactured engine. After 7,000 miles, it came back with a knock. Inspection revealed a broken flex plate, which was replaced. It returned again after another 7,000 miles with a knock, and another broken flex plate. A new GM flex plate was installed. It returned a third time with the same problem.

After the transmission was removed, it was discovered that the replacement engine did not come with the alignment dowels, and this omission was overlooked three times. Installation of the alignment dowels and a new flex plate solved this problem.

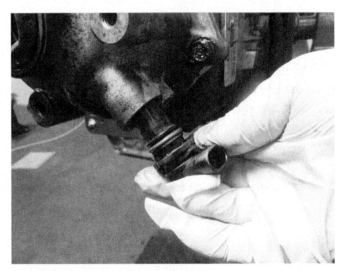

FIGURE 29–43 Installing an output speed sensor that has been equipped with a new O-ring seal.

DYNAMOMETER TESTING

A rebuilt automatic transmission/transaxle can be tested for proper operation on a dynamometer powered by:

- An electric motor. ● **SEE FIGURE 29–44.**
- A gasoline engine. ● **SEE FIGURE 29–45.**

Most dynamometers are equipped with a load applying unit and pressure gauges so that their proper operation can be checked before installation.

- Carefully install the torque converter onto the input shaft, being sure to fully engage the following:

  1. Pump gear
  2. Stator splines
  3. Turbine splines

- Finally, conduct a visual check to make sure that all fasteners are properly tightened.

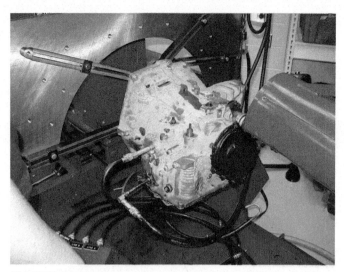

FIGURE 29–44 An electric motor-driven dynamometer being used to check the operation of a transaxle.

FIGURE 29–45 A gasoline-powered dynamometer being used to test a rear-wheel-drive automatic transmission.

FIGURE 29–46 Check the linkage for proper adjustment so that the shift interlock works correctly and the PRNDL is aligned with the transmission range switch.

TRANSMISSION INSTALLATION

STEPS INVOLVED Installing a transmission is the reverse of the removal procedure. The last operation in the removal is usually the first step in the installation.

Installation of an automatic transmission or transaxle usually involves the following steps:

STEP 1 Before installing the transmission, make sure that the transmission alignment dowels and the wiring harness are in place and all of the connectors are properly connected.

STEP 2 Raise the transmission into position and slide it to place it against the engine.

CAUTION: Do not use the bolts to pull the transmission/transaxle to the engine block.

STEP 3 Install the transmission-to-engine bolts and tighten them to the correct torque.

NOTE: Periodically check to make sure the torque converter does not bind as you tighten the bolts to specified torque. The torque converter should turn freely. This ensures that the converter hub will not bind against the pump drive gear.

STEP 4 Place the transmission supports into position, lower the transmission onto the mounts, and tighten the mounting bolts to the correct torque.

STEP 5 Slide the converter forward to align with the flex plate. Install the bolts and tighten them to the correct torque.

STEP 6 Connect the cooler lines and tighten them to the correct torque.

STEP 7 Replace the driveshaft(s) and tighten any retaining bolts to the correct torque.

STEP 8 Reconnect all linkage and wire connections that were disconnected, making sure they are routed properly. ● **SEE FIGURE 29–46.**

STEP 9 If a new TCM has been installed into the vehicle, the new module needs to be reprogrammed.

After installation, the transmission should be filled with the correct amount of ATF and the engine started. Adjust the fluid level after starting the engine and operating the transmission in the different gear ranges.

TRANSMISSION ADAPTIVE LEARNING The purpose of the adapt function is to automatically compensate the shift quality for the various vehicle shift control systems. The adapt function is a continuous process that helps to maintain optimal shift quality throughout the life of the vehicle. A six-speed transmission utilizes a line pressure control system during upshifts to compensate for the normal wear of transmission components. As the apply components within the transmission wear or change over time, shift time increases or decreases.

In order to compensate for these changes, the transmission control module (TCM) adjusts the pressure commands to the various pressure control solenoids to maintain the originally calibrated shift timing.

The TCM's automatic adjusting process is referred to as "**adaptive learning**," and it is used to ensure consistent shift feel plus increase transmission durability. The TCM monitors the automatic transmission input speed sensor and the automatic transmission output speed sensor during commanded shifts to determine if a shift is occurring too fast (harsh) or too slow (soft), and adjusts the corresponding pressure control solenoid signal to maintain the set shift feel.

REPAIR VERIFICATION AND TRANSMISSION ADAPTS RESET
The reset transmission adapts is a procedure for automatic transmissions in which the shift pressure learn values of each individual clutch are reset to zero or a base calibrated value, in the transmission control module.

Once the transmission adapts are set to zero or a calibrated value, the vehicle is then road-tested under various drive-cycle events for the TCM to relearn shift pressure values for the best possible shift feel in all gear ranges.

The reset transmission adapts procedure must be performed when one of the following repairs have been made to the transmission. Failure to perform the procedure after one of the following repairs may result in poor transmission performance, DTCs being set, or customer dissatisfaction.

- Transmission internal service, repair or overhaul
- Valve body repair or replacement
- Control solenoid valve assembly replacement
- Any service/repair in response to a shift quality concern

Listed here are the general steps of the repair verification procedure, including transmission adapt reset. Always refer to service information for the specific vehicle being serviced for details.

STEP 1 The first step of the repair verification is to ensure there is enough transmission fluid inside the transmission to complete a road test. If the transmission is equipped with a fluid level indicator, make sure the transmission fluid is touching the bottom of the indicator. The transmission must be brought up to the correct temperature to properly check the transmission fluid level. If the transmission does not have a fluid level indicator,

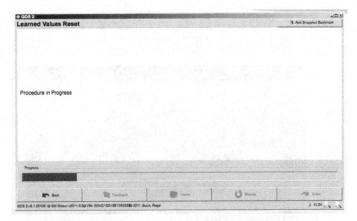

FIGURE 29–47 Use the scan tool to reset the transmission adapts. (Courtesy of General Motors)

check service information (SI) for the correct amount of fluid to add to the transmission after the repair.

STEP 2 Install any components or connectors that have been removed or replaced during diagnosis. Perform any adjustments, programming, or setup procedures that are required when a component or module is removed or replaced. Next, clear any DTCs. Turn the ignition OFF and wait until all vehicle systems are off; this may take up to 2 minutes.

STEP 3 With the ignition ON and the engine running, use a scan tool to reset the transmission adapts. ● **SEE FIGURE 29–47**.

STEP 4 After resetting the transmission adapts, perform a thorough road test as described in SI. Failure to perform the procedure after the repairs are complete may result in poor transmission performance, DTCs being set, or customer dissatisfaction.

During the road test, make sure the transmission completes all of the shifts several times. Operate the vehicle in stop-and-go traffic, as well as at highway speeds. This enables the transmission control module to learn the common shifts and make corrections to the shift quality.

NOTE: After completing the road test, make sure to completely power down the vehicle for at least 2 minutes to ensure the TCM stores the information properly.

STEP 5 Once the road test is complete, restart the vehicle and check the fluid level again. Make any adjustments to fluid level as necessary to bring it to the correct level. The last step of the repair verification is to inspect for any transmission fluid leaks. If any leaks are discovered, make repairs as necessary. If everything is in order, the vehicle is ready to be returned to the customer.[1]

[1]GM Center of Learning Course # 17041.56W3.

ASSEMBLING A 4T65-E TRANSAXLE

1 After cleaning all of the parts, read, understand, and follow the instructions that come with the overhaul kit.

2 A new seal is installed.

3 All bearings and thrust washers should be lubricated with assembly lube during assembly.

4 The band is installed after soaking in ATF.

5 All of the seals being laid out and compared before being installed. They too should be covered with ATF or assembly lube before being installed.

6 All friction discs should be soaked in ATF for at least 20 minutes or until the bubbles stop.

7 All piston seals are replaced as part of the overhaul procedure. The piston is then installed using a lip seal plastic disc to help prevent the seal lip from curling over during installation.

8 Assembling a clutch pack with soaked frictions and then steel plates.

9 The return springs have to be compressed before installing the retaining ring.

10 The drive chain being installed after checking that the black link is up the same way it was when it was disassembled.

11 Before assembling the valve body, always check the valve body gasket labeled "V" and the gasket that goes against the case, label "C" to make sure that they match the ones that were removed when the unit was disassembled.

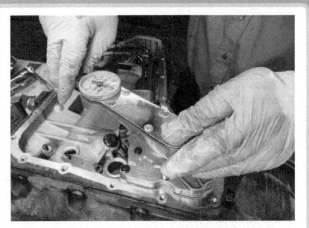

12 All fasteners should be tightened to factory specifications using a torque wrench.

1. A transmission overhaul includes disassembling, cleaning, replacing worn parts, and reassembling to its original clearances.

2. Transmission parts cleaning methods that are commonly used include the following:
   - Hot spray wash
   - Solvent wash
   - Water (aqueous) solution wash
   - Microbe cleaning

3. Bushings and bearings are carefully checked and replaced as necessary. A bushing or thrust washer must have an operating clearance of about 0.003 to 0.005 inches (0.076 to 0.157 mm) to allow a good oil flow across the bearing surface.

4. Clutches are serviced by inspecting and replacing the friction material and seals.

5. Sealing rings must be replaced and the surfaces they seal against must be carefully inspected and serviced as needed. An O-ring should produce some drag and a square-cut seal is normal if it produces a barely noticeable drag.

6. Uncut Teflon rings require two special tools for installation:
   a. An installing tool
   b. A resizing tool

7. Warpage can produce a cross leak, which is a leak from one passage to another. A cross leak can cause an unwanted, partial application of a clutch or band that can lead to an early failure.

8. The pump is disassembled and inspected. The bushings and seals are replaced before reassembly.

9. When rebuilding a clutch, the friction plates, piston seals, and bushings are replaced.

10. Air testing is a valuable diagnostic tool and is also used as a final quality-control check during transmission assembly. Air tests are used to tell if a clutch or band servo operates, and if the passages are properly sealed.

11. For an electronic transmission/transaxle to operate correctly, the transmission adaptive learning memories must be rest using a scan tool and a repair verification road test.

REVIEW QUESTIONS

1. What cleaning methods can be used to clean automatic transmission/transaxle parts?

2. What is a Torrington bearing?

3. Uncut Teflon rings require what two special tools for installation?

4. What are the two ways to check clutch pack clearance?

5. Why should clutches and bands be air checked?

6. Why does the adaptive learning need to be reset after an overhaul?

CHAPTER QUIZ

1. Cleaning methods that are commonly used include _____.
   a. Hot spray wash
   b. Water (aqueous) solution wash
   c. Microbe cleaning
   d. All of the above

2. A radial needle bearing is commonly called a _____
   a. Bushing
   b. Torrington
   c. Bearing
   d. Cup

3. Tapered roller bearings must be adjusted to get the correct end play or preload. This is usually achieved by using _____.
   a. Selective thickness shims
   b. Various sizes of races
   c. Different size rollers
   d. Different tapers used for the bearings

4. New lined material should be soaked in ATF for at least _____ before installation.
   a. 5 minutes
   b. 10 minutes
   c. 20 minutes
   d. 60 minutes (an hour)

5. What is needed to properly fit a Teflon seal?
   a. An installation tool
   b. A sizing tool
   c. Hot water to soften the ring
   d. All of the above

6. Clutch pack clearance can be checked using _____.
   a. A feeler gauge
   b. A dial indicator
   c. Either a or b depending on the clutch and access to measure the clearance
   d. Both methods should be used to insure accuracy

7. Air testing is used to _____.
   a. Check the operation of the pump
   b. Test the valve body valve operation
   c. Test the clutches and bands for proper operation and to detect possible leaks
   d. Operate the speed sensors

8. Technician A says that an end-play check should be performed to make sure that the unit has been correctly assembled. Technician B says that the end-play check can be used to check for proper internal clearances. Which technician is correct?
   a. Technician A only
   b. Technician B only
   c. Both Technicians A and B
   d. Neither Technician A nor B

9. What should be done when installing a transmission/transaxle into a vehicle?
   a. Make sure that the transmission alignment dowels are installed.
   b. Connect the cooler lines and tighten them to the correct torque.
   c. Check the linkage for proper adjustment so that the shift interlock works correctly and the PRNDL is aligned with the transmission range switch.
   d. All of the above

10. The transmission adaptive learned memories are cleared using a _____ before the vehicle is driven.
    a. Pressure gauge   c. Scan tool
    b. Dial indicator   d. Valve body tester

GLOSSARY

Accelerate   To increase speed.

Accumulator   A device that absorbs the shock of sudden pressure surges within a hydraulic system. Accumulators are used in transmission hydraulic systems to control shift quality.

Actuator   A device that translates hydraulic pressure or a computer output voltage signal into mechanical energy.

Adaptive memory   A feature of computer memory that allows the microprocessor to adjust its memory for computing output response based on changes in vehicle-operating conditions.

Additives   Chemicals added to lubricants to improve or modify certain operating characteristics.

Aerobic sealant   A type of sealant that cures in the presence of air.

Aerodynamic drag   The wind resistance of air moving over the size and shape of the vehicle.

All-wheel drive (AWD)   A drive system that can drive both the front and rear wheels through all phases of operation. (Also called full-time 4WD.)

Anaerobic sealant   A type of sealant that cures in the absence of air.

Analog signal   A voltage signal or processing action that is continuously variable relative to the operation being measured or controlled.

Annulus gear   An internal, or ring, gear used in a planetary gear set.

Antifriction bearings   A bearing that uses spherical or cylindrical rollers within a housing to decrease resistance.

Apply devices   Hydraulically operated bands, multidisc clutches, and mechanically operated one-way clutches that drive or hold the members of a planetary gear set.

Asbestos   A generic name for a group of minerals used to line clutch disks in older transmissions.

Automatic locking differential   A final drive differential that has the ability to positively lock the axles to the differential carrier.

Automatic locking hubs   A type of hub that connects the front wheels to the front axle when 4WD is selected.

Automatic transfer case (ATC)   A type of transfer case that operates much like an automatic transmission selecting between 2WD and 4WD.

Automatic transfer case control module   A control computer that monitors input speeds from the front and rear drive shafts' speed sensors to monitor wheel slip. The software then decides to engage or disengage 2WD or 4WD mode.

Automatic transmission fluid (ATF)   The fluid designed for use in an automatic transmission.

Automatic transmission   A transmission that automatically changes forward gear speeds.

Axial load   Any line of force applied parallel to the axis.

Axial motion   Movement along, or parallel to, the centerline (axis) of a shaft. A dynamic seal is required to contain fluids where axial motion is present.

Axial play   Movement along, or parallel to, the centerline (axis) of a shaft. Also called end thrust or end play.

Axis   The centerline around which a gear, wheel, or shaft rotates.

Back taper   An angle cut opposite to the chamfer so that the spine or tooth narrows just behind the chamfered end.

Ball bearing   A bearing that uses round balls between an inner and outer bearing race. They are used in transmissions and drivetrains but are costly to produce and cannot take as much load as sliding bearings.

Bearing cage   A spacer to keep the balls or rollers in a bearing separated and in the proper position.

Bearing cap   A device that is bolted in place to secure a bearing in place.

Bearing cone   The inner race of a tapered roller bearing.

Bearing cup   The outer race for the needles of a U-joint bearing and of a tapered roller bearing.

Bearing race   The hardened surface on which the balls, needles, or rollers of a bearing run.

Bearings   Machine elements placed between any two rotating or moving parts of the drivetrain by engineers to prevent those parts from rubbing directly against each other.

Belleville spring   A conical steel spring that gives a spring action because of its resistance to flattening.

Bell housing   A separate casting that bolts onto the front of the transmission and encloses the entire clutch assembly.

Bellows-type boot   An accordion-pleated rubber cover used to protect a mechanical device inside of it.

Bevel gear   Often used to change the direction of rotation in a drivetrain. Its teeth are cut at an angle to the outside gear surface.

Boots   Rubber or plastic cover that protects the CV joints from contaminants and retain the CV grease.

Boost valve   A device that works against a pressure regulator valve to increase mainline pressure when needed.

Boundary layer   The protective oil film between moving parts.

Boundary lubrication   Lubrication that is required where mounting tolerances are narrow, such as when pressure is applied to one of the components.

Brinelling   Grooves worn on a bearing journal due to impact loading, vibration, or wear.

Burnish   To smooth or polish through rubbing action.

Bus   An electrical conductor, or conductors, serving as a common connection for three or more circuits.

Bushing   A type of sliding bearing. It is a full round sleeve, is usually small, and is pressed into a hole and machined or reamed to fit a shaft.

Cancelling angles   Equal and opposite angles of two U-joints, used to cancel vibrations generated by the U-joints.

Cantilever   A lever that is anchored and supported at one end by its fulcrum and provides an opposing force at its opposite end.

Cardan U-joint   The most common type of U-joint, used in most rear-wheel-drive driveshafts.

Carrier   The casting section of a drive axle that contains the differential and ring and pinion gears.

Case   The rigid housing for a drive axle, transaxle, transmission, or transfer case.

C-clip   A C-shaped locking device used to retain an axle shaft.

Center section   The carrier portion of a drive axle.

Centrifugal force   The force on a revolving object that tries to push it away from the center of revolution.

Chain drive transfer case   A four-wheel-drive transfer case that uses a chain and sprockets to transfer drive torque to the front axle. *See* **gear-to-gear transfer case.**

Chamfer   A beveled edge on a shaft or bore.

Check ball   A type of hydraulic valve, consisting of a ball, that seals an orifice when it is seated and can be unseated to open the orifice.

Circlip   A snap-ring type of ring with a round cross section used to position a shaft in a bore.

Clash   The grinding sound that is heard when trying to mesh two gears that are operating at different speeds.

Cluster gear   A group of gears that are machined from one piece of metal, or individual gears combined into one group so they operate together.

Clutch   A device that controls the power transfer between two points by either allowing or not allowing a transfer.

Clutch assembly   A friction coupling between the engine and transmission.

Clutch drum   A component of a clutch assembly that usually houses the clutch discs and pressure plate. A band often closes around the outside diameter of a clutch drum

Clutch master cylinder   A device that usually mounts in the engine compartment. The fluid reservoir feeds hydraulic fluid into the system as needed to operate the clutch slave cylinder (operating cylinder).

Clutch pack   The assembly of clutch and pressure plates that provides the friction surfaces in a multiple-disc clutch.

Clutch pedal height   The distance from the vehicle floor to the clutch pedal pad.

Clutch plate   A generic term for the friction and steel discs used in a multiple-disc clutch.

Coast   A load condition in which the vehicle is driving the engine, as during deceleration.

Coast side   While the vehicle decelerates, the drive pinion contacts the ring teeth on its coast, or concave, side.

Coefficient of friction   A numerical value expressing the amount of friction between two surfaces. It is obtained by dividing the force required to slide the surfaces across one another by the pressure holding the surfaces together.

Companion flange   A yoke with a bolted mating flange used by some rear axles. It drives the pinion shaft.

Compound planetary gear set   A gear set that contains more than just the three basic members of a simple planetary gear set.

Compressibility   The ability of a gasket to conform to irregularities in the sealing surfaces.

Concave side   *See* **Coast side.**

Consistency   A measure of a grease's resistance to being shaped in the same way that oil viscosity gauges resistance to flow.

Constant velocity (CV) joint   A type of universal joint that transfers torque and speed at a constant rate.

Constant mesh Gears   Gears within a manual transmission that are constantly in mesh. The gears are locked to the output shaft by movement of the synchronizer sleeve when a gear is selected.

Continuously variable transmission (CVT)   A transmission that varies the gear ratio in a continuous, rather than stepwise, manner.

Convex side   When a vehicle accelerates, the drive pinion contacts the ring teeth on its drive, or convex, side.

Corrosion inhibitors   Lubricant additives that help prevent the formation of rust and protect metal parts.

Counter gear   *See* **Countershaft.**

Countershaft   Contains the gears that mesh with output shaft gears to provide gear reduction. It is called a countershaft because it rotates in a direction counter to the main shaft.

Coupling phase   The period of torque converter operation when there is no torque multiplication, and rotary flow causes the stator to unlock and rotate with the impeller and turbine at approximately the same speed.

Cross   Part of a U-joint. Power flows from the first yoke through the cross, and then out through the second yoke.

Crossmember   Supports a typical front-wheel-drive transaxle as well as the rear of the engine; bolts to the chassis.

Crown   It is at the very top of each tooth in a ring gear.

Damper   A device that reduces the torsional vibrations between the engine and transmission.

Decelerate   To reduce speed.

Deflection   Bending or movement caused by a load.

Depth filter   A filter that traps contaminants within the matrix of the filter material. A felt filter is a type of depth filter.

Detent   A spring-loaded device used to position a shift fork correctly.

Detergent additives   Lubricant additives that are designed to reduce varnish deposits that accumulate on piston ring grooves, allowing the rings to seal with maximum effectiveness, which maintains peak engine performance.

Diagnostic trouble code (DTC)   Alpha-numeric identifier for a fault condition.

Dial indicator   A measuring device that indicates linear travel by a rotating needle.

Diaphragm spring   A round, conical-shaped spring; a Belleville spring.

Differential   A gear arrangement that allows the drive wheels to be driven at different speeds.

Direct drive   A 1:1 gear ratio.

Dispersants   Lubricant additives that reduce sludge formation by keeping the contaminants suspended in the oil, which is removed when the oil and filter are changed.

Double-Cardan joint   A type of universal joint that consists of two crosses and a center yoke. The angles between the centerlines of the shafts are cut in half at the centering ball, allowing the speed fluctuations created by the driving yoke to be cancelled out by the driven yoke.

Double-offset joint   A type of universal joint in which the outer race drives the inner bearing race, causing the half shaft to rotate.

Dowel   A round metal pin attached to a casting, which ensures proper alignment as a hole in another casting is placed onto it.

Drag   The resistance or friction created by one object passing by another.

Drain and fill plugs   Threaded plugs that are used to drain and fill the transmission or differential case with lubricant.

Drive   A load condition in which the engine is applying power to the drive wheels.

Drive gear In a transmission, the gear that is inputting power to another gear.

Drive side *See* **Convex side**.

Driveline Another name for a driveshaft.

Driveline windup Occurs while turning a corner on dry pavement while in 4WD.

Driven gear A gear that receives input force from the driving gear.

Driveshaft A device that transmits power from one unit to another. In a vehicle, it transmits power from the transmission to the drive wheels or rear axle.

Drivetrain A device that transfers torque, or the twisting force produced by an automotive engine, to the drive wheels.

Dual-mass flywheel A type of flywheel that is made in two parts that oscillate at slightly different rates, allowing it to absorb a wide range of engine vibrations.

Dyes Colors added to greases by manufacturers to aid in product identification.

Dynamic friction The coefficient of friction between two surfaces that have relative motion between them. Also called kinetic friction.

Dynamic seal A type of oil or grease seal that blocks the passage of fluid between parts that have relative motion between them.

Eccentric Two circles that do not have the same center.

End play The amount of motion a shaft or gear has in a direction that is parallel to the shaft.

Energy The ability to do work.

Engagement modulation The ability to engage the clutch in order to produce a smooth, slip-free engagement.

EP additives Extreme pressure additives; they contain sulfur and phosphorous and are added to the base oil to give gear teeth a protective coating to reduce friction and wear.

Equal-length drive axle system A front-wheel-drive system developed to decrease axle vibration and torque steer, and consists of half shafts of equal length with a CV joint on each end.

External gears Gears, such as spur and helical gears, that have gear teeth on their outside circumference. This type of gear is most commonly used in manual transmissions and transaxles.

Extreme-pressure (EP) lubricant A lubricant designed to stay in place and keep parts from touching when under extremely high pressure.

Feeler gauge Thin metal strips of precise thickness, used to measure the clearance between two parts.

Fiber composites A mixture of fiber threads (glass, graphite, or other materials) and a resin.

Fifth gear In a manual transmission, this is usually an overdrive gear used for highway cruising.

Final drive The last set of reduction gears before the power flows to the differential gears and drive axles.

Final drive gear ratio A ratio of the number of pinion gear teeth to the number of ring gear teeth in the final drive assembly.

Final drive pinion The input or drive component of the rear axle.

First gear The gear used to start the vehicle off from a standstill. Provides high torque but slow speed.

Fixed joints These CV joints, located on the outboard side, allow the wheel to turn at angles as much as 40 degrees to steer the vehicle.

Fixed Rzeppa joint A type of CV joint that operates similar to the plunging double-offset joint, except that the outer race grooves are shorter in length and torque flows in the opposite direction.

Fixed tripod joint A type of CV joint that operates similar to the plunging tripod joint, but has an important difference in that the tulip, instead of being a housing driving the tripod on the half shaft, is now part of the half shaft end driving a tripod encased in a housing.

Flexplate The thin metal plate, used in place of a flywheel, that joins the engine crankshaft to the fluid coupling or torque converter.

Flexible disc A feature of most clutch friction discs. This design allows for some movement between the outer disc assembly and the hub.

Float A load condition in which two parts are turning at the same speed with no driving force between them; also when a shaft is supported by a gear that, in turn, is supported by a bearing.

Float position The intermediate position between drive and coast, when neither the ring gear nor the pinion is driving each other.

Fluoroelastomer rubbers A rubber compound that offers excellent abrasion resistance and has the best high-temperature performance and remains flexible from −40°F to 600°F.

Flywheel The rotating metal mass attached to the crankshaft that helps even out power surges and provides a mounting point and friction surface for the clutch.

Foam inhibitors Reduce lubricant surface tension by reducing the formation of foam, thereby helping to maintain a good oil barrier between moving parts.

Force A push or pull measured in units of weight, like pounds or kilograms.

Formed-in-place gasket (FIPG) A gasket material that comes from a tube, which is applied to metal surfaces before assembly.

Four-wheel drive (4WD) A drive system that can drive both the front and rear wheels.

Fourth gear In a 5-speed manual transmission, fourth gear is usually a direct drive, 1:1 ratio.

Free play A system that allows the pedal to go down about an inch before the operating system starts to transfer any motion to the release bearing. Free play is designed so that the clutch does not immediately begin to disengage as the driver first starts to depress the pedal.

Fretting protection Concerns a specific kind of wear that takes place when two surfaces rub together in a small, repeated motion.

Friction The resistance in motion between two bodies in contact with each other.

Friction disc A flat disc that is faced with friction materials; it is driven when it is clamped between two flat metal surfaces.

Friction modifiers Modifiers added to some gear oils to reduce the amount of friction between contacting metal surfaces.

Front drive axles On 4WD vehicles, they transfer engine torque to the front wheels while allowing the front wheels to turn.

Front propeller shaft Much like the rear propeller shaft, it is usually made of steel with a slip joint incorporated into the shaft.

Front-wheel drive (FWD) A drive system that drives the front wheels.

Fulcrum The pivot or supporting point for a lever.

Full-floating bearing Used on larger trucks, this design places two opposed taper roller bearings between the outside of the axle housing and the inside of the wheel hub.

Full-time four-wheel drive A system that allows the driver to select 2WD or 4WD with similar selector positions as part-time 4WD. Unlike part-time configurations, full-time 4WD includes a differential or viscous coupling that allows the front and rear axles to rotate at different speeds.

Fully synchronized Also called "synchromesh"; in this type of transmission, the gears on the input shaft, countershaft, and output shaft are in constant mesh. Gear ratios are selected by sliding synchronizer rings, as opposed to nonsynchronized transmissions, in which the actual gears slide into and out of mesh.

Galling Wear that transfers metal and is caused by metal-to-metal contact without proper lubrication.

Gasket A compressible material used as a seal between two mating surfaces.

Gear A metal wheel with teeth that transmit power or motion to another gear.

Gear blank A circular piece of metal stock from which gears are cut.

Gear oil A petroleum-based lubricant designed for use in manual transmissions, transaxles, final drives, and differentials.

Gear pump A positive-displacement pump that uses an inner driven gear and an outer driven gear, separated on one side by a crescent, to produce oil flow. Gear pumps may use either helical or spur gears and are sometimes called gear-and-crescent pumps.

Gear ratio The ratio in the number of teeth on the driving and driven gears; it is calculated by dividing the number of teeth on the driven gear by the number of teeth on the driving gear.

Gear reduction A condition in which the driving gear is smaller than the driven gear; the result will be an increase in torque and a reduction in speed.

Gear systems The different types of gears and their functions.

Gear-to-gear transfer cases Simple in design, three gear shafts are in mesh within the transfer case. One gear shaft is attached to the transmission output shaft. The second shaft acts as an idler, and the third shaft is the output to the front axle. *See* **Chain drive transfer case.**

Getrag 5-speed manual transaxle A front-wheel-drive transmission that includes the following features: first and second gears double-coned synchronizer, third, fourth, and fifth gears single-coned synchronizer, and a synchronized reverse gear. The final drive gear is also part of a transaxle.

Governor A hydraulic pressure signal that indicates vehicle road speed.

Governor pressure The transmission hydraulic pressure that is directly related to vehicle speed. Governor pressure increases with vehicle speed and is one of the principle pressures used to control shift points.

Governor valve The valve that regulates governor pressure in relation to vehicle road speed.

Grade resistance One-hundredth of the vehicle weight times the angle of the grade in percent.

Graphite A very fine carbon dust that is used as a dry lubricant or a fiber that is combined with resin to form very strong and lightweight objects, such as driveshaft tubing.

Half shaft The driveshaft used to connect the differential to the drive wheels on drive axles with independent suspension.

Hall effect A signal-generating switch that develops a transverse voltage across a current-carrying semiconductor when subjected to a magnetic field.

Hat Another name for a clutch pressure plate cover.

Heel The outer end of a bevel or hypoid ring gear tooth.

Helical cut final drive gear A gear used in a transaxle when the output shaft is parallel to the axle shafts.

Helical gear A gear with teeth cut at an angle.

Hotchkiss driveshaft A type of rear suspension that uses leaf springs to absorb drive axle housing torque reactions.

Hub The center part of a wheel; the surface where a wheel mounts.

Hunting gear set A gear set in which the driving gear will mesh with every tooth on the driven gear as they rotate.

Hydraulic clutch operating system A clutch operating system that uses hydraulic pressure to transfer motion and pressure.

Hydraulics A branch of science dealing with the transfer of power through fluids under pressure.

Hypoid gear sets A special form of bevel gear that positions the gear axis on nonintersecting planes and is commonly used in drive axles.

Hypoid gears The gears used when the axis of the final drive gear is at a different height than the axis of the ring gear.

Hysteresis bands The areas between two curves on a graph that indicate when a torque converter clutch locks and when it unlocks. Hysteresis bands also exist between graph curves that indicate when a transmission upshifts and when it downshifts between two gears.

Idler gear A gear positioned between two other gears such that it causes a change in the direction of rotation.

Impeller A rotor or rotor blade used to force a gas or liquid in a certain direction under pressure.

Inclinometer A device used to measure mounting positions relative to true level.

Independent rear suspension (IRS) systems A type of rear suspension in which the two rear wheels can move vertically without changing the other's position.

Index To align two parts in the proper position before assembly.

Inertia The physical property maintaining that a body at rest tends to remain at rest and a body in motion tends to remain in motion and travel in a straight line.

Input member The drive member of a planetary gear set.

Input shaft The shaft that carries the driving torque into a gear box.

Integral Manufactured into; part of.

Interaxle differential A device that is used in some 4WD and AWD systems, which prevents driveline harshness and vibration, and serves to maintain smooth operation while making turns in a 4WD/AWD vehicle.

Interlock A transmission mechanism that prevents two shift rails or forks from moving at the same time.

Internal ring gear The outermost member of the gear set, with its teeth pointing inward toward the center of the gear.

Journal A bearing surface for a shaft, gear, or bearing to rotate on.

Lands Areas of a spool valve that control the opening and closing of hydraulic passages.

Lap Matching gear teeth by grinding or use of a grinding compound; on nonhunting and partially nonhunting gears, manufacturers lap the contacting gear teeth to reduce wear.

Lash *See* **Backlash.**

Layshaft *See* **Countershaft.**

LePelletier gear train A compound planetary gear set that combines a simple planetary gear set with a Ravigneaux gear set providing six forward speeds.

Lift pads   The parts of the lift that contact the vehicle manufacturer's recommended lift points.

Limited slip differential (LSD)   A differential that uses internal clutches to limit the speed difference between the axles.

Linkage   The series of rods, levers, cables, and so on used to transmit motion of force from one point to another.

Lip seals   A type of oil seal that is circular and made of rubber-like O-ring and square-cut seals with a metal outer shell. A thin, flexible lip molded onto the seal actually performs the sealing function.

Load-bearing ability   A measurement of a lubricant's strength, determined by the amount of antiwear and EP protection.

Locking differential   A type of differential that has the same parts as an open differential, but adds a mechanical, electric, pneumatic, or hydraulic mechanism to lock the two output pinions together.

Longitudinally mounted   A longitudinally mounted engine means the crankshaft centerlines lie parallel to the length of the vehicle frame with the front of the engine facing the front of the vehicle.

Low gear   First gear in a transmission.

Low-temperature torque   Deals with the amount of resistance to motion caused by a lubricant at cold temperatures.

Lubricants   Substances that reduce friction and wear between two moving parts.

Lubricity   A measure of an oil's flow characteristics, which are affected by temperature; sulfur compounds add lubricity.

Magnetic pulse generator   A signal-generating switch that creates a voltage pulse as magnetic flux changes around a pickup coil.

Mainline pressure   The pressure developed from the fluid output of the pump and controlled by the pressure regulator valve. Mainline pressure operates the apply devices in the transmission and is the source of all other pressures in the hydraulic system.

Malfunction indicator lamp (MIL)   Warning light to alert the driver of a fault that can affect emissions or powertrain performance.

Manual position switch   A switch that returns a switch signal to the powertrain control module or transmission control module to indicate the position of the manual valve.

Manual transmission   A transmission device in which the gear ratios are changed by manually shifting.

Manual transmission case   The main housings of a transmission; it supports the transmission parts and contains the transmission or transaxle lubricant.

Manual valve   The valve that is moved manually, through the shift linkage, to select the transmission drive range. The manual valve directs and blocks fluid flow to various hydraulic circuits.

Manually locking hubs   On a four-wheel-drive vehicle, hubs that connect or disconnect the front hubs to the front drive axles. Manual locking hubs require the driver to exit the vehicle and manually lock the hubs on the front axle.

Marcel   A large series of wave springs between the two lining sections of a clutch disc.

Maximum usable temperature   The application of grease should be limited to where its prolonged operating temperature is significantly below its dropping point temperature.

Mesh   The interlocking of the teeth of two gears.

Micrometer   A precision measuring device, often called a mike, that is used to measure outside diameters or thicknesses, internal diameters, or depths.

Mineral oils   Oils made from crude petroleum; they contain many hydrocarbon chains.

Modified Hotchkiss drivelines   A rear drive axle assembly that uses rear axle control arms supported by coil springs.

Multigrade   Oils that have dual viscosity grade numbers (5W-30, 10W30, etc.), and which meet the low- and high-temperature specifications for both grades of oil indicated.

Multiple-disc clutch   A clutch that uses more than one friction disc.

Multipurpose   Greases having a National Lubricating Grease Institute (NLGI) designation of "GCLB" are multipurpose by definition, which means that they meet the service requirements for chassis, wheel bearing, and universal joint categories.

National Lubricating Grease Institute (NLGI) Classification System   A system that greatly simplifies the process of determining the vehicle manufacturer recommendations and finding a grease product that meets them.

Needle bearing   A very thin roller bearing.

Neutral   A condition in a transmission where the input shaft rotates and the output shaft is not driven.

Newton-meter (Nm)   The metric measurement for torque.

Nitrile rubbers   The rubbers that have excellent abrasion resistance, and some also work well in temperatures from –65°F to 225°F. However, high-temperature performance nitrile-rubber seals have poor low-temperature performance.

NLGI consistency numbers   A characteristic of lubricating grease; lubrication numbers that range from 000, 00, 0, and 1 to 6, with 000 being very soft and 6 being very hard.

Nodular iron   A type of cast iron that incorporates graphite to increase strength.

Nominal shim   A shim of designated thickness used when beginning a gauging process.

Non-hunting gear sets   Final-drive gear sets with final-drive ratios expressible as a whole number. They also require timing marks.

NV 4500 transmission   A type of 5-speed manual transmission with the fifth speed being an overdrive ratio; manufactured by *New Venture Gear* (NVG).

Oil separation   Indicates grease shelf life. Over time, a certain amount of oil separates from the grease; this is called bleed. If too much oil bleeds off in the storage container, the grease lubricating quality decreases.

One-way clutch   A mechanical holding device that prevents rotation in one direction, but overruns to allow it in the other. One-way clutches are either roller or sprag clutches.

One-way sprag clutch   A device that consists of a hub and drum separated by a number of sprags.

One-way valve   A type of switching valve that allows fluid to pass in one direction and only when the pressure is sufficient to unseat the valve.

Operating range   The area of movement of a clutch pedal where the pedal is pushed down past its freeplay to the point that the clutch releases.

O-ring   Round rubber sealing rings.

Orifice   A small opening or restriction, in a line or passage, that is used to regulate pressure and flow.

Output member   The driven member of a planetary gear set.

Output shaft   The shaft that carries the torque out of a gear box.

Overdrive A condition in which the drive gear rotates slower than the driven gear. Output speed of the driven gear is increased, while output torque is reduced. A gear ratio of 0.70:1 is an overdrive gear ratio.

Oxidation When oxygen molecules combine chemically with the base oil, the oil can thicken, resulting in sludge. This process produces oil that is unable to flow to all of the metal surfaces that require lubrication.

Oxidation inhibitors Chemical components that reduce the oxidation problem by interrupting the oxidation chain reaction and altering the chemicals that produce the undesirable oxidation by-product.

Part-time four-wheel drive With this system, the driver may select either two-wheel-drive or four-wheel-drive operation.

Partially non-hunting gear sets Final-drive gear sets with final-drive ratios expressible as a reducible fraction not equaling a whole number. They also require timing marks.

Passing gear A downshift from overdrive to the next lower gear.

Pawl A locking device that holds a gear stationary.

Pedal operating range The range of pedal motion from the point where the disc begins to slip until the clutch fully disengages.

Pedal reserve Clutch pedal travel allowed by the operating system to ensure that the clutch fully disengages under all conditions before the pedal reaches the floor.

Peen A process of striking a metal surface with a hammer or steel shot to upset or harden the surface.

Permanent magnet generator A sensor consisting of a permanent magnet and coil. Used with a reluctor wheel to input the speed of various components in an electronically controlled transmission.

Pinion gear A small gear that meshes with a larger gear.

Pitch diameter The effective diameter of a gear, midpoint of gear tooth. (Also called pitch line.)

Planet carrier assembly Part of a planetary gear set; it holds the pinion gears.

Planetary gear set A gear system composed of a sun gear, a planet carrier with planet pinions, and a ring gear that can produce one or more gear ratios.

Plunging cross-groove CV joint In this joint, the outer race drives the inner race by transferring torque through the cage and bearing assembly.

Plunging joint A CV joint that allows a driveshaft to change length.

Plunging tripod In this joint, the tulip housing drives the tripod assembly, causing the half shaft to rotate.

Polyacrylic rubbers A type of rubber that has fair abrasion resistance, but works better at higher temperatures than nitrile-rubber seals. Disadvantages are high cost, poor dry-running ability, and, with certain lubricant formulations, limited low-temperature performance.

Polymers Recurring molecular chains contained in manmade synthetic fluids.

Positive-displacement pump A pump that delivers the same amount of fluid for reach revolution of the pump.

Positraction Also called limited-slip differential; it uses various mechanisms to allow normal differential action when going around turns. When a wheel slips, positraction allows more torque to be transferred to the nonslipping wheel.

Pour point depressant An oil additive that lowers the temperature at which wax crystals form. As oils cool, wax crystals form, preventing adequate lubrication.

Power The rate at which work is done or force is applied. In mechanics, power is measured as torque times speed and expressed in units such as horsepower or kilowatts.

Power flow The path of drive torque through the transmission or transaxle.

Powertrain The mechanism that transfers and modifies the driving torque from the engine crankshaft to the drive wheels.

Powertrain control module (PCM) It is the computer, the heart of the electronic control system. It receives, processes, and transmits information using voltage and current signals.

Preload A load placed on parts during assembly to maintain critical clearances and adjustments when operating loads are applied.

Preloaded clutches In a limited-slip differential clutch preload determines how much difference in side gear speed locks the side gears. As the difference in axle speed increases, the side gears apply more pressure against the springs. Too little preload causes the side gears to lockup later than normal.

Pressure A force per unit area measured in pounds per square inch (psi) or units of atmospheric pressure (bars or kilopascals).

Pressure plate The metal disc that applies pressure onto the friction disc to transmit torque.

Propeller or prop shaft *See* **Driveshaft**.

Pulse-width modulated (PWM) The signal that controls the transfer case motor/encoder.

Pulse-width modulation A modulation technique that allows a digital output signal to provide varied or analog control of a mechanical device.

Quill The extension from the transmission input bearing retainer that supports the clutch release bearing.

Race A hardened surface for the bearing rollers or balls to roll on.

Radial A direction perpendicular to the rotating axis.

Radial load A line of force applied against the axis at an angle of 90 degrees.

Ravigneaux gear set A compound planetary gear system consisting of two sun gears and two sets of planet pinions that share a common ring gear.

Reaction member The held member of the planetary gear set.

Rear axle The axle that transfers power from the propeller shaft to the drive wheels on rear-wheel-drive vehicles.

Rear axle drive pinion yoke (Flange) In rear-wheel-drive drivelines, it connects the driveshaft to the final drive pinion.

Rear-wheel drive (RWD) A drive system that drives the rear wheels.

Release (slave) cylinder Mounted at the transmission as part of a hydraulic clutch system, it contains a piston and cup seals that move the clutch release fork.

Release bearing The bearing that is forced against the pressure plate assembly to release a clutch. (Also called throw-out bearing.)

Release fork Two types: one-piece fork (most common) and fork with shaft. When the driver moves the clutch pedal, the clutch-operating system moves the release fork.

Resistance to water washout Indicates how well the grease resists being washed away by water.

Reverse gear The gear that helps drive the vehicle in reverse by use of an idler rear in the transmission; gear ratio is usually numerically similar to first gear.

Reverse gear brake The brake used by some transaxles to reduce gear clash on engagement.

Reverse idler gear *See* **Idler gear**.

Reverse idler shaft A shaft that carries the reverse idler gear, which changes the direction of output shaft rotation.

Rigid disc A type of clutch disc; this design does not allow any movement between the outer disc assembly and the hub. Efficient and lightweight design, but can cause rough clutch engagement and noisy vehicle operation. Typically used in high-performance or racing applications.

Ring gear *See* **Annulus gear**.

Roller bearing Used extensively in drive trains, roller bearings are more costly to produce, cannot take as much load as sliding bearings, but are more effective at reducing friction and maintaining proper lubrication.

Roller clutch A one-way clutch that uses a set of rollers and a special cam as the locking mechanism.

Rolling friction The drag of the tires on the road plus bearing friction.

Room-temperature vulcanizing (RTV) compound A silicone sealant compound that begins to dry as soon as it is exposed to air.

Root The depression of a gear lying between two teeth, with the crown at the very top of each tooth.

RTV A formed-in-place gasket material; a rubber-like material that vulcanizes at room temperature.

Rubber dust covers Covers that protect the grease on lubricated parts from dust contamination.

Runout Deviation in an item's rotation or a mounting plane.

S-spring A steel spring shaped like the letter "S"; it provides preload in some limited slip differentials.

Score A scratch, groove, or ridge that mars a finished surface.

Seal compatibility A characteristic of lubricants that keeps the lubricant from damaging or attacking the rubber on the oil seals.

Sealants A material commonly used to fill irregularities between a gasket and the surface it seals. Another use is to lock and seal fastener threads. Two basic types of sealant: aerobic and anaerobic.

Second gear The gear that takes over once the vehicle is in motion and the engine load is reduced. This gear typically has a ratio of approximately 2:1.

Selective-fit thrust washers Thrust washers that are available in different thicknesses, used to adjust end play and absorb axial loads.

Servo A hydraulic piston and cylinder assembly that controls the application and release of a transmission band.

Shift interlock mechanism A mechanism that uses shift rails with machined notches, rs, and pins that keep the other shift rails from moving when one of the shift rails is moved into gear.

Shift valve A spool valve acted on by throttle and governor pressure to time transmission shifts. Also called a "snap" valve or timing valve.

Shim A thin spacer used to adjust clearance or preload.

Side bearings Part of the final drive axle; uses two side bearings to support the differential case on its sides. Usually these are tapered roller bearings and are preloaded to ensure case rotation without axial or radial movement.

Side gears Part of standard differential components. Side gears are splined with each inner axle end and are driven by pinion gears mounted on a shaft.

Silicone rubbers Soft elastomers that have relatively poor resistance to abrasion.

Simpson gear set A compound planetary gear system consisting of two ring gears and two planet carrier assemblies that share a common sun gear.

Sleeve bearings In the category of sliding bearings, these are made in a full circle, have a steel back for support, have a special bearing material on the inside to reduce the effects of friction, and may be inserted in an engine block for a camshaft to turn in.

Slider clutch A clutch designed to slip until a certain rpm to prevent the transfer of too much torque for the drive wheels.

Sliding bearing A type of bearing that is solid, does not move, and is placed between two parts of an engine whose surfaces move against each other.

Sliding reverse gear A type of reverse gear in which the shift linkage slides the reverse idler gear on its shaft until it engages the reverse gears on the countershaft and output shaft gear. This design uses spur, not helical, gears for reverse because the gear teeth must move into and out of mesh.

Slip fit A free-running or sliding fit.

Slip joint A splined joint in a driveshaft to allow it to change length.

Slipping A loss in torque transfer accompanying an increase in engine rpm.

Soap thickener A material contained in grease to keep the grease in place, thus slowly releasing the oil to the surfaces needing lubrication.

Solenoid An electromechanical device that uses magnetism to move an iron core. The core provides mechanical motion to some other system part. A solenoid thus changes electrical voltage and current into mechanical movement.

Solid rear axle assemblies A type of rear axle in which the axles are supported on their outboard side by a roller bearing and by the side gear on the inboard side.

Solvents Substances that are used to clean parts, tools, and other items. The most used are petroleum naphtha, petroleum distillates and additives found in carburetor cleaners, as well as mineral spirits and kerosene.

Spalling A condition where surface metal breaks away from a bearing race.

Speed fluctuation Difference in speed between the ends of a cross-type U joint; as the angle of U-joint shafts increases, the amount of speed fluctuation increases.

Speed ratio The number of revolutions made by the turbine for each revolution of the impeller. Turbine (output) speed is divided by impeller (input) speed and expressed as a percentage.

Spool valve A type of hydraulic valve, consisting of lands and valleys that resemble a spool for thread. The lands seal orifices and the valleys open them.

Spiral bevel final drive gear In the final drive, if the output shaft is at a 90-degree, or right, angle to the axle shafts, then this gear is used.

Spiral bevel gears A type of drive gear that has curved teeth, similar to those on a helical gear, that increase the loads they can carry and decrease the noise they produce.

Spline A slot or groove cut in a shaft or bore that is used to connect to a matching spline.

Split case Where two manual transmission case halves, top-bottom or left-right, bolt together.

Split Hotchkiss drivelines A driveshaft type that uses two driveshafts to transfer torque to the rear axle.

Sprag The locking element in a one-way sprag-type clutch.

Spring pack In a limited-slip differential, springs that push the side gears against the clutches.

Spur gear A gear with teeth cut parallel to the axis of the gear.

Square-cut seals Seals that are circular and have a square or slightly rectangular cross section.

Stall A condition where the engine is running but the transmission input shaft is not rotating.

Stall speed The maximum possible engine and torque converter impeller speed, measured in rpm, with the turbine held stationary and the engine throttle wide open.

Standard transmission *See* **Manual transmission**; at one time the standard equipment on a new vehicle.

Static friction The relative amount of friction between two stationary surfaces or two surfaces that are rotating at the same speed.

Static seal A type of oil seal that blocks the passage of fluid between parts that are in fixed positions relative to each other.

Stator A reaction member of a torque converter mounted on a one-way clutch. Stators multiply torque by redirecting fluid flow from the turbine back to the impeller.

Stepped flywheel A type of flywheel in which the clutch contact surface of the flywheel is recessed, or stepped, so the pressure plate assembly fits within the outer edge of the flywheel.

Sun gear Part of a planetary gear set; it gets its name from its central position, around which pinion gears revolve.

Swaging process A pressing process that may be used by manufacturers to secure the bearing caps inside the bores of the yoke ears.

Synchronize To bring two objects to the same rotating speed; to cause two events to occur at the same time.

Synchronizer assembly A transmission component that matches gear speeds, allowing shifting from one gear to the other. Named for the gears on either side of it, the real "shifting" in a synchromesh transmission takes place here. Most synchronizer assemblies ride on the output shaft between two gears.

Synthetic fluids Manmade lubricants containing recurring molecular chains called polymers.

Tensile strength The greatest longitudinal stress a substance can bear without tearing apart.

Texture Often included in manufacturer product description; a characteristic of grease.

Third gear The gear used for cruising at lower speeds and accelerating at higher cruising speeds.

Throttle pressure The transmission hydraulic pressure that is directly related to engine load. Throttle pressure, which increases with throttle opening and engine torque output, is one of the principle pressures used to control shift points.

Throttle valve The valve that regulates throttle pressure based on throttle butterfly opening or intake manifold vacuum.

Throw-out bearing Another name for a clutch release bearing.

Thrust A motion of a gear of shaft along its axis.

Thrust washer A bearing that is used to separate rotating parts from stationary parts or parts that are rotating at different speeds.

Toe The inner end of a bevel or hypoid ring gear tooth.

Top-loading case A transmission case that has a large covered access hole on the top that conceals the gears and shift forks.

Torque A turning or twisting effort that is normally measured in foot-pounds or Newton-meters.

Torque angle gauge A device that provides a reading that measures how far a bolt is turned.

Torque angle meter A device to measure the exact angle a bolt is turned.

Torque converter A type of fluid coupling that is used with automatic transmissions that will multiply engine torque. It self-releases to allow the vehicle to stop with the engine running and the transmission in gear.

Torque converter capacity The ability of a torque converter to absorb and transmit engine torque in relation to the amount of slippage in the converter.

Torque converter clutch (TCC) Similar to a clutch in a manual transmission, a torque converter clutch uses a friction disc, operated by a hydraulic piston, to mechanically couple the turbine to the impeller.

Torque multiplication Levers can be used to increase or multiply torque.

Torque multiplication factor (TMF) The final gear drive ratio multiplies torque in addition to the driver-selected transmission ratio; both ratios combined determine the overall torque multiplication factor.

Torque multiplication phase The period of torque converter operation when the vortex flow is redirected through the stator to accelerate impeller flow to the turbine and increase engine torque.

Torque steer Occurs in an unequal-length drive axle system, where the wheel attached to the shorter half shaft receives torque first, making the vehicle veer to the side with the longer half shaft on hard acceleration. It is especially noticeable in front-wheel-drive vehicles.

Torque tube A type of driveline found in some late model vehicles with a rear-mounted transmission. It virtually eliminates the effects of rear-end torque on the rear axle.

Torsen differential A type of locking differential that is a torque-sensing, locking design that uses a set of worm side gears in mesh with individual worm wheel pinions that are supported by the differential case.

Torsional The type of vibration released by a spinning, rigid tube. It runs parallel to the shaft centerline and causes a twisting movement.

Traction The relative amount of grip between a tire and the road surface.

Traction control A system used to sense wheel spin and reduce drive wheel torque to the amount of traction.

Tractive effort The amount of thrust that the engine and drivetrain can generate at the road surface.

Tractive resistance The load that the drivetrain works against.

Transaxle A transmission that is combined with the final drive and differential and is normally used in front-wheel-drive and mid-engine vehicles.

Transfer case An auxiliary transmission used in most four-wheel-drive vehicles to divide and control the power flow to the front and rear drive axles.

Transfer case shift motor An electric motor that selects the different operating modes of a transfer case; it consists of a permanent magnet (PM) motor and gear reduction assembly.

Transmission A device in the powertrain that provides different forward gear ratios, a neutral, and a reverse.

Transmission band A flexible steel band lined with friction material that is clamped around a circular drum to hold it from turning.

Transmission fluid pressure switch A set of switches attached to the valve body used to indicate and verify the position of the manual valve.

Transmission identification tag An identification label that is attached to many transmissions. The tag has the model number, part number, and build date stamped on it.

Transversely mounted An engine position that is across the vehicle, rather than parallel with the vehicle's length.

Tremec (Borg-Warner) T5 transmission A type of 5-speed 77 mm manual transmission assembly.

Tremec (Borg-Warner) T56 transmission A type of 6-speed transmission. All of the six forward gears, and the reverse gear, are fully synchronized.

Trunnion The projecting arms of a U-joint cross that form the bearing journals.

Tunnel case A transmission case with a large opening at one end, usually the rear, which the shafts and gears assemble into.

Turbine A driven member that connects to the transmission input shaft and provides torque input to the planetary gear set.

U-joint operating angle The angle between a U-joint's input and output shafts.

Underdrive Also called gear reduction, output shaft speed is less than that, or under, the input shaft speed.

Unequal-length drive axle system A type of front-wheel drive in which the wheel attached to the shorter half shaft receives torque first, making the vehicle veer to the side with the longer half shaft on hard acceleration. This creates the effect called torque steer.

Universal joint (U-joint) A mechanical device used to transfer power and motion at changeable angles.

Valve A device that regulates, restricts, or directs the pressure and flow of transmission fluid.

Valve body The casting that contains most of the valves in a transmission hydraulic system. The valve body also has passages for the flow of hydraulic fluid.

Vane pump A pump that uses a slotted rotor and sliding vanes to produce oil flow. The vane pumps used in automatic transmissions are variable-displacement pumps.

Variable-displacement pump A pump that automatically regulates output volume of fluid based on the needs of the transmission.

Viscosity The resistance to flow of a fluid.

Viscous Thick; tending to resist fluid flow.

Viscous coupling A component of a limited-slip differential assembly that uses a series of closely positioned plates, which do not touch each other. Half of the plates are splined to the case, and the other half are alternately splined to each side gear. The plates are housed in a sealed chamber, which is filled with a thick and viscous silicone-based fluid. The silicone allows normal speed differences between two shafts but resists the high-speed differences associated with wheel spin on one shaft.

Vortex flow The oil flow path, in a fluid coupling or torque converter, that is at a right angle to the rotation of the impeller and rotary flow.

Wave spring A spring that resembles a flat, wavy washer.

Wheel end The outer end of the axle housing where the axle bearing is situated.

Work The transfer of energy from one system to another, particularly through the application of force. The result of this force changes the speed or direction of motion of an object.

Worm gear A type of gear with teeth that resembles screw threads.

Yoke A cross-shaped portion of a shaft that connects to a U-joint cross.

Zerk fitting A snap-on fitting used to lubricate components with grease. In U-joints, grease flows from the zerk fitting through internal passageways to each trunnion, supplying the needle bearings with grease.

INDEX